INSTRUCTOR'S
SOLUTION MANUAL

Daniel Miller

Thinking

MATHEMATICALLY

Third Edition

Blitzer

PEARSON

Prentice
Hall

Upper Saddle River, NJ 07458

Editor-in-Chief: Sally Yagan
Acquisitions Editor: Petra Recter
Supplement Editor: Joanne Wendelken
Executive Managing Editor: Vince O'Brien
Production Editor: Allyson Kloss
Supplement Cover Manager: Paul Gourhan
Supplement Cover Designer: Joanne Alexandris
Manufacturing Buyer: Ilene Kahn

© 2005 Pearson Education, Inc.
Pearson Prentice Hall
Pearson Education, Inc.
Upper Saddle River, NJ 07458

Pearson Prentice Hall® is a trademark of Pearson Education, Inc.

Printed in the United States of America

10 9 8 7 6 5 4 3 2 1

ISBN 0-13-144371-2

Pearson Education Ltd., *London*
Pearson Education Australia Pty. Ltd., *Sydney*
Pearson Education Singapore, Pte. Ltd.
Pearson Education North Asia Ltd., *Hong Kong*
Pearson Education Canada, Inc., *Toronto*
Pearson Educación de Mexico, S.A. de C.V.
Pearson Education—Japan, *Tokyo*
Pearson Education Malaysia, Pte. Ltd.

TABLE OF CONTENTS

Chapter 1
Problem Solving and Critical Thinking

Check Points 1.1

1. Inductive; the general conclusion for all people who increase time spent exercising was based on specific observations.

2. There are many counterexamples including $50 \times 60 = 3000$.

3. **a.** $3 + 6 = 9$
   $9 + 6 = 15$
   $15 + 6 = 21$
   $21 + 6 = 27$
   $27 + 6 = 33$
   $3, 9, 15, 21, 27, \underline{33}$

   b. $2 \times 5 = 10$
   $10 \times 5 = 50$
   $50 \times 5 = 250$
   $250 \times 5 = 1250$
   $2, 10, 50, 250, \underline{1250}$

4. The shapes alternate between rectangle and triangle.
   The number of little legs cycles from 1 to 2 to 3 and then back to 1.
   Therefore the next figure will be a rectangle with 2 little legs.

5. **a.** Conjecture based on results: The original number is doubled.

Select a number	4	10	0	3
Multiply the number by 4.	$4 \times 4 = 16$	$10 \times 4 = 40$	$0 \times 4 = 0$	$3 \times 4 = 12$
Add 6 to the product.	$16 + 6 = 22$	$40 + 6 = 46$	$0 + 6 = 6$	$12 + 6 = 18$
Divide this sum by 2.	$22 \div 2 = 11$	$46 \div 2 = 23$	$6 \div 2 = 3$	$18 \div 2 = 9$
Subtract 3 from the quotient.	$11 - 3 = 8$	$23 - 3 = 20$	$3 - 3 = 0$	$9 - 3 = 6$
Summary of results:	$4 \rightarrow 8$	$10 \rightarrow 20$	$0 \rightarrow 0$	$3 \rightarrow 6$

   b. Select a number: n
   Multiply the number by 4: $4n$
   Add 6 to the product: $4n + 6$

   Divide this sum by 2: $\dfrac{4n+6}{2} = \dfrac{4n}{2} + \dfrac{6}{2} = 2n + 3$

   Subtract 3 from the quotient: $2n + 3 - 3 = 2n$

Exercise Set 1.1

1. Inductive; the general conclusion for all people's fingerprints was based on specific observations.

2. Inductive; the general conclusion for all HMO patients was based on specific observations.

3. Deductive; the specific conclusion about my snake was based on general statements.

4. Deductive; the specific conclusion about Joan was based on general statements.

5. Counterexample: Bill Clinton was younger than 65 at the time of his inauguration.

6. Counterexample: Madonna has appeared in several movies.

7. Counterexample: $5 \times 5 = 25$

8. Counterexample: $101 + 102 = 203$

9. Counterexample: $\dfrac{1}{2} \neq \dfrac{1+1}{2+1} = \dfrac{2}{3}$

10. Counterexample: $8 - 5 = 3$

11. Counterexample: $0 + 0 = 0$

12. Counterexample: $1 \div \frac{1}{3} = 3$

13. Pattern: Add 4
    $24 + 4 = 28$
    8, 12, 16, 20, 24, <u>28</u>

14. Pattern: Add 5
    $39 + 5 = 44$
    19, 24, 29, 34, 39, <u>44</u>

15. Pattern: Subtract 5
    $17 - 5 = 12$
    37, 32, 27, 22, 17, <u>12</u>

16. Pattern: Subtract 4
    $17 - 4 = 13$
    33, 29, 25, 21, 17, <u>13</u>

17. Pattern: Multiply by 3
    $243 \times 3 = 729$
    3, 9, 27, 81, 243, <u>729</u>

18. Pattern: Multiply by 4
    $512 \times 4 = 2048$
    2, 8, 32, 128, 512, <u>2048</u>

19. Pattern: Multiply by 2
    $16 \times 2 = 32$
    1, 2, 4, 8, 16, <u>32</u>

20. Pattern: Multiply by 5
    $125 \times 5 = 625$
    1, 5, 25, 125, <u>625</u>

21. Pattern: 1 alternates with numbers that are multiplied by 2
    $16 \times 2 = 32$
    1, 4, 1, 8, 1, 16, 1, <u>32</u>

22. Pattern: 1 alternates with numbers that are increased by 3
    $10 + 3 = 13$
    1, 4, 1, 7, 1, 10, 1, <u>13</u>

23. Pattern: Subtract 2
    $-4 - 2 = -6$
    4, 2, 0, -2, -4, <u>-6</u>

24. Pattern: Subtract 3
    $-6 - 3 = -9$
    6, 3, 0, -3, -6, <u>-9</u>

25. Pattern: Add 4 to the denominator
    $$\frac{1}{18+4} = \frac{1}{22}$$
    $\frac{1}{2}, \frac{1}{6}, \frac{1}{10}, \frac{1}{14}, \frac{1}{18}, \underline{\frac{1}{22}}$

26. Pattern: Add 1 to the denominator
    $$\frac{1}{5+1} = \frac{1}{6}$$
    $1, \frac{1}{2}, \frac{1}{3}, \frac{1}{4}, \frac{1}{5}, \underline{\frac{1}{6}}$

27. Pattern: Multiply the denominator by 3
    $$\frac{1}{27 \times 3} = \frac{1}{81}$$
    $1, \frac{1}{3}, \frac{1}{9}, \frac{1}{27}, \underline{\frac{1}{81}}$

28. Pattern: Multiply the denominator by 2
    $$\frac{1}{8 \times 2} = \frac{1}{16}$$
    $1, \frac{1}{2}, \frac{1}{4}, \frac{1}{8}, \underline{\frac{1}{16}}$

29. Pattern: Divide by -4
    $$-1 \div (-4) = \frac{1}{4}$$
    $64, -16, 4, -1, \underline{\frac{1}{4}}$

30. Pattern: Divide by -5
    $$-1 \div (-4) = \frac{1}{5}$$
    $125, -25, 5, -1, \underline{\frac{1}{5}}$

31. Pattern: The second value of each pair is 4 less than the first.
    $3 - 4 = -1$
    $(6,2), (0,-4), (7\frac{1}{2}, 3\frac{1}{2}), (2,-2), (3,\underline{-1})$

32. Pattern: The second value of each pair is the square of the first.
    $\left(-\frac{4}{7}\right)^2 = \frac{16}{49}$
    $\left(\frac{2}{3}, \frac{4}{9}\right), \left(\frac{1}{5}, \frac{1}{25}\right), (7, 49), \left(-\frac{5}{6}, \frac{25}{36}\right), \left(-\frac{4}{7}, \underline{\frac{16}{49}}\right)$

33. The figure cycles from square to triangle to circle and then repeats. So the next figure is

34. The figure rotates 90° counterclockwise. So the next figure is

35. The pattern is to add one more letter to the previous figure and use the next consecutive letter in the alphabet. The next figure shown at right.

d	d	d
d	d	

36. The figure alternates from triangle to square and gains one line on the bottom. The next figure is ⬜

37. a. Conjecture based on results: The original number is doubled.

Select a number	4	10	0	3
Multiply the number by 4.	$4 \times 4 = 16$	$10 \times 4 = 40$	$0 \times 4 = 0$	$3 \times 4 = 12$
Add 8 to the product.	$16 + 8 = 24$	$40 + 8 = 48$	$0 + 8 = 8$	$12 + 8 = 20$
Divide this sum by 2.	$24 \div 2 = 12$	$48 \div 2 = 24$	$8 \div 2 = 4$	$20 \div 2 = 10$
Subtract 4 from the quotient.	$12 - 4 = 8$	$24 - 4 = 20$	$4 - 4 = 0$	$10 - 4 = 6$
Summary of results:	$4 \rightarrow 8$	$10 \rightarrow 20$	$0 \rightarrow 0$	$3 \rightarrow 6$

b. $4n$

$4n + 8$

$\dfrac{4n + 8}{2} = \dfrac{4n}{2} + \dfrac{8}{2} = 2n + 4$

$2n + 4 - 4 = 2n$

38. a. Conjecture based on results: The result is always 2.

Select a number	4	10	0	3
Multiply the number by 3.	$4 \times 3 = 12$	$10 \times 3 = 30$	$0 \times 3 = 0$	$3 \times 3 = 9$
Add 6 to the product.	$12 + 6 = 18$	$30 + 6 = 36$	$0 + 6 = 6$	$9 + 6 = 15$
Divide this sum by 3.	$18 \div 3 = 6$	$36 \div 3 = 12$	$6 \div 3 = 2$	$15 \div 3 = 5$
Subtract the original from the quotient.	$6 - 4 = 2$	$12 - 10 - 2$	$2 - 0 = 2$	$5 - 3 = 2$
Summary of results:	$4 \rightarrow 2$	$10 \rightarrow 2$	$0 \rightarrow 2$	$3 \rightarrow 2$

b. $3n$

$3n + 6$

$\dfrac{3n + 6}{3} = \dfrac{3n}{3} + \dfrac{6}{3} = n + 2$

$n + 2 - n = 2$

39. a. Conjecture based on results: The result is always 3.

Select a number.	4	10	0	3
Add 5 to the number.	$4 + 5 = 9$	$10 + 5 = 15$	$0 + 5 = 5$	$3 + 5 = 8$
Double the result.	$9 \times 2 = 18$	$15 \times 2 = 30$	$5 \times 2 = 10$	$8 \times 2 = 16$
Subtract 4.	$18 - 4 = 14$	$30 - 4 = 26$	$10 - 4 = 6$	$16 - 4 = 12$
Divide the result by 2.	$14 \div 2 = 7$	$26 \div 2 = 13$	$6 \div 2 = 3$	$12 \div 2 = 6$
Subtract the original number.	$7 - 4 = 3$	$13 - 10 = 3$	$3 - 0 = 3$	$6 - 3 = 3$
Summary of results:	$4 \rightarrow 3$	$10 \rightarrow 3$	$0 \rightarrow 3$	$3 \rightarrow 3$

b. $n+5$

$2(n+5) = 2n+10$

$2n+10-4 = 2n+6$

$\dfrac{2n+6}{2} = \dfrac{2n}{2} + \dfrac{6}{2} = n+3$

$n+3-n = 3$

40. a. Conjecture based on results: The result is always 5.

Select a number.	4	10	0	3
Add 3 to the number.	$4+3=7$	$10+3=13$	$0+3=3$	$3+3=6$
Double the result.	$7\times 2=14$	$13\times 2=26$	$3\times 2=6$	$6\times 2=12$
Add 4.	$14+4=18$	$26+4=30$	$6+4=10$	$12+4=16$
Divide the result by 2.	$18\div 2=9$	$30\div 2=15$	$10\div 2=5$	$16\div 2=8$
Subtract the original number.	$9-4=5$	$15-10=5$	$5-0=5$	$8-3=5$
Summary of results:	$4 \rightarrow 5$	$10 \rightarrow 5$	$0 \rightarrow 5$	$3 \rightarrow 5$

b. $n+3$

$2(n+3) = 2n+6$

$2n+6+4 = 2n+10$

$\dfrac{2n+10}{2} = \dfrac{2n}{2} + \dfrac{10}{2} = n+5$

$n+5-n = 5$

41. Using inductive reasoning we predict $1+2+3+4+5+6 = \dfrac{6\times 7}{2}$.

Arithmetic verifies this result: $21 = 21$

42. Using inductive reasoning we predict $3+6+9+12+15+18 = \dfrac{18\times 7}{2}$.

Arithmetic verifies this result: $63 = 63$

43. Using inductive reasoning we predict $1+3+5+7+9+11 = 6\times 6$.
Arithmetic verifies this result: $36 = 36$

44. Using inductive reasoning we predict $\dfrac{1}{1\times 2} + \dfrac{1}{2\times 3} + \dfrac{1}{3\times 4} + \dfrac{1}{4\times 5} + \dfrac{1}{5\times 6} = \dfrac{5}{6}$.

$$\dfrac{1}{1\times 2} + \dfrac{1}{2\times 3} + \dfrac{1}{3\times 4} + \dfrac{1}{4\times 5} + \dfrac{1}{5\times 6} = \dfrac{5}{6}$$

$$\dfrac{1}{2} + \dfrac{1}{6} + \dfrac{1}{12} + \dfrac{1}{20} + \dfrac{1}{30} = \dfrac{5}{6}$$

Arithmetic verifies this result:

$$\dfrac{30}{60} + \dfrac{10}{60} + \dfrac{5}{60} + \dfrac{3}{60} + \dfrac{2}{60} = \dfrac{5}{6}$$

$$\dfrac{50}{60} = \dfrac{5}{6}$$

$$\dfrac{5}{6} = \dfrac{5}{6}$$

45. a. $3 - 1 = 2$
$6 - 3 = 3$
$10 - 6 = 4$
$15 - 10 = 5$
$21 - 15 = 6$
The successive differences increase by 1.

b. 1, 3, 6, 10, 15, and 21are followed by
$21 + 7 = 28$
$28 + 8 = 36$
$36 + 9 = 45$
$45 + 10 = 55$
$55 + 11 = 66$
1, 3, 6, 10, 15, 21, 28, 36, 45, 55, and 66.

46. a. $4 - 1 = 3$
$9 - 4 = 5$
$16 - 9 = 7$
$25 - 16 = 9$
The successive differences increase by 2.

b. 1, 4, 9, 16, and 25 are followed by
$25 + 11 = 36$
$36 + 13 = 49$
$49 + 15 = 64$
$64 + 17 = 81$
$81 + 19 = 100$
1, 4, 9, 16, 25, 36, 49, 64, 81, and 100.

47. a. Each additional inch increases the shoe size by 3 units.

Foot length	9	10	11	12	13	14	15	16	17
Shoe size	5	8	11	14	17	20	23	26	29

b. Continuing the pattern suggests Matthew McGrory's feet are 17 inches.

48. Each row begins and ends with 1. Other numbers are the sum of the two values that are diagonally above.

```
            1
          1   1
        1   2   1
      1   3   3   1
    1   4   6   4   1
  1   5  10  10   5   1
```

49-55. Answers will vary.

56. Deductive reasoning; the specific conclusion was based on a general theory.

57. $1 + 1 = 2$; $1 + 2 = 3$; $2 + 3 = 5$; $3 + 5 = 8$; $5 + 8 = 13$; $8 + 13 = 21$; $13 + 21 = 34$; $21 + 34 = 55$
1, 1, 2, 3, 5, 8, 13, 21, 34, <u>55</u>

58. $15 + 8 = 23$; $23 + 10 = 33$; $33 + 12 = 45$; $45 + 14 = 59$
The successive differences increase by 2.
Therefore, the next term is $59 + 16 = \underline{75}$

59. The first multiplier increases by 33.
$132 + 33 = 165$
The second multiplier is 3367.
The product increases by 111,111.
$165 \times 3367 = 555,555$ is correct.

60. The pattern implies we should attach a 6 to the right of the first multiplier. The second multiplier is always 8. The pattern implies we should add 6 to that product to obtain 987,654.
$123,456 \times 8 + 6 = 987,654$ is correct.

61. Answers will vary. Possible answer:
$5 \times 1 = 5$ $5 \times 2^0 = 5$
$5 \times 2 = 10$ $5 \times 2^1 = 10$
$5 \times 3 = 15$ $5 \times 2^2 = 20$

62. a. $6 \times 6 = 36$
$66 \times 66 = 4356$
$666 \times 666 = 443{,}556$
$6666 \times 6666 = 44{,}435{,}556$

  b. An additional digit of 6 is attached to the numbers being multiplied. An additional digit of 4 is attached to the left of the result and an additional digit of 5 is placed between the 3 and the 6.

  c. $66666 \times 66666 = 4{,}444{,}355{,}556$
$666{,}666 \times 666{,}666 = 444{,}443{,}555{,}556$

  d. Inductive reasoning; it uses an observed pattern and draws conclusions from that pattern.

63. a. $3367 \times 3 = 10101$
$3367 \times 6 = 20202$
$3367 \times 9 = 30303$
$3367 \times 12 = 40404$

  b. The first multiplier is always 3367. The second multipliers are successive multiples of 3. The product increases by 10101.

  c. $3367 \times 15 = 50505$
$3367 \times 18 = 60606$

  d. Inductive reasoning; it uses an observed pattern and draws conclusions from that pattern.

Check Points 1.2

1. 58 rounded to the nearest ten is 60.

2. a. $\$2.40 + \$1.25 + \$4.60 + \$4.40 + \$1.40 + \$1.85 + 2.95 \approx \$2 + \$1 + \$5 + \$4 + \$1 + \$2 + 3 \approx \$18$

  b. The bill of $21.85 is not reasonable. It is too high.

3. $\dfrac{0.2489 \times 48}{0.5103} = \dfrac{\frac{1}{4} \times 48}{\frac{1}{2}} = \dfrac{12}{\frac{1}{2}} = 12 \times \dfrac{2}{1} = 24$

4. a. Round $52 per hour to $50 per hour and assume 40 hours per week.
$$\frac{40 \text{ hours}}{\text{week}} \times \frac{\$50}{\text{hour}} = \frac{\$2000}{\text{week}}$$
The architect's salary is $\approx \$2000$ per week.

  b. Round 52 weeks per year to 50 weeks per year.
$$\frac{\$2000}{\text{week}} \times \frac{50 \text{ weeks}}{\text{year}} = \frac{\$100{,}000}{\text{year}}$$
The architect's salary is $\approx \$100{,}000$ per year.

5. First approximate minutes: $\dfrac{10{,}000 \text{ numbers}}{\dfrac{60 \text{ numbers}}{\text{minute}}} = 10{,}000 \text{ numbers} \times \dfrac{\text{minute}}{60 \text{ numbers}} = \dfrac{10{,}000 \text{ minutes}}{60} = 166\dfrac{2}{3} \text{ minutes}.$

$166\dfrac{2}{3}$ minutes equals about 2 hours and 45 minutes. Therefore 3 hours would be a reasonable estimate.

6. **a.** The sector labeled "African American" shows that 13.6% of the U.S. population in 2050 will be African American.

    b. Round 393,931,000 to 400,000,000 and round 8.2% to 8%.

    $400,000,000 \times \dfrac{8}{100} = 32,000,000$ Asian Americans.

7. **a.** 22 is a reasonable estimate for the number of cars per 100 people in Israel.

    b. Number of cars in Israel $\approx \dfrac{6,000,000}{100} \times 22 = 1,200,000$

8. Answers will vary. Possible answer: Table 1.2 show that there were approximately 140,000 federal prisoners in 2001. Figure 1.5 suggests that approximately 60% of federal prisoners were sentenced for drug offenses. $0.6 \times 140,000 \approx 84,000$. Thus, in 2001, approximately 84,000 federal prisoners were sentenced for drug offenses.

Exercise Set 1.2

1. Round $0.19 to $0.20.
    $12 \times \$0.19 \approx 12 \times \$0.20 \approx \$2.40$

2. Round 297 runners to 300.
    Round 19 miles to 20 miles.
    $297 \times 19 \text{ miles} \approx 300 \times 20 \text{ miles} \approx 6000 \text{ miles}$

3. Round 48 mph to 50 mph.
    Round 7 hours and 8 minutes to 7 hours.
    $48 \text{ mph} \times (7 \text{ hours} + 8 \text{ minutes})$
    $\approx 50 \text{ mph} \times 7 \text{ hours}$
    $\approx 350 \text{ miles}$

4. Round 32.7 hours to 30 hours.
    Round $8.95 to $9.00
    $32.7 \text{ hours} \times \$8.95 \approx 30 \text{ hours} \times \$9.00 \approx \$270$

5. $\$3.47 + \$5.89 + \$19.98 + \$2.03 + \$11.85 + \$0.23$
    $\approx \$3 + \$6 + \$20 + \$2 + \$12 + \$0$
    $\approx \$43$

6. $137 + 146 + 172 + 197 \approx 140 + 150 + 170 + 200$
    $\approx 660 \text{ pounds}$

7. $\$2037 \times 0.05 \approx \dfrac{\$2000 \times 0.10}{2}$
    $\approx \dfrac{\$200}{2}$
    $\approx \$100$

8. 21% of $585,000 \approx 20\%$ of $600,000$
    $\approx 0.20 \times 600,000$
    $\approx 120,000$

9. Round $19.50 to $20 per hour.
    40 hours per week
    (40 × $20) per week = $800/week
    Round 52 weeks to 50 weeks per year.
    50 weeks per year
    (50 × $800) per year = $40,000
    $19.50 per hour $\approx$ $40,000 per year

10. Round $9.87 to $10 per hour.
    40 hours per week
    (40 × $10) per week = $400/week
    Round 52 weeks to 50 weeks per year.
    50 weeks per year
    (50 × $400) per year = $20,000
    $9.87 per hour $\approx$ $20,000 per year

11. $\dfrac{0.57 \times 68}{0.493} \approx \dfrac{0.5 \times 68}{0.5} \approx 68$

12. $17\dfrac{7}{8} \div 2\dfrac{11}{12} \approx 18 \div 3 \approx 6$

13. Hours in a year:
    Round 365 days/year to 400 days/year.
    Round 24 hours/day to 25 hours/day
    Hours in a year
    $\approx 400 \text{ days/year} \times 25 \text{ hours/day}$
    $\approx (400 \times 25) \text{ hours}$
    $\approx 10,000 \text{ hours}$

14. Hours in a decade:
Round 365 days/year to 400 days/year.
Round 24 hours/day to 20 hours/day.
Hours in a decade

$\approx 10 \text{ years} \times 400 \text{ days/year} \times 25 \text{ hours/day}$

$\approx (10 \times 400 \times 25) \text{ hours}$

$\approx 100,000 \text{ hours}$

15. Round 78 years to 80 years.
Round 365 days per year to 400 days per year.
Round 24 hours per day to 25 hours per day.
$\approx (80 \text{ years})(400 \text{ days per year})(25 \text{ hours per day})$

$\approx (80 \times 400 \times 25) \text{ hours}$

$\approx 800,000 \text{ hours}$

16. Round 39 years to 40 years.
Round 365 days per year to 400 days per year.
Round 24 hours per day to 25 hours per day.
$\approx (40 \text{ years})(400 \text{ days per year})(25 \text{ hours per day})$

$\approx (40 \times 400 \times 25) \text{ hours}$

$\approx 400,000 \text{ hours}$

17. Round $61,500 to $60,000 per year.
Round 52 weeks per year to 50 weeks per year.
50 weeks $\times$ 40 hours per week = 2000 hours
$60,000 $\div$ 2000 hours = $30 per hour
$61,500 per year $\approx$ $30 per hour

18. Round $38,950 to $40,000 per year.
Round 52 weeks per year to 50 weeks per year.
50 weeks $\times$ 40 hours per week = 2000 hours
$40,000 $\div$ 2000 hours = $20 per hour
$38,950 per year $\approx$ $20 per hour

19. Round the raise of $310,000 to $300,000.
Round the 294 professors to 300.
$300,000 $\div$ 300 professors = $1000 per professor.
$310,000 raise $\approx$ $1000 per professor.

20. Round the raise of $310,000 to $300,000.
Round the 196 professors to 200.
$300,000 $\div$ 200 professors = $1500 per professor.
$310,000 raise $\approx$ $1500 per professor.

21. Round the $605 monthly payment to $600.
3 years is 36 months.
Round the 36 months to 40 months.
$600 $\times$ 40 months = $24,000 total cost.
$605 monthly payment for 3 years $\approx$ $24,000 total cost.

22. Round the $415 monthly payment to $400.
4 years is 48 months.
Round the 48 months to 50 months.
$400 $\times$ 50 months = $20,000 total cost.
$415 monthly payment for 3 years $\approx$ $20,000 total cost.

23. Round the $21.36 to $20.
15% of $20 is a $3.00 tip.

24. Round the $28.70 to $30.
15% of $30 is a $4.50 tip.

25. a. The distance on map is about 3 inches. So, at 80 miles/inch this means the total distance $\approx 3 \times 80 \text{ miles} \approx 240 \text{ miles}$.

b. $\dfrac{240 \text{ miles}}{40 \text{ miles / hour}} = 6 \text{ hours}$
Travel time $\approx$ 6 hours

26. a. The distance on the map is about $\frac{1}{4}$ inch. So, at 80 miles/inch, this means the distance is

$(80 \text{ miles / inch})\left(\dfrac{1}{4} \text{ inch}\right) = 20 \text{ miles}$

Distance $\approx$ 20 miles

b. At distance of 20 miles at speed of 40 mph
$\dfrac{20 \text{ miles}}{40 \text{ mph}} = \dfrac{1}{2} \text{ hour}$

Travel time $\approx \dfrac{1}{2}$ hour

27. Round US population to 300,000,000 people. Round percentage of Protestants to 60%.

    Protestant population $\approx \dfrac{6}{10}$ (300,000,000 people) $\approx 180{,}000{,}000$ people.

28. Round US population to 300,000,000 people.

    25% means $\dfrac{1}{4}$

    Catholic population $\approx \dfrac{300{,}000{,}000 \text{ people}}{4}$

    $\approx 75{,}000{,}000$ people

29. Round the 9976 hate crimes to 10,000. Round percentage motivated by race to 60%.

    Hate crimes motivated by race $\approx \dfrac{6}{10}$ (10,000 crimes motivated by race) ≈ 6000 crimes motivated by race.

30. Round the 10,021 hate crimes to 10,000. Hate crimes motivated by sexual orientation

    $\approx \dfrac{14}{100}$ (10,000 crimes motivated by sexual orientation) ≈ 1400 crimes motivated by race.

31. The graph indicates that approximately 33% of vacations include shopping.

32. The graph indicates that approximately 11% of vacations include beaches.

33. historical places and museums, outdoor recreation, and shopping

34. historical places and museums, and outdoor recreation

35. The life expectancy for men born in 1900 was approximately 48 years.

36. The life expectancy for women born in 2050 will be approximately 83 years.

37. Approximately 8 years more. The life expectancy for women born in 1980 was approximately 78 years. The life expectancy for men born in 1980 was approximately 70 years.

38. Approximately 7 years more. The life expectancy for women born in 1996 was approximately 79 years. The life expectancy for men born in 1996 was approximately 72 years.

39. Approximately $470

40. Approximately $425

41. Approximately $20

42. Approximately $30

43. For the period shown, a maximum of about 22% occurred in 1960.

44. For the period shown, a minimum of about 11% occurred in 2000.

45. $0.20 \times 180{,}000{,}000 \approx 36{,}000{,}000$. Thus approximately 36 million lived below the poverty level in 1960.

46. $0.10 \times 280{,}000{,}000 \approx 28{,}000{,}000$. Thus approximately 28 million lived below the poverty level in 2000.

47. 1832; approximately 20%

48. 1960; approximately 62%

49. Approximately 52%

50. Approximately 22%

51-60. Answers will vary.

61. The graphs indicate that the populations will both be about 9 million in 2030.

62. $\dfrac{24{,}000 \times 5124}{14{,}730} \approx \dfrac{24{,}000 \times 5000}{15{,}000}$

    $= \dfrac{24{,}000 \times \cancel{5000}}{\cancel{15{,}000}_{\,3}}$

    $= \dfrac{24{,}000}{3}$

    $= 8000$

63. 20 dimes stack to about 1 inch.

$$\frac{5280 \text{ feet}}{\text{mile}} \times \frac{12 \text{ inches}}{\text{foot}} = 63,360 \text{ inches per mile}$$

Round 63,360 to 60,000 inches per mile.

$$1,000,000 \text{ dimes} \times \frac{\text{inch}}{20 \text{ dimes}} \times \frac{\text{mile}}{60,000 \text{ inches}}$$

$$= \frac{1,000,000}{1,200,000} \text{ miles} = \frac{5}{6} \text{ mile}$$

$$1,000,000 \text{ dimes} \approx \frac{5}{6} \text{ mile}$$

64. Round days in a year to 400.

$$\frac{\$1,000,000,000}{\$1000 / \text{day}} = 1,000,000 \text{ days}$$

$$\approx \frac{1,000,000 \text{ days}}{400 \text{ days} / \text{year}}$$

$$\approx 2500 \text{ years}$$

65. a. Answers will vary.;

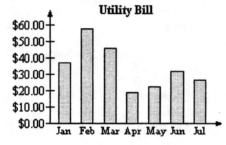

b. Answers will vary.;

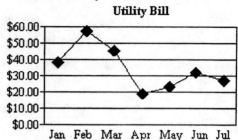

c. Answers will vary.;

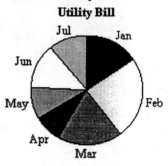

Check Points 1.3

1. The amount of money given to the cashier is unknown.

2. Step 1: Understand the problem.
   Bottles: 128 ounces costs $5.39
   Boxes: a 9-pack of 6.75 ounce boxes costs $3.15
   We must determine whether bottles or boxes are the better value.
   Step 2: Devise a plan.
   Dividing the cost by the number of ounces will give us the cost per ounce. We will need to multiply 9 by 6.75 to determine the total number of ounces the boxes contain. The lower cost per ounce is the best value.
   Step 3: Carry out the plan and solve the problem.

   Unit price for the bottles: $\dfrac{\$5.39}{128 \text{ ounces}} \approx \$0.042$ per ounce

   Unit price for the boxes: $\dfrac{\$3.15}{9 \times 6.75 \text{ ounces}} = \dfrac{\$3.15}{60.75 \text{ ounces}} \approx \$0.052$ per ounce

   Bottles have a lower price per ounce and are the better value.
   Step 4: Look back and check the answer.
   This answer satisfies the conditions of the problem.

3. Step 1: Understand the problem.
   We are given the cost of the computer, the amount of cash paid up front, and the amount paid each month. We must determine the number of months it will take to finish paying for the computer.
   Step 2: Devise a plan.
   Subtract the amount paid in cash from the cost of the computer. This results in the amount still to be paid. Because the monthly payments are $45, divide the amount still to be paid by 45. This will give the number of months required to pay for the computer.
   Step 3: Carry out the plan and solve the problem.
   The balance is $980 - $350 = $630. Now divide the $630 balance by $45, the monthly payment.

$$\$630 \div \frac{\$45}{\text{month}} = \$630 \times \frac{\text{month}}{\$45} = \frac{630 \text{ months}}{45} = 14 \text{ months}.$$

   Step 4: Look back and check the answer.
   This answer satisfies the conditions of the problem. 14 monthly payments at $45 each gives $14 \times \$45 = \$630$. Adding in the up front cash payment of $350 gives us $630 + $350 = $980. $980 is the cost of the computer.

4. Step 1: Understand the problem.
   Step 2: Devise a plan.
   Make a list of all possible coin combinations. Begin with the coins of larger value and work toward the coins of smaller value.

   Step 3: Carry out the plan and solve the problem.

Quarters	Dimes	Nickels
1	0	1
0	3	0
0	2	2
0	1	4
0	0	6

   There are 5 combinations.
   Step 4: Look back and check the answer.
   Check to see that no combinations are omitted, and that those given total 30 cents. Also double-check the count.

5. Step 1: Understand the problem.
   We must determine the number of jeans/T-shirt combinations that we can make.
   For example, one such combination would be to wear the blue jeans with the beige shirt.
   Step 2: Devise a plan.
   Each pair of jeans could be matched with any of the three shirts. We will make a tree diagram to show all combinations.
   Step 3: Carry out the plan and solve the problem.

JEANS	T-SHIRT	COMBINATIONS
	Beige shirt	Blue jeans-Beige shirt
Blue jeans	Yellow shirt	Blue jeans-Yellow shirt
	Blue shirt	Blue jeans-Blue shirt
	Beige shirt	Black jeans-Beige shirt
Black jeans	Yellow shirt	Black jeans-Yellow shirt
	Blue shirt	Black jeans-Blue shirt

   There are 6 different outfits possible.
   Step 4: Look back and check the answer.
   Check to see that no combinations are omitted, and double-check the count.

6. Step 1: Understand the problem.
   There are many possible ways to visit each city once and then return home. We must find a route that costs less than $1460.
   Step 2: Devise a plan.
   From city A fly to the city with the cheapest available flight. Repeat this until all cities have been visited and then fly home. If this cost is above $1460 then use trial and error to find other alternative routes.
   Step 3: Carry out the plan and solve the problem.
   A to D costs $185, D to E costs $302, E to C costs $165, C to B costs $305, B back to A costs $500
   $185 + $302 + $165 + $305 + $500 = $1457
   The route A, D, E, C, B, A costs less than $1460
   Step 4: Look back and check the answer.
   This answer satisfies the conditions of the problem.

7. Step 1: Understand the problem.
   Despite this person's apparent irresponsibility, she/he is your friend. You would like to see your friend's attendance and academic achievement improve.
   Step 2: Devise a plan.
   List as many ideas as possible.
   Step 3: Carry out the plan and solve the problem.
   Your list might include…
   - Offer to drive your friend to school.
   - Suggest the friend take later classes in future semesters. (or see if instructor has later sections of the course)
   - Offer a reward to your friend based on good attendance or grades.
   - Offer help with assignments.
   - Try to address the reasons your friend is absent. (ex. offer to baby-sit)
   Step 4: Look back and check the answer.
   Real-life situations often have more than one solution. Also, some of the ideas in our list may be inappropriate or make matters worse. Choose carefully.

Trick Questions 1.3

1. The farmer has 12 sheep left since all but 12 sheep died.

2. All 12 months have [at least] 28 days.

3. The doctor and brother are brother and sister.

4. You should light the match first.

Exercise Set 1.3

1. The price of the computer is needed.

2. The weight of the steak is needed.

3. The number of words per page is needed.

4. The amount of the payments is needed.

5. Weekly salary is unnecessary information.
   $212 - 200 = 12$ items sold in excess of 200
   $12 \times \$15 = \$180$ extra is received.

6. Tire weight is not necessary.
   $4 \times (\$42 + \$2.50) = 4 \times \$44.50 = \$178.00$
   $\$250 - \$178 = \$72$ remaining after purchase.

7. How much the attendant was given is not necessary.
   There were 5 hours of parking.
   1st hour is $2.50
   4 hours at $0.50/hr
   $\$2.50 + (4 \times \$0.50) = \$2.50 + \$2.00$
   $= \$4.50$
   $4.50 was charged.

8. The width of the house is not necessary.
   $90 \text{ feet} = 15 \times 6 \text{ feet}$
   The line representing the length is 15 inches.

9. a. Step 1: Understand the problem.
Box #1: 15.3 ounces costs $3.37
Box #2: 24 ounces costs $4.59
We must determine whether Box #1 or Box #2 is the better value.
Step 2: Devise a plan.
Dividing the cost by the number of ounces will give us the cost per ounce. The lower cost per ounce is the best value.
Step 3: Carry out the plan and solve the problem.

Unit price for Box #1: $\dfrac{\$3.37}{15.3 \text{ ounces}} \approx \$0.22$ per ounce

Unit price for Box #2: $\dfrac{\$4.59}{24 \text{ ounces}} \approx \$0.19$ per ounce

The cereal that is 24 ounces for $4.59 is the better value.
Step 4: Look back and check the answer.
This answer satisfies the conditions of the problem.

b. Unit price for Box #1: $0.22 per ounce

Unit price for Box #2: $\dfrac{\$4.59}{24 \text{ ounces}} \times \dfrac{16 \text{ ounces}}{\text{pound}} \approx \$3.06$ per pound

c. No, explanations will vary

10. a. Step 1: Understand the problem.
Jar #1: 12 ounces costs $2.25
Jar #2: 18 ounces costs $3.24
We must determine whether Jar #1 or Jar #2 is the better value.
Step 2: Devise a plan.
Dividing the cost by the number of ounces will give us the cost per ounce. The lower cost per ounce is the best value.
Step 3: Carry out the plan and solve the problem.

Unit price for Jar #1: $\dfrac{\$2.25}{12 \text{ ounces}} \approx \$0.19$ per ounce

Unit price for Jar #2: $\dfrac{\$3.24}{18 \text{ ounces}} \approx \$0.18$ per ounce

The honey that is 18 ounces for $3.24 is the better value.
Step 4: Look back and check the answer.
This answer satisfies the conditions of the problem.

b. Unit price for Jar #1: $0.19 per ounce

Unit price for Jar #2: $\dfrac{\$3.24}{18 \text{ ounces}} \times \dfrac{32 \text{ ounces}}{\text{quart}} \approx \$5.76$ per quart

c. No, explanations will vary

11. Step 1: Comparing two yearly salaries
Step 2:
We need to convert the second person's wages to yearly salary.
Step 3:
The person that earns $3750/month earns
$12 \times \$3750 = \$45,000$/year. The person that earns $48,000/year gets $3000 more per year.
Step 4:
It appears to satisfy the conditions of the problem.

13

12. Step 1:
Finding out the car's mileage for one year, and gas usage.
Step 2:
Subtract beginning odometer reading from ending reading.
Step 3:
37,364 miles – 25,124 miles = 12,240 miles
$$\frac{12,240 \text{ miles}}{24 \text{ mpg}} = 510 \text{ gallons}$$
Step 4:
It satisfies the conditions of the problem.

13. Step 1:
We are trying the difference between two methods of payment.
Step 2:
Compute total costs and compare two figures.
Step 3:
By spreading purchase out, the total comes to:
$100 + 14($50) = $100 + $700 = $800
$800 – $750 = $50 saved by paying all at once
Step 4:
It satisfies the conditions of problem.

14. Step 1: Trying to determine which team won.
Step 2: Compile point totals and compare.
Step 3:
Bulldogs: $34 \times 2 + 13 = 68 + 13 = 81$ points
Panthers: $38 \times 2 + 8 = 76 + 8 = 84$ points
Panthers won by 3 points
Step 4:
It satisfies the conditions of the problem.

15. Step 1:
Trying to determine profit on goods sold.
Step 2:
Find total cost of buying product and comparing with gross sales.
Step 3:
Purchased: ($65 per dozen)(6 dozen) = $390
Sold: 6 dozen = 72 calculators
$$\frac{72}{3} = 24 \text{ groups of 3 at \$20 per group.}$$
$24 \times $20 = $480
$480 – $390 = $90 profit
Step 4:
It satisfies the conditions of the problem.

16. Step 1: Determine profit.
Step 2:
Determine cost of purchase and compare with gross sales.

Step 3:
Bought:
($0.95/dozen)(15 dozen) = $14.25
Sold:
15 dozen = 180 pens
$$\frac{180}{4} = 45 \text{ packs}$$
45 packs $\times$ $2.25 = $101.25
Profit = $101.25 – $14.25 = $87
Step 4:
It satisfies the conditions of the problem.

17. Step 1: Determine profit for ten-day period.
Step 2: Compare totals
Step 3:
(200 slices)($1.50) = $300 for pizza
(85 sandwiches)($2.50) = $212.50 for sandwiches
For 10 day period:
Gross: 10($300) + 10($212.50) = $3000 + $2125.00
$$= $5125.00$$
Expenses: 10($60) = $600
Profit: $5125.00 – $600 = $4525
Step 4:
It satisfies the conditions of the problem.

18. Step 1: Determine how much was earned over two-week period.
Step 2: Compute each week's earnings and total.
Step 3:
1st week:
(40 hours)($5.15 per hour) + (2 hours)($5.15 + $1.20)
= $206 + (2 hours)($6.35)
= $206 + $12.70
= $218.70
2nd week:
(40 hours)($ 5.15 per hour) + (5 hours)($ 6.35)
= $206 + $31.75
= $237.75
Total is $218.70 + $237.75 = $456.45
Step 4:
It satisfies the conditions of problem.

19. Step 1:
We are trying to compute total rental cost.
Step 2:
Add rental cost and mileage cost to get total cost.
Step 3:
Rental costs:
(2 weeks)($220 per week) = $440
Mileage: (500 miles)($0.25) = $125
Total: $440 + $125 = $565
Step 4:
It satisfies the conditions of problem.

20. Step 1:
We are trying to figure out an annual budget and see how much is left to buy stock and how many shares of stock.
Step 2:

Determine annual earnings and compare with budget.

Step 3:

Salary:

(12 months/year)($2750/month) = $33,000

Expenses:

$4800 + $8200 + $3750 + $4250 + $3000

= $24,000

Available to buy stocks:

$33,000 − $24,000 = $9000

Number of stocks: $\dfrac{\$9000}{\$375 \text{ / share}}$ = 24 shares

Step 4:

It satisfies the conditions of problem.

21. Step 1:

A round trip was made; we need to determine how much was walked or ridden.

Step 2:

Add up the totals walked and ridden and compare.

Step 3:

It is 5 miles between the homes or a 10 mile round trip. The first 3 were covered with the bicycle, leaving 7 miles covered by walking.

7 miles − 3 miles = 4 miles more that was walked.

Step 4:

It satisfies the conditions of the problem.

22. Step 1:

Trying to determine the profit on goods sold

Step 2:

Determine the cost of obtaining product and compare with gross sales.

Step 3:

Cost:

200 containers at $0.75 apiece = $150

Cost = $150

Gross sales: (150 containers)($1.25) = $187.50

50 containers returned for $0.50 refund:

50($0.50) = $25.00

Total received: $187.50 + $25.00 = $212.50

Total Profit: $212.50 − $150.00 = $62.50

Step 4:

It satisfies the conditions of the problem.

23. Step 1:

To determine profit by comparing expenses with gross sales

Step 2:

Calculate expenses and gross sales and compare.

Step 3:

Expense:

(25 calculators)($30) = $750

Gross Sales:

(22 calculators)($35.00) = $770

The storeowner receives $30 − $2 = $28 for each returned calculator.

(3 calculators)($28) = $84

Total Income:

$770 + $84 = $854

Profit = Income − Expenses

$\qquad$ = $854 − $750

$\qquad$ = $104

Step 4:
It satisfies the conditions of the problem.

24. When the drivers meet for lunch they have been traveling for 2 hours and 24 minutes or 2.4 hours.
The car from New York City has traveled
(2.4 hours)(55 miles per hour) = 132 miles.
The car from D.C. has traveled
(2.4 hours)(45 miles per hour) = 108 miles.

25. Use a list.

2 Quarters	3 Dimes	5 Nickels
1	2	0
1	1	2
1	0	4
0	3	3
0	2	5

There are 5 ways.

26. Use a list.

Pennies	Nickels	Dimes
25	0	0
20	1	0
15	2	0
15	0	1
10	3	0
10	1	1
5	4	0
5	2	1
5	0	2
0	5	0
0	3	1
0	1	2

There are 12 ways.

27. Make a list of all possible orders:
TFFF, FTFF, FFTF, FFFT
The "True" could be written 1st, 2nd, 3rd, or 4th.
There are 4 ways.

28. Represent the 5 people as A, B, C, D, and E and make a list of all possible handshakes:
AB, AC, AD, AE, BC, BD, BE, CD, CE and DE.
There are 10 handshakes exchanged.

29. The order the racers finished was; Andy, Darnell, Caleb, Beth, Ella.

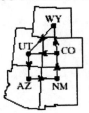

30. To determine a winner, seven teams must be eliminated. Since each game eliminates one team, this tournament will take seven games.

31. Home→Bank→Post Office→Dry Cleaners→Home will take 11.5 miles.

32. Home→Post Office→Dry Cleaners→Bank→Home will take 12.5 miles.

33. CO→WY→UT→AZ→NM→CO→UT

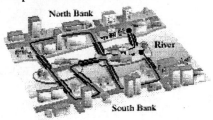

34. One possible route is indicated:

35. The problem states that the psychology major knocks on Jose's wall, and Jose's dorm is adjacent to Bob's dorm but not Tony's. Therefore Bob is the psychology major.

36. Answers will vary

37.

```
        156
    28)4368
        28
        156
        140
        168
        168
          0
```

38. The first area code's sum is nine. The second area code starts with 6, cannot contain a 1 or 2, and therefore it must end with 30 or 03 to have the proper sum. The third area code ends with 1. Therefore, the first two digits of this area code must total eight. 7 and 1 are the only remaining pair of digits that meet all the criteria. The third area code is 711.

2 5 2

6 3 0 or 6 0 3

7 1 1

39. The completed diagonal has a sum of 75. Use this sum to complete rows or columns that have two known values. For example, the middle number of the right column must be $75 - 30 - 40 = 5$. Continuing this process results in the magic square shown at right.

10	35	30
45	25	5
20	15	40

40. The given diagonal has a sum of 15. Use this sum to complete rows or columns that have two known values. For example, the middle number of the right column must be $15 - 8 - 4 = 3$. Continuing this process results in the magic square shown at right.

6	1	8
7	5	3
2	9	4

41. The figure has 9 one by one's ▢, 4 two by two's ⊞, and 1 three by three ⊞.
Giving a total of $9 + 4 + 1 = 14$ squares.

42. The figure has 16 one by one's ▢, 9 two by two's ⊞, 4 three by three's ⊞, and 1 four by four ⊞.
Giving a total of $16 + 9 + 4 + 1 = 30$ squares.

43. Move the 3 shaded toothpicks as shown. Notice that there are 4 little squares and 1 big square.

44. Assemble the pieces as shown:

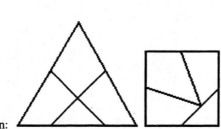

45. The message is: ESCAPE TONIGHT

46. 21 cubes are needed for the fifth solid. The first three solids contain 1, 6, and 11 cubes respectively. This pattern suggests that the number of cubes needed by each successive solid is 5 more than the previous solid. Giving the sequence 1, 6, 11, 16, and 21.

47-53. Answers will vary.

54. Make a list of every instance of a seven: 7, 17, 27, 37, 47, 57, 67, 70, 71, 72, 73, 74, 75, 76, 77, 78, 79, 87, 97
A total of twenty 7s are needed.

55. You should choose the dentist whose teeth show the effects of poor dental work because he took good care of the other dentist's teeth.

56. Use one plank diagonally across one corner of the square. Use the other plank to go from the first plank to the stone.

57. The farmer can use the following strategy: Take the goat to the other side of the stream and return to get either the wolf or cabbage. The farmer should take that across the stream and bring the goat back to the original side. He then takes across the cabbage or wolf, whichever remains, and leaves it on the other side while he returns to get the goat.

58. From the middle rung the firefighter went up 4, down 6, up 7, and up 4 to reach the top rung. This is a net climb of up 9. Since there are 9 rungs above the middle rung, there must also be 9 rungs below.
9 above + 9 below + 1 middle = 19 rungs.

59. Answers will vary.

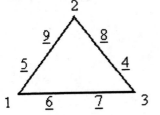

60. Answers will vary. One method is to start by multiplying 30 by each state's fraction of the population.

State A: $30 \times \dfrac{275}{1890} \approx 4.365$ or 4

State B: $30 \times \dfrac{383}{1890} \approx 6.079$ or 6

State C: $30 \times \dfrac{465}{1890} \approx 7.381$ or 7

State D: $30 \times \dfrac{767}{1890} \approx 12.175$ or 12

Notice that 4, 6, 7, and 12 add to 29, so there is 1 more representative to be allocated. We could give this extra representative to state C because it had the largest decimal part (0.381). This leads to an allocation of state A: 4, state B: 6, state C: 8, and state D: 12.

Chapter 1 Review Exercises

1. Deductive; the specific conclusion about *Carrie* was based on a general statement about all Stephen King books.

2. Inductive; the general conclusion for this next book was based on past specific observations.

3. Vermont, Virginia, Washington, West Virginia, Wisconsin and Wyoming are all counterexamples.

4. Any two consecutive odd numbers, like 5 and 7, are a counterexample.

5. Counterexample: $2 > -5$ but $(2)^2 < (-5)^2$. That is 4 is less than 25

6. Pattern: Add 5
   $19 + 5 = 24$
   $4, 9, 14, 19, \underline{24}$

7. Pattern: Multiply by 2
   $56 \times 2 = 112$
   $7, 14, 28, 56, \underline{112}$

8. Pattern: Numbers added increase by 1
   $1 + 2 = 3$
   $3 + 3 = 6$
   $6 + 4 = 10$
   $10 + 5 = 15$
   $15 + 6 = 21$
   $1, 3, 6, 10, 15, \underline{21}$

9. Notice that $\dfrac{1}{2} = \dfrac{3}{6}$

Pattern: Add 1 to the denominator

$$\dfrac{3}{7+1} = \dfrac{3}{8}$$

$$\dfrac{3}{4}, \dfrac{3}{5}, \dfrac{3}{6}, \dfrac{3}{7}, \underline{\dfrac{3}{8}} \text{ or}$$

$$\dfrac{3}{4}, \dfrac{3}{5}, \dfrac{1}{2}, \dfrac{3}{7}, \underline{\dfrac{3}{8}}$$

10. Pattern: Divide by -2

$$-5 \div (-2) = \dfrac{-5}{-2} = \dfrac{5}{2} \text{ or } 2\dfrac{1}{2}$$

$$40, -20, 10, -5, \dfrac{5}{2}$$

10. Pattern: Subtract 60

$$-140 - 60 = -200$$

$$40, -20, -80, -140, \underline{-200}$$

12. The pattern is alternating between square and circle while the line rotates 90° clockwise. The next figure is shown at right.

13. a. Conjecture based on results: The result is the original number.

Select a number	4	10	0	3
Double the number.	$4 \times 2 = 8$	$10 \times 2 = 20$	$0 \times 2 = 0$	$3 \times 2 = 6$
Add 4 to the product.	$8 + 4 = 12$	$20 + 4 = 24$	$0 + 4 = 4$	$6 + 4 = 10$
Divide this sum by 2.	$12 \div 2 = 6$	$24 \div 2 = 12$	$4 \div 2 = 2$	$10 \div 2 = 5$
Subtract 2 from the quotient.	$6 - 2 = 4$	$12 - 2 = 10$	$2 - 2 = 0$	$5 - 2 = 3$
Summary of results:	$4 \rightarrow 4$	$10 \rightarrow 10$	$0 \rightarrow 0$	$3 \rightarrow 3$

b. $2n$

$2n + 4$

$$\dfrac{2n+4}{2} = \dfrac{2n}{2} + \dfrac{4}{2} = n + 2$$

$n + 2 - 2 = n$

14. $8.47 + \$0.89 + \$2.79 + \$0.14 + \$1.19 + \$4.76$

$\approx \$8 + \$1 + \$3 + \$0 + \$1 + \$5$

$\approx \$18$

15. Round 78 hours to 80, round \$6.85 to \$7.00. $78 \times \$6.85 \approx 80 \times \$7.00 \approx \$560$

16. $60 \dfrac{\text{seconds}}{\text{minute}} \times 60 \dfrac{\text{minutes}}{\text{hour}} = 3600 \dfrac{\text{seconds}}{\text{hour}}$

Round $3600 \dfrac{\text{seconds}}{\text{hour}}$ to $4000 \dfrac{\text{seconds}}{\text{hour}}$.

Round $24 \dfrac{\text{hours}}{\text{day}}$ to $20 \dfrac{\text{hours}}{\text{day}}$.

$20 \dfrac{\text{hours}}{\text{day}} \times 4000 \dfrac{\text{seconds}}{\text{hour}} = 80,000 \dfrac{\text{seconds}}{\text{day}}$

$3600 \dfrac{\text{seconds}}{\text{hour}} \times 24 \dfrac{\text{hours}}{\text{day}} \approx 80,000 \dfrac{\text{seconds}}{\text{day}}$

17. Round $27 \dfrac{19}{20}$ to 28.

Round 6.823 to 7.

$27 \dfrac{19}{20} \div 6.823 \approx 28 \div 7 \approx 4$

18. Round book price to $1.00 each.
Round chair price to $12.00 each.
Round plate price to $15.00.
$(21 \times \$0.85) + (2 \times \$11.95) + \$14.65$
$\approx (21 \times \$1) + (2 \times \$12) + \$15$
$\approx \$21 + \$24 + \$15$
$\approx \$60$

19. Approximate gallons used by toilets: $0.25 \times 30 \times 360 \approx 2700$

20. The veterinary costs for cats in 1983 was approximately $1 billion.

21. The veterinary costs for dogs in 1996 was approximately $8 billion.

22. The veterinary costs for cats in 2000 was approximately $6 billion. The veterinary costs for dogs in 2000 was approximately $14 billion. The difference between the two was approximately $8 billion.

23. This occurs for dogs in 1991, for cats in 1996, and for cats in 2000. Note that the wording in the question *excludes* dogs in 1987 but *includes* cats in 2000.

24. There were approximately 7 murders per 100,000 people in 2000.

25. For the period shown, the maximum murder rate occurred in 1980. There were approximately 10 or 11 murders per 100,000 people in 1980.

26. To estimate, use the values from 1970, 1980, 1990, and 2000. These values are approximately 8, 11, 10, and 7.

The average is $\dfrac{8 + 11 + 10 + 7}{4} = \dfrac{36}{4} = 9$ murders per 100,000 people.

27. The weight of the child is needed.

28. The unnecessary information is the customer giving the driver a $20 bill.
For a 6 mile trip, the first mile is $3.00, and the next 5 miles are $0.50/half-mile or $1.00/mile. The cost is
$\$3.00 + (5 \times \$1.00) = \$3.00 + \$5.00$
$= \$8.00.$

29. Total of $28 \times 2 = 56$ frankfurters would be needed. $\dfrac{56}{7} = 8$. Therefore, 8 pounds would be needed.

30. Rental for 3 weeks at $175 per week is
$3 \times \$175 = \$525$. Mileage for 1200 miles at $0.30 per mile is $1200 \times \$0.30 = \$360$. Total cost is $\$525 + \$360 = \$885$.

31. Healthy Bodies is a better deal by $40 for the year.
Superfit: $\$500 + 80(\$1.00) = \$580$; Healthy Bodies: $\$400 + 80(\$1.75) = \$400 + \$140 = \$540$

32. The flight leaves Miami at 7:00 A.M. Pacific Standard Time. With a lay-over of 45 minutes, it arrives in San Francisco at 1:30 P.M. Pacific Standard Time, 6 hrs 30 min. − 45 min = 5 hours 45 minutes.

33. At steady decrease in value: $\dfrac{\$37,000 - \$2600}{8 \text{ years}} = \dfrac{\$34,400}{8 \text{ years}} = \$4300 / \text{ year}$

After 5 years: $\$4300 \times 5 = \$21,500$ decrease in value
Value of car: $\$37,000 - \$21,500 = \$15,500$

34. The machine will accept nickels, dimes, quarters.

nickels	dimes	quarters
7	0	0
5	1	0
3	2	0
2	0	1
1	3	0
0	1	1

There are 6 combinations.

Chapter 1 Test

1. One possible answer is: $25 \times 4 = 100$ which is a three-digit number.

2. $0 + 5 = 5$
$5 + 5 = 10$
$10 + 5 = 15$
$15 + 5 = 20$
$0, 5, 10, 15, \underline{20}$

3. $\dfrac{1}{6 \times 2} = \dfrac{1}{12}$

$\dfrac{1}{12 \times 2} = \dfrac{1}{24}$

$\dfrac{1}{24 \times 2} = \dfrac{1}{48}$

$\dfrac{1}{48 \times 2} = \dfrac{1}{96}$

$\dfrac{1}{6}, \dfrac{1}{12}, \dfrac{1}{24}, \dfrac{1}{48}, \dfrac{1}{\underline{96}}$

4. The outer figure is always a square. The inner figure appears to cycle from triangle to circle to square. The line segments at the bottom alternate from two to one. The next shape is shown at right.

5. a. Conjecture based on results: The original number is doubled.

Select a number	4	10	3
Multiply the number by 4.	$4 \times 4 = 16$	$10 \times 4 = 40$	$3 \times 4 = 12$
Add 8 to the product.	$16 + 8 = 24$	$40 + 8 = 48$	$12 + 8 = 20$
Divide this sum by 2.	$24 \div 2 = 12$	$48 \div 2 = 24$	$20 \div 2 = 10$
Subtract 4 from the quotient.	$12 - 4 = 8$	$24 - 4 = 20$	$10 - 4 = 6$
Summary of results:	$4 \rightarrow 8$	$10 \rightarrow 20$	$3 \rightarrow 6$

b. $4n$

$4n + 8$

$$\frac{4n + 8}{2} = \frac{4n}{2} + \frac{8}{2} = 2n + 4$$

$2n + 4 - 4 = 2n$

6. Round $47.00 to $50.00.
   Round $311.00 to $310.00.
   Round $405.00 to $410.00.
   Round $681.79 to $680.00.
   Total needed for expenses:
   $47.00 + $311.00 + $405.00
   $\approx$ $50.00 + $310.00 + $410.00
   $\approx$ $770.00
   Additional money needed:
   $770.00 − $681.79 $\approx$ $770.00 − $680.00
   $\approx$ $90

7. Round $485,000 to $500,000.
   Round number of people to 20.
   $$\frac{\$485,000}{19 \text{ people}} \approx \frac{\$500,000}{20 \text{ people}}$$
   $\approx$ $25,000 per person

8. $0.48992 \times 120 \approx 0.5 \times 120 \approx 60$

9. World population living in free countries in 2002: 0.40×6 billion ≈ 2.4 billion

10. Carter appointed approximately 250 federal judgeships.

11. Carter, Reagan, and Bush each appointed between 20 and 50 women to federal judgeships.

12. Clinton appointed about 60 African Americans to federal judgeships. Bush appointed about 10 African Americans to federal judgeships. Thus, Clinton appointed approximately 50 more than Bush.

13. A minimum of approximately 54 million was reached in 1980.

14. For 3 hours:

    Estes: $9 per $\frac{1}{4}$ hour

    $3 \times 4 = 12$ quarter-hours $\rightarrow 12 \times \$9 = \$108$

    Ship and Shore: $20 per $\frac{1}{2}$ hour

    $3 \times 2 = 6$ half-hours $\rightarrow 6 \times \$20 = \$120$
    Estes is a better deal by
    $120 − $108 = $12.00.

15. 20 round trips mean 40 one-way trips at $11/trip.
    (40 trips)(32 passengers)($11)
    = $14,080 in one day

16. $960 − $50 = $910 remaining to pay

    $$\frac{\$910}{\$35 \text{ per week}} = 26 \text{ weeks}$$

Chapter 2
Set Theory

Check Points 2.1

1. Set L is the set of the first six lowercase letters in the English alphabet.

2. $D = \{3, 7, 4, 1, 8\}$

3. $L = \{m, a, r, c, h\}$

4. **a.** True; 8 is an element of the given set.

   b. True; r is not an element of the given set.

   c. False; {Monday} is a set and the set {Monday} is not an element of the given set.

5. **a.** $A = \{1, 2, 3\}$

   b. $B = \{15, 16, 17, \ldots\}$

   c. $O = \{1, 3, 5, \ldots\}$

   d. $F = \{12, 13\}$

6. **a.** $n(A) = 5$; the set has 5 elements

   b. $n(B) = 1$; the set has only 1 element

   c. $n(C) = 8$; Though this set lists only five elements, the three dots indicate 12, 13, and 14 are also elements.

   d. $n(D) = 0$ because the set has no elements.

7. **a.** True, $\{O, L, D\} = \{D, O, L\}$ because the sets contain exactly the same elements.

   b. False, the two sets do not contain exactly the same elements.

8. **a.** No, they are not equal because they have different elements.

   b. Yes, they are equivalent because they have the same number of elements.

Exercise Set 2.1

1. The set of known planets in our Solar System.

2. The set of weekend days.

3. The set of months that begin with J.

4. The set of signs of the zodiac.

5. The set of odd natural numbers less than 100.

6. The set of natural numbers which are multiples of 5.

7. {winter, spring, summer, fall}

8. {April, June, September, November}

9. {September, October, November, December}

10. {e, f, g, h, i}

11. {1, 2, 3}

12. {1, 2, 3, 4, 5, 6}

13. {1, 3, 5, 7, 9, 11}

14. {2, 4, 6, 8}

15. {101, 102, 103, ...}

16. {51, 52, 53, ...}

17. {11, 12, 13, 14, 15}

18. {24, 25, 26, 27, 28}

19. {10, 11, 12, 13, 14, 15, 16}

20. {23, 24, 25, 26, 27, 28, 29}

21. {2}

22. {6}

23. $\{x \mid x$ is a day of the week that begins with T}

24. $\{x \mid x$ is a letter that follows g and comes before l}

25. $\{x \mid x \in N$ and x is less than 6}

26. $\{x \mid x \in N$ and x is less than 7}

27. $\{x \mid x \in N$ and lies between 3 and 5, inclusive} or $\{x \mid x \in N$ and lies between 2 and 6}

28. $\{x \mid x \in N$ and lies between 4 and 6, inclusive} or $\{x \mid x \in N$ and lies between 3 and 7}

29. $\{x \mid x \in N$ and is greater than 2}

30. $\{x \mid x \in N$ and is greater than 3}

31. True
3 is a member of the set.

32. True
6 is a member of the set.

33. True
12 is a member of the set.

34. True
10 is a member of the set.

35. False
5 is *not* a member of the set.

36. False
8 is *not* a member of the set.

37. True
11 is *not* a member of the set.

38. True.
17 is *not* a member of the set.

39. False
37 is a member of the set.

40. False
26 is a member of the set.

41. False
4 is a member of the set.

42. False
2 is *not* a member of the set.

43. False
16 is *not* a member of the set.

44. True
18 is *not* a member of the set.

45. False
The set {3} is *not* a member of the set.

46. False
The set {7} is *not* a member of the set.

47. $\notin$
Mark McGwire is not, nor has ever been, President.

48. $\notin$
Atlanta is not a U.S. state.

49. $\in$
13,791 is an odd natural number.

50. $\in$
26,794 is an even natural number.

51. $\notin$
$\varnothing$ is not a member of { }

52. $\notin$
0 is not a member of $\varnothing$, since $\varnothing$ is a null set.

53. $\notin$
0 is not a natural number.

54. $\notin$
−1 is not a natural number.

55. $n(A) = 5$; There are 5 elements in the set.

56. $n(A) = 6$; There are 6 elements in the set.

57. $n(B) = 25$; There are 25 elements in the set.

58. $n(B) = 24$; There are 24 elements in the set.

59. $n(C) = 0$; There are *no* days of the week beginning with A.

60. $n(C) = 0$; There are no such months.

61. $n(D) = 1$; There is 1 element in the set.

62. $n(D) = 1$; There is 1 element in the set.

63. True; These two sets contain exactly the same elements.

64. True; These two sets contain exactly the same elements.

65. False; These two sets do not contain the exact same elements.

66. False; These two sets do not contain the exact same elements.

67. True; These two sets contain exactly the same elements.

68. True; These two sets contain exactly the same elements.

69. a. Not equal
The two sets contain different elements.

    b. Not equivalent
The number of elements is not the same.

70. a. Not equal
The two sets contain different elements.

    b. Equivalent
The number of elements is the same.

71. a. Not equal
The elements are not exactly the same.

    b. Equivalent
The number of elements is the same.

72. a. Not equal
The elements are not exactly the same.

    b. Equivalent
The number of elements is the same.

73. a. Equal
The elements are exactly the same.

    b. Equivalent
The number of elements is the same.

74. a. Equal
The elements are exactly the same.

    b. Equivalent
Number of elements is the same.

75. {amusement parks, gardening, movies, exercise}

76. {home improvement, amusement parks, gardening, movies, exercise}

77. {home improvement, amusement parks, gardening}

78. {amusement parks, gardening}

79. {Chicago, Newark, LaGuardia}

80. {San Francisco, Chicago, Newark, LaGuardia}

81. {Atlanta, Philadelphia, Boston}

82. {Philadelphia, Boston, San Francisco}

83. {75}

84. {85}

85-93. Answers will vary.

94. d

95. a

96. This question contains a paradox. Sweeney Todd cannot shave himself because he does not shave any men who shave themselves. That suggests that $s \notin A$ which implies $s \in B$. However, if Sweeney Todd does not shave himself, the question states he shaves all such men who do not shave themselves. That suggests that he does shave himself, giving $s \in A$ which implies $s \notin B$. Therefore, paradoxically, s belongs and does not belong in both sets.

Check Points 2.2

1. U is the set of TV game shows.

2. $A' = \{b, c, e\}$; those are the elements in U but not in A.

3. $U = \{a, b, c, d, e\}$; $A = \{a, d\}$; and $A' = \{b, c, e\}$

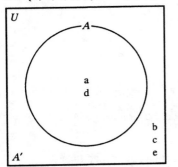

4. a. $\not\subseteq$; because 7 is not in set B.

b. $\subseteq$; because all elements in set A are also in set B.

c. $\subseteq$; because all elements in set A are also in set B.

5. a. $\subseteq$

b. Both $\subseteq$ and $\subset$ are correct.

6. Yes, the empty set is a subset of any set.

7. a. This set has 3 elements. Therefore there are $2^3 = 2 \times 2 \times 2 = 8$ subsets. This number means that there are 8 ways to make a selection, including the option to bring no books.

b.

No books packed:	{ }	
One book packed:	{*The Color Purple*}	
	{*Hannibal*}	
	{*The Royals*}	
Two books packed:	{*The Color Purple, Hannibal*}	
	{*The Color Purple, The Royals*}	
	{*Hannibal, The Royals*}	
Three books packed:	{*The Color Purple, Hannibal, The Royals*}	

c. 7 of the 8 subsets are proper subsets. {*The Color Purple, Hannibal, The Royals*} is not a proper subset.

Exercise Set 2.2

1. U is the set of composers.

2. U is the set of authors or playwrights.

3. U is the set of soft drinks.

4. U is the set of automobile brands.

5. $A' = \{c, d, e\}$

6. $B' = \{a, b, f, g\}$

7. $C' = \{b, c, d, e, f\}$

8. $D' = \{g\}$

9. $A' = \{6, 7, 8, \ldots, 20\}$

10. $B' = \{1, 2, 3, 4, 5, 10, 11, 12, 13, 14, 15, 16, 17, 18, 19, 20\}$

11. $C' = \{2, 4, 6, 8, \ldots, 20\}$

12. $D' = \{1, 3, 5, 7, \ldots, 19\}$

13. $A' = \{21, 22, 23, 24, \ldots\}$

14. $B' = \{51, 52, 53, 54, \ldots\}$

15. $C' = \{1, 3, 5, 7, \ldots\}$

16. $D' = \{2, 4, 6, 8, \ldots\}$

17. $A' = \{3, 4, 6, 7\}$

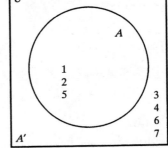

18. $A' = \{1, 4, 5, 7\}$

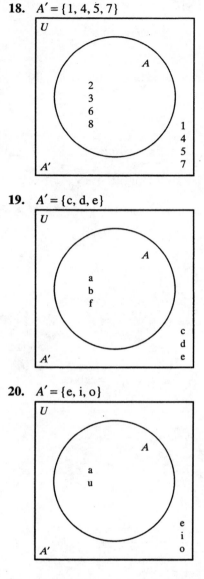

19. $A' = \{c, d, e\}$

20. $A' = \{e, i, o\}$

21. $U = \{0, 1, 2, 3, 4, 5, 6, 7, 8, 9, 10, 11, 12\}$
$A = \{1, 3, 5, 7, 9\}$ Cross out these elements from U
$A' \cancel{U} = \{0, \cancel{1}, 2, \cancel{3}, 4, \cancel{5}, 6, \cancel{7}, 8, \cancel{9}, 10, 11, 12\}$
$A' = \{0, 2, 4, 6, 8, 10, 11, 12\}$

22. $U = \{0, 1, 2, 3, 4, 5, 6, 7, 8, 9, 10\}$
$A = \{2, 4, 6, 8, 10\}$ Cross out these elements from U
$A' \cancel{U} = \{0, 1, \cancel{2}, 3, \cancel{4}, 5, \cancel{6}, 7, \cancel{8}, 9, \cancel{10}\}$
$A' = \{0, 1, 3, 5, 7, 9\}$

23. $\subseteq$

24. $\subseteq$

25. $\not\subseteq$

26. $\not\subseteq$

27. $\not\subseteq$

28. $\not\subseteq$

29. $\not\subseteq$
Subset cannot be larger than the set.

30. $\not\subseteq$
Subset cannot be larger than the set.

31. $\subseteq$

32. $\subseteq$

33. $\not\subseteq$

34. $\not\subseteq$

35. $\subseteq$ or $\subset$

36. $\subseteq$ or $\subset$

37. $\subseteq$

38. $\subseteq$

39. Neither symbol will make the statement true.
The second set is smaller than the first.

40. Neither symbol will make the statement true.
The second set is smaller than the first.

41. True

42. True

43. False
{Ralph} is a subset, not Ralph.

44. False
{Canada} is a subset, not Canada.

45. True

46. True

47. False
The symbol "$\varnothing$" is not a member of the set.

48. True

49. True

50. True

51. False
All elements of $\{1, 4\}$ are members of $\{4, 1\}$

52. True

53. True

54. True

55. $\{ \}$ {Border Collie} {Poodle} {Border Collie, Poodle}

56. $\{ \}$ {Romeo} {Juliet} {Romeo, Juliet}

57. $\{ \}$ {t} {a} {b} {t, a} {t, b} {a, b} {t, a, b}

58. $\{ \}$ {I} {II} {III} {I, II} {I, III} {II, III} {I, II, III }

59. $\{ \}$ {0}

60. $\varnothing$

61. 16 subsets, 15 proper subsets
There are 4 elements, which means there are 2^4 or 16 subsets. There are $2^4 - 1$ proper subsets or 15.

62. 16 subsets, 15 proper subsets
There are 4 elements, which means there are 2^4 or 16 subsets. There are $2^4 - 1$ proper subsets or 15.

63. 64 subsets, 63 proper subsets
There are 6 elements, which means there are 2^6 or 64 subsets. There are $2^6 - 1$ proper subsets or 63.

64. 64 subsets, 63 proper subsets
There are 6 elements, which means there are 2^6 or 64 subsets. There are $2^6 - 1$ proper subsets or 63.

65. 128 subsets, 127 proper subsets
There are 7 elements, which means there are 2^7 or 128 subsets. There are $2^7 - 1$ proper subsets or 127.

66. 32 subsets, 31 proper subsets
There are 5 elements, which means there are 2^5 or 32 subsets. There are $2^5 - 1$ proper subsets or 31.

67. 8 subsets, 7 proper subsets
There are 3 elements, which means there are 2^3 or 8 subsets. There are $2^3 - 1$ proper subsets or 7.

68. 32 subsets, 31 proper subsets
There are 5 elements, which means there are 2^5 or 32 subsets. There are $2^5 - 1$ proper subsets or 31.

69. $2^5 = 32$ option combinations

70. $2^9 = 512$ topping combinations

71. $2^6 = 64$ viewing combinations

72. $2^4 = 16$ response options

73. $2^8 = 256$ city combinations

74. $2^7 = 128$ viewing combinations

75-85. Answers will vary.

86. b

87. 0, 5¢, 10¢, 25¢, 40¢, 15¢, 30¢, 35¢
Since there are 3 elements or coins, there are 2^3 or 8 different coin combinations.

88. Number of proper subsets is $2^n - 1$, which means there are 128 total subsets (127 + 1).
128 is 2^7, so there are 7 elements.

Check Points 2.3

1. a. $\{1, 3, 5, \underline{7}, \underline{10}\} \cap \{6, \underline{7}, \underline{10}, 11\} = \{7, 10\}$

 b. $\{1, 2, 3\} \cap \{4, 5, 6, 7\} = \varnothing$

 c. $\{1, 2, 3\} \cap \varnothing = \varnothing$

2. a. $\{1, 3, 5, 7, 10\} \cup \{6, 7, 10, 11\}$
 $= \{1, 3, 5, 6, 7, 10, 11\}$

 b. $\{1, 2, 3\} \cup \{4, 5, 6, 7\} = \{1, 2, 3, 4, 5, 6, 7\}$

 c. $\{1, 2, 3\} \cup \varnothing = \{1, 2, 3\}$

3. a. $A \cup B = \{b, c, e\}$
 $(A \cup B)' = \{a, d\}$

 b. $A' = \{a, d, e\}$
 $B' = \{a, d\}$
 $A' \cap B' = \{a, d\}$

Exercise Set 2.3

1. $A = \{1, 3, 5, 7\}$
 $B = \{1, 2, 3\}$
 $A \cap B = \{1, 3\}$

2. $B = \{1, 2, 3\}$
   $C = \{2, 3, 4, 5, 6\}$
   $B \cap C = \{2, 3\}$

3. $A = \{1, 3, 5, 7\}$
   $B = \{1, 2, 3\}$
   $A \cup B = \{1, 2, 3, 5, 7\}$

4. $B = \{1, 2, 3\}$
   $C = \{2, 3, 4, 5, 6\}$
   $B \cup C = \{1, 2, 3, 4, 5, 6\}$

5. $A = \{1, 3, 5, 7\}$
   $U = \{1, 2, 3, 4, 5, 6, 7\}$
   $A' = \{2, 4, 6\}$

6. $B = \{1, 2, 3\}$
   $U = \{1, 2, 3, 4, 5, 6, 7\}$
   $B' = \{4, 5, 6, 7\}$

7. $A' = \{2, 4, 6\}$
   $B' = \{4, 5, 6, 7\}$
   $A' \cap B' = \{4, 6\}$

8. $B' = \{4, 5, 6, 7\}$
   $C = \{2, 3, 4, 5, 6\}$
   $B' \cap C = \{4, 5, 6\}$

9. $A = \{1, 3, 5, 7\}$
   $C' = \{1, 7\}$
   $A \cup C' = \{1, 3, 5, 7\}$

10. $B = \{1, 2, 3\}$
    $C' = \{1, 7\}$
    $B \cup C' = \{1, 2, 3, 7\}$

11. $A = \{1, 3, 5, 7\}$
    $C = \{2, 3, 4, 5, 6\}$
    $A \cap C = \{3, 5\}$
    $(A \cap C)' = \{1, 2, 4, 6, 7\}$

12. $A = \{1, 3, 5, 7\}$
    $B = \{1, 2, 3\}$
    $A \cap B = \{1, 3\}$
    $(A \cap B)' = \{2, 4, 5, 6, 7\}$

13. $A = \{1, 3, 5, 7\}$ $C = \{2, 3, 4, 5, 6\}$
    $A' = \{2, 4, 6\}$ $C' = \{1, 7\}$
    $A' \cup C' = \{1, 2, 4, 6, 7\}$

14. $A = \{1, 3, 5, 7\}$
    $B = \{1, 2, 3\}$

$A' = \{2, 4, 6\}$
$B' = \{4, 5, 6, 7\}$
$A' \cup B' = \{2, 4, 5, 6, 7\}$

15. $A = \{1, 3, 5, 7\}$ $B = \{1, 2, 3\}$
    $(A \cup B) = \{1, 2, 3, 5, 7\}$
    $(A \cup B)' = \{4, 6\}$

16. $A = \{1, 3, 5, 7\}$
    $C = \{2, 3, 4, 5, 6\}$
    $A \cup C = \{1, 2, 3, 4, 5, 6, 7\}$
    $(A \cup C)' = \varnothing$

17. $A = \{1, 3, 5, 7\}$
    $A \cup \varnothing = \{1, 3, 5, 7\}$

18. $C = \{2, 3, 4, 5, 6\}$
    $C \cup \varnothing = \{2, 3, 4, 5, 6\}$

19. $A \cap \varnothing = \varnothing$

20. $C \cap \varnothing = \varnothing$

21. $A \cup U = U$
    $U = \{1, 2, 3, 4, 5, 6, 7\}$

22. $B \cup U = U$
    $U = \{1, 2, 3, 4, 5, 6, 7\}$

23. $A \cap U = A$
    $A = \{1, 3, 5, 7\}$

24. $B \cap U = B$
    $B = \{1, 2, 3\}$

25. $A = \{a, g, h\}$
    $B = \{b, g, h\}$
    $A \cap B = \{g, h\}$

26. $B = \{b, g, h\}$
    $C = \{b, c, d, e, f\}$
    $B \cap C = \{b\}$

27. $A = \{a, g, h\}$
    $B = \{b, g, h\}$
    $A \cup B = \{a, b, g, h\}$

28. $B = \{b, g, h\}$
    $C = \{b, c, d, e, f\}$
    $B \cup C = \{b, c, d, e, f, g, h\}$

29. $A = \{a, g, h\}$
$U = \{a, b, c, d, e, f, g, h\}$
$A' = \{b, c, d, e, f\}$

30. $B = \{b, g, h\}$
$U = \{a, b, c, d, e, f, g, h\}$
$B' = \{a, c, d, e, f\}$

31. $A' = \{b, c, d, e, f\}$
$B' = \{a, c, d, e, f\}$
$A' \cap B' = \{c, d, e, f\}$

32. $B' = \{a, c, d, e, f\}$
$C = \{b, c, d, e, f\}$
$B' \cap C = \{c, d, e, f\}$

33. $A = \{a, g, h\}$
$C' = \{a, g, h\}$
$A \cup C' = \{a, g, h\}$

34. $B = \{b, g, h\}$
$C = \{b, c, d, e, f\}$
$C' = \{a, g, h\}$
$B \cup C' = \{a, b, g, h\}$

35. $A = \{a, g, h\}$
$C = \{b, c, d, e, f\}$
$A \cap C = \varnothing$
$(A \cap C)' = \{a, b, c, d, e, f, g, h\}$

36. $A = \{a, g, h\}$
$B = \{b, g, h\}$
$A \cap B = \{g, h\}$
$(A \cap B)' = \{a, b, c, d, e, f\}$

37. $A' = \{b, c, d, e, f\}$
$C' = \{a, g, h\}$
$A' \cup C' = \{a, b, c, d, e, f, g, h\}$

38. $A' = \{b, c, d, e, f\}$
$B' = \{a, c, d, e, f\}$
$A' \cup B' = \{a, b, c, d, e, f\}$

39. $A = \{a, g, h\}$
$B = \{b, g, h\}$
$A \cup B = \{a, b, g, h\}$
$(A \cup B)' = \{c, d, e, f\}$

40. $A = \{a, g, h\}$
$C = \{b, c, d, e, f\}$
$A \cup C = \{a, b, c, d, e, f, g, h\}$
$(A \cup C)' = \varnothing$

41. $A \cup \varnothing = A$
$A = \{a, g, h\}$

42. $C \cup \varnothing = C$
$C = \{b, c, d, e, f\}$

43. $A \cap \varnothing = \varnothing$

44. $C \cap \varnothing = \varnothing$

45. $A = \{a, g, h\}$
$U = \{a, b, c, d, e, f, g, h\}$
$A \cup U = \{a, b, c, d, e, f, g, h\}$

46. $B = \{b, g, h\}$
$U = \{a, b, c, d, e, f, g, h\}$
$B \cup U = \{a, b, c, d, e, f, g, h\}$

47. $A = \{a, g, h\}$
$U = \{a, b, c, d, e, f, g, h\}$
$A \cap U = \{a, g, h\}$

48. $B = \{b, g, h\}$
$U = \{a, b, c, d, e, f, g, h\}$
$B \cap U = \{b, g, h\}$

49. $A = \{1, 3, 5, 7\}$
$B = \{2, 4, 6, 8\}$
$A \cup B = \{1, 2, 3, 4, 5, 6, 7, 8\}$

50. $B = \{2, 4, 6, 8\}$
$C = \{2, 3, 4, 5\}$
$B \cup C = \{2, 3, 4, 5, 6, 8\}$

51. $U = \{1, 2, 3, 4, 5, 6, 7, 8\}$
$A = \{1, 3, 5, 7\}$
$A \cap U = \{1, 3, 5, 7\}$

52. $U = \{1, 2, 3, 4, 5, 6, 7, 8\}$
$A = \{1, 3, 5, 7\}$
$A \cup U = \{1, 2, 3, 4, 5, 6, 7, 8\}$

53. $A = \{1, 3, 5, 7\}$
$C' = \{1, 6, 7, 8\}$
$A \cap C' = \{1, 7\}$

54. $A = \{1, 3, 5, 7\}$

$B' = \{1, 3, 5, 7\}$

$A \cap B' = \{1, 3, 5, 7\}$

55. $U = \{1, 2, 3, 4, 5, 6, 7, 8\}$

$B = \{2, 4, 6, 8\}$

$C = \{2, 3, 4, 5\}$

$B \cap C = \{2, 4\}$

$(B \cap C)' = \{1, 3, 5, 6, 7, 8\}$

56. $U = \{1, 2, 3, 4, 5, 6, 7, 8\}$

$A = \{1, 3, 5, 7\}$

$C = \{2, 3, 4, 5\}$

$A \cap C = \{3, 5\}$

$(A \cap C)' = \{1, 2, 4, 6, 7, 8\}$

57. $A = \{1, 3, 4, 7\}$

58. $B = \{2, 3, 5, 6, 7\}$

59. $U = \{1, 2, 3, 4, 5, 6, 7, 8, 9\}$

60. $A \cup B = \{1, 2, 3, 4, 5, 6, 7\}$

61. $A \cap B = \{3, 7\}$

62. $A' = \{2, 5, 6, 8, 9\}$

63. $B' = \{1, 4, 8, 9\}$

64. $(A \cap B)' = \{1, 2, 4, 5, 6, 8, 9\}$

65. $(A \cup B)' = \{8, 9\}$

66. $A' = \{2, 5, 6, 8, 9\}$

$B = \{2, 3, 5, 6, 7\}$

$A' \cap B = \{2, 5, 6\}$

67. {spatial-temporal, sports equipment, toy cars and trucks} $\cap$ {dollhouses, spatial-temporal, sports equipment, toy cars and trucks}
= {spatial-temporal, sports equipment, toy cars and trucks}

68. {dollhouses, domestic accessories, dolls} $\cap$ {dollhouses, spatial-temporal, sports equipment, toy cars and trucks}
= {dollhouses}

69. {spatial-temporal, sports equipment, toy cars and trucks} $\cup$ {dollhouses, spatial-temporal, sports equipment, toy cars and trucks}
= {dollhouses, spatial-temporal, sports equipment, toy cars and trucks}

70. {dollhouses, domestic accessories, dolls} $\cup$ {dollhouses, spatial-temporal, sports equipment, toy cars and trucks}
= {dollhouses, domestic accessories, dolls, spatial-temporal, sports equipment, toy cars and trucks}

71. {toy cars and trucks} $\cap$ {dollhouses, domestic accessories, dolls, spatial-temporal, sports equipment}
= $\varnothing$

72. {toy cars and trucks} $\cup$ {dollhouses, domestic accessories, dolls, spatial-temporal, sports equipment}
= {dollhouses, domestic accessories, dolls, spatial-temporal, sports equipment, toy cars and trucks}

73-78. Answers will vary.

79. b is true.

80. d is true.

81. Example of a possible answer: Suppose there is an element in set A that is not also in set B. This element would be part of $A \cup B$ *and* B'. This element would then be part of $A' \cup B'$. However, since this element is part of $A \cup B$ it is *not* part of $(A \cup B)'$. Since this element is a part of $A' \cup B'$ but *not* $(A \cup B)'$, this serves as a counterexample to the proposition that $(A \cup B)' = A' \cup B'$.

Check Points 2.4

1. a. $B \cap C = \{b, f\}$
$A \cup (B \cap C) = \{a, b, c, d, f\}$

b. $A \cup B = \{a, b, c, d, f\}$
$A \cup C = \{a, b, c, d, f\}$
$(A \cup B) \cap (A \cup C) = \{a, b, c, d, f\}$

c. $C' = \{a, d, e\}$
$B \cup C' = \{a, b, d, e, f\}$
$A \cap (B \cup C') = \{a, b, d\}$

2. a. Regions IV, V, VI, and VII

b. Regions II, III, IV, V, VI, and VII

c. Regions IV and V

d. Regions I, II, III, and VIII

e. Regions I, II, III, IV, V, VI, VII

3. a. $A \cup B$ is represented by regions I, II, and III. Therefore $(A \cup B)'$ is represented by region IV.

b. A' is represented by regions III and IV.
B' is represented by regions I and IV.
Therefore $A' \cap B'$ is represented by region IV.

c. $(A \cup B)' = A' \cap B'$ because they both represent region IV.

4. a. $B \cup C$ is represented by regions II, III, IV, V, VI, and VII.
Therefore $A \cap (B \cup C)$ is represented by regions II, IV, and V.

b. $A \cap B$ is represented by regions II and V.
$A \cap C$ is represented by regions IV and V.
Therefore $(A \cap B) \cup (A \cap C)$ is represented by regions II, IV, and V.

c. $A \cap (B \cup C) = (A \cap B) \cup (A \cap C)$ because they both represent region IV.

Exercises 2.4

1. $B \cap C = \{2, 3\}$
$A \cup (B \cap C) = \{1, 2, 3, 5, 7\}$

2. $B \cup C = \{1, 2, 3, 4, 5, 6\}$
$A \cap (B \cup C) = \{1, 3, 5\}$

3. $A \cup B = \{1, 2, 3, 5, 7\}$
$A \cup C = \{1, 2, 3, 4, 5, 6, 7\}$
$(A \cup B) \cap (A \cup C) = \{1, 2, 3, 5, 7\}$

4. $(A \cap B) = \{1, 3\}$
$(A \cap C) = \{3, 5\}$
$(A \cap B) \cup (A \cap C) = \{1, 3, 5\}$

5. $A' = \{2, 4, 6\}$ $C' = \{1, 7\}$
$B \cup C' = \{1, 2, 3, 7\}$
$A' \cap (B \cup C') = \{2\}$

6. $B' = \{4, 5, 6, 7\}$
$C' = \{1, 7\}$
$A \cup B' = \{1, 3, 4, 5, 6, 7\}$
$C' \cap (A \cup B') = \{1, 7\}$

7. $A' = \{2, 4, 6\}$ $C' = \{1, 7\}$
$A' \cap B = \{2\}$
$A' \cap C' = \emptyset$
$(A' \cap B) \cup (A' \cap C') = \{2\}$

8. $B' = \{4, 5, 6, 7\}$
$C' = \{1, 7\}$
$(C' \cap A) = \{1, 7\}$
$(C' \cap B') = \{7\}$
$(C' \cap A) \cup (C' \cap B') = \{1, 7\}$

9. $A = \{1, 3, 5, 7\}$
$B = \{1, 2, 3\}$
$C = \{2, 3, 4, 5, 6\}$
$A \cup B \cup C = \{1, 2, 3, 4, 5, 6, 7\}$
$(A \cup B \cup C)' = \emptyset$

10. $A = \{1, 3, 5, 7\}$
$B = \{1, 2, 3\}$
$C = \{2, 3, 4, 5, 6\}$
$A \cap B \cap C = \{3\}$
$(A \cap B \cap C)' = \{1, 2, 4, 5, 6, 7\}$

11. $A = \{1, 3, 5, 7\}$
    $B = \{1, 2, 3\}$
    $A \cup B = \{1, 2, 3, 5, 7\}$
    $(A \cup B)' = \{4, 6\}$
    $C = \{2, 3, 4, 5, 6\}$
    $(A \cup B)' \cap C = \{4, 6\}$

12. $B \cup C = \{1, 2, 3, 4, 5, 6\}$
    $(B \cup C)' = \{7\}$
    $(B \cup C)' \cap A = \{7\}$

13. $B \cap C = \{b\}$
    $A \cup (B \cap C) = \{a, b, g, h\}$

14. $B \cup C = \{b, c, d, e, f, g, h\}$
    $A \cap (B \cup C) = \{g, h\}$

15. $A \cup B = \{a, b, g, h\}$
    $A \cup C = \{a, b, c, d, e, f, g, h\}$
    $(A \cup B) \cap (A \cup C) = \{a, b, g, h\}$

16. $A \cap B = \{g, h\}$
    $A \cap C = \varnothing$
    $(A \cap B) \cup (A \cap C) = \{g, h\}$

17. $A' = \{b, c, d, e, f\}$
    $C' = \{a, g, h\}$
    $B \cup C' = \{a, b, g, h\}$
    $A' \cap (B \cup C') = \{b\}$

18. $C' = \{a, g, h\}$
    $B' = \{a, c, d, e, f\}$
    $A \cup B' = \{a, c, d, e, f, g, h\}$
    $C' \cap (A \cup B') = \{a, g, h\}$

19. $A' = \{b, c, d, e, f\}$
    $A' \cap B = \{b\}$
    $C' = \{a, g, h\}$
    $A' \cap C' = \varnothing$
    $(A' \cap B) \cup (A' \cap C') = \{b\}$

20. $C' = \{a, g, h\}$
    $B' = \{a, c, d, e, f\}$
    $C' \cap A = \{a, g, h\}$
    $C' \cap B' = \{a\}$
    $(C' \cap A) \cup (C' \cap B') = \{a, g, h\}$

21. $A \cup B \cup C = \{a, b, c, d, e, f, g, h\}$
    $(A \cup B \cup C)' = \varnothing$

22. $A \cap B \cap C = \varnothing$
    $(A \cap B \cap C)' = \{a, b, c, d, e, f, g, h\}$

23. $A \cup B = \{a, b, g, h\}$
    $(A \cup B)' = \{c, d, e, f\}$
    $(A \cup B)' \cap C = \{c, d, e, f\}$

24. $B \cup C = \{b, c, d, e, f, g, h\}$
    $(B \cup C)' = \{a\}$
    $(B \cup C)' \cap A = \{a\}$

25. II, III, V, VI

26. IV, V, VI, VII

27. I, II, IV, V, VI, VII

28. II, III, IV, V, VI, VII

29. II, V

30. IV, V

31. I, IV, VII, VIII

32. I, II, III, VIII

33. $A = \{1, 2, 3, 4, 5, 6, 7, 8\}$

34. $B = \{4, 5, 6, 9, 10, 11\}$

35. $A \cup B = \{1, 2, 3, 4, 5, 6, 7, 8, 9, 10, 11\}$

36. $B = \{4, 5, 6, 9, 10, 11\}$
    $C = \{6, 7, 8, 9, 12\}$
    $B \cup C = \{4, 5, 6, 7, 8, 9, 10, 11, 12\}$

37. $A = \{1, 2, 3, 4, 5, 6, 7, 8\}$
    $B = \{4, 5, 6, 9, 10, 11\}$
    $A \cup B = \{1, 2, 3, 4, 5, 6, 7, 8, 9, 10, 11\}$
    $(A \cup B)' = \{12, 13\}$

38. $B = \{4, 5, 6, 9, 10, 11\}$
    $C = \{6, 7, 8, 9, 12\}$
    $B \cup C = \{4, 5, 6, 7, 8, 9, 10, 11, 12\}$
    $(B \cup C)' = \{1, 2, 3, 13\}$

39. The set contains the elements in the two regions where the circles representing sets A and B overlap.
$A \cap B = \{4, 5, 6\}$

40. The set contains the elements in the two regions where the circles representing sets A and C overlap.
$A \cap C = \{6, 7, 8\}$

41. The set contains the element in the center region where the circles representing sets A, B, and C overlap.
$A \cap B \cap C = \{6\}$

42. The set contains the elements in the seven regions of the circles representing sets A, B, and C. Only element 13 lies outside these regions.
$A \cup B \cup C = \{1, 2, 3, 4, 5, 6, 7, 8, 9, 10, 11, 12\}$

43. $A \cap B \cap C = \{6\}$
$(A \cap B \cap C)' = \{1, 2, 3, 4, 5, 7, 8, 9, 10, 11, 12, 13\}$

44. $A \cup B \cup C = \{1, 2, 3, 4, 5, 6, 7, 8, 9, 10, 11, 12\}$
$(A \cup B \cup C)' = \{13\}$

45. a. II

    b. II

    c. $A \cap B = B \cap A$

46. a. I, II, III

    b. I, II, III

    c. $A \cup B = B \cup A$

47. a. I, III, IV

    b. IV

    c. No, $(A \cap B)' \neq A' \cap B'$

48. a. IV

    b. I, III, IV

    c. No, $(A \cup B)' \neq A' \cup B'$

49. Set A is represented by regions I and II.
Set A' is represented by regions III and IV.
Set B is represented by regions II and III.
Set B' is represented by regions I and IV.
$A' \cup B$ is represented by regions II, III, and IV.
$A \cap B'$ is represented by region I.

Thus, $A' \cup B$ and $A \cap B'$ are not equal for all sets A and B.

50. Set A is represented by regions I and II.
Set A' is represented by regions III and IV.
Set B is represented by regions II and III.
Set B' is represented by regions I and IV.
$A' \cap B$ is represented by region III.
$A \cup B'$ is represented by regions I, II, and IV.
Thus, $A' \cap B$ and $A \cup B'$ are not equal for all sets A and B.

51. Set A is represented by regions I and II.
Set B is represented by regions II and III.

$(A \cup B)'$ is represented by region IV.

$(A \cap B)'$ is represented by regions I, III, and IV.

Thus, $(A \cup B)'$ and $(A \cap B)'$ are not equal for all sets A and B.

52. Set A is represented by regions I and II.
Set B is represented by regions II and III.

$(A \cup B)'$ is represented by region IV.

$A' \cap B$ is represented by region III.

Thus, $(A \cup B)'$ and $A' \cap B$ are not equal for all sets A and B.

53. Set A is represented by regions I and II.
Set A' is represented by regions III and IV.
Set B is represented by regions II and III.
Set B' is represented by regions I and IV.

$(A' \cap B)'$ is represented by regions I, II, and IV.

$A \cup B'$ is represented by regions I, II, and IV.
Thus, $A' \cap B$ and $A \cup B'$ are equal for all sets A and B.

54. Set A is represented by regions I and II.
Set A' is represented by regions III and IV.
Set B is represented by regions II and III.
Set B' is represented by regions I and IV.

$(A \cup B')'$ is represented by region III.

$A' \cap B$ is represented by region III.
Thus, $A' \cap B$ and $A \cup B'$ are equal for all sets A and B.

55. a. II, IV, V, VI, VII

    b. II, IV, V, VI, VII

    c. $(A \cap B) \cup C = (A \cup C) \cap (B \cup C)$

56. a. IV, V, VI

 b. IV, V, VI

 c. $(A \cup B) \cap C = (A \cap C) \cup (B \cap C)$

57. a. II, IV, V

 b. I, II, IV, V, VI

 c. No
 The results in **a** and **b** show
 $A \cap (B \cup C) \neq A \cup (B \cap C)$ because of the
 different regions represented.

58. a. II, IV, V, VI, VII

 b. IV, V, VI

 c. No
 The results in **a** and **b** show
 $C \cup (B \cap A) \neq C \cap (B \cup A)$ because of the
 different regions represented.

59. $A \cap (B \cup C)$ is represented by regions II, IV, and
 V.
 $(A \cap B) \cup C$ is represented by regions II, IV, V, VI
 and VII.
 Thus, $A \cap (B \cup C)$ and $(A \cap B) \cup C$ are not equal
 for all sets A, B, and C.

60. $A \cup (B \cap C)$ is represented by regions I, II, IV, V,
 and VI.
 $(A \cup B) \cap C$ is represented by regions IV, V, and
 VI.
 Thus, $A \cup (B \cap C)$ and $(A \cup B) \cap C$ are not equal
 for all sets A, B, and C.

61. $B \cup (A \cap C)$ is represented by regions II, III, IV, V,
 and VI.
 $(A \cup B) \cap (B \cup C)$ is represented by regions II, III,
 IV, V, and VI.
 Thus, $B \cup (A \cap C)$ and $(A \cup B) \cap (B \cup C)$ are
 equal for all sets A, B, and C.

62. $B \cap (A \cup C)$ is represented by regions II, V, and
 VI.
 $(A \cap B) \cup (B \cap C)$ is represented by regions II, V,
 and VI.
 Thus, $B \cap (A \cup C)$ and $(A \cap B) \cup (B \cap C)$ are
 equal for all sets A, B, and C.

63. $A \cap (B \cup C)'$ is represented by region I.
 $A \cap (B' \cap C')$ is represented by region I.
 Thus, $A \cap (B \cup C)'$ and $A \cap (B' \cap C')$ are equal for
 all sets A, B, and C.

64. $A \cup (B \cap C)'$ is represented by regions I, II, III, IV,
 V, VII, and VIII.
 $A \cup (B' \cup C')$ is represented by region I, II, III, IV,
 V, VII, and VIII.
 Thus, $A \cup (B \cap C)'$ and $A \cup (B' \cup C')$ are equal for
 all sets A, B, and C.

65. I

66. VII

67. II

68. VI

69. V

70. V

71. V

72. VI

73. IV

74. VIII

75-76. Answers will vary

77. AB^+

78. O^-

79. No

80. Yes

Check Points 2.5

 1. a. $55 + 20 = 75$

 b. $20 + 70 = 90$

 c. 20

 d. $55 + 20 + 70 = 145$

 e. 55

f. 70

g. 30

h. $55 + 20 + 70 + 30 = 175$

2. $n(A \cup B) = n(A) + n(B) - n(A \cap B)$
$$= 45 + 15 - 5$$
$$= 55$$

3. The 50 Hispanic Americans that agreed with the statement belong in region II. Since region II accounts for 50 of the 550 people who agreed with the statement, the remaining 500 people belong in region III. Since region II also accounts for 50 of the 250 Hispanic Americans, the remaining 200 Hispanic Americans belong in region I. Regions I, II, and III account for a total of 750 of the 1000 people surveyed. This leaves 250 people in region IV.

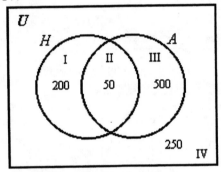

a. 500 non-Hispanics agreed with the statement. (Region III)

b. 250 non-Hispanics disagreed with the statement. (Region IV)

4. **a.** $9 + 4 + 7 + 6 + 3 + 5 = 34$ people surveyed liked comedies or dramas.

b. $7 + 3 = 10$ people surveyed liked dramas but not science fiction.

Exercise Set 2.5

1. 26

2. 20

3. 17

4. 11

5. 37

6. 9

7. 7

8. 44

9. $n(A \cup B) = n(A) + n(B) - n(A \cap B)$
$$= 17 + 20 - 6$$
$$= 31$$

10. $n(A \cup B) = n(A) + n(B) - n(A \cap B)$
$$= 30 + 18 - 5$$
$$= 43$$

11. $n(A \cup B) = n(A) + n(B) - n(A \cap B)$
$$= 17 + 17 - 7$$
$$= 27$$

12. $n(A \cup B) = n(A) + n(B) - n(A \cap B)$
$$= 30 + 24 - 7$$
$$= 47$$

13. $4 + 5 + 2 + 7 = 18$ respondents agreed with the statement.

14. $8 + 2 + 3 + 9 = 22$ respondents disagreed with the statement.

15. $2 + 7 = 9$ women agreed with the statement.

16. $4 + 2 = 6$ people who are not African American agreed with the statement.

17. 9 women who are not African American disagreed with the statement.

18. 8 men who are not African American agreed with the statement.

19. Parts b, c, and d are labeled.

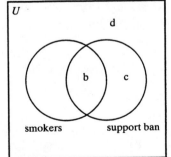

20. Parts b, c, and d are labeled.

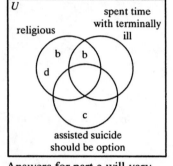

21. Parts b, c, and d are labeled.

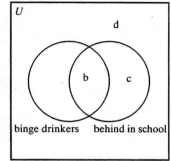

Answers for part e will vary.

22. Parts b, c, and d are labeled.

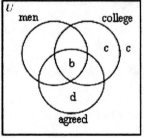

Answers for part e will vary.

23. Begin by placing 7 in the region that represents both newspapers and television.

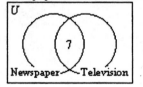

a. Since 29 students got news from newspapers, $29 - 7 = 22$ got news from only newspapers.

b. Since 43 students got news from television, $43 - 7 = 36$ got news from only television.

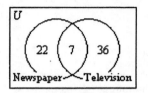

c. $22 + 7 + 36 = 65$ students who got news from newspapers or television.

d. Since 75 students were surveyed, $75 - 65 = 10$ students who did not get news from either.

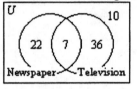

24. Begin by placing 40 in the region that represents both math and English.

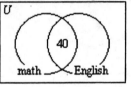

a. Since 75 students registered for math, $75 - 40 = 35$ registered for only math.

b. Since 65 students registered for English, $65 - 40 = 25$ registered for only English.

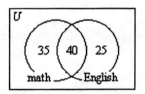

c. $35 + 40 + 25 = 100$ students who registered for math or English.

d. Since 120 students were surveyed, $120 - 100 = 20$ students who did not register for either.

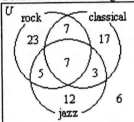

25. Construct a Venn diagram.

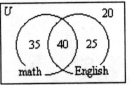

a. 23

b. 3

c. $17 + 3 + 12 = 32$

d. $23 + 17 + 12 = 52$

e. $7 + 3 + 5 = 15$

f. 6

26. Construct a Venn diagram.

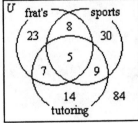

a. 30

b. 8

c. $23 + 8 + 30 = 61$

d. $23 + 30 + 14 = 67$

e. $8 + 7 + 9 = 24$

f. 84

27-28. Answers will vary.

29. b

30. a. 0; This would assume none of the psychology students were taking mathematics.

b. 30; This would assume all 30 students taking psychology were taking mathematics.

c. 60; $U = 150$ so with 90 taking mathematics, if we assume all the psychology students are taking mathematics courses, $U - 90 = 60$.

31. Under the conditions given concerning enrollment in math, chemistry, and psychology courses, the total number of students is 100, not 90.

Chapter 2 Review Exercises

1. Possible description: Natural numbers less than 11.

2. {Tuesday, Thursday}

3. $\{x \mid x \in N$ and lies between 5 and 7, inclusive$\}$ or $\{x \mid x \in N$ and lies between 4 and 8$\}$

4. $\in$
93 is an element of the set.

5. $\notin$
{d} is a subset, not a member; "d" would be a member.

6. 12
12 months in the year.

7. 15

8. Not equal
The two sets do not contain exactly the same elements.

9. Not equal
One set is infinite. The other is finite.

10. Equivalent
Same number of elements, but different elements.

11. Equal and equivalent
The two sets have exactly the same elements.

12. $A' = \{1, 2, 8, 9\}$

13. {January, February, March, May, July, August, October, December}

14. $\subseteq$

15. $\not\subseteq$

16. $\subseteq$

17. $\subseteq$

18. Both $\subseteq$ and $\subset$ are correct.

19. False
Texas is not a member of the set.

20. False
4 is not a subset. {4} is a subset.

21. True

22. False
It is a subset but not a proper subset.

23. True

24. False
The set {six} has only one element.

25. True

26. $\varnothing$ {1} {5} {1, 5}
{1, 5} is not a proper subset.

27. There are 5 elements. This means there are $2^5 = 32$ subsets.
There are $2^5 - 1 = 31$ proper subsets.

28. {January, June, July}
There are 3 elements. This means there are $2^3 = 8$ subsets.
There are $2^3 - 1 = 7$ proper subsets.

29. $A \cap B = \{1, 2, 4\}$

30. $A \cup B' = \{1, 2, 3, 4, 6, 7, 8\}$

31. $A' \cap B = \{5\}$

32. $(A \cup B)' = \{6, 7, 8\}$

33. $A' \cap B' = \{6, 7, 8\}$

34. $\{4, 5, 6\}$

35. $\{2, 3, 6, 7\}$

36. $\{1, 4, 5, 6, 8, 9\}$

37. $\{4, 5\}$

38. $\{1, 2, 3, 6, 7, 8, 9\}$

39. $\{2, 3, 7\}$

40. $\{6\}$

41. $\{1, 2, 3, 4, 5, 6, 7, 8, 9\}$

42. $B \cap C = \{1, 5\}$
$A \cup (B \cap C) = \{1, 2, 3, 4, 5\}$

43. $A \cap C = \{1\}$
$(A \cap C)' = (2, 3, 4, 5, 6, 7, 8)$
$(A \cap C)' \cup B = \{1, 2, 3, 4, 5, 6, 7, 8\}$

44. {c, d, e, f, k, p, r}

45. {f, p}

46. {c, d, f, k, p, r}

47. {c, d, e}

48. {a, b, c, d, e, g, h, p, r}

49. {f}

50. The shaded regions are the same for $(A \cup B)'$ and $A' \cap B'$. Therefore $(A \cup B)' = A' \cap B'$

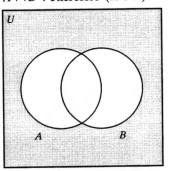

51. The statement is false because the shaded regions are different.

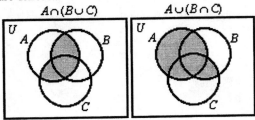

52. $n(A \cup B) = n(A) + n(B) - n(A \cap B)$
$\qquad = 25 + 17 - 9$
$\qquad = 33$

53. a. Parts b and c are labeled.

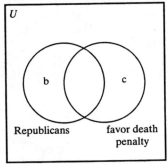

54. Begin by placing 400 in the region that represents both stocks and bonds.

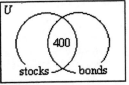

a. Since 650 respondents invested in stocks, $650 - 400 = 250$ invested in only stocks.

Furthermore, since 550 respondents invested in bonds, $550 - 400 = 150$ invested in only bonds. Place this data in the Venn diagram.

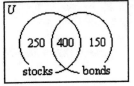

b. $250 + 400 + 150 = 800$ respondents invested in stocks or bonds.

c. Since 1000 people were surveyed, $1000 - 800 = 200$ respondents who did not invest in either.

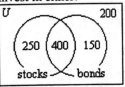

55. Construct a Venn diagram.

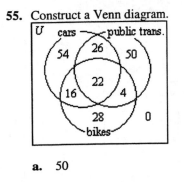

a. 50

b. 26

c. $54 + 26 + 50 = 130$

d. $26 + 16 + 4 = 46$

e. 0

Chapter 2 Test

1. {18, 19, 20, 21, 22, 23, 24, 25}

2. 12

3. False, {6} is not an element of the set, but 6 is an element.

4. True, both sets have seven elements.

5. True

6. False, g is not an element in the larger set.

7. True

8. False, 14 is an element of the set.

9. False, Number of subsets: 2^N where N is the number of elements. There are 5 elements. $2^5 = 32$ subsets

10. False, $\varnothing$ is *not* a proper subset of itself.

11. $\varnothing$ {6} {9} {6, 9}
    {6, 9} is not a proper subset.

12. {a, b, c, d, e, f}

13. $B \cap C = \{e\}$
    $(B \cap C)' = \{a, b, c, d, f, g\}$

14. $C' = \{b, c, d, f\}$
    $A \cap C' = \{b, c, d\}$

15. $A \cup B = \{a, b, c, d, e, f\}$
    $(A \cup B) \cap C = \{a, e\}$

16. I, II, IV, V, VI

17. **a.**

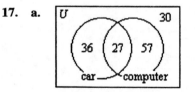

   b. Car Only: $63 - 27 = 36$
      Computer Only: $84 - 27 = 57$
      Both: 27
      $150 - 36 - 57 - 27 = 30$

   c. 57

   d. 36

   e. 120

Chapter 3
Logic

Check Points 3.1

1. **a.** Paris is not the capital of Spain.

   b. July is a month.

2. **a.** ~p

   b. ~q

3. Tom Hanks is not a jazz singer.

4. Some new tax dollars will not be used to improve education.
   At least one new tax dollar will not be used to improve education.

Exercise Set 3.1

1. Statement

2. Statement

3. Statement

4. Statement

5. Not a statement

6. Not a statement

7. Not a statement

8. Not a statement

9. Statement

10. Statement

11. Statement

12. Statement

13. It is not raining.

14. It is not snowing.

15. Macbeth is a comedy show on television.

16. Albert Einstein was offered the presidency of Israel.

17. ~p

18. ~q

19. ~r

20. ~s

21. *I Love Lucy* is not a Broadway musical.

22. Bruce Springsteen is not a U.S. President.

23. Benjamin Franklin invented the rocking chair.

24. Bill Clinton was impeached.

25. The United States is not the country with the most Internet users.

26. New Jersey is not a planet.

27. Michael is the most common boys' name.

28. The final exam was comprehensive.

29. **a.** There are no whales that are not mammals.

    b. Some whales are not mammals.

30. **a.** There are no journalists who are not writers.

    b. Some journalists are not writers.

31. **a.** There exists at least one student that is a business major.

    b. No students are business majors.

32. **a.** There exists at least one movie that is a comedy.

    b. No movies are comedies.

33. **a.** At least one thief is not a criminal.

    b. All thieves are criminals.

34. **a.** At least one pianist is not a keyboard player.

    b. All pianists are keyboard players.

35. **a.** All Democratic presidents have not been impeached.

    b. Some Democratic presidents have been impeached.

36. **a.** All women have not served as Supreme Court justices.

    b. Some women have served as Supreme Court justices.

37. b

38. c

39-45. Answers will vary.

46. Answers will vary. Possible answer: Everything I say or write is false.

47. Answers will vary. Possible answer: Some mammals are not cats (true). Some cats are not mammals (false).

48. The statement could mean that she *is* dating him, but that his muscularity is *not* the reason. The statement could also mean that she *is not* dating him because she does not like the fact that he is muscular.

Check Points 3.2

1. a. $p \wedge q$ **b.** $\sim p \wedge q$

2. a. $p \vee \sim q$ **b.** $q \vee p$

3. a. $p \rightarrow q$ **b.** $\sim p \rightarrow \sim q$
   c. $\sim q \rightarrow \sim p$

4. a. $q \leftrightarrow p$ **b.** $\sim p \leftrightarrow \sim q$

5. a. It is not true that Steven Spielberg is an actor and a director.

    b. Steven Spielberg is not an actor and Steven Spielberg is a director.

    c. It is not true that Steven Spielberg is an actor or a director.

6. a. If the plant is fertilized and the plant is watered, then the plant does not wilt.

    b. The plant is fertilized, and if the plant is watered then the plant does not wilt.

Exercise Set 3.2

1. $p \wedge q$;

$$\underbrace{\textit{I Love Lucy} \text{ is a television show}}_{p} \underbrace{\text{and}}_{\wedge}$$
$$\underbrace{\textit{Macbeth} \text{ is a television show.}}_{q}$$

2. $q \wedge p$;

$$\underbrace{\textit{Macbeth} \text{ is a television show}}_{q} \underbrace{\text{and}}_{\wedge}$$
$$\underbrace{\textit{I Love Lucy} \text{ is a television show.}}_{p}$$

3. $p \wedge \sim q$;

$$\underbrace{\textit{I Love Lucy} \text{ is a television show}}_{p} \underbrace{\text{and}}_{\wedge}$$
$$\underbrace{\textit{Macbeth} \text{ is not a television show.}}_{\sim q}$$

4. $\sim q \wedge p$;

$$\underbrace{\textit{Macbeth} \text{ is not a television show}}_{\sim q} \underbrace{\text{and}}_{\wedge}$$
$$\underbrace{\textit{I Love Lucy} \text{ is a television show.}}_{p}$$

5. $p \vee q$; $\quad \underbrace{\text{I study}}_{p} \underbrace{\text{or}}_{\vee} \underbrace{\text{I pass the course.}}_{q}$

6. $q \vee p$; $\quad \underbrace{\text{I pass the course}}_{q} \underbrace{\text{or}}_{\vee} \underbrace{\text{I study.}}_{p}$

7. $p \vee \sim q$; $\quad \underbrace{\text{I study}}_{p} \underbrace{\text{or}}_{\vee} \underbrace{\text{I do not pass the course.}}_{\sim q}$

8. $\sim p \vee \sim q$;

$$\underbrace{\text{I do not study}}_{\sim p} \underbrace{\text{or}}_{\vee} \underbrace{\text{I do not pass the course.}}_{\sim q}$$

9. $p \rightarrow q$;

$$\underbrace{\text{If}} \underbrace{\text{this is an alligator,}}_{p} \underbrace{\text{then}}_{\rightarrow} \underbrace{\text{this is a reptile.}}_{q}$$

10. $q \rightarrow p$;

$$\underbrace{\text{If}} \underbrace{\text{this is a reptile,}}_{q} \underbrace{\text{then}}_{\rightarrow} \underbrace{\text{this is an alligator.}}_{p}$$

11. $\sim p \rightarrow \sim q$;

$$\underbrace{\text{If}} \underbrace{\text{this is not an alligator,}}_{\sim p} \underbrace{\text{then}}_{\rightarrow}$$
$$\underbrace{\text{this is not a reptile.}}_{\sim q}$$

12. $\sim q \to \sim p$;

If	this is not a reptile,	then
	$\sim q$	$\to$

this is not an alligator.
$\sim p$

13. $p \leftrightarrow q$;

The campus is closed | if and only if | it is Sunday.
p | $\leftrightarrow$ | q

14. $q \leftrightarrow p$;

It is Sunday | if and only if | the campus is closed.
q | $\leftrightarrow$ | p

15. $\sim q \leftrightarrow \sim p$;

It is not Sunday | if and only if
$\sim q$ | $\leftrightarrow$

the campus is not closed.
$\sim p$

16. $\sim p \leftrightarrow \sim q$;

The campus is not closed | if and only if
$\sim p$ | $\leftrightarrow$

it is not Sunday.
$\sim q$

17. The heater is not working and the house is cold.

18. The heater is working and the house is not cold.

19. The heater is working or the house is not cold.

20. The heater is not working or the house is cold.

21. If the heater is working then the house is not cold.

22. If the house is cold then the heater is not working.

23. The heater is working if and only if the house is not cold.

24. The heater is not working if and only if the house is cold.

25. It is July 4th and we are not having a barbeque.

26. It is not July 4th and we are having a barbeque.

27. It is not July 4th or we are having a barbeque.

28. It is July 4th or we are not having a barbeque.

29. If we are having a barbeque, then it is not July 4th.

30. If it is July 4th, then we are not having a barbeque.

31. It is not July 4th if and only if we are having a barbeque.

32. It is July 4th if and only if we are not having a barbeque.

33. It is not true that Romeo loves Juliet and Juliet loves Romeo.

34. It is not true that Juliet loves Romeo and Romeo loves Juliet.

35. Romeo does not love Juliet and Juliet loves Romeo.

36. Juliet does not love Romeo and Romeo loves Juliet.

37. Neither Juliet loves Romeo nor Romeo loves Juliet.

38. Neither Romeo loves Juliet nor Juliet loves Romeo.

39. Juliet does not love Romeo or Romeo loves Juliet.

40. Romeo does not love Juliet or Juliet loves Romeo.

41. Romeo does not love Juliet and Juliet does not love Romeo.

42. Juliet does not love Romeo and Romeo does not love Juliet.

43. $(p \land q) \lor r$;

The temperature outside is freezing | and | the heater is working, | or | the house is cold.
p | $\land$ | q | $\lor$ | r

44. $p \to (q \lor \sim r)$;

If the temperature outside is freezing, | then | the heater is working | or | the house is not cold.
p | $\to$ | q | $\lor$ | $\sim r$

45. $(p \lor \sim q) \to r$;

If the temperature outside is freezing | or | the heater is not working, | then | the house is cold.
p | $\lor$ | $\sim q$ | $\to$ | r

46. $\sim(r \to \sim q)$; $\quad$ It is not the case that $\Big($ if the house is cold then the heater is not working. $\Big)$
$\qquad\qquad\qquad\quad \sim \qquad\qquad\qquad\qquad r \qquad \to \qquad\qquad \sim q$

47. $r \leftrightarrow (p \wedge \sim q)$; $\quad$ The house is cold if and only if $\Big($ the temperature outside is freezing and the heater isn't working. $\Big)$
$\qquad\qquad\qquad\qquad\quad r \qquad\qquad\qquad \leftrightarrow \qquad\qquad p \qquad\qquad\qquad\qquad \wedge \qquad\qquad \sim q$

48. $q \to (p \leftrightarrow r)$; $\quad$ If the heater is working, then $\Big($ the temperature outside is freezing if and only if the house is cold. $\Big)$
$\qquad\qquad\qquad\qquad\quad\quad q \qquad\qquad \to \qquad\qquad\quad p \qquad\qquad\qquad\qquad\qquad \leftrightarrow \qquad\qquad\quad r$

49. If the temperature is above 85° and we finished studying, then we go to the beach.

50. If we finished studying and we go to the beach, then the temperature is above 85°.

51. The temperature is above 85°, and if we finished studying then we go to the beach.

52. The temperature is above 85°, and if we go to the beach then we finished studying.

53. If we do not go to the beach, then the temperature is not above 85° or we did not finish studying.

54. If the temperature is not above 85°, then we finished studying or we go to the beach.

55. If we do not go to the beach then we didn't finish studying, or the temperature is above 85°.

56. If the temperature is not above 85° then we don't go to the beach, or we finished studying.

57. We go to the beach if and only if the temperature is above 85° and we finished studying.

58. We go to the beach if and only if we finished studying and the temperature is above 85°.

59. The temperature is above 85° if and only if we finished studying, and we go to the beach.

60. If we finished studying, then we go to the beach if and only if the temperature is above 85°.

61. If we don't go to the beach, then it is not true that the temperature is above 85° and we finished studying.

62. If it is not true that the temperature is above 85° and we finished studying, then we won't go to the beach.

63. p: You can get rid of the family skeleton.
q: You may as well make it dance.
$\sim p \to q$

64. p: I would turn out the way I did.
q: I did have all the old-fashioned values to rebel.
$\sim q \to \sim p$

65. p: You know what you believe.
q: It makes it a lot easier to answer questions.
r: I can answer your questions.
$(p \to q) \wedge \sim r$

66. p: You do like what you are doing.
q: You can always pick up your needle and move to another groove.
$\sim p \to q$

67. p: I am an intellectual.
q: I would be pessimistic about America.
$((p \rightarrow q) \wedge \sim p) \rightarrow \sim q$

68. p: You can be a good socializer.
q: You can be a good writer.
$\sim (p \wedge q)$

69-75. Answers will vary.

76. $\left(\underset{p}{\underline{\text{Shooting unarmed civilians is morally justifiable}}} \; \underset{\leftrightarrow}{\underline{\text{if and only if}}} \right.$

$\left. \underset{q}{\underline{\text{bombing unarmed civilians is morally justifiable,}}} \right) \; \underset{\wedge}{\underline{\text{and}}} \; \left(\underset{\sim p}{\underline{\text{as the former is not morally justifiable,}}} \; \underset{\wedge \; \sim q}{\underline{\text{neither is the latter.}}} \right)$

Check Points 3.3

1. The statement is <u>true</u> because it is of the form: [true] *and* [true].

2. The statement is <u>false</u> because it is of the form: [false] *or* [false].

3. $\sim(p \vee q)$

p	q	$p \vee q$	$\sim(p \vee q)$
T	T	T	F
T	F	T	F
F	T	T	F
F	F	F	T

4. $\sim p \wedge \sim q$

p	q	$\sim p$	$\sim q$	$\sim p \wedge \sim q$
T	T	F	F	F
T	F	F	T	F
F	T	T	F	F
F	F	T	T	T

5. Will Smith is not an actor or Bob Dylan is not an actor.

6. $(p \wedge \sim q) \vee \sim p$

p	q	$\sim p$	$\sim q$	$p \wedge \sim q$	$(p \wedge \sim q) \vee \sim p$
T	T	F	F	F	F
T	F	F	T	T	T
F	T	T	F	F	T
F	F	T	T	F	T

Exercise Set 3.3

1. p: The Beatles were a rock group – true
q: Ernest Hemingway was a writer – true
A conjunction is true when both statements are true.
Hence, $p \wedge q$ is true.

2. p: John Travolta is an actor – true
q: Abraham Lincoln was a U.S. President – true
A conjunction is true when both statements are true.
Hence, $p \wedge q$ is true.

3. p: $3 + 2 = 5$ – true
q: 3 is an even number – false
A conjunction is true when both statements are true.
Hence, $p \wedge q$ is false.

4. p: $7 \times 5 = 35$ – true
q: 6 is an odd number – false
A conjunction is true when both statements are true.
Hence, $p \wedge q$ is false.

5. p: Fir trees produce fur coats – false
q: Some first basemen are right-handed– true
A conjunction is true when both statements are true.
Hence, $p \wedge q$ is false.

6. p: Some dogs are not mammals – false
q: No number can exceed one million – false
A conjunction is true when both statements are true.
Hence, $p \wedge q$ is false.

7. p: $7 \times 3 = 21$ – true
q: Martin Luther King fought for racial equality – true
A disjunction is false when both statements are false.
Hence, $p \vee q$ is true.

8. p: $11 - 4 = 7$ – true
q: George Washington was the first U.S. President – true
A disjunction is false when both statements are false.
Hence, $p \vee q$ is true.

9. p: Some athletes are not college professors – true
q: Sammy Sosa was a U.S. President – false
A disjunction is false when both statements are false.
Hence, $p \vee q$ is true.

10. p: London is the capital of France – false
q: Some students are not psychology majors – true
A disjunction is false when both statements are false.
Hence, $p \vee q$ is true.

11. p: All politicians have law degrees – false
q: No students are business majors – false
A disjunction is false when both statements are false.
Hence, $p \vee q$ is false.

12. p: All computers cost more than $1000 – false
q: No colleges have athletic programs – false
A disjunction is false when both statements are false.
Hence, $p \vee q$ is false.

13. $p \vee \sim p$

p	$\sim p$	$p \vee \sim p$
T	F	T
F	T	T

14. $p \wedge \sim p$

p	$\sim p$	$p \wedge \sim p$
T	F	F
F	T	F

15. $\sim p \wedge q$

p	q	$\sim p$	$\sim p \wedge q$
T	T	F	F
T	F	F	F
F	T	T	T
F	F	T	F

16. $\sim p \vee q$

p	q	$\sim p$	$\sim p \vee q$
T	T	F	T
T	F	F	F
F	T	T	T
F	F	T	T

17. $\sim(p \vee q)$

p	q	$p \vee q$	$\sim(p \vee q)$
T	T	T	F
T	F	T	F
F	T	T	F
F	F	F	T

18. $\sim(p \vee \sim q)$

p	q	$\sim q$	$p \vee \sim q$	$\sim(p \vee \sim q)$
T	T	F	T	F
T	F	T	T	F
F	T	F	F	T
F	F	T	T	F

19. $\sim p \wedge \sim q$

p	q	$\sim p$	$\sim q$	$\sim p \wedge \sim q$
T	T	F	F	F
T	F	F	T	F
F	T	T	F	F
F	F	T	T	T

20. $p \wedge \sim q$

p	q	$\sim q$	$p \wedge \sim q$
T	T	F	F
T	F	T	T
F	T	F	F
F	F	T	F

21. $p \vee \sim q$

p	q	$\sim q$	$p \vee \sim q$
T	T	F	T
T	F	T	T
F	T	F	F
F	F	T	T

22. $\sim q \wedge p$

p	q	$\sim q$	$\sim q \wedge p$
T	T	F	F
T	F	T	T
F	T	F	F
F	F	T	F

23. $\sim(\sim p \vee q)$

p	q	$\sim p$	$\sim p \vee q$	$\sim(\sim p \vee q)$
T	T	F	T	F
T	F	F	F	T
F	T	T	T	F
F	F	T	T	F

24. $\sim(p \wedge \sim q)$

p	q	$\sim q$	$p \wedge \sim q$	$\sim(p \wedge \sim q)$
T	T	F	F	T
T	F	T	T	F
F	T	F	F	T
F	F	T	F	T

25. $(p \vee q) \wedge \sim p$

p	q	$\sim p$	$p \vee q$	$(p \vee q) \wedge \sim p$
T	T	F	T	F
T	F	F	T	F
F	T	T	T	T
F	F	T	F	F

26. $(p \wedge q) \vee \sim p$

p	q	$\sim p$	$p \wedge q$	$(p \wedge q) \vee \sim p$
T	T	F	T	T
T	F	F	F	F
F	T	T	F	T
F	F	T	F	T

27. $\sim p \vee (p \wedge \sim q)$

p	q	$\sim p$	$\sim q$	$p \wedge \sim q$	$\sim p \vee (p \wedge \sim q)$
T	T	F	F	F	F
T	F	F	T	T	T
F	T	T	F	F	T
F	F	T	T	F	T

28. $\sim p \wedge (p \vee \sim q)$

p	q	$\sim p$	$\sim q$	$p \vee \sim q$	$\sim p \wedge (p \vee \sim q)$
T	T	F	F	T	F
T	F	F	T	T	F
F	T	T	F	F	F
F	F	T	T	T	T

29. $(p \vee q) \wedge (\sim p \vee \sim q)$

p	q	$\sim p$	$\sim q$	$p \vee q$	$\sim p \vee \sim q$	$(p \vee q) \wedge (\sim p \vee \sim q)$
T	T	F	F	T	F	F
T	F	F	T	T	T	T
F	T	T	F	T	T	T
F	F	T	T	F	T	F

30. $(p \wedge \sim q) \vee (\sim p \wedge q)$

p	q	$\sim p$	$\sim q$	$p \wedge \sim q$	$\sim p \wedge q$	$(p \wedge \sim q) \vee (\sim p \wedge q)$
T	T	F	F	F	F	F
T	F	F	T	T	F	T
F	T	T	F	F	T	T
F	F	T	T	F	F	F

31. $(p \wedge \sim q) \vee (p \wedge q)$

p	q	$\sim q$	$p \wedge \sim q$	$p \wedge q$	$(p \wedge \sim q) \vee (p \wedge q)$
T	T	F	F	T	T
T	F	T	T	F	T
F	T	F	F	F	F
F	F	T	F	F	F

32. $(p \vee \sim q) \wedge (p \vee q)$

p	q	$\sim q$	$p \vee \sim q$	$p \vee q$	$(p \vee \sim q) \wedge (p \vee q)$
T	T	F	T	T	T
T	F	T	T	T	T
F	T	F	F	T	F
F	F	T	T	F	F

33. Texas is not a state or Paris is not a state.

34. Michael Jordan is not a musician or Garth Brooks is not a musician.

35. *Romeo and Juliet* was not written by Shakespeare or *Jurassic Park* was not written by Shakespeare.

36. *Star Wars* is not a movie or *Frasier* is not a movie.

37. Two statements linked by "and."
p: A motorist in Los Angeles averages more than 80 hours in traffic per year. – true
q: motorists in Atlanta average less hours in traffic per year than in Seattle. – true
Both statements are true, so $p \wedge q$ is true.

38. Two statements linked by "and."
p: A motorist in Los Angeles averages more than 80 hours in traffic per year. – true
q: motorists in Houston average less hours in traffic per year than in Dallas. – false
The first statement is true, second is false; so $p \wedge q$ is false.

39. Two statements linked by "or."
p: The average life expectancy for men born in 2000 is longer than the average life expectancy women born in 2000. – false
q: People in the U.S. are living longer with increasing birth years. – true.
First statement is false, second is true; so $p \vee q$ is true.

40. Two statements linked by "or."
p: Men born in 1950 have a life expectancy of 80 years. – false
q: The average life expectancy for women born in any year between 1950 and 2050 is longer than the average life expectancy for men born in the same year. – true
First statement is false, second is true; so $p \vee q$ is true.

41. The chance of divorce peaks during the fourth year of marriage and the chance of divorce does not decrease after 4 years of marriage. This statement is false.

42. The chance of divorce peaks during the fourth year of marriage and more than 2% of all divorces do not occur during the 25th year of marriage. This statement is true.

43. The chance of divorce does not peak during the fourth year of marriage and more than 2% of all divorces occur during the 25th year of marriage. This statement is false.

44. The chance of divorce decreases after four years of marriage and the chance of divorce does not peak during the fourth year of marriage. This statement is false.

45. The chance of divorce peaks during the fourth year of marriage or the chance of divorce does not decrease after four years of marriage. This statement is true.

46. The chance of divorce peaks during the fourth year of marriage or more than 2% of divorces do not occur during the 25th year of marriage. This statement is true.

47. The chance of divorce does not peak during the fourth year of marriage or more than 2% of divorces occur during the 25th year of marriage. This statement is false.

48. The chance of divorce decreases after four years of marriage or the chance of divorce does not peak during the fourth year of marriage. This statement is true.

49. The chance of divorce peaks during the fourth year of marriage and the chance of divorce decreases after four years of marriage, or more than 2% of divorces occur during the 25th year of marriage. This statement is true.

50. The chance of divorce peaks during the fourth year of marriage, and either the chance of divorce decreases after four years of marriage or more than 2% of divorces occur during the 25th year of marriage. This statement is true.

51-60. Answers will vary.

61. p and q are both false when $\sim(p \vee q)$ is true.

$\sim(p \vee q)$

p	q	$p \vee q$	$\sim(p \vee q)$
T	T	T	F
T	F	T	F
F	T	T	F
F	F	F	T

62. $p \veebar q$

p	q	$p \veebar q$
T	T	F
T	F	T
F	T	T
F	F	F

Check Points 3.4

1. $\sim p \rightarrow \sim q$

p	q	$\sim p$	$\sim q$	$\sim p \rightarrow \sim q$
T	T	F	F	T
T	F	F	T	T
F	T	T	F	F
F	F	T	T	T

The rightmost column shows that the statement is false when p is false and q is true; otherwise the statement is true.

2. If Shakespeare is not the author, then the play is not *Macbeth*.

3. $[(p \rightarrow q) \wedge \sim q] \rightarrow \sim p$ is a tautology because the final column is always true.

p	q	$\sim p$	$\sim q$	$p \rightarrow q$	$(p \rightarrow q) \wedge \sim q$	$[(p \rightarrow q) \wedge \sim q] \rightarrow \sim p$
T	T	F	F	T	F	T
T	F	F	T	F	F	T
F	T	T	F	T	F	T
F	F	T	T	T	T	T

4. $(p \rightarrow q) \wedge (\sim p \rightarrow \sim q)$

p	q	$\sim p$	$\sim q$	$p \rightarrow q$	$\sim p \rightarrow \sim q$	$(p \rightarrow q) \wedge (\sim p \rightarrow \sim q)$
T	T	F	F	T	T	T
T	F	F	T	F	T	F
F	T	T	F	T	F	F
F	F	T	T	T	T	T

5. $(p \vee q) \leftrightarrow (\sim p \rightarrow q)$ is a tautology.

p	q	$\sim p$	$p \vee q$	$\sim p \rightarrow q$	$(p \vee q) \leftrightarrow (\sim p \rightarrow q)$
T	T	F	T	T	T
T	F	F	T	T	T
F	T	T	T	T	T
F	F	T	F	F	T

6. $(p \rightarrow q) \wedge r$ is not a tautology.

p	q	r	$p \rightarrow q$	$(p \rightarrow q) \wedge r$
T	T	T	T	T
T	T	F	T	F
T	F	T	F	F
T	F	F	F	F
F	T	T	T	T
F	T	F	T	F
F	F	T	T	T
F	F	F	T	F

7. p: 17.6% of freshman are conservative (True).
q: 29.6% of freshman are liberal (False).
r: The percentage of liberals exceeds the percentage of conservative and far-right freshman combined. (True)
Substituting the truth values into the compound statement shows the statement to be false.

$$(p \vee q) \leftrightarrow \sim r$$
$$(T \vee F) \leftrightarrow \sim T$$
$$T \leftrightarrow F$$
$$F$$

Exercise Set 3.4

1. $p \rightarrow \sim q$

p	q	$\sim q$	$p \rightarrow \sim q$
T	T	F	F
T	F	T	T
F	T	F	T
F	F	T	T

2. $\sim p \rightarrow q$

p	q	$\sim p$	$\sim p \rightarrow q$
T	T	F	T
T	F	F	T
F	T	T	T
F	F	T	F

3. $\sim(q \rightarrow p)$

p	q	$q \rightarrow p$	$\sim(q \rightarrow p)$
T	T	T	F
T	F	T	F
F	T	F	T
F	F	T	F

4. $\sim(p \rightarrow q)$

p	q	$p \rightarrow q$	$\sim(p \rightarrow q)$
T	T	T	F
T	F	F	T
F	T	T	F
F	F	T	F

5. $(p \wedge q) \rightarrow (p \vee q)$

p	q	$p \wedge q$	$p \vee q$	$(p \wedge q) \rightarrow (p \vee q)$
T	T	T	T	T
T	F	F	T	T
F	T	F	T	T
F	F	F	F	T

6. $(p \vee q) \rightarrow (p \wedge q)$

p	q	$p \vee q$	$p \wedge q$	$(p \vee q) \rightarrow (p \wedge q)$
T	T	T	T	T
T	F	T	F	F
F	T	T	F	F
F	F	F	F	T

7. $(p \rightarrow q) \wedge \sim q$

p	q	$p \rightarrow q$	$\sim q$	$(p \rightarrow q) \wedge \sim q$
T	T	T	F	F
T	F	F	T	F
F	T	T	F	F
F	F	T	T	T

8. $(p \rightarrow q) \wedge \sim p$

p	q	$p \rightarrow q$	$\sim p$	$(p \rightarrow q) \wedge \sim p$
T	T	T	F	F
T	F	F	F	F
F	T	T	T	T
F	F	T	T	T

9. If I do not live in Washington, then I do not live in Seattle.

10. If I do not live in Utah, then I do not live in Salt Lake City.

11. If a plant does not wilt, then it is watered.

12. If I go out tonight, then the exam is not tomorrow.

13. $[(p \to q) \land q] \to p$ is not a tautology.

p	q	$p \to q$	$(p \to q) \land q$	$[(p \to q) \land q] \to p$
T	T	T	T	T
T	F	F	F	T
F	T	T	T	F
F	F	T	F	T

14. $\left[(p \to q) \land p \right] \to q$ is a tautology.

p	q	$p \to q$	$(p \to q) \land p$	$\left[(p \to q) \land p \right] \to q$
T	T	T	T	T
T	F	F	F	T
F	T	T	F	T
F	F	T	F	T

15. $\left[(p \to q) \land \sim q \right] \to \sim p$ is a tautology.

p	q	$\sim p$	$\sim q$	$p \to q$	$(p \to q) \land \sim q$	$\left[(p \to q) \land \sim q \right] \to \sim p$
T	T	F	F	T	F	T
T	F	F	T	F	F	T
F	T	T	F	T	F	T
F	F	T	T	T	T	T

16. $\left[(p \to q) \land \sim p \right] \to \sim q$ is not a tautology.

p	q	$\sim p$	$\sim q$	$p \to q$	$(p \to q) \land \sim p$	$\left[(p \to q) \land \sim p \right] \to \sim q$
T	T	F	F	T	F	T
T	F	F	T	F	F	T
F	T	T	F	T	T	F
F	F	T	T	T	T	T

17. $\left[(p \lor q) \land p \right] \to \sim q$ is not a tautology.

p	q	$\sim q$	$p \lor q$	$(p \lor q) \land p$	$\left[(p \lor q) \land p \right] \to \sim q$
T	T	F	T	T	F
T	F	T	T	T	T
F	T	F	T	F	T
F	F	T	F	F	T

18. $[(p \vee q) \wedge \sim q] \rightarrow p$ is a tautology.

p	q	$\sim q$	$p \vee q$	$(p \vee q) \wedge \sim q$	$[(p \vee q) \wedge \sim q] \rightarrow p$
T	T	F	T	F	T
T	F	T	T	T	T
F	T	F	T	F	T
F	F	T	F	F	T

19. $(p \rightarrow q) \rightarrow (\sim p \vee q)$ is a tautology.

p	q	$\sim p$	$p \rightarrow q$	$\sim p \vee q$	$(p \rightarrow q) \rightarrow (\sim p \vee q)$
T	T	F	T	T	T
T	F	F	F	F	T
F	T	T	T	T	T
F	F	T	T	T	T

20. $(q \rightarrow p) \rightarrow (p \vee \sim q)$ is a tautology.

p	q	$\sim q$	$q \rightarrow p$	$p \vee \sim q$	$(q \rightarrow p) \rightarrow (p \vee \sim q)$
T	T	F	T	T	T
T	F	T	T	T	T
F	T	F	F	F	T
F	F	T	T	T	T

21. $(p \wedge q) \wedge (\sim p \vee \sim q)$ is not a tautology.

p	q	$\sim p$	$\sim q$	$p \wedge q$	$\sim p \vee \sim q$	$(p \wedge q) \wedge (\sim p \vee \sim q)$
T	T	F	F	T	F	F
T	F	F	T	F	T	F
F	T	T	F	F	T	F
F	F	T	T	F	T	F

22. $(p \vee q) \wedge (\sim p \wedge \sim q)$ is not a tautology.

p	q	$\sim p$	$\sim q$	$p \vee q$	$\sim p \wedge \sim q$	$(p \vee q) \wedge (\sim p \wedge \sim q)$
T	T	F	F	T	F	F
T	F	F	T	T	F	F
F	T	T	F	T	F	F
F	F	T	T	F	T	F

23. $p \leftrightarrow \sim q$

p	q	$\sim q$	$p \leftrightarrow \sim q$
T	T	F	F
T	F	T	T
F	T	F	T
F	F	T	F

24. $\sim p \leftrightarrow q$

p	q	$\sim p$	$\sim p \leftrightarrow q$
T	T	F	F
T	F	F	T
F	T	T	T
F	F	T	F

25. $\sim(p \leftrightarrow q)$

p	q	$p \leftrightarrow q$	$\sim(p \leftrightarrow q)$
T	T	T	F
T	F	F	T
F	T	F	T
F	F	T	F

26. $\sim(q \leftrightarrow p)$

p	q	$q \leftrightarrow p$	$\sim(q \leftrightarrow p)$
T	T	T	F
T	F	F	T
F	T	F	T
F	F	T	F

27. $(p \leftrightarrow q) \rightarrow p$

p	q	$p \leftrightarrow q$	$(p \leftrightarrow q) \rightarrow p$
T	T	T	T
T	F	F	T
F	T	F	T
F	F	T	F

28. $(p \leftrightarrow q) \rightarrow q$

p	q	$p \leftrightarrow q$	$(p \leftrightarrow q) \rightarrow q$
T	T	T	T
T	F	F	T
F	T	F	T
F	F	T	F

29. $(\sim p \leftrightarrow q) \rightarrow (\sim p \rightarrow q)$

p	q	$\sim p$	$\sim p \leftrightarrow q$	$\sim p \rightarrow q$	$(\sim p \leftrightarrow q) \rightarrow (\sim p \rightarrow q)$
T	T	F	F	T	T
T	F	F	T	T	T
F	T	T	T	T	T
F	F	T	F	F	T

30. $(p \leftrightarrow \sim q) \rightarrow (q \rightarrow \sim p)$

p	q	$\sim p$	$\sim q$	$p \leftrightarrow \sim q$	$q \rightarrow \sim p$	$(p \leftrightarrow \sim q) \rightarrow (q \rightarrow \sim p)$
T	T	F	F	F	F	T
T	F	F	T	T	T	T
F	T	T	F	T	T	T
F	F	T	T	F	T	T

31. $[(p \wedge q) \wedge (q \rightarrow p)] \leftrightarrow (p \wedge q)$

p	q	$p \wedge q$	$q \rightarrow p$	$(p \wedge q) \wedge (q \rightarrow p)$	$[(p \wedge q) \wedge (q \rightarrow p)] \leftrightarrow (p \wedge q)$
T	T	T	T	T	T
T	F	F	T	F	T
F	T	F	F	F	T
F	F	F	T	F	T

32. $\left[(p \to q) \vee (p \wedge \sim p)\right] \leftrightarrow (\sim q \to \sim p)$

p	q	$\sim p$	$\sim q$	$p \to q$	$p \wedge \sim p$	$(p \to q) \vee (p \wedge \sim p)$	$\sim q \to \sim p$	$\left[(p \to q) \vee (p \wedge \sim p)\right] \leftrightarrow (\sim q \to \sim p)$
T	T	F	F	T	F	T	T	T
T	F	F	T	F	F	F	F	T
F	T	T	F	T	F	T	T	T
F	F	T	T	T	F	T	T	T

33. $\sim(p \wedge q) \leftrightarrow (\sim p \wedge \sim q)$ is not a tautology.

p	q	$\sim p$	$\sim q$	$p \wedge q$	$\sim(p \wedge q)$	$\sim p \wedge \sim q$	$\sim(p \wedge q) \leftrightarrow (\sim p \wedge \sim q)$
T	T	F	F	T	F	F	T
T	F	F	T	F	T	F	F
F	T	T	F	F	T	F	F
F	F	T	T	F	T	T	T

34. $\sim(p \vee q) \leftrightarrow (\sim p \wedge \sim q)$ is a tautology.

p	q	$\sim p$	$\sim q$	$p \vee q$	$\sim(p \vee q)$	$\sim p \wedge \sim q$	$\sim(p \vee q) \leftrightarrow (\sim p \wedge \sim q)$
T	T	F	F	T	F	F	T
T	F	F	T	T	F	F	T
F	T	T	F	T	F	F	T
F	F	T	T	F	T	T	T

35. $(p \to q) \leftrightarrow (q \to p)$ is not a tautology.

p	q	$p \to q$	$q \to p$	$(p \to q) \leftrightarrow (q \to p)$
T	T	T	T	T
T	F	F	T	F
F	T	T	F	F
F	F	T	T	T

36. $(p \to q) \leftrightarrow (\sim p \to \sim q)$ is not a tautology.

p	q	$\sim p$	$\sim q$	$p \to q$	$\sim p \to \sim q$	$(p \to q) \leftrightarrow (\sim p \to \sim q)$
T	T	F	F	T	T	T
T	F	F	T	F	T	F
F	T	T	F	T	F	F
F	F	T	T	T	T	T

37. $(p \to q) \leftrightarrow (\sim p \vee q)$ is a tautology.

p	q	$\sim p$	$p \to q$	$\sim p \vee q$	$(p \to q) \leftrightarrow (\sim p \vee q)$
T	T	F	T	T	T
T	F	F	F	F	T
F	T	T	T	T	T
F	F	T	T	T	T

38. $(p \to q) \leftrightarrow (p \lor \sim q)$ is not a tautology.

p	q	$\sim q$	$p \to q$	$p \lor \sim q$	$(p \to q) \leftrightarrow (p \lor \sim q)$
T	T	F	T	T	T
T	F	T	F	T	F
F	T	F	T	F	F
F	F	T	T	T	T

39. $(p \leftrightarrow q) \leftrightarrow [(q \to p) \land (p \to q)]$ is a tautology.

p	q	$q \to p$	$p \to q$	$p \leftrightarrow q$	$(q \to p) \land (p \to q)$	$(p \leftrightarrow q) \leftrightarrow [(q \to p) \land (p \to q)]$
T	T	T	T	T	T	T
T	F	T	F	F	F	T
F	T	F	T	F	F	T
F	F	T	T	T	T	T

40. $(q \leftrightarrow p) \leftrightarrow [(p \to q) \land (q \to p)]$ is a tautology.

p	q	$q \leftrightarrow p$	$p \to q$	$q \to p$	$(p \to q) \land (q \to p)$	$(q \leftrightarrow p) \leftrightarrow [(p \to q) \land (q \to p)]$
T	T	T	T	T	T	T
T	F	F	F	T	F	T
F	T	F	T	F	F	T
F	F	T	T	T	T	T

41. $(p \land \sim q) \lor r$

p	q	r	$\sim q$	$p \land \sim q$	$(p \land \sim q) \lor r$
T	T	T	F	F	T
T	T	F	F	F	F
T	F	T	T	T	T
T	F	F	T	T	T
F	T	T	F	F	T
F	T	F	F	F	F
F	F	T	T	F	T
F	F	F	T	F	F

43. $(p \lor q) \to r$ is not a tautology.

p	q	r	$p \lor q$	$(p \lor q) \to r$
T	T	T	T	T
T	T	F	T	F
T	F	T	T	T
T	F	F	T	F
F	T	T	T	T
F	T	F	T	F
F	F	T	F	T
F	F	F	F	T

42. $(p \lor \sim q) \land r$

p	q	r	$\sim q$	$p \lor \sim q$	$(p \lor \sim q) \land r$
T	T	T	F	T	T
T	T	F	F	T	F
T	F	T	T	T	T
T	F	F	T	T	F
F	T	T	F	F	F
F	T	F	F	F	F
F	F	T	T	T	T
F	F	F	T	T	F

44. $p \to (q \lor r)$ is not a tautology.

p	q	r	$q \lor r$	$p \to (q \lor r)$
T	T	T	T	T
T	T	F	T	T
T	F	T	T	T
T	F	F	F	F
F	T	T	T	T
F	T	F	T	T
F	F	T	T	T
F	F	F	F	T

45. $(p \wedge q) \rightarrow (p \vee r)$ is a tautology.

p	q	r	$p \wedge q$	$p \vee r$	$(p \wedge q) \rightarrow (p \vee r)$
T	T	T	T	T	T
T	T	F	T	T	T
T	F	T	F	T	T
T	F	F	F	T	T
F	T	T	F	T	T
F	T	F	F	F	T
F	F	T	F	T	T
F	F	F	F	F	T

46. $(p \vee r) \rightarrow (q \wedge r)$ is not a tautology.

p	q	r	$p \vee r$	$q \wedge r$	$(p \vee r) \rightarrow (q \wedge r)$
T	T	T	T	T	T
T	T	F	T	F	F
T	F	T	T	F	F
T	F	F	T	F	F
F	T	T	T	T	T
F	T	F	F	F	T
F	F	T	T	F	F
F	F	F	F	F	T

47. $r \rightarrow (p \wedge q)$ is not a tautology.

p	q	r	$p \wedge q$	$r \rightarrow (p \wedge q)$
T	T	T	T	T
T	T	F	T	T
T	F	T	F	F
T	F	F	F	T
F	T	T	F	F
F	T	F	F	T
F	F	T	F	F
F	F	F	F	T

48. $r \rightarrow (p \vee q)$ is not a tautology.

p	q	r	$p \vee q$	$r \rightarrow (p \vee q)$
T	T	T	T	T
T	T	F	T	T
T	F	T	T	T
T	F	F	T	T
F	T	T	T	T
F	T	F	T	T
F	F	T	F	F
F	F	F	F	T

49. $[(p \rightarrow q) \wedge (q \rightarrow r)] \rightarrow (p \rightarrow r)$ is a tautology.

p	q	r	$p \rightarrow q$	$q \rightarrow r$	$(p \rightarrow q) \wedge (q \rightarrow r)$	$p \rightarrow r$	$[(p \rightarrow q) \wedge (q \rightarrow r)] \rightarrow (p \rightarrow r)$
T	T	T	T	T	T	T	T
T	T	F	T	F	F	F	T
T	F	T	F	T	F	T	T
T	F	F	F	T	F	F	T
F	T	T	T	T	T	T	T
F	T	F	T	F	F	T	T
F	F	T	T	T	T	T	T
F	F	F	T	T	T	T	T

50. $\left[(p \to q) \wedge (q \to r)\right] \to (\sim r \to \sim p)$ is a tautology.

p	q	r	$\sim p$	$\sim r$	$p \to q$	$q \to r$	$(p \to q) \wedge (q \to r)$	$\sim r \to \sim p$	$\left[(p \to q) \wedge (q \to r)\right] \to (\sim r \to \sim p)$
T	T	T	F	F	T	T	T	T	T
T	T	F	F	T	T	F	F	F	T
T	F	T	F	F	F	T	F	T	T
T	F	F	F	T	F	T	F	F	T
F	T	T	T	F	T	T	T	T	T
F	T	F	T	T	T	F	F	T	T
F	F	T	T	F	T	T	T	T	T
F	F	F	T	T	T	T	T	T	T

51. $\sim(p \to q)$

$\quad \sim(F \to T)$

$\qquad \sim T$

$\qquad F$

52. $\sim(p \leftrightarrow q)$

$\quad \sim(F \leftrightarrow T)$

$\qquad \sim F$

$\qquad T$

53. $\sim p \leftrightarrow q$

$\quad \sim F \leftrightarrow T$

$\quad T \leftrightarrow T$

$\qquad T$

54. $\sim p \to q$

$\quad \sim F \to T$

$\quad T \to T$

$\qquad T$

55. $q \to (p \wedge r)$

$\quad T \to (F \wedge F)$

$\qquad T \to F$

$\qquad F$

56. $(p \wedge r) \to q$

$\quad (F \wedge F) \to T$

$\qquad F \to T$

$\qquad T$

57. $(\sim p \wedge q) \leftrightarrow \sim r$

$\quad (\sim F \wedge T) \leftrightarrow \sim F$

$\quad (T \wedge T) \leftrightarrow T$

$\qquad T \leftrightarrow T$

$\qquad T$

58. $\sim p \leftrightarrow (\sim q \wedge r)$

$\quad \sim F \leftrightarrow (\sim T \wedge F)$

$\quad T \leftrightarrow (F \wedge F)$

$\quad T \leftrightarrow F$

$\qquad F$

59. $\sim\left[(p \to \sim r) \leftrightarrow (r \wedge \sim p)\right]$

$\quad \sim\left[(F \to \sim F) \leftrightarrow (F \wedge \sim F)\right]$

$\quad \sim\left[(F \to T) \leftrightarrow (F \wedge T)\right]$

$\qquad \sim[T \leftrightarrow F]$

$\qquad \sim F$

$\qquad T$

60. $\sim\left[(\sim p \to r) \leftrightarrow (p \vee \sim q)\right]$

$\quad \sim\left[(\sim F \to F) \leftrightarrow (F \vee \sim T)\right]$

$\quad \sim\left[(T \to F) \leftrightarrow (F \vee F)\right]$

$\qquad \sim[F \leftrightarrow F]$

$\qquad \sim T$

$\qquad F$

61. The statement is of the form $p \to q$ with p true and q false.

$\qquad p \to q$

$\qquad T \to F$

$\qquad\quad F$

Therefore the statement is false.

62. The statement is of the form $p \to q$ with p false and q false.

$\qquad p \to q$

$\qquad F \to F$

$\qquad\quad T$

Therefore the statement is true.

63. The statement is of the form $(p \rightarrow q) \vee r$ with p true, q true, and r false.

$$(p \rightarrow q) \vee r$$
$$(T \rightarrow T) \vee F$$
$$T \vee F$$
$$T$$

Therefore the statement is true.

64. The statement is of the form $(p \wedge q) \vee r$ with p true, q true, and r false.

$$(p \wedge q) \vee r$$
$$(T \wedge T) \vee F$$
$$T \vee F$$
$$T$$

Therefore the statement is true.

65. The statement is of the form $p \wedge (\sim q \rightarrow r)$ with p true, q true, and r true.

$$p \wedge (\sim q \rightarrow r)$$
$$T \wedge (\sim T \rightarrow T)$$
$$T \wedge (F \rightarrow T)$$
$$T \wedge T$$
$$T$$

Therefore the statement is true.

66. The statement is of the form $p \leftrightarrow (q \vee r)$ with p true, q false, and r true.

$$p \leftrightarrow (q \vee r)$$
$$T \leftrightarrow (F \vee T)$$
$$T \leftrightarrow T$$
$$T$$

Therefore the statement is true.

67. The statement is of the form $(p \vee q) \leftrightarrow r$ with p false, q true, and r false.

$$(p \vee q) \leftrightarrow r$$
$$(F \vee T) \leftrightarrow F$$
$$T \leftrightarrow F$$
$$F$$

Therefore the statement is false.

68. The statement is of the form $(p \wedge q) \leftrightarrow r$ with p false, q true, and r false.

$$(p \wedge q) \leftrightarrow r$$
$$(F \wedge T) \leftrightarrow F$$
$$F \leftrightarrow F$$
$$T$$

Therefore the statement is true.

69. The statement is of the form $p \to (q \wedge r)$ with p true, q false, and r true.

$$p \to (q \wedge r)$$
$$T \to (F \wedge T)$$
$$T \to F$$
$$F$$

Therefore the statement is false.

70. The statement is of the form $p \to (q \vee r)$ with p false, q false, and r true.

$$p \to (q \vee r)$$
$$F \to (F \vee T)$$
$$F \to T$$
$$T$$

Therefore the statement is true.

71-76. Answers will vary.

77. d is true. For example: if p is false and q is false, $p \to q$ is true.

78. No, you cannot conclude you got an A. The person could still take you out to dinner if you received a different grade. That would be an example of an *if-then* statement with a false antecedent and a true consequent.

79. Answers will vary. Possible column headings:

p	q	$p \to q$	$\sim p$	$(p \to q) \vee \sim p$	$[(p \to q) \vee \sim p] \leftrightarrow (p \to q)$

80. Answers will vary. Possible column headings:

p	q	$p \vee q$	$p \wedge q$	$\sim(p \wedge q)$	$(p \vee q) \to \sim(p \wedge q)$

81. If there are n simple statements, then there are 2^n true-false combinations.

Check Points 3.5

1. a. $p \vee q$ and $\sim q \to p$ are equivalent.

p	q	$\sim q$	$p \vee q$	$\sim q \to p$
T	T	F	T	T
T	F	T	T	T
F	T	F	T	T
F	F	T	F	F

The statements are equivalent since their truth values are the same.

b.
$$\underline{ p \vee q }$$
I attend classes or I lose my scholarship.

...is equivalent to...
$$\underline{ \sim q \to p }$$
If I do not lose my scholarship, then I attend classes.

2. $\sim p$ and $\sim[\sim(\sim p)]$ are equivalent.

p	$\sim p$	$\sim(\sim p)$	$\sim[\sim(\sim p)]$
T	F	T	F
F	T	F	T

The statements are equivalent since their truth values are the same.

3. Given: If it's raining, then I need a jacket.
   p: It's raining.
   q: I need a jacket.
   a: It's not raining or I need a jacket.
   b: I need a jacket or it's not raining.
   c: If I need a jacket, then it's raining.
   d: If I do not need a jacket, then it's not raining.

The given is *not* equivalent to statement **c**.

				Given	a	b	c	d
p	*q*	~*p*	~*q*	$p \rightarrow q$	~$p \vee q$	$q \vee$~p	$q \rightarrow p$	~$q \rightarrow$~p
T	T	F	F	T	T	T	T	T
T	F	F	T	F	F	F	T	F
F	T	T	F	T	T	T	F	T
F	F	T	T	T	T	T	T	T

4. **a.** If you do not pay a fine, then the book is not overdue.

   b. If we use the pool, then it is not cold.

   c. If supervision is needed, then some students do not take exams honestly.

   d. $q \rightarrow$ ~p

5. Converse: If it can fly, then it's a bird.
   Inverse: If it's not a bird, then it can not fly.

6. The triangle is isosceles and it does not have two equal sides.

7. Kelsey Grammer is not an actor or Katie Couric is not an actor.

8. Oprah Winfrey is not a jazz musician and Oprah Winfrey is not a presidential candidate.
   Alternatively: Oprah Winfrey is neither a jazz musician nor a presidential candidate.

9. You do not leave by 5 P.M. and you arrive home on time.

10. *p*: It is windy.
    q: We can swim.
    r: We can sail.
    The statement can be represented symbolically as ~$p \rightarrow (q \wedge$~$r)$.
    Next write the contrapositive and simplify.
    $$\sim(q \wedge \sim r) \rightarrow \sim(\sim p)$$
    $$[\sim q \vee \sim(\sim r)] \rightarrow p$$
    $$(\sim q \vee r) \rightarrow p$$
    Thus, ~$p \rightarrow (q \wedge$~$r) \equiv (\sim q \vee r) \rightarrow p$.
    The original statement is equivalent to "If we cannot swim or we can sail, then it is windy."

Exercise Set 3.5

1. a. $p \rightarrow q$ and $\sim p \vee q$ are equivalent.

p	q	$\sim p$	$p \rightarrow q$	$\sim p \vee q$
T	T	F	T	T
T	F	F	F	F
F	T	T	T	T
F	F	T	T	T

b.

If a number is even, then it is divisible by 2.

$\qquad\qquad\quad p \qquad\qquad \rightarrow \qquad\qquad q$

...is equivalent to...

$\qquad\qquad \sim p \qquad\qquad \vee \qquad\qquad q$

A number is not even or it is divisible by 2.

2. a. $\sim p \rightarrow q$ and $p \vee q$ are equivalent.

p	q	$\sim p$	$\sim p \rightarrow q$	$p \vee q$
T	T	F	T	T
T	F	F	T	T
F	T	T	T	T
F	F	T	F	F

b.

If a major dam on the upper Nile River is not in place, then the lower Nile overflows its banks each year.

$\qquad\qquad\qquad \sim p \qquad\qquad\qquad\qquad \rightarrow \qquad\qquad\qquad q$

...is equivalent to...

$\qquad\qquad\qquad p \qquad\qquad\qquad \vee \qquad\qquad\qquad q$

A major dam on the upper Nile River is in place or the lower Nile overflows its banks each year.

3. Given: I saw *Rent* or *Ragtime*.

p: I saw *Rent*.

q: I saw *Ragtime*.

a: If I did not see *Rent*, I saw *Ragtime*.

b: I saw both *Rent* and *Ragtime*.

c: If I saw *Rent*, I did not see *Ragtime*.

d: If I saw *Ragtime*, I did not see *Rent*.

The given is equivalent to statement **a.**

p	q	Given $p \vee q$	a $\sim p \rightarrow q$	b $p \wedge q$	c $p \rightarrow \sim q$	d $q \rightarrow \sim p$
T	T	T	T	T	F	F
T	F	T	T	F	T	T
F	T	T	T	F	T	T
F	F	F	F	F	T	T

4. Given: *Citizen Kane* or *Howard the Duck* appear in a list of greatest U.S. movies.

p: *Citizen Kane* appears in a list of greatest U.S. movies.

q: *Howard the Duck* appears in a list of greatest U.S. movies.

a: If *Citizen Kane* appears in the list of greatest U.S. movies, *Howard the Duck* does not.

b: If *Howard the Duck* does not appear in the list of greatest U.S. movies, then *Citizen Kane* does.

c: Both *Citizen Kane* and *Howard the Duck* appear in a list of greatest U.S. movies.

d: If *Howard the Duck* appears in the list of greatest U.S. movies, *Citizen Kane* does not.

The given is equivalent to statement **b.**

p	q	Given $p \vee q$	a $p \rightarrow \sim q$	b $\sim q \rightarrow p$	c $p \wedge q$	d $q \rightarrow \sim p$
T	T	T	F	T	T	F
T	F	T	T	T	F	T
F	T	T	T	T	F	T
F	F	F	T	F	F	T

5. Given: It is not true that Sondheim and Picasso are both musicians.
   p: Sondheim is a musician.
   q: Picasso is a musician.
   a: Sondheim is not a musician or Picasso is not a musician.
   b: If Sondheim is a musician, then Picasso is not a musician.
   c: Sondheim is not a musician and Picasso is not a musician.
   d: If Picasso is a musician, then Sondheim is not a musician.

   The given is *not* equivalent to statement **c**.

		Given	a	b	c	d
p	*q*	~(*p* ∧ *q*)	~*p*∨~*q*	*p* → ~*q*	~*p*∧~*q*	*q* → ~*p*
T	T	F	F	F	F	F
T	F	T	T	T	F	T
F	T	T	T	T	F	T
F	F	T	T	T	T	T

6. Given: It is not true that England and Africa are both countries.
   p: England is a country.
   q: Africa is a country.
   a: If England is a country, then Africa is not a country.
   b: England is not a country and Africa is not a country.
   c: England is not a country or Africa is not a country.
   d: If Africa is a country, then England is not a country.

   The given is *not* equivalent to statement **b**.

		Given	a	b	c	d
p	*q*	~(*p* ∧ *q*)	*p* → ~*q*	~*p*∧~*q*	~*p*∨~*q*	*p* → ~*q*
T	T	F	F	F	F	F
T	F	T	T	F	T	T
F	T	T	T	F	T	T
F	F	T	T	T	T	T

7. If I am not in Illinois, I am not in Chicago.

8. If I am not in the South, I am not in Birmingham.

9. If I can hear you, then the stereo is not playing.

10. If it is an apple, it is not blue.

11. If you don't die, you laugh.

12. If you do not acquit, then it fits..

13. If some troops were not withdrawn, then the president was not telling the truth.

14. If some students fail the test, then the review session was not successful.

15. If no people suffer, then some institutions do not profit above human need.

16. If all people are hard workers, then some hard workers are not successful.

17. *r* → *q*

18. ~*r* → *p*

19. Converse: If you get a skin rash, then you have touched poison oak.
    Inverse: If you have not touched poison oak, then you will not get a skin rash.

20. Converse: If I miss class, then I am sick.
    Inverse: If I am not sick, then I will not miss class.

21. Converse: If Shakespeare is the author, then the play is *Macbeth*.
    Inverse: If the play is not *Macbeth*, then Shakespeare is not the author.

22. Converse: If Tom Hanks appears, then the movie is *Saving Private Ryan*.
    Inverse: If the movie is not *Saving Private Ryan*, then Tom Hanks does not appear.

23. Converse: If you are not sleeping, then you are driving the car.
Inverse: If you are not driving the car, then you are sleeping.

24. Converse: If you are not listening to the radio, then you are in class.
Inverse: If you are not in class, then you are listening to the radio.

25. Converse: If I am not in the West, then I am in Charleston.
Inverse: If I am not in Charleston, then I am in the West.

26. Converse: If I am not in Spain, then I am in London.
Inverse: If I am not in London, then I am in Spain.

27. Converse: If some people wear green, then it is St. Patrick's Day.
Inverse: If it's not St. Patrick's Day, then no people wear green.

28. Converse: If some people eat turkey, then it's Thanksgiving.
Inverse: If it's not Thanksgiving, then no people eat turkey.

29. Converse: $\sim r \rightarrow \sim q$
Inverse: $q \rightarrow r$

30. Converse:. $r \rightarrow \sim p$
Inverse: $p \rightarrow \sim r$

31. The negation of $p \rightarrow q$ is $p \wedge \sim q$: I am in Los Angeles and not in California.

32. The negation of $p \rightarrow q$ is $p \wedge \sim q$: I am in Houston and not in Texas.

33. The negation of $p \rightarrow q$ is $p \wedge \sim q$: It is purple and it is a carrot.

34. The negation of $p \rightarrow q$ is $p \wedge \sim q$: The TV is playing and I can concentrate.

35. The negation of $p \rightarrow q$ is $p \wedge \sim q$: He doesn't, and I won't.

36. The negation of $p \rightarrow q$ is $p \wedge \sim q$: She says "yes," and he does not say "no."

37. The negation of $p \rightarrow q$ is $p \wedge \sim q$: There is a blizzard, and yet some schools are not closed.

38. The negation of $p \rightarrow q$ is $p \wedge \sim q$: There is a tax cut, and some people do not have extra spending money.

39. The negation of $\sim q \rightarrow \sim r$ is $\sim q \wedge r$

40. The negation of $\sim p \rightarrow r$ is $\sim p \wedge \sim r$

41. Australia is not an island or China is not an island.

42. Florida is not a peninsula or California is not a peninsula.

43. My high school did not encourage creativity or did not encourage diversity.

44. The course does not cover logic or does not cover dream analysis.

45. Babe Ruth was not a writer and was not a lawyer.

46. Martin Luther King supported neither violent protests nor the Vietnam War.

47. The United States has eradicated neither poverty nor racism.

48. The movie was neither interesting nor entertaining.

49. $\sim(\sim p \wedge q)$
$\sim(\sim p) \vee \sim q$
$p \vee \sim q$

50. $\sim(p \vee \sim q)$
$\sim p \wedge \sim(\sim q)$
$\sim p \wedge q$

51. p: You attend lecture.

q: You study.

r: You succeed.

The statement can be represented symbolically as $(p \wedge q) \rightarrow r$.

Next write the contrapositive and simplify.

$\sim r \rightarrow \sim (p \wedge q)$

$\sim r \rightarrow (\sim p \vee \sim q)$

Thus, $(p \wedge q) \rightarrow r \equiv \sim r \rightarrow (\sim p \vee \sim q)$.

The original statement is equivalent to "If you do not succeed, then you did not attend lecture or did not study."

52. p: A number is a natural number.

q: A number is a whole number.

r: The number is 0.

The statement can be represented symbolically as $(p \wedge q) \rightarrow r$.

Next write the contrapositive and simplify.

$\sim r \rightarrow \sim (p \wedge q)$

$\sim r \rightarrow (\sim p \vee \sim q)$

Thus, $(p \wedge q) \rightarrow r \equiv \sim r \rightarrow (\sim p \vee \sim q)$.

The original statement is equivalent to "If a number is not 0, then the number is not a natural number or not a whole number."

53. p: He cooks.

q: His wife cooks.

r: His child cooks.

The statement can be represented symbolically as $\sim p \rightarrow (q \vee r)$.

Next write the contrapositive and simplify.

$\sim (q \vee r) \rightarrow \sim (\sim p)$

$(\sim q \wedge \sim r) \rightarrow p$

Thus, $\sim p \rightarrow (q \vee r) \equiv (\sim q \wedge \sim r) \rightarrow p$.

The original statement is equivalent to "If his wife does not cook and child does not cook, then he does."

54. p: It is Saturday.

q: It is Sunday.

r: I work.

The statement can be represented symbolically as $(p \vee q) \rightarrow \sim r$.

Next write the contrapositive and simplify.

$\sim (\sim r) \rightarrow \sim (p \vee q)$

$r \rightarrow (\sim p \wedge \sim q)$

Thus, $(p \vee q) \rightarrow \sim r \equiv r \rightarrow (\sim p \wedge \sim q)$.

The original statement is equivalent to "If I work, then it is not Saturday and it is not Sunday."

55. Write the contrapositive of $p \rightarrow (q \vee \sim r)$ and simplify.

$\sim (q \vee \sim r) \rightarrow \sim p$

$[\sim q \wedge \sim (\sim r)] \rightarrow \sim p$

$(\sim q \wedge r) \rightarrow \sim p$

Thus, $p \rightarrow (q \vee \sim r) \equiv (\sim q \wedge r) \rightarrow \sim p$.

56. Write the contrapositive of $p \rightarrow (\sim q \wedge \sim r)$ and simplify.

$\sim(\sim q \wedge \sim r) \rightarrow \sim p$

$\left[q \vee \sim(\sim r) \right] \rightarrow \sim p$

$(q \vee r) \rightarrow \sim p$

Thus, $p \rightarrow (\sim q \wedge \sim r) \equiv (q \vee r) \rightarrow \sim p$.

57. I'm going to neither Seattle nor San Francisco.

58. This course covers neither logic nor statistics.

59. I do not study and I pass.

60. I did not give up tobacco and I am healthy.

61. I am going or he is not going.

62. I did apply myself or I do not succeed.

63. A bill does not become law or it receives majority approval.

64. They do not see the show or they have tickets.

65. Write the negation of $p \vee \sim q$ and simplify.

$\sim(p \vee \sim q)$

$\sim p \wedge \sim(\sim q)$

$\sim p \wedge q$

Thus the negation of $p \vee \sim q$ is $\sim p \wedge q$.

66. Write the negation of $\sim p \vee q$ and simplify.

$\sim(\sim p \vee q)$

$\sim(\sim p) \wedge \sim q$

$p \wedge \sim q$

Thus the negation of $\sim p \vee q$ is $p \wedge \sim q$.

67. Write the negation of $p \wedge (q \vee r)$ and simplify.

$\sim\left[p \wedge (q \vee r) \right]$

$\sim p \vee \sim(q \vee r)$

$\sim p \vee (\sim q \wedge \sim r)$

Thus the negation of $p \wedge (q \vee r)$ is $\sim p \vee (\sim q \wedge \sim r)$.

68. Write the negation of $p \vee (q \wedge r)$ and simplify.

$\sim\left[p \vee (q \wedge r) \right]$

$\sim p \wedge \sim(q \wedge r)$

$\sim p \wedge (\sim q \vee \sim r)$

Thus the negation of $p \vee (q \wedge r)$ is $\sim p \wedge (\sim q \vee \sim r)$.

69. None are equivalent.

		a	b	c
p	q	$p \rightarrow \sim q$	$\sim p \vee q$	$\sim p \rightarrow q$
T	T	F	T	T
T	F	T	T	F
F	T	T	T	T
F	F	T	F	T

70. a and b are equivalent.

		a	b	c
p	q	$p \rightarrow \sim q$	$p \vee q$	$q \rightarrow \sim p$
T	T	F	T	F
T	F	T	T	T
F	T	T	T	T
F	F	T	F	T

71. None are equivalent.

		a	b	c
p	q	$\sim(p \wedge \sim q)$	$\sim p \wedge q$	$p \vee \sim q$
T	T	T	F	T
T	F	F	F	T
F	T	T	T	F
F	F	T	F	T

72. a and b are equivalent.

		a	b	c
p	q	$p \vee \sim q$	$\sim(\sim p \wedge q)$	$\sim p \wedge q$
T	T	T	T	F
T	F	T	T	F
F	T	F	F	T
F	F	T	T	F

73. None are equivalent.

			a	b	c
p	q	r	$p \to \sim(q \vee r)$	$(q \wedge r) \to \sim p$	$\sim p \to (q \wedge r)$
T	T	T	F	F	T
T	T	F	F	T	T
T	F	T	F	T	T
T	F	F	T	T	T
F	T	T	T	T	T
F	T	F	T	T	F
F	F	T	T	T	F
F	F	F	T	T	F

74. None are equivalent.

			a	b	c
p	q	r	$(\sim p \vee q) \to r$	$(p \wedge \sim q) \to \sim r$	$\sim r \to (p \vee \sim q)$
T	T	T	T	T	T
T	T	F	F	T	T
T	F	T	T	F	T
T	F	F	T	T	T
F	T	T	T	T	T
F	T	F	F	T	F
F	F	T	T	T	T
F	F	F	F	T	T

75. a and b are equivalent.

			a	b	c
p	q	r	$p \wedge (q \vee r)$	$p \wedge \sim(\sim q \wedge \sim r)$	$p \to (q \vee r)$
T	T	T	T	T	T
T	T	F	T	T	T
T	F	T	T	T	T
T	F	F	F	F	F
F	T	T	F	F	T
F	T	F	F	F	T
F	F	T	F	F	T
F	F	F	F	F	T

76. a and c are equivalent.

			a	b	c
p	q	r	$p \wedge (q \to r)$	$r \leftrightarrow (q \wedge p)$	$p \wedge (\sim r \to \sim q)$
T	T	T	T	T	T
T	T	F	F	F	F
T	F	T	T	F	T
T	F	F	T	T	T
F	T	T	F	F	F
F	T	F	F	T	F
F	F	T	F	F	F
F	F	F	F	T	F

77. a. The given statement is true.

   b. If it is not the case that 96% of the patients are women, then the procedure is not a chemical peel.
True

   c. If 96% of the patients are women, then the procedure is a chemical peel.
Not necessarily true

   d. If the procedure is not a chemical peel, then it is not the case that 96% of the patients are women.
Not necessarily true

   e. The procedure is a chemical peel and it is not the case that 96% of the patients are women.
False

78. a. The given statement is false.

   b. There are not 51,072 liposuctions each year or it is not the case that 93% of the liposuction patients are women.

   c. The negation is true.

79. a. The given statement is true.

   b. There are not 32,283 face lifts per year and it is not the case that 8% of the facelift patients are men.

   c. The negation is false.

80-88. Answers will vary.

89. b is true.

90. Rewrite the given statement: If I observe the speed limit, then I do not get a ticket.
Contrapositive: If I get a ticket, then I did not observe the speed limit.
Alternative form of Contrapositive: I did not observe the speed limit if I got a ticket.

91. We will replace or repair the roof, *or* we will not sell the house.

Check Points 3.6

1. The argument is valid. p: I study for 5 hours. q: I fail.

$$
\begin{array}{c}
p \vee q \\
\sim p \\
\hline
\therefore q
\end{array}
$$

p	q	$\sim p$	$p \vee q$	$(p \vee q) \wedge \sim p$	$[(p \vee q) \wedge \sim p] \to q$
T	T	F	T	F	T
T	F	F	T	F	T
F	T	T	T	T	T
F	F	T	F	F	T

2. The argument is invalid. p: I study for 5 hours. q: I fail.

$$
\begin{array}{c}
p \vee q \\
p \\
\hline
\therefore \sim q
\end{array}
$$

p	q	$p \vee q$	$(p \vee q) \wedge p$	$[(p \vee q) \wedge p] \to \sim q$
T	T	T	T	T
T	F	T	T	F
F	T	T	F	T
F	F	F	F	T

3. The argument is invalid.
   p: You do not know how to read. *q*: You cannot read "War and Peace." *r*: Leo Tolstoy will hate you.

$p \rightarrow q$

$q \rightarrow r$

$\therefore \sim p \rightarrow \sim r$

p	*q*	*r*	~*p*	~*r*	$p \rightarrow q$	$q \rightarrow r$	$\sim p \rightarrow \sim r$	$(p \rightarrow q) \wedge (q \rightarrow r)$	$[(p \rightarrow q) \wedge (q \rightarrow r)] \rightarrow (\sim p \rightarrow \sim r)$
T	T	T	F	F	T	T	T	T	T
T	T	F	F	T	T	F	T	F	T
T	F	T	F	F	F	T	T	F	T
T	F	F	F	T	F	T	T	F	T
F	T	T	T	F	T	T	F	T	F
F	T	F	T	T	T	F	T	F	T
F	F	T	T	F	T	T	F	T	F
F	F	F	T	T	T	T	T	T	T

4. Using the contrapositive reasoning form of a valid argument, the following can be concluded: It is not midnight.

Exercise Set 3.6

1. This is an invalid argument.

p	*q*	~*p*	~*q*	$p \rightarrow q$	$(p \rightarrow q) \wedge \sim p$	$[(p \rightarrow q) \wedge \sim p] \rightarrow \sim q$
T	T	F	F	T	F	T
T	F	F	T	F	F	T
F	T	T	F	T	T	F
F	F	T	T	T	T	T

2. This.is an invalid argument.

p	*q*	~*p*	$p \rightarrow q$	$(p \rightarrow q) \wedge \sim p$	$[(p \rightarrow q) \wedge \sim p] \rightarrow q$
T	T	F	T	F	T
T	F	F	F	F	T
F	T	T	T	T	T
F	F	T	T	T	F

3. This is a valid argument.

p	*q*	~*p*	~*q*	$p \rightarrow \sim q$	$(p \rightarrow \sim q) \wedge q$	$[(p \rightarrow \sim q) \wedge q] \rightarrow \sim p$
T	T	F	F	F	F	T
T	F	F	T	T	F	T
F	T	T	F	T	T	T
F	F	T	T	T	F	T

4. This is a valid argument.

p	*q*	~*p*	~*q*	$\sim p \rightarrow q$	$(\sim p \rightarrow q) \wedge \sim q$	$[(\sim p \rightarrow q) \wedge \sim q] \rightarrow p$
T	T	F	F	T	F	T
T	F	F	T	T	T	T
F	T	T	F	T	F	T
F	F	T	T	F	F	T

5. This is a valid argument.

p	q	$\sim q$	$p \wedge \sim q$	$(p \wedge \sim q) \wedge p$	$[(p \wedge \sim q) \wedge p] \rightarrow \sim q$
T	T	F	F	F	T
T	F	T	T	T	T
F	T	F	F	F	T
F	F	T	F	F	T

6. This is a valid argument.

p	q	$\sim p$	$\sim p \vee q$	$(\sim p \vee q) \wedge p$	$[(\sim p \vee q) \wedge p] \rightarrow q$
T	T	F	T	T	T
T	F	F	F	F	T
F	T	T	T	F	T
F	F	T	T	F	T

7. This is an invalid argument.

p	q	$p \rightarrow q$	$q \rightarrow p$	$p \wedge q$	$[(p \rightarrow q) \wedge (q \rightarrow p)]$	$[(p \rightarrow q) \wedge (q \rightarrow p)] \rightarrow (p \wedge q)$
T	T	T	T	T	T	T
T	F	F	T	F	F	T
F	T	T	F	F	F	T
F	F	T	T	F	T	F

8. This is a valid argument.

p	q	$p \rightarrow q$	$q \rightarrow p$	$(p \rightarrow q) \wedge (q \rightarrow p)$	$[(p \rightarrow q) \wedge (q \rightarrow p)] \wedge p$	$p \vee q$
T	T	T	T	T	T	T
T	F	F	T	F	F	T
F	T	T	F	F	F	T
F	F	T	T	T	F	F

$\big[[(p \rightarrow q) \wedge (q \rightarrow p)] \wedge p\big] \rightarrow (p \vee q)$
T
T
T
T

9. This is a valid argument. p: It is cold. q: Motorcycle started.

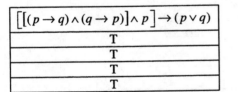

p	q	$\sim p$	$\sim q$	$p \rightarrow \sim q$	$(p \rightarrow \sim q) \wedge q$	$[(p \rightarrow \sim q) \wedge q \rightarrow \sim p]$
T	T	F	F	F	F	T
T	F	F	T	T	F	T
F	T	T	F	T	T	T
F	F	T	T	T	F	T

10. This is a valid argument. p: Metrorail system is in operation. q: There are traffic delays.

$\sim p \rightarrow q$

$\sim q$

$\therefore p$

p	q	$\sim p$	$\sim q$	$\sim p \rightarrow q$	$(\sim p \rightarrow q) \wedge \sim q$	$[(\sim p \rightarrow q) \wedge \sim q] \rightarrow p$
T	T	F	F	T	F	T
T	F	F	T	T	T	T
F	T	T	F	T	F	T
F	F	T	T	F	F	T

11. This an invalid argument. **p:** There is a dam. **q:** There is flooding.

$p \lor q$

q

$\therefore \sim p$

p	q	$\sim p$	$p \lor q$	$(p \lor q) \land q$	$[(p \lor q) \land q] \to \sim p$
T	T	F	T	T	F
T	F	F	T	F	T
F	T	T	T	T	T
F	F	T	F	F	T

12. This is an invalid argument. **p:** You eat well. **q:** You are healthy.

$p \lor \sim q$

p

$\therefore q$

p	q	$\sim q$	$p \lor \sim q$	$(p \lor \sim q) \land p$	$[(p \lor \sim q) \land p] \to q$
T	T	F	T	T	T
T	F	T	T	T	F
F	T	F	F	F	T
F	F	T	T	F	T

13. This is an invalid argument. **p:** All people obey the law. **q:** No jails are needed.

$p \to q$

$\sim p$

$\therefore \sim q$

p	q	$\sim p$	$\sim q$	$p \to q$	$(p \to q) \land \sim p$	$[(p \to q) \land \sim p] \to \sim q$
T	T	F	F	T	F	T
T	F	F	T	F	F	T
F	T	T	F	T	T	F
F	F	T	T	T	T	T

14. This is a valid argument. **p:** All people obey the law. **q:** No jails are needed.

$p \to q$

$\sim q$

$\therefore \sim p$

p	q	$\sim p$	$\sim q$	$p \to q$	$(p \to q) \land \sim q$	$[(p \to q) \land \sim q] \to \sim p$
T	T	F	F	T	F	T
T	F	F	T	F	F	T
F	T	T	F	T	F	T
F	F	T	T	T	T	T

15. This is an invalid argument.

p	q	r	$p \to q$	$q \to r$	$r \to p$	$(p \to q) \land (q \to r)$	$[(p \to q) \land (q \to r)] \to (r \to p)$
T	T	T	T	T	T	T	T
T	T	F	T	F	T	F	T
T	F	T	F	T	T	F	T
T	F	F	F	T	T	F	T
F	T	T	T	T	F	T	F
F	T	F	T	F	T	F	T
F	F	T	T	T	F	T	F
F	F	F	T	T	T	T	T

16. This is an invalid argument.

p	q	r	$\sim p$	$\sim r$	$p \rightarrow q$	$q \rightarrow r$	$\sim p \rightarrow \sim r$	$(p \rightarrow q) \wedge (q \rightarrow r)$	$[(p \rightarrow q) \wedge (q \rightarrow r)] \rightarrow (\sim p \rightarrow \sim r)$
T	T	T	F	F	T	T	T	T	T
T	T	F	F	T	T	F	T	F	T
T	F	T	F	F	F	T	T	F	T
T	F	F	F	T	F	T	T	F	T
F	T	T	T	F	T	T	F	T	F
F	T	F	T	T	T	F	T	F	T
F	F	T	T	F	T	T	F	T	F
F	F	F	T	T	T	T	T	T	T

17. This is a valid argument.

p	q	r	$p \rightarrow q$	$q \wedge r$	$p \vee r$	$(p \rightarrow q) \wedge (q \wedge r)$	$[(p \rightarrow q) \wedge (q \wedge r)] \rightarrow (p \vee r)$
T	T	T	T	T	T	T	T
T	T	F	T	F	T	F	T
T	F	T	F	F	T	F	T
T	F	F	F	F	T	F	T
F	T	T	T	T	T	T	T
F	T	F	T	F	F	F	T
F	F	T	T	F	T	F	T
F	F	F	T	F	F	F	T

18. This is an invalid argument.

p	q	r	$\sim p$	$\sim p \wedge q$	$p \rightarrow r$	$r \rightarrow p$	$p \leftrightarrow r$	$p \wedge r$	$(\sim p \wedge q) \wedge (p \leftrightarrow r)$	$[(\sim p \wedge q) \wedge (p \leftrightarrow r)] \rightarrow (p \wedge r)$
T	T	T	F	F	T	T	T	T	F	T
T	T	F	F	F	F	T	F	F	F	T
T	F	T	F	F	T	T	T	T	F	T
T	F	F	F	F	F	T	F	F	F	T
F	T	T	T	T	T	F	F	F	F	T
F	T	F	T	T	T	T	T	F	T	F
F	F	T	T	F	T	F	F	F	F	T
F	F	F	T	F	T	T	T	F	F	T

19. This is a valid argument.

p	q	r	$\sim p$	$\sim r$	$p \leftrightarrow q$	$q \rightarrow r$	$\sim r \rightarrow \sim p$	$(p \leftrightarrow q) \wedge (q \rightarrow r)$	$[(p \leftrightarrow q) \wedge (q \rightarrow r)] \rightarrow (\sim r \rightarrow \sim p)$
T	T	T	F	F	T	T	T	T	T
T	T	F	F	T	T	F	F	F	T
T	F	T	F	F	F	T	T	F	T
T	F	F	F	T	F	T	F	F	T
F	T	T	T	F	F	T	T	F	T
F	T	F	T	T	F	F	T	F	T
F	F	T	T	F	T	T	T	T	T
F	F	F	T	T	T	T	T	T	T

20. This is an invalid argument.

p	q	r	$\sim p$	$q \to \sim p$	$q \wedge r$	$r \to p$	$(q \to \sim p) \wedge (q \wedge r)$	$[(q \to \sim p) \wedge (q \wedge r)] \to (r \to q)$
T	T	T	F	F	T	T	F	T
T	T	F	F	F	F	T	F	T
T	F	T	F	T	F	T	F	T
T	F	F	F	T	F	T	F	T
F	T	T	T	T	T	F	T	F
F	T	F	T	T	F	T	F	T
F	F	T	T	T	F	F	F	T
F	F	F	T	T	F	T	F	T

21. This is a valid argument. p: Tim plays q: Janet plays r: Team wins

$(p \wedge q) \to r$

$p \wedge \sim r$

$\therefore \sim q$

p	q	r	$\sim q$	$\sim r$	$p \wedge q$	$p \wedge \sim r$	$(p \wedge q) \to r$
T	T	T	F	F	T	F	T
T	T	F	F	T	T	T	F
T	F	T	T	F	F	F	T
T	F	F	T	T	F	T	T
F	T	T	F	F	F	F	T
F	T	F	F	T	F	F	T
F	F	T	T	F	F	F	T
F	F	F	T	T	F	F	T

$[(p \wedge q) \to r] \wedge (p \wedge \sim r)$	$[[(p \wedge q) \to r] \wedge (p \wedge \sim r)] \to \sim q$
F	T
F	T
F	T
T	T
F	T
F	T
F	T
F	T

22. This is a valid argument.
p: *The Graduate* was shown q: *Midnight Cowboy* was shown r: performance was sold out

$(p \wedge q) \to r$

$q \wedge \sim r$

$\therefore \sim p$

p	q	r	$\sim p$	$\sim r$	$p \wedge q$	$(p \wedge q) \to r$	$q \wedge \sim r$
T	T	T	F	F	T	T	F
T	T	F	F	T	T	F	T
T	F	T	F	F	F	T	F
T	F	F	F	T	F	T	F
F	T	T	T	F	F	T	F
F	T	F	T	T	F	T	T
F	F	T	T	F	F	T	F
F	F	F	T	T	F	T	F

$[(p \wedge q) \rightarrow r] \wedge (q \wedge {\sim} r)$	$[[(p \wedge q) \rightarrow r] \wedge (q \wedge {\sim} r)] \rightarrow {\sim}p$
F	T
F	T
F	T
F	T
F	T
T	T
F	F
F	T

23. This is a valid argument. **p:** It rains **q:** It snows **r:** I read

$(p \vee q) \rightarrow r$

${\sim}r$

$\therefore {\sim}(p \vee q)$

p	q	r	${\sim}r$	$p \vee q$	${\sim}(p \vee q)$	$(p \vee q) \rightarrow r$
T	T	T	F	T	F	T
T	T	F	T	T	F	F
T	F	T	F	T	F	T
T	F	F	T	T	F	F
F	T	T	F	T	F	T
F	T	F	T	T	F	F
F	F	T	F	F	T	T
F	F	F	T	F	T	T

$[(p \vee q) \rightarrow r] \wedge {\sim} r$	$[[(p \vee q) \rightarrow r] \wedge {\sim} r] \rightarrow {\sim}(p \vee q)$
F	T
F	T
F	T
F	T
F	T
F	T
F	T
T	T

24. This is a valid argument. **p:** I am tired. **q:** I am hungry. **r:** I can't concentrate.

$(p \vee q) \rightarrow r$

${\sim}r$

$\therefore {\sim}(p \vee q)$

p	q	r	${\sim}r$	$p \vee q$	${\sim}(p \vee q)$	$(p \vee q) \rightarrow r$
T	T	T	F	T	F	T
T	T	F	T	T	F	F
T	F	T	F	T	F	T
T	F	F	T	T	F	F
F	T	T	F	T	F	T
F	T	F	T	T	F	F
F	F	T	F	F	T	T
F	F	F	T	F	T	T

$[(p \lor q) \to r] \land \sim r$	$[[(p \lor q) \to r] \land \sim r] \to \sim(p \lor q)$
F	T
F	T
F	T
F	T
F	T
F	T
F	T
T	T

25. This is an invalid argument. *p*: It rains *q*: It snows *r*: I read

$(p \lor q) \to r$

r
_____

$\therefore p \lor q$

p	q	r	$p \lor q$	$(p \lor q) \to r$	$[(p \lor q) \to r] \land r$	$[[(p \lor q) \to r] \land r] \to (p \lor q)$
T	T	T	T	T	T	T
T	T	F	T	F	F	T
T	F	T	T	T	T	T
T	F	F	T	F	F	T
F	T	T	T	T	T	T
F	T	F	T	F	F	T
F	F	T	F	T	T	F
F	F	F	F	T	F	T

26. This is an invalid argument. *p*: I am tired. *q*: I am hungry. *r*: I can't concentrate.

$(p \lor q) \to r$

r
_____

$\therefore p \lor q$

p	q	r	$p \lor q$	$(p \lor q) \to r$	$[(p \lor q) \to r] \land r$	$[[(p \lor q) \to r] \land r] \to (p \lor q)$
T	T	T	T	T	T	T
T	T	F	T	F	F	T
T	F	T	T	T	T	T
T	F	F	T	F	F	T
F	T	T	T	T	T	T
F	T	F	T	F	F	T
F	F	T	F	T	T	F
F	F	F	F	T	F	T

27. This is an invalid argument. **p:** It's hot. **q:** It's humid. **r:** I complain.

$(p \wedge q) \to r$

$\dfrac{\sim p \vee \sim q}{\therefore \sim r}$

p	q	r	$\sim p$	$\sim q$	$\sim r$	$p \wedge q$	$\sim p \vee \sim q$	$(p \wedge q) \to r$
T	T	T	F	F	F	T	F	T
T	T	F	F	F	T	T	F	F
T	F	T	F	T	F	F	T	T
T	F	F	F	T	T	F	T	T
F	T	T	T	F	F	F	T	T
F	T	F	T	F	T	F	T	T
F	F	T	T	T	F	F	T	T
F	F	F	T	T	T	F	T	T

$[(p \wedge q) \to r] \wedge (\sim p \vee \sim q)$	$\big[[(p \wedge q) \to r] \wedge (\sim p \vee \sim q)\big] \to \sim r$
F	T
F	T
T	F
T	T
T	F
T	T
T	F
T	T

28. This is an invalid argument.
p: I watch *Schindler's List*
q: I watch *Guess Who's Coming to Dinner*
r: I am aware of the destructive nature of intolerance.

$(p \wedge q) \to r$

$\dfrac{\sim p \vee \sim q}{\therefore \sim r}$

p	q	r	$\sim p$	$\sim q$	$\sim r$	$p \wedge q$	$\sim p \vee \sim q$	$(p \wedge q) \to r$
T	T	T	F	F	F	T	F	T
T	T	F	F	F	T	T	F	F
T	F	T	F	T	F	F	T	T
T	F	F	F	T	T	F	T	T
F	T	T	T	F	F	F	T	T
F	T	F	T	F	T	F	T	T
F	F	T	T	T	F	F	T	T
F	F	F	T	T	T	F	T	T

$[(p \wedge q) \to r] \wedge (\sim p \vee \sim q)$	$\big[[(p \wedge q) \to r] \wedge (\sim p \vee \sim q)\big] \to \sim r$
F	T
F	T
T	F
T	T
T	F
T	T
T	F
T	T

29. *p*: We close the door.
    q: There is less noise.

$$p \rightarrow q$$
$$\underline{q}$$
$$\therefore p$$
Invalid, by fallacy of the converse.

30. *p*: Temperature is in the 90s.
    q: At least 2 county pools are open.

$$p \rightarrow q$$
$$\underline{p}$$
$$\therefore q$$
Valid, by direct reasoning.

31. *p*: We criminalize drugs.
    q: We damage the future of young people.

$$p \vee q$$
$$\underline{\sim q}$$
$$\therefore p$$
Valid, by disjunctive reasoning.

32. *p*: He is intelligent.
    q: He is an over-achiever.

$$p \vee q$$
$$\underline{p}$$
$$\therefore \sim q$$
Invalid, by misuse of disjunctive reasoning.

33. *p*: I am at the beach.
    q: I swim in the ocean.
    r: I feel refreshed.

$$p \rightarrow q$$
$$\underline{q \rightarrow r}$$
$$\therefore p \rightarrow r$$
Valid, by transitive reasoning.

34. *p*: I'm tired.
    q: I'm edgy.
    r: I'm nasty.

$$p \rightarrow q$$
$$\underline{q \rightarrow r}$$
$$\therefore \sim r \rightarrow \sim p$$
Valid, by transitive reasoning.

35. *p*: I'm at the beach.
    q: I swim in the ocean.
    r: I feel refreshed.

$$p \rightarrow q$$
$$\underline{q \rightarrow r}$$
$$\therefore \sim p \rightarrow \sim r$$
Invalid, by misuse of transitive reasoning.

36. *p*: I'm tired.
    q: I'm edgy.
    r: I'm nasty.

$$p \rightarrow q$$
$$\underline{q \rightarrow r}$$
$$\therefore r \rightarrow p$$
Invalid, by misuse of transitive reasoning.

37. *p*: A person is a chemist.
    q: A person has a college degree.

$$p \rightarrow q$$
$$\underline{\sim q}$$
$$\therefore \sim p$$
My best friend is not a chemist. By contrapositive reasoning.

38. *p*: Expressway is not in operation.
    q: Traffic is bad.

$$p \rightarrow q$$
$$\underline{p}$$
$$\therefore q$$
Traffic is bad. By direct reasoning. i.e. On June 2nd, the Eastside Expressway looked like a parking lot.

39. *p*: Writers improve.
    q: "My Mother the Car" dropped from primetime.

$$p \vee q$$
$$\underline{\sim p}$$
$$\therefore q$$
"My Mother the Car" was dropped from primetime. By disjunctive reasoning.

40. p: I exercise.
    q: I do not feel energized.

$p \vee q$

$\underline{\sim p}$

$\therefore q$

I do not feel energized. By disjunctive reasoning.

41. p: All electricity off.
    q: No lights work.

$p \rightarrow q$

$\underline{\sim q}$

$\therefore \sim p$

Some electricity is not off. By contrapositive reasoning.

42. p: All houses meet the hurricane code.
    q: None are destroyed by category 4 hurricane.
$p \rightarrow q$

$\underline{\sim q}$

$\therefore \sim p$

Some houses did not meet the hurricane code. By contrapositive reasoning.

43. p: I vacation in Paris.
    q: I eat French pastries.
    r: I gain weight.

$p \rightarrow q$
$\underline{q \rightarrow r}$
$\therefore \ p \rightarrow r$

If I vacation in Paris I gain weight. By transitive reasoning.

44. p: I am a full-time student.
    q: I cannot work.
    r: I cannot afford a rental apartment costing more than $500 per month.

$p \rightarrow q$
$\underline{q \rightarrow r}$
$\therefore \ p \rightarrow r$

If I am a full-time student I cannot afford more than $500 a month in rent. By transitive reasoning.

45. If the power comes on, then Mr. Scott is still with us.

46. p: Poverty causes crime.
    q: Crime sweeps American cities during the Great Depression.

$p \rightarrow q$

$\underline{\sim q}$

$\therefore \sim p$

Valid. By contrapositive reasoning.

47. If one is Mabel, then one knows very little.
I know very little.
Therefore, I am Mabel.
$p \rightarrow q$

$\underline{q}$

$\therefore p$

Invalid.

48. p: Invitation is not genuine.
    q: People would not spend £125.

$p \rightarrow q$

$\underline{\sim q}$

$\therefore \sim p$

Valid. By contrapositive reasoning.

49-55. Answers will vary.

56. *p*: You only spoke when spoken to, and
I only speak when spoken to.
q: Nobody would ever say anything.

$p \rightarrow q$

$\dfrac{\sim q}{}$

$\therefore \sim p$

People sometimes speak without being spoken to.

p	*q*	~*p*	~*q*	$p \rightarrow q$	$(p \rightarrow q) \wedge \sim q$	$[(p \rightarrow q) \wedge \sim q] \rightarrow \sim p$
T	T	F	F	T	F	T
T	F	F	T	F	F	T
F	T	T	F	T	F	T
F	F	T	T	T	T	T

57. This is a valid argument.
p: Secondary cigarette smoke is a health threat.
q: It's wrong to smoke in public.
r: The ALA says that secondary cigarette smoke is a health threat.

$p \rightarrow q$

$\sim p \rightarrow \sim r$

$\dfrac{r}{}$

$\therefore q$

p	*q*	*r*	~*p*	~*r*	$p \rightarrow q$	$\sim p \rightarrow \sim r$	$[(p \rightarrow q) \wedge (\sim p \rightarrow \sim r)] \wedge r$	$[[(p \rightarrow q) \wedge (\sim p \rightarrow \sim r)] \wedge r] \rightarrow q$
T	T	T	F	F	T	T	T	T
T	T	F	F	T	T	T	F	T
T	F	T	F	F	F	T	F	T
T	F	F	F	T	F	T	F	T
F	T	T	T	F	T	F	F	T
F	T	F	T	T	T	T	F	T
F	F	T	T	F	T	F	F	T
F	F	F	T	T	T	T	F	T

Check Points 3.7

1. The argument is valid.

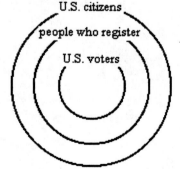

2. The argument is invalid.

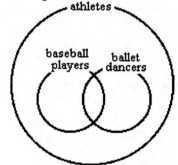

3. The argument is valid.

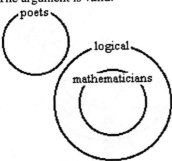

4. The argument is invalid.

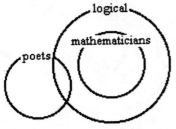

5. The argument is invalid.

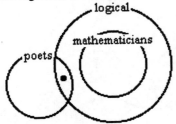

6. The argument is invalid.
   The ● is Euclid.

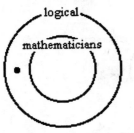

Exercise Set 3.7

1. Valid

2. Valid.

3. Invalid.

4. Invalid.

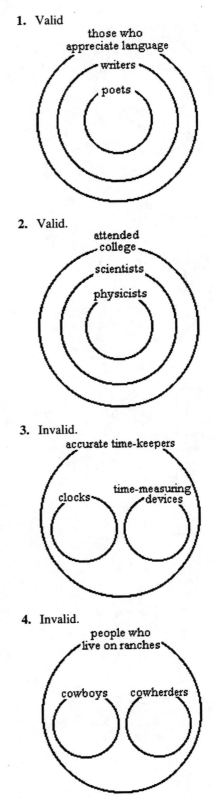

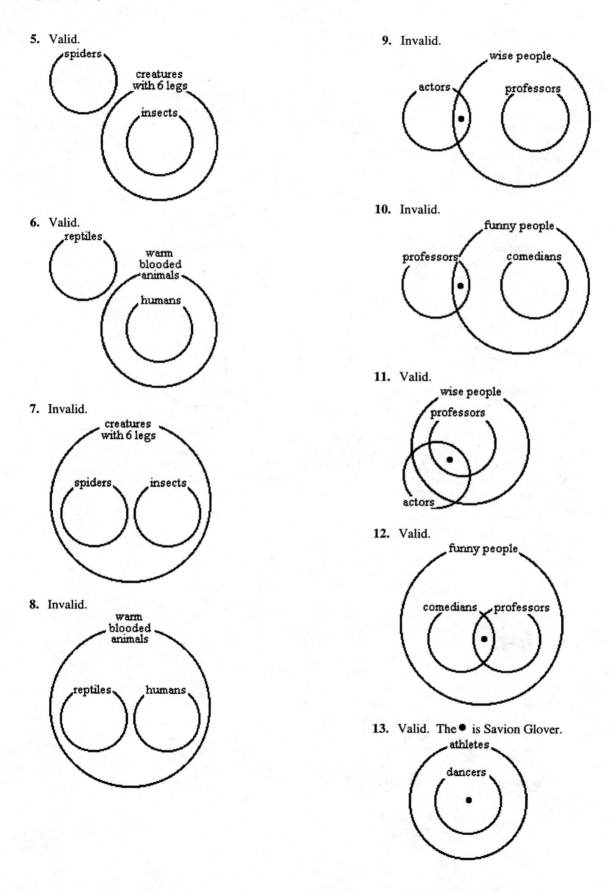

5. Valid.

spiders

creatures
with 6 legs

insects

6. Valid.

reptiles

warm
blooded
animals

humans

7. Invalid.

creatures
with 6 legs

spiders   insects

8. Invalid.

warm
blooded
animals

reptiles   humans

9. Invalid.

wise people

actors   professors

10. Invalid.

funny people

professors   comedians

11. Valid.

wise people

professors

actors

12. Valid.

funny people

comedians professors

13. Valid. The ● is Savion Glover.

athletes

dancers

14. Valid. The ● is Kim Basinger.

artists

actors

●

15. Invalid. The ● is Savion Glover.

athletes

dancers

●

16. Invalid. The ● is Kim Basinger.

artists

actors

●

17. Invalid.

people

people who enjoy reading

people who enjoy TV

●   *

18. Valid.

immoral acts

thefts

●

justifiable thefts

19. Valid.

animals with fleas

dogs

●

animals with rabies

20. Invalid.

makes sense

jokes

logic problems

●

21. Valid.

disks without data

blank disks

●

formatted disks

22. Invalid.

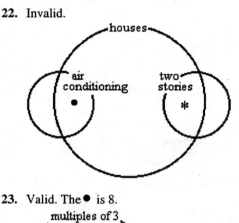

23. Valid. The ● is 8.

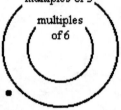

24. Invalid. The ● is 8.

25. Valid.

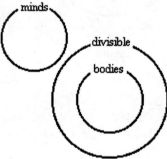

26. Valid.

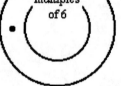

27-29. Answers will vary.

30. b is true.

31. All opera singers take voice lessons.

32. Some teachers are amusing people.

Chapter 3 Review Exercises

1. If the temperature is below 32° and we finished studying, then we go to the movies.

2. If we don't go to the movies, then the temperature is not below 32° or we did not finish studying.

3. The temperature is below 32°, and if we finished studying, we go to the movies.

4. We go to the movies if and only if the temperature is below 32° and we finished studying.

5. It is not true that the temperature is below 32° and we finished studying.

6. We won't go to the movies if and only if the temperature is not below 32° or we have not finished studying.

7. $(p \wedge q) \vee r$

8. $(p \vee \sim q) \rightarrow r$

9. $q \rightarrow (p \leftrightarrow r)$

10. $r \leftrightarrow (p \wedge \sim q)$

11. Some houses are not made of wood.

12. Some students major in business.

13. No crimes are motivated by passion.

14. All Democrats are registered voters.

15. Some new taxes are not for education.

16. The statement is <u>false</u> because it is of the form: [true] *and* [false].

17. The statement is <u>true</u> because it is of the form: [true] *or* [false].

18. The statement is <u>true</u> because it is of the form: If [false], then [false].

19. $p \vee (\sim p \wedge q)$

p	q	$\sim p$	$\sim p \wedge q$	$p \vee (\sim p \wedge q)$
T	T	F	F	T
T	F	F	F	T
F	T	T	T	T
F	F	T	F	F

20. $\sim p \vee \sim q$

p	q	$\sim p$	$\sim q$	$\sim p \vee \sim q$
T	T	F	F	F
T	F	F	T	T
F	T	T	F	T
F	F	T	T	T

21. $p \rightarrow (\sim p \vee q)$

p	q	$\sim p$	$\sim p \vee q$	$p \rightarrow (\sim p \vee q)$
T	T	F	T	T
T	F	F	F	F
F	T	T	T	T
F	F	T	T	T

22. $p \leftrightarrow \sim q$

p	q	$\sim q$	$p \leftrightarrow \sim q$
T	T	F	F
T	F	T	T
F	T	F	T
F	F	T	F

23. $\sim (p \vee q) \rightarrow (\sim p \wedge \sim q)$

p	q	$\sim p$	$\sim q$	$p \vee q$	$\sim (p \vee q)$	$\sim p \wedge \sim q$	$\sim (p \vee q) \rightarrow (\sim p \wedge \sim q)$
T	T	F	F	T	F	F	T
T	F	F	T	T	F	F	T
F	T	T	F	T	F	F	T
F	F	T	T	F	T	T	T

24. $(p \vee q) \rightarrow \sim r$

p	q	r	$\sim r$	$p \vee q$	$(p \vee q) \rightarrow \sim r$
T	T	T	F	T	F
T	T	F	T	T	T
T	F	T	F	T	F
T	F	F	T	T	T
F	T	T	F	T	F
F	T	F	T	T	T
F	F	T	F	F	T
F	F	F	T	F	T

25. $(p \wedge q) \leftrightarrow (p \wedge r)$

p	q	r	$p \wedge q$	$p \wedge r$	$(p \wedge q) \leftrightarrow (p \wedge r)$
T	T	T	T	T	T
T	T	F	T	F	F
T	F	T	F	T	F
T	F	F	F	F	T
F	T	T	F	F	T
F	T	F	F	F	T
F	F	T	F	F	T
F	F	F	F	F	T

26. The statement is of the form $p \rightarrow (q \vee r)$ with p true, q true, and r false.

$T \rightarrow (T \vee F)$

$\quad T \rightarrow T$

$\quad\quad T$

Therefore the statement is true.

27. The statement is of the form $(p \leftrightarrow q) \wedge r$ with p true, q false, and r true.

$(T \leftrightarrow F) \wedge T$

$\quad F \wedge T$

$\quad\quad F$

Therefore the statement is false.

28. $\sim(q \leftrightarrow r)$

$\sim(F \leftrightarrow F)$

$\quad \sim T$

$\quad\quad F$

29. $(p \wedge q) \rightarrow (p \vee r)$

$(T \wedge F) \rightarrow (T \vee F)$

$\quad F \rightarrow T$

$\quad\quad T$

30. $(\sim q \rightarrow p) \vee (r \wedge \sim p)$

$(\sim F \rightarrow T) \vee (F \wedge \sim T)$

$(T \rightarrow T) \vee (F \wedge F)$

$\quad\quad T \vee F$

$\quad\quad\quad T$

31. a. $\sim p \vee q \equiv p \rightarrow q$

p	q	$\sim p$	$\sim p \vee q$	$p \rightarrow q$
T	T	F	T	T
T	F	F	F	F
F	T	T	T	T
F	F	T	T	T

   b. If the triangle is isosceles, then it has two equal sides.

32. c

33. If I am not in the South, then I am not in Atlanta.

34. If today is a holiday, then I'm not in class.

35. If I do not pass some course, then I did not work hard.

36. Converse: If classes are cancelled, then there is a storm.
Inverse: If there is no storm, then classes are not cancelled.

37. Converse: If we do not talk, then the television is on.
Inverse: If the television is not on, then we talk.

38. I am in Bogota and I am not in Columbia.

39. I do not work hard and I succeed.

40. Chicago is not a city or Maine is not a city.

41. Ernest Hemingway was neither a musician nor an actor.

42. If a number is not 0, the number is positive or negative.

43. I don't work hard and I succeed.

44. She is using her car or she is not taking a bus.

45. Write the negation of $\sim p \vee q$ and simplify.

$\sim(\sim p \vee q)$

$\sim(\sim p) \wedge \sim q$

$\quad p \wedge \sim q$

46. a and c are equivalent.

		a	b	c
p	q	$p \rightarrow q$	$\sim p \rightarrow \sim q$	$\sim p \vee q$
T	T	T	T	T
T	F	F	T	F
F	T	T	F	T
F	F	T	T	T

47. a and b are equivalent.

		a	b	c
p	q	$\sim p \rightarrow q$	$\sim q \rightarrow p$	$\sim p \wedge \sim q$
T	T	T	T	F
T	F	T	T	F
F	T	T	T	F
F	F	F	F	T

48. a and c are equivalent.

		a	b	c
p	q	$p \vee \sim q$	$\sim q \rightarrow p$	$\sim(\sim p \wedge q)$
T	T	T	T	T
T	F	T	T	T
F	T	F	T	F
F	F	T	F	T

49. The argument is invalid.

p	q	$\sim q$	$p \rightarrow q$	$(p \rightarrow q) \wedge \sim q$	$[(p \rightarrow q) \wedge \sim q] \rightarrow p$
T	T	F	T	F	T
T	F	T	F	F	T
F	T	F	T	F	T
F	F	T	T	T	F

50. The argument is valid.

p	q	r	$p \wedge q$	$q \rightarrow r$	$p \rightarrow r$	$(p \wedge q) \wedge (q \rightarrow r)$	$[(p \wedge q) \wedge (q \rightarrow r)] \rightarrow (p \rightarrow r)$
T	T	T	T	T	T	T	T
T	T	F	T	F	F	F	T
T	F	T	F	T	T	F	T
T	F	F	F	T	F	F	T
F	T	T	F	T	T	F	T
F	T	F	F	F	T	F	T
F	F	T	F	T	T	F	T
F	F	F	F	T	T	F	T

51. The argument is valid. **p:** Good baseball player. **q:** Good hand–eye coordination.

$p \rightarrow q$

$\sim q$

$\sim p$

p	q	$\sim p$	$\sim q$	$p \rightarrow q$	$(p \rightarrow q) \wedge \sim q$	$[(p \rightarrow q) \wedge \sim q] \rightarrow \sim p$
T	T	F	F	T	F	T
T	F	F	T	F	F	T
F	T	T	F	T	F	T
F	F	T	T	T	T	T

52. The argument is invalid. **p:** Tony plays. **q:** Team wins.

$p \rightarrow q$

q

$\therefore p$

p	q	$p \rightarrow q$	$(p \rightarrow q) \wedge q$	$[(p \rightarrow q) \wedge q] \rightarrow p$
T	T	T	T	T
T	F	F	F	T
F	T	T	T	F
F	F	T	F	T

53. The argument is invalid. **p:** Plant is fertilized. **q:** Plant turns yellow.

$p \vee q$

q

$\therefore \sim p$

p	q	$\sim p$	$p \vee q$	$(p \vee q) \wedge q$	$[(p \vee q) \wedge q] \rightarrow \sim p$
T	T	F	T	T	F
T	F	F	T	F	T
F	T	T	T	T	T
F	F	T	F	F	T

54. The argument is valid. **p:** A majority of legislators vote for a bill. **q:** Bill does not become law.

$p \vee q$

$\sim p$

$\therefore q$

p	q	$\sim p$	$p \vee q$	$(p \vee q) \wedge \sim p$	$[(p \vee q) \wedge \sim p] \rightarrow q$
T	T	F	T	F	T
T	F	F	T	F	T
F	T	T	T	T	T
F	F	T	F	F	T

55. The argument is invalid.

    p: I purchase season tickets to the football games.
    q: I do not attend all the lectures.
    r: I do not do well in school.

    $p \rightarrow q$
    $\underline{q \rightarrow r}$
    $\therefore r \rightarrow p$

p	*q*	*r*	$p \rightarrow q$	$q \rightarrow r$	$r \rightarrow p$	$(p \rightarrow q) \wedge (q \rightarrow r)$	$[(p \rightarrow q) \wedge (q \rightarrow r)] \rightarrow (r \rightarrow p)$
T	T	T	T	T	T	T	T
T	T	F	T	F	T	F	T
T	F	T	F	T	T	F	T
T	F	F	F	T	T	F	T
F	T	T	T	T	F	T	F
F	T	F	T	F	T	F	T
F	F	T	T	T	F	T	F
F	F	F	T	T	T	T	T

56. Invalid.

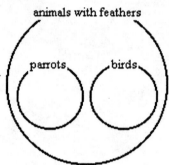

57. Valid.

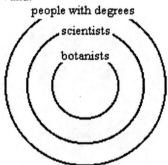

58. Valid.

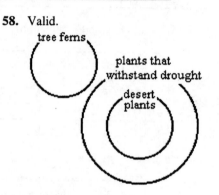

59. Invalid.

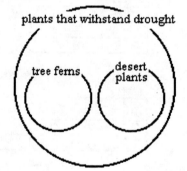

60. Invalid.

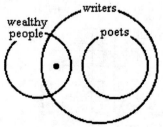

Chapter 3 Test

1. If I'm registered and I'm a citizen, then I vote.

2. I don't vote if and only if I'm not registered or I'm not a citizen.

3. I'm neither registered nor a citizen.

4. $(p \wedge q) \vee {\sim}r$

5. $({\sim}p \vee {\sim}q) \rightarrow {\sim}r$

6. Some numbers are not divisible by 5.

7. No people wear glasses.

8. $p \wedge ({\sim}p \vee q)$

p	q	${\sim}p$	${\sim}p \vee q$	$p \wedge ({\sim}p \vee q)$
T	T	F	T	T
T	F	F	F	F
F	T	T	T	F
F	F	T	T	F

9. ${\sim}(p \wedge q) \leftrightarrow ({\sim}p \vee {\sim}q)$

p	q	${\sim}p$	${\sim}q$	$p \wedge q$	${\sim}(p \wedge q)$	$({\sim}p \vee {\sim}q)$	${\sim}(p \wedge q) \leftrightarrow ({\sim}p \vee {\sim}q)$
T	T	F	F	T	F	F	T
T	F	F	T	F	T	T	T
F	T	T	F	F	T	T	T
F	F	T	T	F	T	T	T

10. $p \leftrightarrow (q \vee r)$

p	q	r	$q \vee r$	$p \leftrightarrow (q \vee r)$
T	T	T	T	T
T	T	F	T	T
T	F	T	T	T
T	F	F	F	F
F	T	T	T	F
F	T	F	T	F
F	F	T	T	F
F	F	F	F	T

11. ${\sim}(q \rightarrow r)$

   ${\sim}(T \rightarrow F)$

   ${\sim}F$

   T

12. $(p \lor r) \leftrightarrow (\sim r \land p)$

$(F \lor F) \leftrightarrow (\sim F \land F)$

$F \leftrightarrow (T \land F)$

$F \leftrightarrow F$

T

13. b

14. If it snows, then it is not August.

15. Converse: If I cannot concentrate, then the radio is playing.

Inverse: If the radio is not playing, then I can concentrate.

16. It is cold and we use the pool.

17. The test is not today and the party is not tonight.

18. The banana is not green or it is ready to eat.

19. a and b are equivalent.

		a	b	c
p	q	$\sim p \rightarrow q$	$p \lor q$	$p \rightarrow \sim q$
T	T	T	T	F
T	F	T	T	T
F	T	T	T	T
F	F	F	F	T

20. a and c are equivalent.

		a	b	c
p	q	$\sim(p \lor q)$	$\sim p \rightarrow \sim q$	$\sim p \land \sim q$
T	T	F	T	F
T	F	F	T	F
F	T	F	F	F
F	F	T	T	T

21. The argument is invalid. p: Parrot talks. q: It is intelligent.

$p \rightarrow q$

q

$\therefore p$

22. The argument is valid. p: I am sick. q: I am tired.

$p \lor q$

$\sim q$

$\therefore p$

23. The argument is invalid. p: I am going. q: You are going.

$p \leftrightarrow \sim q$

q

$\therefore p$

24. Invalid.

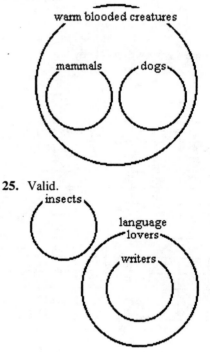

25. Valid.

Chapter 4
Number Representation and Calculation

Check Points 4.1

1. **a.** $10^5 = 10 \times 10 \times 10 \times 10 \times 10 = 100,000$ **b.** $10^6 = 10 \times 10 \times 10 \times 10 \times 10 \times 10 = 1,000,000$

2. **a.** $8^2 = 8 \times 8 = 64$ **b.** $6^3 = 6 \times 6 \times 6 = 216$

   c. $2^5 = 2 \times 2 \times 2 \times 2 \times 2 = 32$ **d.** $18^1 = 18$

3. **a.** $4026 = (4 \times 10^3) + (0 \times 10^2) + (2 \times 10^1) + (6 \times 1) = (4 \times 1000) + (0 \times 100) + (2 \times 10) + (6 \times 1)$

   b. $24,232 = (2 \times 10^4) + (4 \times 10^3) + (2 \times 10^2) + (3 \times 10^1) + (2 \times 1)$
   $$= (2 \times 10,000) + (4 \times 1000) + (2 \times 100) + (3 \times 10) + (2 \times 1)$$

4. **a.** $6000 + 70 + 3 = 6073$ **b.** $80,000 + 900 = 80,900$

5.
$$\begin{array}{ccc} \lor\lor\lor & << & <<<\lor \\ \downarrow & \downarrow & \downarrow \end{array}$$
$$(3 \times 60^2) + (2 \times 60) + (31 \times 1)$$
$$= (3 \times 3600) + (2 \times 60) + (31 \times 1)$$
$$= 10,800 + 1200 + 31$$
$$= 12,031$$

6.
$$\begin{array}{rcrcr} 11 & \times & 7200 & = & 79,200 \\ 3 & \times & 360 & = & 1080 \\ 0 & \times & 20 & = & 0 \\ 13 & \times & 1 & = & \underline{13} \\ & & & & 80,293 \end{array}$$

Exercise Set 4.1

1. $5^2 = 5 \times 5 = 25$

2. $6^2 = 6 \times 6 = 36$

3. $2^3 = 2 \times 2 \times 2 = 8$

4. $4^3 = 4 \times 4 \times 4 = 64$

5. $3^4 = 3 \times 3 \times 3 \times 3 = 81$

6. $2^4 = 2 \times 2 \times 2 \times 2 = 16$

7. $10^5 = 10 \times 10 \times 10 \times 10 \times 10 = 100,000$

8. $10^6 = 10 \times 10 \times 10 \times 10 \times 10 \times 10 = 1,000,000$

9. $36 = (3 \times 10^1) + (6 \times 1) = (3 \times 10) + (6 \times 1)$

10. $65 = (6 \times 10^1) + (5 \times 1) = (6 \times 10) + (5 \times 1)$

11. $249 = (2 \times 10^2) + (4 \times 10^1) + (9 \times 1) = (2 \times 100) + (4 \times 10) + (9 \times 1)$

12. $698 = (6 \times 10^2) + (9 \times 10^1) + (8 \times 1) = (6 \times 100) + (9 \times 10) + (8 \times 1)$

13. $703 = (7 \times 10^2) + (0 \times 10^1) + (3 \times 1) = (7 \times 100) + (0 \times 10) + (3 \times 1)$

14. $902 = (9 \times 10^2) + (0 \times 10^1) + (2 \times 1) = (9 \times 100) + (0 \times 10) + (2 \times 1)$

15. $4856 = (4 \times 10^3) + (8 \times 10^2) + (5 \times 10^1) + (6 \times 1) = (4 \times 1000) + (8 \times 100) + (5 \times 10) + (6 \times 1)$

16. $5749 = (5 \times 10^3) + (7 \times 10^2) + (4 \times 10^1) + (9 \times 1) = (5 \times 1000) + (7 \times 100) + (4 \times 10) + (9 \times 1)$

17. $3070 = (3 \times 10^3) + (0 \times 10^2) + (7 \times 10^1) + (0 \times 1) = (3 \times 1000) + (0 \times 100) + (7 \times 10) + (0 \times 1)$

18. $9007 = (9 \times 10^3) + (0 \times 10^2) + (0 \times 10^1) + (7 \times 1) = (9 \times 1000) + (0 \times 100) + (0 \times 10) + (7 \times 1)$

19. $34,569 = (3 \times 10^4) + (4 \times 10^3) + (5 \times 10^2) + (6 \times 10^1) + (9 \times 1)$
    $= (3 \times 10,000) + (4 \times 1000) + (5 \times 100) + (6 \times 10) + (9 \times 1)$

20. $67,943 = (6 \times 10^4) + (7 \times 10^3) + (9 \times 10^2) + (4 \times 10^1) + (3 \times 1)$
    $= (6 \times 10,000) + (7 \times 1000) + (9 \times 100) + (4 \times 10) + (3 \times 1)$

21. $230,007,004 = (2 \times 10^8) + (3 \times 10^7) + (0 \times 10^6) + (0 \times 10^5) + (0 \times 10^4) + (7 \times 10^3) + (0 \times 10^2) + (0 \times 10^1) + (4 \times 1)$
    $= (2 \times 100,000,000) + (3 \times 10,000,000) + (0 \times 1,000,000) + (0 \times 100,000)$
    $\quad + (0 \times 10,000) + (7 \times 1000) + (0 \times 100) + (0 \times 10) + (4 \times 1)$

22. $909,006,070$
    $= (9 \times 10^8) + (0 \times 10^7) + (9 \times 10^6) + (0 \times 10^5) + (0 \times 10^4) + (6 \times 10^3) + (0 \times 10^2) + (7 \times 10^1) + (0 \times 1)$
    $= (9 \times 100,000,000) + (0 \times 10,000,000) + (9 \times 1,000,000) + (0 \times 100,000) + (0 \times 10,000) + (6 \times 1000)$
    $\quad + (0 \times 100) + (7 \times 10) + (0 \times 1)$

23. $70 + 3 = 73$

24. $90 + 4 = 94$

25. $300 + 80 + 5 = 385$

26. $700 + 50 + 3 = 753$

27. $500,000 + 20,000 + 8000 + 700 + 40 + 3 = 528,743$

28. $7,000,000 + 400,000 + 20,000 + 3000 + 100 + 90 + 6 = 7,423,196$

29. $7000 + 2 = 7002$

30. $90,000 + 40 + 5 = 90,045$

31. $600,000,000 + 2000 + 7 = 600,002,007$

32. $300,000,000 + 50,000 + 4 = 300,050,004$

33. $(10 + 10 + 1 + 1 + 1) \times 1 = 23 \times 1 = 23$

34. $(10 + 10 + 10 + 1 + 1) \times 1 = 32 \times 1 = 32$

35. $(10 + 10 + 1) \times 60^1 + (1 + 1) \times 1 = (21 \times 60) + 2 = 1260 + 2 = 1262$

36. $(10 + 10) \times 60^1 + (10 + 1 + 1) \times 1 = (20 \times 60) + 12 = 1200 + 12 = 1212$

37. $(1 + 1 + 1) \times 60^2 + (10 + 1 + 1) \times 60^1 + (1 + 1 + 1) \times 1 = (3 \times 3600) + (12 \times 60) + 3 = 10,800 + 720 + 3 = 11,523$

38.
$$(1 + 1) \times 60^2 + (10 + 1) \times 60^1 + (10 + 10 + 1 + 1) \times 1 = (2 \times 3600) + (11 \times 60) + (22 \times 1)$$
$$= 7200 + 660 + 22$$
$$= 7882$$

39.
$$(10 + 1) \times 60^3 + (10 + 1) \times 60^2 + (10 + 1) \times 60^1 + (10 + 1) \times 1$$
$$= (11 \times 60^3) + (11 \times 60^2) + (11 \times 60^1) + (11 \times 1)$$
$$= (11 \times 216,000) + (11 \times 3600) + (11 \times 60) + 11$$
$$= 2,376,000 + 39,600 + 660 + 11$$
$$= 2,416,271$$

40.
$$(10 + 10) \times 60^3 + (10 + 10) \times 60^2 + (10 + 1 + 1) \times 60^1 + (10 + 1 + 1) \times 1$$
$$= (20 \times 216,000) + (20 \times 3600) + (12 \times 60) + (12 \times 1)$$
$$= 4,320,000 + 72,000 + 720 + 12$$
$$= 4,392,732$$

41. $14 \times 1 = 14$

42. $13 \times 1 = 13$

43.
$$
\begin{array}{rcrcr}
19 & \times & 360 & = & 6840 \\
0 & \times & 20 & = & 0 \\
6 & \times & 1 & = & \underline{6} \\
& & & & 6846
\end{array}
$$

44.
$$
\begin{array}{rcrcr}
19 & \times & 360 & = & 6840 \\
0 & \times & 20 & = & 0 \\
5 & \times & 1 & = & \underline{5} \\
& & & & 6845
\end{array}
$$

45.

$$
\begin{aligned}
8 \times 360 &= 2880 \\
8 \times 20 &= 160 \\
8 \times 1 &= \underline{8} \\
&\,3048
\end{aligned}
$$

46.

$$
\begin{aligned}
6 \times 360 &= 2160 \\
6 \times 20 &= 120 \\
6 \times 1 &= \underline{6} \\
&\,2286
\end{aligned}
$$

47.

$$
\begin{aligned}
2 \times 7200 &= 14,400 \\
0 \times 360 &= 0 \\
0 \times 20 &= 0 \\
11 \times 1 &= \underline{11} \\
&\,14,411
\end{aligned}
$$

48.

$$
\begin{aligned}
3 \times 7200 &= 21,600 \\
10 \times 360 &= 3,600 \\
0 \times 20 &= 0 \\
0 \times 1 &= \underline{0} \\
&\,25,200
\end{aligned}
$$

49.

$$
\begin{aligned}
10 \times 7200 &= 72,000 \\
10 \times 360 &= 3,600 \\
0 \times 20 &= 0 \\
10 \times 1 &= \underline{10} \\
&\,75,610
\end{aligned}
$$

50.

$$
\begin{aligned}
10 \times 7200 &= 72,000 \\
0 \times 360 &= 0 \\
10 \times 20 &= 200 \\
10 \times 1 &= \underline{10} \\
&\,72,210
\end{aligned}
$$

51.

$$
\begin{aligned}
4 \times 360 &= 1440 \\
16 \times 20 &= 320 \\
16 \times 1 &= \underline{16} \\
&\,1776
\end{aligned}
$$

Declaration of Independence

52. $(10+10+1+1+1+1) \times 60^1 + (10+10+10+10+10+1+1) \times 1$

$= (24 \times 60) + (52 \times 1)$

$= 1440 + 52$

$= 1492$ Columbus discovers America

53-60. Answers will vary.

94

61. Change to Hindu-Arabic:

$(1 \times 60^2) + (10+1+1) \times 60^1 + (10+1) \times 1$

$= 3600 + (12 \times 60) + 11$

$= 3600 + 720 + 11 = 4331$

Change to Mayan:

$12 \times 360 = 4320$

$0 \times 20 = 0$

$11 \times 1 = \underline{11}$

4331

62. Change to Hindu-Arabic:

$7 \times 360 = 2520$

$7 \times 20 = 140$

$7 \times 1 = \underline{7}$

2667

Change to Babylonian:

$= 2667$

$= 2640 + 27$

$= (44 \times 60) + 27$

$= (10+10+10+10+1+1+1+1) \times 60 + (10+10+1+1+1+1+1+1+1) \times 1$

< < < < ∨ ∨ ∨ ∨   < < ∨ ∨ ∨ ∨ ∨ ∨ ∨

63. *Writing the numeral that precedes:*
Subtract 1 or ∨ from the numeral on the right:

< ∨   < < < < < ∨ ∨ ∨ ∨ ∨ ∨ ∨ ∨

Writing the numeral that follows:
First, add 1, or ∨, to the numeral on the right:
< ∨   < < < < < ∨ ∨ ∨ ∨ ∨ ∨ ∨ ∨ ∨ ∨
Next, change the 10 ∨'s to a <:
< ∨   < < < < < <
Since < < < < < < has a value of 60 it
can be carried as a ∨ in the next higher place:
< ∨ ∨ (note the missing place value)
The missing place value is indicated by $\genfrac{}{}{0pt}{}{<}{<}$

giving a final answer of: < ∨ ∨ $\genfrac{}{}{0pt}{}{<}{<}$

64. $4^5 = 1024$

65. $5^4 = 625$

66. $2^9 = 512$

67. $84^3 = 592,704$

Chapter 4: Number Representation and Calculation

Check Points 4.2

1. $3422_{\text{five}} = (3 \times 5^3) + (4 \times 5^2) + (2 \times 5^1) + (2 \times 1)$
   $= (3 \times 5 \times 5 \times 5) + (4 \times 5 \times 5) + (2 \times 5) + (2 \times 1)$
   $= 375 + 100 + 10 + 2$
   $= 487$

2. $110011_{\text{two}} = (1 \times 2^5) + (1 \times 2^4) + (0 \times 2^3) + (0 \times 2^2) + (1 \times 2^1) + (1 \times 1)$
   $= (1 \times 32) + (1 \times 16) + (0 \times 8) + (0 \times 4) + (1 \times 2) + (1 \times 1)$
   $= 32 + 16 + 2 + 1$
   $= 51$

3. $AD4_{\text{sixteen}} = (10 \times 16^2) + (13 \times 16^1) + (4 \times 1)$
   $= (10 \times 16 \times 16) + (13 \times 16) + (4 \times 1)$
   $= 2560 + 208 + 4$
   $= 2772$

4. $6_{\text{ten}} = (1 \times 5) + (1 \times 1) = 11_{\text{five}}$

5. The place values in base 7 are $...7^4,\ 7^3,\ 7^2,\ 7^1,\ 1$ or $...2401,\ 343,\ 49,\ 7,\ 1$

$$
\begin{array}{ccc}
\overset{1}{343)\overline{365}} & \overset{0}{49)\overline{22}} & \overset{3}{7)\overline{22}} \\
\underline{343} & \underline{0} & \underline{21} \\
22 & 22 & 1
\end{array}
$$

   $365_{\text{ten}} = (1 \times 343) + (0 \times 49) + (3 \times 7) + (1 \times 1)$
   $= (1 \times 7^3) + (0 \times 7^2) + (3 \times 7^1) + (1 \times 1)$
   $= 1031_{\text{seven}}$

6. The place values in base 5 are $...5^4,\ 5^3,\ 5^2,\ 5^1,\ 1$ or $...3125,\ 625,\ 125,\ 25,\ 5,\ 1$

$$
\begin{array}{cccc}
\overset{4}{625)\overline{2763}} & \overset{2}{125)\overline{263}} & \overset{0}{25)\overline{13}} & \overset{2}{5)\overline{13}} \\
\underline{2500} & \underline{250} & \underline{0} & \underline{10} \\
263 & 13 & 13 & 3
\end{array}
$$

   $2763_{\text{ten}} = (4 \times 625) + (2 \times 125) + (0 \times 25) + (2 \times 5) + (3 \times 1)$
   $= (4 \times 5^4) + (2 \times 5^3) + (0 \times 5^2) + (2 \times 5^1) + (3 \times 1)$
   $= 42023_{\text{five}}$

Exercise Set 4.2

1. $(4 \times 5^1) + (3 \times 1)$
   $= 20 + 3$
   $= 23$

2. $(3 \times 5^1) + (4 \times 1) = 15 + 4 = 19$

3. $(5 \times 8^1) + (2 \times 1)$
   $= 40 + 2$
   $= 42$

4. $(6 \times 8^1) + (7 \times 1) = 48 + 7 = 55$

5. $(1 \times 4^2) + (3 \times 4^1) + (2 \times 1)$
   $= 16 + 12 + 2$
   $= 30$

6. $(3 \times 4^2) + (2 \times 4^1) + (1 \times 1) = 48 + 8 + 1 = 57$

7. $(1 \times 2^3) + (0 \times 2^2) + (1 \times 2^1) + (1 \times 1)$
   $= 8 + 0 + 2 + 1 = 11$

8. $(1 \times 2^3) + (1 \times 2^2) + (0 \times 2^1) + (1 \times 1) = 8 + 4 + 0 + 1$
   $= 13$

9. $(2 \times 6^3) + (0 \times 6^2) + (3 \times 6^1) + (5 \times 1) = 432 + 0 + 18 + 5$
   $= 455$

10. $(2 \times 9^3) + (0 \times 9^2) + (7 \times 9^1) + (3 \times 1) = 1458 + 0 + 63 + 3$
    $= 1524$

11. $(7 \times 8^4) + (0 \times 8^3) + (3 \times 8^2) + (5 \times 8^1) + (5 \times 1) = 28,672 + 0 + 192 + 40 + 5$
    $= 28,909$

12. $(4 \times 6^4) + (1 \times 6^3) + (5 \times 6^2) + (0 \times 6^1) + (2 \times 1) = 5184 + 216 + 180 + 0 + 2$
    $= 5582$

13. $(2 \times 16^3) + (0 \times 16^2) + (9 \times 16^1) + (6 \times 1) = 8192 + 0 + 144 + 6$
    $= 8342$

14. $(3 \times 15^3) + (1 \times 15^2) + (0 \times 15^1) + (4 \times 1) = 10,125 + 225 + 0 + 4$
    $= 10,354$

15. $(1 \times 2^5) + (1 \times 2^4) + (0 \times 2^3) + (1 \times 2^2) + (0 \times 2^1) + (1 \times 1) = 32 + 16 + 0 + 4 + 0 + 1$
    $= 53$

16. $(1 \times 2^5) + (0 \times 2^4) + (1 \times 2^3) + (1 \times 2^2) + (0 \times 2^1) + (1 \times 1) = 32 + 0 + 8 + 4 + 0 + 1$
    $= 45$

17. $(10 \times 16^3) + (12 \times 16^2) + (14 \times 16^1) + (5 \times 1) = 40,960 + 3072 + 224 + 5$
    $= 44,261$

18. $(14 \times 16^3) + (13 \times 16^2) + (15 \times 16^1) + (7 \times 1) = 57,344 + 3328 + 240 + 7$
    $= 60,919$

19. 12_{five}

20. 14_{five}

21. 14_{seven}

22. 15_{seven}

23. 10_{two}

24. 11_{two}

25. 31_{four}

26. 103_{four}

27. 101_{six}

28. 41_{six}

29.
$$25\overline{)87} \qquad 5\overline{)12}$$
$$\underline{75} \qquad\quad \underline{10}$$
$$\;\;12 \qquad\qquad 2$$
$$87 = 322_{five}$$

30.
$$49\overline{)85} \qquad 7\overline{)36}$$
$$\underline{49} \qquad\quad \underline{35}$$
$$\;\;36 \qquad\qquad 1$$
$$85 = 151_{seven}$$

31.
$$64\overline{)108} \qquad 16\overline{)44} \qquad 4\overline{)12}$$
$$\underline{64} \qquad\qquad \underline{32} \qquad\quad \underline{12}$$
$$\;\;44 \qquad\qquad\;\; 12 \qquad\qquad 0$$
$$108 = 1230_{four}$$

32.
$$64\overline{)199} \qquad 16\overline{)7} \qquad 4\overline{)7}$$
$$\underline{192} \qquad\qquad \underline{0} \qquad\quad \underline{4}$$
$$\;\;\;7 \qquad\qquad\quad 7 \qquad\qquad 3$$
$$199 = 3013_{four}$$

33.
$$16\overline{)19} \qquad 8\overline{)3} \qquad 4\overline{)3} \qquad 2\overline{)3}$$
$$\underline{16} \qquad\quad \underline{0} \qquad\quad \underline{0} \qquad\quad \underline{2}$$
$$\;\;3 \qquad\qquad 3 \qquad\qquad 3 \qquad\qquad 1$$
$$19 = 10011_{two}$$

34.
$$16\overline{)23} \qquad 8\overline{)7} \qquad 4\overline{)7} \qquad 2\overline{)3}$$
$$\underline{16} \qquad\quad \underline{0} \qquad\quad \underline{4} \qquad\quad \underline{2}$$
$$\;\;7 \qquad\qquad 7 \qquad\qquad 3 \qquad\qquad 1$$
$$23 = 10111_{two}$$

35.
$$81\overline{)138} \qquad 27\overline{)57} \qquad 9\overline{)3} \qquad 3\overline{)3}$$
$$\underline{81} \qquad\qquad \underline{54} \qquad\quad \underline{0} \qquad\quad \underline{3}$$
$$\;\;57 \qquad\qquad\;\; 3 \qquad\qquad 3 \qquad\qquad 0$$
$$138 = 12010_{three}$$

36.
$$81\overline{)129} \qquad 27\overline{)48} \qquad 9\overline{)21} \qquad 3\overline{)3}$$
$$\underline{81} \qquad\qquad \underline{27} \qquad\quad \underline{18} \qquad\quad \underline{3}$$
$$\;\;48 \qquad\qquad\;\; 21 \qquad\qquad 3 \qquad\qquad 0$$
$$129 = 11210_{three}$$

37.
$$216\overline{)386} \qquad 36\overline{)170} \qquad 6\overline{)26}$$
$$\underline{216} \qquad\qquad \underline{144} \qquad\quad \underline{24}$$
$$\;\;170 \qquad\qquad\;\; 26 \qquad\qquad 2$$
$$386 = 1442_{six}$$

38.
$$81\overline{)428} \qquad 9\overline{)23}$$
$$\underline{405} \qquad\quad \underline{18}$$
$$\;\;23 \qquad\qquad 5$$
$$428 = 525_{nine}$$

39.
$$343\overline{)1599} \qquad 49\overline{)227} \qquad 7\overline{)31}$$
$$\underline{1372} \qquad\qquad \underline{196} \qquad\quad \underline{28}$$
$$\;\;227 \qquad\qquad\;\; 31 \qquad\qquad 3$$
$$1599 = 4443_{seven}$$

40.
$$512\overline{)1346} \qquad 64\overline{)322} \qquad 8\overline{)2}$$
$$\underline{1024} \qquad\qquad \underline{320} \qquad\quad \underline{0}$$
$$\;\;322 \qquad\qquad\;\; 2 \qquad\qquad 2$$
$$1346 = 2502_{eight}$$

41. 21 weeks = 147 days

153 days = 21 weeks, 6 days

42. 273 hours $\div 24 = 11.375$

11 days = 264 hours

273 hours = 11 days, 9 hours

43. Example:

$\$8.79 \div 0.25 = 35.16$

35 quarters = $\$8.75$

$\$8.79 = 35$ quarters + 4 pennies

44-46. Answers will vary.

47.

Preceding:	Following:
888_{nine}	888_{nine}
$-\;\;\;1_{nine}$	$+\;\;\;1_{nine}$
887_{nine}	1000_{nine}

48. Preceding: Following:

$$\begin{array}{r} EC5_{sixteen} \\ -\ 1_{sixteen} \\ \hline EC4_{sixteen} \end{array} \qquad \begin{array}{r} EC5_{sixteen} \\ +\ 1_{sixteen} \\ \hline EC6_{sixteen} \end{array}$$

49. 11111011_{two}

$(1 \times 2^7) + (1 \times 2^6) + (1 \times 2^5) + (1 \times 2^4) + (1 \times 2^3) + (0 \times 2^2) + (1 \times 2^1) + (1 \times 1)$
$= 128 + 64 + 32 + 16 + 8 + 0 + 2 + 1$
$= 251$
$3A6_{twelve}$
$(3 \times 12^2) + (10 \times 12^1) + (6 \times 1) = 432 + 120 + 6 = 558$
673_{eight}
$(6 \times 8^2) + (7 \times 8^1) + (3 \times 1) = 384 + 56 + 3 = 443$
11111011_{two}, 673_{eight}, $3A6_{twelve}$

50. 55_{eight}

51. 37

52. $25_{sixteen}$

53. 1000110111_{two}

54. $DB_{sixteen}$

Check Points 4.3

1.
$$\begin{array}{r} {}^1\ \\ 3\,2_{five} \\ +44_{five} \\ \hline 131_{five} \end{array}$$

$2 + 4 = 6 = (1 \times 5^1) + (1 \times 1) = 11_{five}$

$1 + 3 + 4 = 8 = (1 \times 5^1) + (3 \times 1) = 13_{five}$

2.
$$\begin{array}{r} {}^{11}\ \\ 111_{two} \\ +111_{two} \\ \hline 1110_{two} \end{array}$$

$1 + 1 = 2 = (1 \times 2^1) + (0 \times 1) = 10_{two}$

$1 + 1 + 1 = 3 = (1 \times 2^1) + (1 \times 1) = 11_{two}$

3.
$$\begin{array}{r} {}^{3\ 6}\ \\ 4\,1_{five} \\ -23_{five} \\ \hline 13_{five} \end{array}$$

4.
$$\begin{array}{r} {}^{4\,8\,3\,1\,1}\ \\ 5144_{seven} \\ -3236_{seven} \\ \hline 1605_{seven} \end{array}$$

5.
$$\begin{array}{r} {}^2\ \\ 45_{seven} \\ \times\ 3_{seven} \\ \hline 201_{seven} \end{array}$$

$3 \times 5 = 15 = (2 \times 7^1) + (1 \times 1) = 21_{seven}$

$(3 \times 4) + 2 = 14 = (2 \times 7^1) + (0 \times 1) = 20_{seven}$

6.
$$\begin{array}{r} 23\ \\ 2_{four}\overline{)112_{four}} \\ \underline{10}\ \ \ \\ 12\ \\ \underline{12}\ \\ 0\ \\ 23_{four} \end{array}$$

Chapter 4: Number Representation and Calculation

Exercise Set 4.3

Note: Numbers with no base specified are base 10.

1.
$$\overset{1}{2}3_{four}$$
$$+13_{four}$$
$$\overline{102_{four}}$$

$$3+3 = 6 = (1\times4^{1})+(2\times1) = 12_{four}$$
$$1+2+1 = 4 = (1\times4^{1})+(0\times1) = 10_{four}$$

2.
$$31_{four}$$
$$+22_{four}$$
$$\overline{113_{four}}$$

$$3+2 = 5 = (1\times4^{1})+(1\times1) = 11_{four}$$

3.
$$\overset{1}{1}1_{two}$$
$$+11_{two}$$
$$\overline{110_{two}}$$

$$1+1+1 = 3 = (1\times2^{1})+(1\times1) = 11_{two}$$

4.
$$\overset{1\;1}{1}01_{two}$$
$$+\;11_{two}$$
$$\overline{1000_{two}}$$

5.
$$\overset{1\;1}{3}42_{five}$$
$$+413_{five}$$
$$\overline{1310_{five}}$$

$$2+3 = 5 = (1\times5^{1})+(0\times1) = 10_{five}$$
$$1+4+1 = 6 = (1\times5^{1})+(1\times1) = 11_{five}$$
$$1+3+4 = 8 = (1\times5^{1})+(3\times1) = 13_{five}$$

6.
$$323_{five}$$
$$+421_{five}$$
$$\overline{1244_{five}}$$

$$3+4 = 7 = (1\times5^{1})+(2\times1) = 12_{five}$$

7.
$$\overset{1\;1}{6}45_{seven}$$
$$+324_{seven}$$
$$\overline{1302_{seven}}$$

$$5+4 = 9 = (1\times7^{1})+(2\times1) = 12_{seven}$$
$$1+4+2 = 7 = (1\times7^{1})+(0\times1) = 10_{seven}$$
$$1+6+3 = 10 = (1\times7^{1})+(3\times1) = 13_{seven}$$

8.
$$\overset{1}{6}32_{seven}$$
$$+\;564_{seven}$$
$$\overline{1526_{seven}}$$

$$3+6 = 9 = (1\times7^{1})+(2\times1) = 12_{seven}$$
$$1+6+5 = 12 = (1\times7^{1})+(5\times1) = 15_{seven}$$

9.
$$\overset{1\;1\;1}{6}784_{nine}$$
$$+7865_{nine}$$
$$\overline{15760_{nine}}$$

$$4+5 = 9 = (1\times9^{1})+(0\times1) = 10_{nine}$$
$$1+8+6 = 15 = (1\times9^{1})+(6\times1) = 16_{nine}$$
$$1+7+8 = 16 = (1\times9^{1})+(7\times1) = 17_{nine}$$
$$1+6+7 = 14 = (1\times9^{1})+(5\times1) = 15_{nine}$$

10.
$$\overset{1}{1}021_{three}$$
$$+2011_{three}$$
$$\overline{10102_{three}}$$

$$2+1 = 3 = (1\times3^{1})+(0\times1) = 10_{three}$$

11.
$$\overset{11}{1}4632_{seven}$$
$$+5604_{seven}$$
$$\overline{23536_{seven}}$$

$$6+6 = 12 = (1\times7^{1})+(5\times1) = 15_{seven}$$
$$1+4+5 = 10 = (1\times7^{1})+(3\times1) = 13_{seven}$$

12.
$$53B_{sixteen}$$
$$+ \ 694_{sixteen}$$
$$BCF_{sixteen}$$

$B + 4 = 11 + 4 = 15 = F_{sixteen}$
$3 + 9 = 12 = C_{sixteen}$
$5 + 6 = 11 = B_{sixteen}$

13.
$$\overset{2\,6}{3\,2}_{four}$$
$$-13_{four}$$
$$13_{four}$$

14.
$$\overset{1\,5}{2\,1}_{four}$$
$$-12_{four}$$
$$3_{four}$$

15.
$$\overset{1\,8}{2\,3}_{five}$$
$$-14_{five}$$
$$4_{five}$$

16.
$$\overset{2\,9}{3\,2}_{seven}$$
$$-16_{seven}$$
$$13_{seven}$$

17.
$$\overset{6\,13}{47\,5}_{eight}$$
$$-267_{eight}$$
$$206_{eight}$$

18.
$$\overset{6\,9\,11}{71\,2}_{nine}$$
$$-483_{nine}$$
$$218_{nine}$$

19.
$$\overset{4\,12\ \ 10}{5\,6\,3}_{seven}$$
$$-164_{seven}$$
$$366_{seven}$$

20.
$$\overset{\ \ \ \ 13}{\overset{3\,5\,10}{45\,2}}_{eight}$$
$$-\ 177_{eight}$$
$$263_{eight}$$

21.
$$\overset{0\,1\,2}{100\,1}_{two}$$
$$-111_{two}$$
$$10_{two}$$

22.
$$\overset{0\,1\,1\,2}{100\,0}_{two}$$
$$-\ \ 101_{two}$$
$$11_{two}$$

23.
$$\overset{1\,2\,3}{120\,0}_{three}$$
$$-1012_{three}$$
$$111_{three}$$

24.
$$\overset{B\ \ \ 22}{4C\,6}_{sixteen}$$
$$-19\ 8_{sixteen}$$
$$3\ 2\ E_{sixteen}$$

25.
$$\overset{3}{25}_{six}$$
$$\times 4_{six}$$
$$152_{six}$$

$(2_{six} \times 4_{six}) + 3_{six} = 8_{ten} + 3_{six}$
$$= 12_{six} + 3_{six}$$
$$= 15_{six}$$

26.
$$\overset{2}{34}_{five}$$
$$\times \ \ 3_{five}$$
$$212_{five}$$

$(3_{five} \times 3_{five}) + 2_{five} = 9_{ten} + 2_{five}$
$$= (1 \times 5^1 + 4 \times 5^0) + 2_{five}$$
$$= 14_{five} + 2_{five}$$
$$= 21_{five}$$

27.
$$11_{two}$$
$$\underline{\times\ 1_{two}}$$
$$11_{two}$$

28.
$$21_{four}$$
$$\underline{\times\ 3_{four}}$$
$$123_{four}$$

$$2_{four} \times 3_{four} = 6_{ten}$$
$$= (1 \times 4^1) + (2 \times 1)$$
$$= 12_{four}$$

29.
$$\overset{3\ 2}{543}_{seven}$$
$$\underline{\times\ \ \ 5_{seven}}$$
$$4011_{seven}$$

$$3 \times 5 = 15 = (2 \times 7^1) + (1 \times 1) = 21_{seven}$$
$$(4 \times 5) + 2 = 22 = (3 \times 7^1) + (1 \times 1) = 31_{seven}$$
$$(5 \times 5) + 3 = 28 = (4 \times 7^1) + (0 \times 1) = 40_{seven}$$

30.
$$\overset{2\ 2}{243}_{nine}$$
$$\underline{\times\ \ \ 6_{nine}}$$
$$1580_{nine}$$

$$3 \times 6 = 18 = (2 \times 9^1) + (0 \times 1) = 20_{nine}$$
$$(4 \times 6) + 2 = 26 = (2 \times 9^1) + (8 \times 1) = 28_{nine}$$
$$(2 \times 6) + 2 = 14 = (1 \times 9^1) + (5 \times 1) = 15_{nine}$$

31.
$$\overset{1\ 1}{623}_{eight}$$
$$\underline{\times\ \ \ 4_{eight}}$$
$$3114_{eight}$$

$$(3_{eight} \times 4_{eight}) = 12_{ten}$$
$$= (1 \times 8^1) + (4 \times 1)$$
$$= 14_{eight}$$
$$(2_{eight} \times 4_{eight}) + 1_{eight} = 8_{ten} + 1_{ten}$$
$$= 9_{ten}$$
$$= (1 \times 8^1) + (1 \times 1)$$
$$= 11_{eight}$$
$$(6_{eight} \times 4_{eight}) + 1_{eight} = 24_{ten} + 1_{ten}$$
$$= 25_{ten}$$
$$= (3 \times 8^1) + (1 \times 1)$$
$$= 31_{eight}$$

32.
$$\overset{3\ 2}{543}_{six}$$
$$\underline{\times\ \ \ 5_{six}}$$
$$4443_{six}$$

$$3_{six} \times 5_{six} = 15_{ten} = (2 \times 6^1) + (3 \times 1)$$
$$= 23_{six}$$
$$(4_{six} \times 5_{six}) + 2_{six} = 20_{ten} + 2_{ten}$$
$$= 22_{ten}$$
$$= (3 \times 6^1) + (4 \times 1)$$
$$= 34_{six}$$
$$(5_{six} \times 5_{six}) + 3_{six} = 25_{ten} + 3_{ten}$$
$$= 28_{ten}$$
$$= (4 \times 6^1) + (4 \times 1)$$
$$= 44_{six}$$

33.
$$21_{four}$$
$$\underline{\times 12_{four}}$$
$$102$$
$$\underline{210}$$
$$312_{four}$$

$$21_{four} \times 2_{four} = 9_{ten} \times 2_{ten}$$
$$= 18$$
$$= (1 \times 4^2) + (0 \times 4) + (2 \times 1)$$
$$= 102_{four}$$
$$21_{four} \times 1_{four} = 21_{four}$$

34.
$$\begin{array}{r} 1 \\ 32_{four} \\ \times\ 23_{four} \\ \hline 222_{four} \\ 1300_{four} \\ \hline 2122_{four} \end{array}$$

$$\begin{aligned} 32_{four} \times 3_{four} &= 14_{ten} \times 3_{ten} \\ &= 42 \\ &= (2 \times 4^2) + (2 \times 4^1) + (2 \times 1) \\ &= 222_{four} \\ 32_{four} \times 2_{four} &= 14_{ten} \times 2_{ten} \\ &= 28 \\ &= (1 \times 4^2) + (3 \times 4^1) + (0 \times 1) \\ &= 130_{four} \end{aligned}$$

35.
$$\begin{array}{r} 20 \\ 2_{four}\overline{)100_{four}} \\ 10 \\ \hline 00 \end{array}$$

$$20_{four}$$

36.
$$\begin{array}{r} 130 \\ 2_{four}\overline{)321_{four}} \\ 2 \\ \hline 12 \\ 12 \\ \hline 01 \\ 0 \\ \hline 1 \end{array}$$

$$130_{four} \text{ remainder of } 1$$

37.
$$\begin{array}{r} 41 \\ 3_{five}\overline{)224_{five}} \\ 22 \\ \hline 04 \\ 3 \\ \hline 1 \end{array}$$

$$41_{five} \text{ remainder of } 1$$

38.
$$\begin{array}{r} 21 \\ 4_{five}\overline{)134_{five}} \\ 13 \\ \hline 04 \\ 4 \\ \hline 0 \end{array}$$

$$21_{five}$$

39-41. Answers will vary.

42.
$$\begin{array}{r} 56_{seven} \\ 31_{seven}\overline{)2426_{seven}} \\ 215 \\ \hline 246 \\ 246 \\ \hline 0 \end{array}$$

43. 1367_{eight}

44. 235_{eight}

45. $12F_{sixteen}$

46. $D9_{sixteen}$

Check Points 4.4

1. $100,000 + 100,000 + 100,000 + 100 + 100 + 10 + 10 + 1 + 1 = 300,222$

2. $2563 = 1000 + 1000 + 100 + 100 + 100 + 100 + 100 + 10 + 10 + 10 + 10 + 10 + 10 + 1 + 1 + 1$

   𒀭𒀭𓆼𓆼𓆼𓆼𓆼𓎆𓎆𓎆𓎆𓎆|||

3. $MCCCLXI = 1000 + 100 + 100 + 100 + 50 + 10 + 1 = 1361$

4. $MCDXLVII = \overbrace{1000}^{M} + \overbrace{(500-100)}^{CD} + \overbrace{(50-10)}^{XL} + \overset{V}{5} + \overset{I}{1} + \overset{I}{1} = 1000 + 400 + 40 + 5 + 1 + 1 = 1447$

5. $399 = 100 + 100 + 100 + 90 + 9 = \underbrace{100}_{C} + \underbrace{100}_{C} + \underbrace{100}_{C} + \overbrace{(100-10)}^{XC} + \overbrace{(10-1)}^{IX} = CCCXCIX$

6. $2693 = 2000 + 600 + 90 + 3$

   二
   千
   六
   百
   九
   十
   三

7. $\omega\pi\varepsilon = 800 + 80 + 5 = 885$

Exercise Set 4.4

1. 322

2. 3,040,214

3. 300,423

4. 200,213

5. 132

6. 121,302

7. $423 = (4 \times 100) + (2 \times 10) + (3 \times 1)$

   𓆼𓆼𓆼𓆼𓎆𓎆|||

8. $825 = (8 \times 100) + (2 \times 10) + (5 \times 1)$

   𓆼𓆼𓆼𓆼𓆼𓆼𓆼𓆼𓎆𓎆|||||

9. $1846 = (1 \times 1000) + (8 \times 100) + (4 \times 10) + (6 \times 1)$

   𒀭𓆼𓆼𓆼𓆼𓆼𓆼𓆼𓆼𓎆𓎆𓎆𓎆||||||

10. $1425 = (1 \times 1000) + (4 \times 100) + (2 \times 10) + (5 \times 1)$

    𒀭𓆼𓆼𓆼𓆼𓎆𓎆|||||

11. $23,547 = (2 \times 10,000) + (3 \times 1000) + (5 \times 100) + (4 \times 10) + (7 \times 1)$

    𐡀𐡀𒀭𒀭𒀭𓆼𓆼𓆼𓆼𓆼𓎆𓎆𓎆|||||||

12. $2,346,031 = (2 \times 1,000,000) + (3 \times 100,000) + (4 \times 10,000) + (6 \times 1000) + (0 \times 100) + (3 \times 10) + (1 \times 1)$

13. XI = 11

14. CL = 150

15. XVI = 16

16. LVII = 57

17. XL = 40

18. CM = 900

19. LIX = 59

20. XLIV = 44

21. CXLVI = 146

22. CLXI = 161

23. MDCXXI = 1621

24. MMCDXLV = 2445

25. MMDCLXXVII = 2677

26. MDCXXVI = 1626

27. $\overline{\text{IX}}$CDLXVI = 9466

28. $\overline{\text{V}}$MCCXI = 6211

29. 43 = XLIII

30. 96 = XCVI

31. 129 = CXXIX

32. 469 = CDLXIX

33. 1896 = MDCCCXCVI

34. 4578 = $\overline{\text{IV}}$DLXXVIII

35. 6892 = $\overline{\text{VI}}$DCCCXCII

36. 5847 = $\overline{\text{V}}$DCCCXLVII

37. $80 + 8 = 88$

$\left.\begin{array}{l} 8 \\ 10 \end{array}\right\} 80$

$8 \} 8$

38. $700 + 5 = 705$

$\left.\begin{array}{l} 7 \\ 100 \end{array}\right\} 700$

$5 \} 5$

39. $500 + 20 + 7 = 527$

$\left.\begin{array}{l} 5 \\ 100 \end{array}\right\} 500$

$\left.\begin{array}{l} 2 \\ 10 \end{array}\right\} 20$

$7 \} 7$

40. $3000 + 80 + 1 = 3081$

$\left.\begin{array}{l} 3 \\ 1000 \end{array}\right\} 3000$

$\left.\begin{array}{l} 8 \\ 10 \end{array}\right\} 80$

$1 \} 1$

41. $2000 + 700 + 70 + 6 = 2776$

$\left.\begin{array}{l} 2 \\ 1000 \end{array}\right\} 2000$

$\left.\begin{array}{l} 7 \\ 100 \end{array}\right\} 700$

$\left.\begin{array}{l} 7 \\ 10 \end{array}\right\} 70$

$6 \} 6$

42. $8000 + 200 + 30 + 6 = 8236$

$\left.\begin{array}{l} 8 \\ 1000 \end{array}\right\} 8000$

$\left.\begin{array}{l} 2 \\ 100 \end{array}\right\} 200$

$\left.\begin{array}{l} 3 \\ 10 \end{array}\right\} 30$

$6 \} 6$

43.

44.

二
百
六
十
九

45.

五
百
八
十
三

46.

二
千
九
百
六
十
五

47.

四
千
八
百
七
十

48.

七
千
六
百
五

49. $\iota\beta = 12$

50. $\varphi\varepsilon = 505$

51. $\sigma\lambda\delta = 234$

52. $\psi o\theta = 779$

53. $43 = \mu\gamma$

54. $257 = \sigma\nu\zeta$

55. $483 = \upsilon\pi\gamma$

56. $895 = \omega Q\varepsilon$

57. MDCCLXXVI = 1776—Declaration of Independence

58. 1989—it is too recent to be an "old" building.

59-63. Answers will vary.

64. 428, 431, 449 or

四
百
二
十
八, ⑨⑨⑨⑨∩∩∩I, CCCCXLIX

65. Preceding: ⑨⑨∩∩∩∩∩∩∩∩IIIIIIII
Following: ⑨⑨⑨

66. Roman: XLVI = 46
Egyptian: = 32
Chinese: = 20
Greek: $200 - 46 - 32 - 20 = 102 = \rho\beta$

Chapter 4 Review Exercises

1. $11^2 = 11\times11 = 121$

2. $7^3 = 7\times7\times7 = 343$

3. $472 = (4\times10^2) + (7\times10^1) + (2\times1) = (4\times100) + (7\times10) + (2\times1)$

4. $8076 = (8\times10^3) + (0\times10^2) + (7\times10^1) + (6\times1) = (8\times1000) + (0\times100) + (7\times10) + (6\times1)$

5. $70,329 = (7\times10^4) + (0\times10^3) + (3\times10^2) + (2\times10^1) + (9\times1)$
$= (7\times10,000) + (0\times1000) + (3\times100) + (2\times10) + (9\times1)$

6. 706,953

7. 740,000,306

8. <∨ <∨∨∨ $= (10+1)\times60^1 + (10+1+1+1)\times1$
$= (11\times60^1) + (13\times1)$
$= 660 + 13$
$= 673$

9. ∨∨ << <<<
$= (1+1)\times60^2 + (10+10)\times60^1 + (10+10+10)\times1$
$= (2\times60^2) + (20\times60) + (30\times1)$
$= (2\times3600) + 1200 + 30$
$= 7200 + 1230$
$= 8430$

10. $6\times360 = 2160$
$8\times20 \;=\; 160$
$11\times1 \;=\; \underline{\quad 11}$
$\qquad\qquad 2331$

11. $9\times7200 = 64,800$
$2\times360 = \quad 720$
$0\times20 = \qquad 0$
$16\times1 \;= \quad \underline{\quad 16}$
$\qquad\qquad 65,536$

12. Each position represents a particular value. The symbol in each position tells how many of that value are represented.

13. $34_{\text{five}} = (3\times5^1) + (4\times1)$
$= 15 + 4$
$= 19$

14. $110_{\text{two}} = (1\times2^2) + (1\times2^1) + (0\times1)$
$= 4 + 2 + 0$
$= 6$

15. $643_{\text{seven}} = (6\times7^2) + (4\times7^1) + (3\times1)$
$= 294 + 28 + 3$
$= 325$

16. $1084_{\text{nine}} = (1\times9^3) + (0\times9^2) + (8\times9^1) + (4\times1)$
$= 729 + 0 + 72 + 4$
$= 805$

17. $\text{FD3}_{\text{sixteen}} = (15\times16^2) + (13\times16^1) + (3\times1)$
$= 3840 + 208 + 3$
$= 4051$

18. $202202_{\text{three}} = (2\times3^5) + (0\times3^4) + (2\times3^3) + (2\times3^2) + (0\times3^1) + (2\times1)$
$= 486 + 0 + 54 + 18 + 0 + 2$
$= 560$

19. $89 = (3\times5^2) + (2\times5^1) + (4\times1)$
$= 324_{\text{five}}$

20. $21 = (1\times2^4) + (0\times2^3) + (1\times2^2) + (0\times2^1) + (1\times1)$
$= 10101_{\text{two}}$

21. $473 = (1\times3^5) + (2\times3^4) + (2\times3^3) + (1\times3^2) + (1\times3^1) + (2\times1)$
$= 243 + 162 + 54 + 9 + 3 + 2$
$= 122112_{\text{three}}$

22. $7093 = (2 \times 7^4) + (6 \times 7^3) + (4 \times 7^2) + (5 \times 7^1) + (2 \times 1)$
$= 4802 + 2058 + 196 + 35 + 2$
$= 26452_{\text{seven}}$

23. $9348 = (1 \times 6^5) + (1 \times 6^4) + (1 \times 6^3) + (1 \times 6^2) + (4 \times 6^1) + (0 \times 1)$
$= 7776 + 1296 + 216 + 36 + 24$
$= 111140_{\text{six}}$

24. $554 = (3 \times 12^2) + (A \times 12^1) + (2 \times 1)$
$= 3A2_{\text{twelve}}$

25.
$$\begin{array}{r} \overset{1}{}46_{\text{seven}} \\ +\,53_{\text{seven}} \\ \hline 132_{\text{seven}} \end{array}$$

26.
$$\begin{array}{r} \overset{1\ 1}{}574_{\text{eight}} \\ +\,605_{\text{eight}} \\ \hline 1401_{\text{eight}} \end{array}$$

27.
$$\begin{array}{r} \overset{1111}{11011_{\text{two}}} \\ 10101_{\text{two}} \\ \hline 110000_{\text{two}} \end{array}$$

28.
$$\begin{array}{r} \overset{1}{}43C_{\text{sixteen}} \\ +\,694_{\text{sixteen}} \\ \hline AD0_{\text{sixteen}} \end{array}$$

29.
$$\begin{array}{r} \overset{2\ 10}{\cancel{3}\cancel{4}_{\text{six}}} \\ 25_{\text{six}} \\ \hline 5_{\text{six}} \end{array}$$

30.
$$\begin{array}{r} \overset{5\ \ 8\ \ 11}{\cancel{6}\,\cancel{2}\,\cancel{4}_{\text{seven}}} \\ -\,246_{\text{seven}} \\ \hline 345_{\text{seven}} \end{array}$$

31.
$$\begin{array}{r} \overset{0\ 1\ 2}{10\cancel{0}1_{\text{two}}} \\ -\,110_{\text{two}} \\ \hline 11_{\text{two}} \end{array}$$

32.
$$\begin{array}{r} \overset{3\ 6\ 1\ 6}{4\cancel{1}\cancel{2}\cancel{1}_{\text{five}}} \\ -\,1312_{\text{five}} \\ \hline 2304_{\text{five}} \end{array}$$

33.
$$\begin{array}{r} \overset{1}{}32_{\text{four}} \\ \times\ \ 3_{\text{four}} \\ \hline 222_{\text{four}} \end{array}$$

34.
$$\begin{array}{r} \overset{2}{}43_{\text{seven}} \\ \times\ \ 6_{\text{seven}} \\ \hline 354_{\text{seven}} \end{array}$$

35.
$$\begin{array}{r} \overset{2\ 2}{123_{\text{five}}} \\ 4_{\text{five}} \\ \hline 1102_{\text{five}} \end{array}$$

36.
$$\begin{array}{r} 133 \\ 2_{\text{four}}\overline{)332_{\text{four}}} \\ \underline{2} \\ 13 \\ \underline{12} \\ 12 \\ \underline{12} \\ 0 \end{array}$$
133_{four}

37.
$$\begin{array}{r} 12 \\ 4_{\text{five}}\overline{)103_{\text{five}}} \\ \underline{4} \\ 13 \\ \underline{13} \\ 0 \end{array}$$
12_{five}

38. 1246

39. 12,432

40. $2486 = (2 \times 1000) + (4 \times 100) + (8 \times 10) + (6 \times 1)$

卐卐@@@@∩∩∩∩∩∩∩∩IIIIII

41. $34{,}573 = (3\times10{,}000)+(4\times1000)+(5\times100)+(7\times10)+(3\times1)$

〔〔〔𓏢𓏢𓏢𓏢𓆐𓆐𓆐𓆐𓆐∩∩∩∩∩∩∩|||

42. DDCCCBAAAA = 2314

43. 5492 = DDDDDCCCCBBBBBBBBBAA

44. Answers will vary.

45. CLXIII = 163

46. MXXXIV = 1034

47. MCMXC = 1990

48. 49 = XLIX

49. 2965 = MMCMLXV

50. If symbols increase in value from left to right, subtract the value of the symbol on the left from the symbol on the right.

51. $500+50+4=554$

$\left.\begin{array}{l}5\\100\end{array}\right\}500$

$\left.\begin{array}{l}5\\10\end{array}\right\}50$

$4\}4$

52. $8000+200+50+3=8253$

$\left.\begin{array}{l}8\\1000\end{array}\right\}8000$

$\left.\begin{array}{l}2\\100\end{array}\right\}200$

$\left.\begin{array}{l}5\\10\end{array}\right\}50$

$3\}3$

53.

二
百
七
十
四

54.

三
千
五
百
八
十
七

55. 365

56. 4520

57. G Y I X C

58. F Z H Y E X D

59. Answers will vary.

60. $\chi\nu\gamma = 653$

61. $\chi o\eta = 678$

62. $453 = \upsilon\nu\gamma$

63. $902 = \pi\beta$

64. UNG = 357

65. mhZRD = 37,894

66. rXJH = 80,618

67. 597 = WRG

68. $25{,}483 = $ lfVQC

69. Answers will vary.

Chapter 4: Number Representation and Calculation

Chapter 4 Test

1. $9 \times 9 \times 9 = 729$

2. $567 = (5 \times 10^2) + (6 \times 10^1) + (7 \times 1)$
    $= (5 \times 100) + (6 \times 10) + (7 \times 1)$

3. $63,028 = (6 \times 10^4) + (3 \times 10^3) + (0 \times 10^2) + (2 \times 10^1) + (8 \times 1)$
    $= (6 \times 10,000) + (3 \times 1000) + (0 \times 100) + (2 \times 10) + (8 \times 1)$

4. $7000 + 400 + 90 + 3 = 7493$

5. $400,000 + 200 + 6 = 400,206$

6-7.   Answers will vary.

8. $<< <\vee\vee\ \ <\vee = (10+10) \times 60^2 + (10+1+1) \times 60^1 + (10+1) \times 1$
    $= (20 \times 60^2) + (12 \times 60) + (11 \times 1) = 72,000 + 720 + 11 = 72,731$

9. $\begin{array}{rr} 4 \times 360 = & 1440 \\ 6 \times 20 = & 120 \\ 0 \times 1 = & \underline{0} \\ & 1560 \end{array}$

10. $423_{five} = (4 \times 5^2) + (2 \times 5^1) + (3 \times 1) = 4 \times 25 + 10 + 3 = 100 + 10 + 3 = 113$

11. $267_{nine} = (2 \times 9^2) + (6 \times 9^1) + (7 \times 1) = 2 \times 81 + 54 + 7 = 162 + 54 + 7 = 223$

12. $110101_{two} = (1 \times 2^5) + (1 \times 2^4) + (0 \times 2^3) + (1 \times 2^2) + (0 \times 2^1) + (1 \times 1) = 32 + 16 + 0 + 4 + 0 + 1 = 53$

13. $77 = (2 \times 3^3) + (2 \times 3^2) + (1 \times 3^1) + (2 \times 1) = 2212_{three}$

14. $56 = (1 \times 2^5) + (1 \times 2^4) + (1 \times 2^3) + (0 \times 2^2) + (0 \times 2^1) + (0 \times 1) = 111000_{two}$

15. $1844 = (2 \times 5^4) + (4 \times 5^3) + (3 \times 5^2) + (3 \times 5^1) + (4 \times 1) = 1250 + 500 + 75 + 15 + 4 = 24334_{five}$

16. $\begin{array}{r} \overset{1\ 1}{234_{five}} \\ +423_{five} \\ \hline 1212_{five} \end{array}$

17. $\begin{array}{r} \overset{5\ 9}{5\,\cancel{6}2_{seven}} \\ -145_{seven} \\ \hline 414_{seven} \end{array}$

18. $\begin{array}{r} \overset{2}{54_{six}} \\ \times\ \ 3_{six} \\ \hline 250_{six} \end{array}$

19.

$$
\begin{array}{r}
221 \\
3_{\text{five}} \overline{)\ 1213_{\text{five}}} \\
\underline{11} \\
11 \\
\underline{11} \\
03 \\
\underline{3} \\
0
\end{array}
$$

221_{five}

20. 20,303

21. $32,634 = (3 \times 10,000) + (2 \times 1000) + (6 \times 100) + (3 \times 10) + (4 \times 1)$

ℂℂℂ⚱⚱ↅↅↅↅↅↅↅ∩∩∩⦙⦙⦙⦙

22. $\text{MCMXCIV} = \overset{M}{\overbrace{1000}} + \overset{CM}{\overbrace{(1000-100)}} + \overset{XC}{\overbrace{(100-10)}} + \overset{IV}{\overbrace{(5-1)}} = 1000 + 900 + 90 + 4 = 1994$

23. $459 = \overset{CD}{\overbrace{(500-100)}} + \overset{L}{\overbrace{50}} + \overset{IX}{\overbrace{(10-1)}} = \text{CDLIX}$

24. Answers will vary.

Chapter 5
Number Theory and the Real Number System

Check Points 5.1

1. The statement given in part (b) is true.

   a. False, 8 does not divide 48,324 because 8 does not divide 324.

   b. True, 6 divides 48,324 because both 2 and 3 divide 48,324. 2 divides 48,324 because the last digit is 4. 3 divides 48,324 because the sum of the digits, 21, is divisible by 3.

   c. False, 4 *does* divide 48,324 because the last two digits form 24 which is divisible by 4.

2.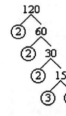

   $$120 = 2^3 \cdot 3 \cdot 5$$

3. $225 = 3^2 \cdot 5^2$
   $825 = 3 \cdot 5^2 \cdot 11$
   Greatest Common Divisor: $3 \cdot 5^2 = 75$

4. $192 = 2^6 \cdot 3$
   $288 = 2^5 \cdot 3^2$
   Greatest Common Divisor: $2^5 \cdot 3 = 96$
   The largest number of people that can be placed in each singing group is 96.

5. $18 = 2 \cdot 3^2$
   $30 = 2 \cdot 3 \cdot 5$
   Least common multiple is: $90 = 2 \cdot 3^2 \cdot 5$

6. $40 = 2^3 \cdot 5$
   $60 = 2^2 \cdot 3 \cdot 5$
   Least common multiple is: $120 = 2^3 \cdot 3 \cdot 5$
   It will be 120 minutes, or 2 hours, until both movies begin again at the same time. The time will be 5:00 PM.

Exercise Set 5.1

1. 6944

   a. Yes. The last digit is four.

   b. No. The sum of the digits is 23, which is not divisible by 3.

   c. Yes. The last two digits form 44, which is divisible by 4.

   d. No. The number does not end in 0 or 5.

   e. No. The number is not divisible by both 2 and 3.

   f. Yes. The last three digits form 944, which is divisible by 8.

   g. No. The sum of the digits is 23, which is not divisible by 9.

   h. No. The number does not end in 0.

   i. No. The number is not divisible by both 3 and 4.

2. 7245

   a. No. The last digit is five.

   b. Yes. The sum of the digits is 18, which is divisible by 3.

   c. No. The last two digits form 45, which is not divisible by 4.

   d. Yes. The number ends with 5.

   e. No. The number is not divisible by both 2 and 3.

   f. No. The last 3 digits form 245, which is not divisible by 8.

   g. Yes. The sum of the digits is 18, which is divisible by 9.

   h. No. The number does not end in 0.

   i. No. The number is not divisible by both 3 and 4.

3. 21,408

   a. Yes. The last digit is eight.

   b. Yes. The sum of the digits is 15, which is divisible by 3.

   c. Yes. The last two digits form 08, which is divisible by 4.

   d. No. The number does not end in 0 or 5.

   e. Yes. The number is divisible by both 2 and 3.

   f. Yes. The last three digits form 408, which is divisible by 8.

   g. No. The sum of the digits is 15, which is not divisible by 9.

   h. No. The number does not end in 0.

   i. Yes. The number is divisible by both 3 and 4.

4. 25,025

   a. No. The last digit is 5.

   b. No. The sum of the digits is 14, which is not divisible by 3.

   c. No. The last two digits form 25 which is not divisible by 4.

   d. Yes. The last digit is 5.

   e. No. The number is not divisible by 2 and 3.

   f. No. The last three digits form 025 which is not divisible by 8.

   g. No. The sum of the digits is 14, which is not divisible by 9.

   h. No. The number does not end in 0.

   i. No. The number is not divisible by 3 and 4.

5. 26,428

   a. Yes. The last digit is 8.

   b. No. The sum of the digits is 22, which is not divisible by 3.

   c. Yes. The last 2 digits form 28, which is divisible by 4.

   d. No. The last digit is eight.

e. No. The number is not divisible by both two and three.

f. No. The last three digits form 428, which is not divisible by 8.

g. No. The sum of the digits is 22, which is not divisible by 9.

h. No. The number does not end in 0.

i. No. The number is not divisible by 3 and 4.

6. 89,001

   a. No. The last digit is one.

   b. Yes. The sum of the digits is 18, which is divisible by 3.

   c. No. The last two digits form 01, which is not divisible by 4.

   d. No. The last digit is one.

   e. No. The number is not divisible by two and three.

   f. No. The last three digits form 001, which is not divisible by 8.

   g. Yes. The sum of the digits is 18, which is divisible by 9.

   h. No. The number does not end in 0.

   i. No. The number is not divisible by 3 and 4.

7. 374,832

   a. Yes. The last digit is 2.

   b. Yes. The sum of the digits is 27, which is divisible by 3.

   c. Yes. The last two digits form 32, which is divisible by 4.

   d. No. The last digit is two.

   e. Yes. The number is divisible by 2 and 3.

   f. Yes. The last 3 digits form 832, which is divisible by 8.

   g. Yes. The sum of the digits is 27, which is divisible by 9.

   h. No. The last digit is 2.

    i.   Yes. The number is divisible by both 3 and 4.

8. 347,712

    a.   Yes. The last digit is 2.

    b.   Yes. The sum of the digits is 24, which is divisible by 3.

    c.   Yes. The last two digits form 12, which is divisible by 4.

    d.   No. The last digit is 2.

    e.   Yes. The number is divisible by both 2 and 3.

    f.   Yes. The last 3 digits form 712, which is divisible by 8.

    g.   No. The sum of the digits is 24, which is not divisible by 9.

    h.   No. The last digit is 2.

    i.   Yes. The number is divisible by both 3 and 4.

9. 6,126,120

    a.   Yes. The last digit is 0.

    b.   Yes. The sum of the digits is 18, which is divisible by 3.

    c.   Yes. The last two digits form 20, which is divisible by 4.

    d.   Yes. The last digit is 0.

    e.   Yes. The number is divisible by both 2 and 3.

    f.   Yes. The last 3 digits form 120, which is divisible by 8.

    g.   Yes. The sum of the digits is 18, which is divisible by 9.

    h.   Yes. The last digit is 0.

    i.   Yes. The number is divisible by both 3 and 4.

10. 5,941,221

    a.   No. The last digit is 1.

    b.   Yes. The sum of the digits is 24, which is divisible by 3.

    c.   No. The last two digits form 21, which is not divisible by 4.

    d.   No. The last digit is 1.

    e.   No. The number is not divisible by both 2 and 3.

    f.   No. The last 3 digits form 221, which is not divisible by 8.

    g.   No. The sum of the digits is 24, which is not divisible by 9.

    h.   No. The last digit is 1.

    i.   No. The number is not divisible by both 3 and 4.

11. True. $5958 \div 3 = 1986$
The sum of the digits is 27, which is divisible by 3.

12. True. $8142 \div 3 = 2714$
The sum of the digits is 15, which is divisible by 3.

13. True. $10,612 \div 4 = 2653$
The last two digits form 12, which is divisible by 4.

14. True. $15,984 \div 4 = 3996$
The last two digits form 84, which is divisible by 4.

15. False

16. False

17. True. $104,538 \div 6 = 17,423$
The number is divisible by both 2 and 3.

18. True. $163,944 \div 6 = 27,324$
The number is divisible by both 2 and 3.

19. True. $20,104 \div 8 = 2513$
The last three digits form 104, which is divisible by 8.

20. True. $28,096 \div 8 = 3512$
The last three digits form 96, which is divisible by 8.

21. False

22. False

23. True. $517,872 \div 12 = 43,156$
The number is divisible by both 3 and 4.

24. True. $785,172 \div 12 = 65,431$
The number is divisible by both 3 and 4.

25.

26.

27.

28.

29.

30.

31.

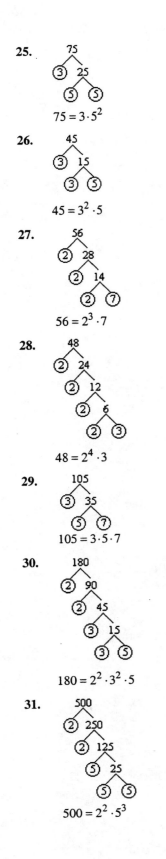

32.

33.

34.

35.

36.

37.

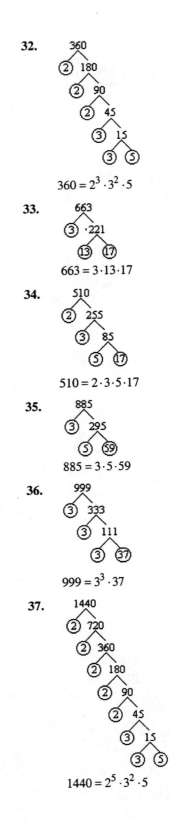

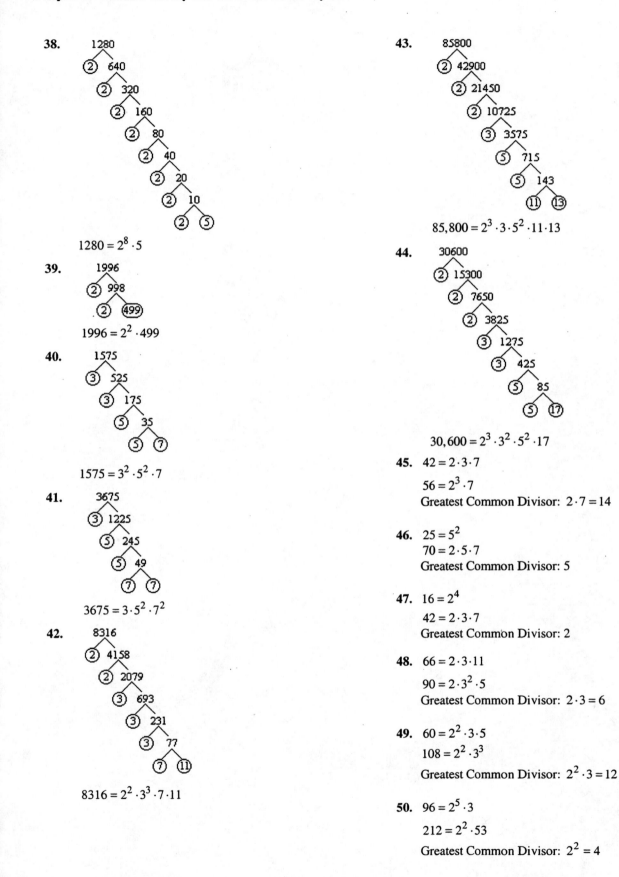

38. 1280

$1280 = 2^8 \cdot 5$

39. 1996

$1996 = 2^2 \cdot 499$

40. 1575

$1575 = 3^2 \cdot 5^2 \cdot 7$

41. 3675

$3675 = 3 \cdot 5^2 \cdot 7^2$

42. 8316

$8316 = 2^2 \cdot 3^3 \cdot 7 \cdot 11$

43. 85800

$85,800 = 2^3 \cdot 3 \cdot 5^2 \cdot 11 \cdot 13$

44. 30600

$30,600 = 2^3 \cdot 3^2 \cdot 5^2 \cdot 17$

45. $42 = 2 \cdot 3 \cdot 7$

$56 = 2^3 \cdot 7$

Greatest Common Divisor: $2 \cdot 7 = 14$

46. $25 = 5^2$

$70 = 2 \cdot 5 \cdot 7$

Greatest Common Divisor: 5

47. $16 = 2^4$

$42 = 2 \cdot 3 \cdot 7$

Greatest Common Divisor: 2

48. $66 = 2 \cdot 3 \cdot 11$

$90 = 2 \cdot 3^2 \cdot 5$

Greatest Common Divisor: $2 \cdot 3 = 6$

49. $60 = 2^2 \cdot 3 \cdot 5$

$108 = 2^2 \cdot 3^3$

Greatest Common Divisor: $2^2 \cdot 3 = 12$

50. $96 = 2^5 \cdot 3$

$212 = 2^2 \cdot 53$

Greatest Common Divisor: $2^2 = 4$

51. $72 = 2^3 \cdot 3^2$

$120 = 2^3 \cdot 3 \cdot 5$

Greatest Common Divisor: $2^3 \cdot 3 = 24$

52. $220 = 2^2 \cdot 5 \cdot 11$

$400 = 2^4 \cdot 5^2$

Greatest Common Divisor: $2^2 \cdot 5 = 20$

53. $324 = 2 \cdot 3^2 \cdot 19$

$380 = 2^2 \cdot 5 \cdot 19$

Greatest Common Divisor: $2 \cdot 19 = 38$

54. $224 = 2^5 \cdot 7$

$430 = 2 \cdot 5 \cdot 43$

Greatest Common Divisor: 2

55. $240 = 2^4 \cdot 3 \cdot 5$

$285 = 3 \cdot 5 \cdot 19$

Greatest Common Divisor: $3 \cdot 5 = 15$

56. $150 = 2 \cdot 3 \cdot 5^2$

$480 = 2^5 \cdot 3 \cdot 5$

Greatest Common Divisor: $2 \cdot 3 \cdot 5 = 30$

57. $42 = 2 \cdot 3 \cdot 7$

$56 = 2^3 \cdot 7$

Least Common Multiple: $2^3 \cdot 3 \cdot 7 = 168$

58. $25 = 5^2$

$70 = 2 \cdot 5 \cdot 7$

Least Common Multiple: $2 \cdot 5^2 \cdot 7 = 350$

59. $16 = 2^4$

$42 = 2 \cdot 3 \cdot 7$

Least Common Multiple: $2^4 \cdot 3 \cdot 7 = 336$

60. $66 = 2 \cdot 3 \cdot 11$

$90 = 2 \cdot 3^2 \cdot 5$

Least Common Multiple $= 2 \cdot 3^2 \cdot 5 \cdot 11 = 990$

61. $60 = 2^2 \cdot 3 \cdot 5$

$108 = 2^2 \cdot 3^3$

Least Common Multiple: $2^2 \cdot 3^3 \cdot 5 = 540$

62. $96 = 2^5 \cdot 3$

$212 = 2^2 \cdot 53$

Least Common Multiple $= 2^5 \cdot 3 \cdot 53 = 5088$

63. $72 = 2^3 \cdot 3^2$

$120 = 2^3 \cdot 3 \cdot 5$

Least Common Multiple: $2^3 \cdot 3^2 \cdot 5 = 360$

64. $220 = 2^2 \cdot 5 \cdot 11$

$400 = 2^4 \cdot 5^2$

Least Common Multiple $= 2^4 \cdot 5^2 \cdot 11 = 4400$

65. $342 = 2 \cdot 3^2 \cdot 19$

$380 = 2^2 \cdot 5 \cdot 19$

Least Common Multiple: $2^2 \cdot 3^2 \cdot 5 \cdot 19 = 3420$

66. $224 = 2^5 \cdot 7$

$430 = 2 \cdot 5 \cdot 43$

Least Common Multiple

$= 2^5 \cdot 5 \cdot 7 \cdot 43$

$= 48{,}160$

67. $240 = 2^4 \cdot 3 \cdot 5$

$285 = 3 \cdot 5 \cdot 19$

Least Common Multiple

$= 2^4 \cdot 3 \cdot 5 \cdot 19$

$= 4560$

68. $150 = 2 \cdot 3 \cdot 5^2$

$480 = 2^5 \cdot 3 \cdot 5$

Least Common Multiple

$= 2^5 \cdot 3 \cdot 5^2$

$= 2400$

69. The numbers are the prime numbers less than 100.

70. a. Multiples of 18: 18, 36, 54, 72, 90, 108, 126, 144, 162, 180, 198, 216
Multiples of 12: 12, 24, 36, 48, 60, 72, 84, 96, 108, 120, 132, 144, 156, 168, 180, 192, 204, 216
Common multiples of 12 and 18: 36, 72, 108, 144, 180, 216
Over a 216-year period, the two species will share the forest 6 times (once every 36 years).

b. The least common multiple of 17 and 13 is 221. The two species will share the forest once every 221 years.

c. By having a prime number as the length of its life cycle, the species will share the forest with other species less often.

71. $300 = 2^2 \cdot 3 \cdot 5^2$

$144 = 2^4 \cdot 3^2$

Greatest Common Divisor: $2^2 \cdot 3 = 12$
There would be 25 groups with 12 bottles of water each. There would be 12 groups with 12 cans of food each.

72. $180 = 2^2 \cdot 3^2 \cdot 5$

$144 = 2^4 \cdot 3^2$

Greatest Common Divisor: $2^2 \cdot 3^2 = 36$
There would be 5 all-male groups of 36.
There would be 4 all-female groups of 36.

73. $310 = 2 \cdot 5 \cdot 31$

$460 = 2^2 \cdot 5 \cdot 23$

Greatest Common Divisor: $2 \cdot 5 = 10$
There would be 31 groups of 10 five-dollar bills.
There would be 46 groups of
10 ten-dollar bills.

74. $360 = 2^3 \cdot 3^2 \cdot 5$

$432 = 2^4 \cdot 3^3$

Greatest Common Divisor: $2^3 \cdot 3^2 = 72$
There would be 5 groups of 72 football cards.
There would be 6 groups of 72 baseball cards.

75. $6 = 2 \cdot 3$

$10 = 2 \cdot 5$

Least Common Multiple is: $2 \cdot 3 \cdot 5 = 30$
It will be 30 more nights until both have the evening off, or July 1.

76. $40 = 2^3 \cdot 5$

$100 = 2^2 \cdot 5^2$

Least common multiple is: $2^3 \cdot 5^2 = 200$
It will be 200 minutes until each movie starts at the same time, or 3 hours and 20 minutes. The time would be 3:20 PM.

77. $15 = 3 \cdot 5$

$18 = 2 \cdot 3^2$

Least Common Multiple is: $2 \cdot 3^2 \cdot 5 = 90$
It take 90 minutes.

78. $40 = 2^3 \cdot 5$

$45 = 3^2 \cdot 5$

Least common multiple is: $2^3 \cdot 3^2 \cdot 5 = 360$
It will take 360 seconds or 6 minutes.

79-89. Answers will vary.

90. Ex: 1020 is divisible by 4 but not by 8.

91. a. GCD $= 2^{14} \cdot 3^{25} \cdot 5^{30}$

b. LCM $= 2^{17} \cdot 3^{37} \cdot 5^{31}$

92. 53
His age was prime 6 years ago at the age of 47. His age will be prime again in 6 years at the age of 59.

93. $85 + 15 = 100 = 2^2 \cdot 5^2$

$100 + 15 = 115 = 5 \cdot 23$

LCM $= 2^2 \cdot 5 \cdot 23 = 2300$
The films will begin at the same time

2300 min $\left(= 38\frac{1}{3}\text{hr} \right)$ after noon (today), or at 2:20

A.M. on the third day.

94. Yes, since 96 is divisible by 4, then 67,234,096 is divisible by 4.

95. No, since $1 + 2 + 5 + 4 + 1 + 7 + 5 + 0 = 25$ is not divisible by 3, then 12,541,750 is not divisible by 3.

96. Yes, since $4 + 8 + 2 + 0 + 1 + 6 + 5 + 1 = 27$ is divisible by 9, then 48,201,651 is divisible by 9.

Check Points 5.2

1.

2. a. $6 > -7$ because 6 is to the right of -2 on the number line.

b. $-8 < -1$ because -8 is to the left of -1 on the number line.

c. $-25 < -2$ because -25 is to the left of -2 on the number line.

d. $-14 < 0$ because -14 is to the left of 0 on the number line.

3. a. $|-8| = 8$ because -8 is 8 units from 0.

  b. $|6| = 6$ because 6 is 6 units from 0.

4. a. $30 - (-7) = 30 + 7 = 37$

  b. $-14 - (-10) = -14 + 10 = -4$

  c. $-14 - 10 = -24$

5. The difference in elevation is
    $8848 - (-10,915) = 8848 + 10,915 = 19,763$ m.

6. a. $8^2 = 8 \cdot 8 = 64$

  b. $(-8)^2 = (-8)(-8) = 64$

  c. $7^3 = 7 \cdot 7 \cdot 7 = 49 \cdot 7 = 343$

  d. $(-7)^3 = (-7)(-7)(-7) = 49(-7) = -343$

  e. $(-3)^4 = (-3)(-3)(-3)(-3) = 81$

7. $7^2 - 48 \div 4^2 \cdot 5 + 2$
    $= 49 - 48 \div 16 \cdot 5 + 2$
    $= 49 - 3 \cdot 5 + 2$
    $= 49 - 15 + 2$
    $= 34 + 2$
    $= 36$

8. $(-8)^2 - (10-13)^2(-2)$
    $= (-8)^2 - (-3)^2(-2)$
    $= 64 - (9)(-2)$
    $= 64 - (-18)$
    $= 64 + (+18)$
    $= 82$

Exercise Set 5.2

1.

2.

3.

4.

5. $-2 < 7$ because -2 is to the left of 7 on the number line.

6. $-1 < 13$ because -1 is to the left of 13 on the number line.

7. $-13 < -2$ because -13 is to the left of -2 on the number line.

8. $-1 > -13$ because -1 is to the right of -13 on the number line.

9. $8 > -50$ because 8 is to the right of -50 on the number line.

10. $7 > -9$ because 7 is to the right of -9 on the number line.

11. $-100 < 0$ because -100 is to the left of 0 on the number line.

12. $0 > -300$ because 0 is to the right of -300 on the number line.

13. $|-14| = 14$ because -14 is 14 units from 0.

14. $|-16| = 16$ because -16 is 16 units from 0.

15. $|14| = 14$ because 14 is 14 units from 0.

16. $|16| = 16$ because 16 is 16 units from 0.

17. $|-300,000| = 300,000$ because $-300,000$ is 300,000 units from 0.

18. $|-1,000,000| = 1,000,000$ because $-1,000,000$ is 1,000,000 units from 0.

19. $-7 + (-5) = -12$

20. $-3 + (-4) = -7$

21. $12 + (-8) = 4$

22. $13 + (-5) = 8$

23. $6 + (-9) = -3$

24. $3 + (-11) = -8$

25. $-9 + (+4) = -5$

26. $-7 + (+3) = -4$

27. $-9 + (-9) = -18$

28. $-13 + (-13) = -26$

29. $9 + (-9) = 0$

30. $13 + (-13) = 0$

31. $13 - 8 = 5$

32. $14 - 3 = 11$

33. $8 - 15 = 8 + (-15) = -7$

34. $9 - 20 = 9 + (-20) = -11$

35. $4 - (-10) = 4 + 10 = 14$

36. $3 - (-17) = 3 + 17 = 20$

37. $-6 - (-17) = -6 + 17 = 11$

38. $-4 - (-19) = -4 + 19 = 15$

39. $-12 - (-3) = -12 + 3 = -9$

40. $-19 - (-2) = -19 + 2 = -17$

41. $-11 - 17 = -11 + (-17) = -28$

42. $-19 - 21 = -19 + (-21) = -40$

43. $6(-9) = -54$

44. $5(-7) = -35$

45. $(-7)(-3) = 21$

46. $(-8)(-5) = 40$

47. $(-2)(6) = -12$

48. $(-3)(10) = -30$

49. $(-13)(-1) = 13$

50. $(-17)(-1) = 17$

51. $0(-5) = 0$

52. $0(-8) = 0$

53. $5^2 = 5 \cdot 5 = 25$

54. $6^2 = 6 \cdot 6 = 36$

55. $(-5)^2 = (-5) \cdot (-5) = 25$

56. $(-6)^2 = (-6)(-6) = 36$

57. $4^3 = 4 \cdot 4 \cdot 4 = 64$

58. $2^3 = 2 \cdot 2 \cdot 2 = 8$

59. $(-5)^3 = (-5)(-5)(-5) = 25(-5) = -125$

60. $(-4)^3 = (-4)(-4)(-4) = 16(-4) = -64$

61. $(-5)^4 = (-5)(-5)(-5)(-5) = 625$

62. $(-4)^4 = (-4)(-4)(-4)(-4) = 256$

63. $-3^4 = -[3 \cdot 3 \cdot 3 \cdot 3] = -81$

64. $-1^4 = -[1 \cdot 1 \cdot 1 \cdot 1] = -1$

65. $(-3)^4 = (-3)(-3)(-3)(-3) = 81$

66. $(-1)^4 = (-1)(-1)(-1)(-1) = 1$

67. $\dfrac{-12}{4} = -3$

68. $\dfrac{-40}{5} = -8$

69. $\dfrac{21}{-3} = -7$

70. $\dfrac{60}{-6} = -10$

71. $\dfrac{-90}{-3} = 30$

72. $\dfrac{-66}{-6} = 11$

73. $\dfrac{0}{-7} = 0$

74. $\dfrac{0}{-8} = 0$

75. $\dfrac{-7}{0}$ is undefined

76. $\dfrac{0}{0}$ is undefined.

77. $(-480) \div 24 = \dfrac{-480}{24} = -20$

78. $(-300) \div 12 = \dfrac{-300}{12} = -25$

79. $(465) \div (-15) = \dfrac{465}{-15} = -31$

80. $(-594) \div (-18) = \dfrac{-594}{-18} = 33$

81. $7 + 6 \cdot 3 = 7 + 18 = 25$

82. $-5 + (-3) \cdot 8 = -5 + (-24) = -29$

83. $(-5) - 6(-3) = -5 + 18 = 13$

84. $-8(-3) - 5(-6) = 24 - (-30) = 24 + 30 = 54$

85. $6 - 4(-3) - 5 = 6 - (-12) - 5$
$\qquad\qquad = 6 + 12 - 5$
$\qquad\qquad = 18 - 5$
$\qquad\qquad = 13$

86. $3 - 7(-1) - 6 = 3 - (-7) - 6$
$\qquad\qquad = 3 + 7 - 6$
$\qquad\qquad = 10 - 6$
$\qquad\qquad = 4$

87. $3 - 5(-4 - 2) = 3 - 5(-6)$
$\qquad\qquad = 3 - (-30)$
$\qquad\qquad = 3 + 30$
$\qquad\qquad = 33$

88. $3 - 9(-1 - 6) = 3 - 9(-7)$
$\qquad\qquad = 3 - (-63)$
$\qquad\qquad = 3 + 63$
$\qquad\qquad = 66$

89. $(2 - 6)(-3 - 5) = (-4)(-8) = 32$

90. $9 - 5(6 - 4) - 10 = 9 - 5(2) - 10$
$\qquad\qquad = 9 - 10 - 10$
$\qquad\qquad = -1 - 10$
$\qquad\qquad = -11$

91. $3(-2)^2 - 4(-3)^2 = 3(4) - 4(9)$
$\qquad\qquad = 12 - 36$
$\qquad\qquad = -24$

92. $5(-3)^2 - 2(-2)^3 = 5(9) - 2(-8)$
$\qquad\qquad = 45 - (-16)$
$\qquad\qquad = 45 + 16$
$\qquad\qquad = 61$

93. $(2 - 6)^2 - (3 - 7)^2 = (-4)^2 - (-4)^2$
$\qquad\qquad = 16 - 16$
$\qquad\qquad = 0$

94. $(4 - 6)^2 - (5 - 9)^3 = (-2)^2 - (-4)^3$
$\qquad\qquad = 4 - (-64)$
$\qquad\qquad = 4 + 64$
$\qquad\qquad = 68$

95. $6(3 - 5)^3 - 2(1 - 3)^3 = 6(-2)^3 - 2(-2)^3$
$\qquad\qquad = 6(-8) - 2(-8)$
$\qquad\qquad = -48 + 16$
$\qquad\qquad = -32$

96. $-3(-6 + 8)^3 - 5(-3 + 5)^3 = -3(2)^3 - 5(2)^3$
$\qquad\qquad = -3(8) - 5(8)$
$\qquad\qquad = -24 - 40$
$\qquad\qquad = -64$

97. $8^2 - 16 \div 2^2 \cdot 4 - 3 = 64 - 16 \div 4 \cdot 4 - 3$
$\qquad\qquad = 64 - 4 \cdot 4 - 3$
$\qquad\qquad = 64 - 16 - 3$
$\qquad\qquad = 45$

98. $10^2 - 100 \div 5^2 \cdot 2 - (-3)$

$= 10^2 - 100 \div 25 \cdot 2 - (-3)$

$= 100 - 4 \cdot 2 + 3$

$= 100 - 8 + 3$

$= 92 + 3$

$= 95$

99. $-2°F$

100. $-7°F$

101. The high temperature was $-56 + 100 = 44$ degrees.

102. The high temperature was $-4 + 49 = 45$ degrees.

103. The difference in elevation $= 19,321 - (-436)$
$19,321 + 436 = 19,757$ feet.

104. The difference in elevation $= 14,494 - (-282)$
$14,494 + 282 = 14,776$ feet.

105. $2,025,200 - 1,788,800 = 236,400$ which represents a surplus.

106. $1,946,100 - 2,052,300 = -106,200$ which represents a deficit.

107. The average low in March is $2 - (-19) = 21$ degrees warmer than February's.

108. The average low in October is $6 - (-12) = 18$ degrees warmer than November's.

109. The average low in February is $-19 - (-22) = 3$ degrees warmer than January's.

110. The average low in November is $-12 - (-19) = 7$ degrees warmer than December's.

111. The difference in Ford's profits in 1988 and their losses in 2002 was about $22 - (-1) = 23$ billion.

112. The difference in Ford's losses in 2002 and their losses in 2001 was about $-1 - (-5) = 4$ billion.

113-121. Answers will vary.

122. $8 - 2 \cdot (3 - 4) = 10$

123. $(8 - 2) \cdot 3 - 4 = 14$

124. -7

125. -36

126. 150

Check Points 5.3

1. $72 = 2^3 \cdot 3^2$

$90 = 2 \cdot 5 \cdot 3^2$

Greatest Common Divisor is $2 \cdot 3^2$ or 18.

$\dfrac{72}{90} = \dfrac{72 \div 18}{90 \div 18} = \dfrac{4}{5}$

2. $2\dfrac{5}{8} = \dfrac{8 \cdot 2 + 5}{8} = \dfrac{16 + 5}{8} = \dfrac{21}{8}$

3. $\dfrac{5}{3} = 1\dfrac{2}{3}$

4. a. $\dfrac{3}{8} = 0.375$

$$
\begin{array}{r}
0.375 \\
8\overline{)3.000} \\
24 \\
\hline
60 \\
56 \\
\hline
40 \\
40 \\
\hline
0
\end{array}
$$

b. $\dfrac{5}{11} = 0.\overline{45}$

$$
\begin{array}{r}
0.4545\ldots \\
11\overline{)5.0000} \\
44 \\
\hline
60 \\
55 \\
\hline
50 \\
44 \\
\hline
60 \\
55 \\
\hline
5
\end{array}
$$

5. a. $0.9 = \dfrac{9}{10}$

b. $0.86 = \dfrac{86}{100} = \dfrac{86 \div 2}{100 \div 2} = \dfrac{43}{50}$

c. $0.053 = \dfrac{53}{1000}$

6. $n = 0.\overline{2}$

$n = 0.22222\ldots$

$10n = 2.22222\ldots$

$10n = 2.2222\ldots$

$\underline{-n = 0.2222\ldots}$

$9n = 2.0$

$n = \dfrac{2}{9}$

7. $n = 0.\overline{79}$

$n = 0.7979\ldots$

$100n = 79.7979\ldots$

$100n = 79.7979\ldots$

$\underline{-\quad n = 0.7979\ldots}$

$99n = 79$

$n = \dfrac{79}{99}$

8. a. $\dfrac{4}{11}\cdot\dfrac{2}{3} = \dfrac{8}{33}$

b. $\left(-\dfrac{3}{7}\right)\left(-\dfrac{14}{4}\right) = \dfrac{42}{28} = \dfrac{42\div14}{28\div14} = \dfrac{3}{2}$ or $1\dfrac{1}{2}$

c. $\left(3\dfrac{2}{5}\right)\left(1\dfrac{1}{2}\right) = \dfrac{17}{5}\cdot\dfrac{3}{2} = \dfrac{51}{10}$ or $5\dfrac{1}{10}$

9. a. $\dfrac{9}{11}\div\dfrac{5}{4} = \dfrac{9}{11}\cdot\dfrac{4}{5} = \dfrac{36}{55}$

b. $-\dfrac{8}{15}\div\dfrac{2}{5} = -\dfrac{8}{15}\cdot\dfrac{5}{2} = -\dfrac{40}{30} = -\dfrac{4}{3}$ or $-1\dfrac{1}{3}$

c. $3\dfrac{3}{8}\div2\dfrac{1}{4} = \dfrac{27}{8}\div\dfrac{9}{4} = \dfrac{27}{8}\cdot\dfrac{4}{9} = \dfrac{108}{72} = \dfrac{3}{2}$ or $1\dfrac{1}{2}$

10. a. $\dfrac{5}{12}+\dfrac{3}{12} = \dfrac{5+3}{12} = \dfrac{8}{12} = \dfrac{2}{3}$

b. $\dfrac{7}{4}-\dfrac{1}{4} = \dfrac{7-1}{4} = \dfrac{6}{4} = \dfrac{3}{2}$ or $1\dfrac{1}{2}$

c. $-3\dfrac{3}{8}-\left(-1\dfrac{1}{8}\right) = -\dfrac{27}{8}-\left(-\dfrac{9}{8}\right)$

$= -\dfrac{27}{8}+\dfrac{9}{8}$

$= \dfrac{-27+9}{8}$

$= \dfrac{-18}{8}$

$= -\dfrac{9}{4}$

or $-2\dfrac{1}{4}$

11. $\dfrac{1}{5}+\dfrac{3}{4} = \dfrac{1}{5}\cdot\dfrac{4}{4}+\dfrac{3}{4}\cdot\dfrac{5}{5} = \dfrac{4}{20}+\dfrac{15}{20} = \dfrac{19}{20}$

12. $\dfrac{3}{10}-\dfrac{7}{12} = \dfrac{3}{10}\cdot\dfrac{6}{6}-\dfrac{7}{12}\cdot\dfrac{5}{5} = \dfrac{18}{60}-\dfrac{35}{60} = -\dfrac{17}{60}$

13. First, find the sum:

$\dfrac{1}{3}+\dfrac{1}{2} = \dfrac{1}{3}\cdot\dfrac{2}{2}+\dfrac{1}{2}\cdot\dfrac{3}{3} = \dfrac{2}{6}+\dfrac{3}{6} = \dfrac{5}{6}$

Next, divide by 2: $\dfrac{5}{6}\div\dfrac{2}{1} = \dfrac{5}{6}\cdot\dfrac{1}{2} = \dfrac{5}{12}$

14. Amount of eggs needed

$= \dfrac{\text{desired serving size}}{\text{recipe serving size}}\times\text{eggs in recipe}$

$= \dfrac{7\ \text{dozen}}{5\ \text{dozen}}\times2\ \text{eggs}$

$= \dfrac{14}{5}\ \text{eggs}$

$= 2\dfrac{4}{5}\ \text{eggs}$

$\approx 3\ \text{eggs}$

Exercise Set 5.3

1. $10 = 2 \cdot 5$

$15 = 3 \cdot 5$

Greatest Common Divisor is 5.

$\dfrac{10}{15} = \dfrac{10 \div 5}{15 \div 5} = \dfrac{2}{3}$

2. $18 = 2 \cdot 3^2$

$45 = 3^2 \cdot 5$

Greatest Common Divisor is 3^2 or 9.

$\dfrac{18}{45} = \dfrac{18 \div 9}{45 \div 9} = \dfrac{2}{5}$

3. $15 = 3 \cdot 5$

$18 = 2 \cdot 3^2$

Greatest Common Divisor is 3.

$\dfrac{15}{18} = \dfrac{15 \div 3}{18 \div 3} = \dfrac{5}{6}$

4. $16 = 2^4$

$64 = 2^6$

Greatest Common Divisor is 2^4 or 16.

$\dfrac{16}{64} = \dfrac{16 \div 16}{64 \div 16} = \dfrac{1}{4}$

5. $24 = 2^3 \cdot 3$

$42 = 2 \cdot 3 \cdot 7$

Greatest Common Divisor is $2 \cdot 3$ or 6.

$\dfrac{24}{42} = \dfrac{24 \div 6}{42 \div 6} = \dfrac{4}{7}$

6. $32 = 2^5$

$80 = 2^4 \cdot 5$

Greatest Common Divisor is 2^4 or 16.

$\dfrac{32}{80} = \dfrac{32 \div 16}{80 \div 16} = \dfrac{2}{5}$

7. $60 = 2^2 \cdot 3 \cdot 5$

$108 = 2^2 \cdot 3^3$

Greatest Common Divisor is $2^2 \cdot 3$ or 12.

$\dfrac{60}{108} = \dfrac{60 \div 12}{108 \div 12} = \dfrac{5}{9}$

8. $112 = 2^4 \cdot 7$

$128 = 2^7$

Greatest Common Divisor is 2^4 or 16.

$\dfrac{112}{128} = \dfrac{112 \div 16}{128 \div 16} = \dfrac{7}{8}$

9. $342 = 2 \cdot 3^2 \cdot 19$

$380 = 2^2 \cdot 5 \cdot 19$

Greatest Common Divisor is $2 \cdot 19$ or 38.

$\dfrac{342}{380} = \dfrac{342 \div 38}{380 \div 38} = \dfrac{9}{10}$

10. $210 = 2 \cdot 3 \cdot 5 \cdot 7$

$252 = 2^2 \cdot 3^2 \cdot 7$

Greatest Common Divisor is $2 \cdot 3 \cdot 7$ or 42.

$\dfrac{210}{252} = \dfrac{210 \div 42}{252 \div 42} = \dfrac{5}{6}$

11. $308 = 2^2 \cdot 7 \cdot 11$

$418 = 2 \cdot 11 \cdot 19$

Greatest Common Divisor is $2 \cdot 11$ or 22.

$\dfrac{308}{418} = \dfrac{308 \div 22}{418 \div 22} = \dfrac{14}{19}$

12. $144 = 2^4 \cdot 3^2$

$300 = 2^2 \cdot 3 \cdot 5^2$

Greatest Common Divisor is $2^2 \cdot 3$ or 12.

$\dfrac{144}{300} = \dfrac{144 \div 12}{300 \div 12} = \dfrac{12}{25}$

13. $2\dfrac{3}{8} = \dfrac{8 \cdot 2 + 3}{8} = \dfrac{16 + 3}{8} = \dfrac{19}{8}$

14. $2\dfrac{7}{9} = \dfrac{9 \cdot 2 + 7}{9} = \dfrac{18 + 7}{9} = \dfrac{25}{9}$

15. $-7\dfrac{3}{5} = -\dfrac{5 \cdot 7 + 3}{5} = -\dfrac{35 + 3}{5} = -\dfrac{38}{5}$

16. $-6\dfrac{2}{5} = -\dfrac{5 \cdot 6 + 2}{5} = -\dfrac{30 + 2}{5} = -\dfrac{32}{5}$

17. $12\dfrac{7}{16} = \dfrac{16 \cdot 12 + 7}{16} = \dfrac{192 + 7}{16} = \dfrac{199}{16}$

18. $11\dfrac{5}{16} = \dfrac{16 \cdot 11 + 5}{16} = \dfrac{176 + 5}{16} = \dfrac{181}{16}$

19. $\dfrac{23}{5} = 4\dfrac{3}{5}$

20. $\dfrac{47}{8} = 5\dfrac{7}{8}$

21. $-\dfrac{76}{9} = -8\dfrac{4}{9}$

22. $-\dfrac{59}{9} = -6\dfrac{5}{9}$

23. $\dfrac{711}{20} = 35\dfrac{11}{20}$

24. $\dfrac{788}{25} = 31\dfrac{13}{25}$

25. $\dfrac{3}{4} = 0.75$

$$
\begin{array}{r}
0.75 \\
4\overline{)3.00} \\
28 \\
\hline
20 \\
20 \\
\hline
0
\end{array}
$$

26. $\dfrac{3}{5} = 0.6$

$$
\begin{array}{r}
0.6 \\
5\overline{)3.0} \\
30 \\
\hline
0
\end{array}
$$

27. $\dfrac{7}{20} = 0.35$

$$
\begin{array}{r}
0.35 \\
20\overline{)7.00} \\
60 \\
\hline
100 \\
100 \\
\hline
0
\end{array}
$$

28. $\dfrac{3}{20} = 0.15$

$$
\begin{array}{r}
0.15 \\
20\overline{)3.00} \\
20 \\
\hline
100 \\
100 \\
\hline
0
\end{array}
$$

29. $\dfrac{7}{8} = 0.875$

$$
\begin{array}{r}
0.875 \\
8\overline{)7.000} \\
64 \\
\hline
60 \\
56 \\
\hline
40 \\
40 \\
\hline
0
\end{array}
$$

30. $\dfrac{5}{16} = 0.3125$

$$
\begin{array}{r}
0.3125 \\
16\overline{)5.0000} \\
48 \\
\hline
20 \\
16 \\
\hline
40 \\
32 \\
\hline
80
\end{array}
$$

31. $\dfrac{9}{11} = 0.\overline{81}$

$$
\begin{array}{r}
0.8181\ldots \\
11\overline{)9.0000} \\
88 \\
\hline
20 \\
11 \\
\hline
90 \\
88 \\
\hline
20 \\
11 \\
\hline
9
\end{array}
$$

32. $\dfrac{3}{11} = 0.\overline{27}$

$$
\begin{array}{r}
0.2727\ldots \\
11\overline{)3.0000} \\
22 \\
\hline
80 \\
77 \\
\hline
30 \\
22 \\
\hline
80 \\
77 \\
\hline
3
\end{array}
$$

33. $\dfrac{22}{7} = 3.\overline{142857}$

$$
\begin{array}{r}
3.142857\ldots \\
7)\overline{22.000000} \\
\underline{21} \\
10 \\
\underline{7} \\
\overline{30} \\
\underline{28} \\
\overline{20} \\
\underline{14} \\
\overline{60} \\
\underline{56} \\
\overline{40} \\
\underline{35} \\
\overline{50} \\
\underline{49} \\
\overline{10}
\end{array}
$$

34. $\dfrac{20}{3} = 6.\overline{6}$

$$
\begin{array}{r}
6.66\ldots \\
3)\overline{20.00} \\
\underline{18} \\
20 \\
\underline{18} \\
\overline{20} \\
\underline{18} \\
\overline{2}
\end{array}
$$

35. $\dfrac{2}{7} = 0.\overline{285714}$

$$
\begin{array}{r}
0.2857142\ldots \\
7)\overline{2.000000} \\
\underline{14} \\
60 \\
\underline{56} \\
\overline{40} \\
\underline{35} \\
\overline{50} \\
\underline{49} \\
\overline{10} \\
\underline{7} \\
\overline{30} \\
\underline{28} \\
\overline{20} \\
\underline{14} \\
\overline{6}
\end{array}
$$

36. $\dfrac{5}{7} = 0.\overline{714285}$

$$
\begin{array}{r}
0.7142857\ldots \\
7)\overline{5.000000} \\
\underline{49} \\
10 \\
\underline{7} \\
\overline{30} \\
\underline{28} \\
\overline{20} \\
\underline{14} \\
\overline{60} \\
\underline{56} \\
\overline{40} \\
\underline{35} \\
\overline{50} \\
\underline{49} \\
\overline{1}
\end{array}
$$

37. $0.3 = \dfrac{3}{10}$

38. $0.9 = \dfrac{9}{10}$

39. $0.4 = \dfrac{4}{10} = \dfrac{4 \div 2}{10 \div 2} = \dfrac{2}{5}$

40. $0.6 = \dfrac{6}{10} = \dfrac{6 \div 2}{10 \div 2} = \dfrac{3}{5}$

41. $0.39 = \dfrac{39}{100}$

42. $0.59 = \dfrac{59}{100}$

43. $0.82 = \dfrac{82}{100} = \dfrac{82 \div 2}{100 \div 2} = \dfrac{41}{50}$

44. $0.64 = \dfrac{64}{100}$

$64 = 2^6$

$100 = 2^2 \cdot 5^2$

Greatest Common Divisor is 2^2 or 4.

$\dfrac{64}{100} = \dfrac{64 \div 4}{100 \div 4} = \dfrac{16}{25}$

45. $0.725 = \dfrac{725}{1000}$

$725 = 5^2 \cdot 29$

$1000 = 2^3 \cdot 5^3$

Greatest Common Divisor is 5^2 or 25.

$\dfrac{725}{1000} = \dfrac{725 \div 25}{1000 \div 25} = \dfrac{29}{40}$

46. $0.625 = \dfrac{625}{1000}$

$625 = 5^4$

$1000 = 2^3 \cdot 5^3$

Greatest Common Divisor is 5^3 or 125.

$\dfrac{625 \div 125}{1000 \div 125} = \dfrac{5}{8}$

47. $0.5399 = \dfrac{5399}{10,000}$

48. $0.7006 = \dfrac{7006}{10,000}$

$7006 = 2 \cdot 31 \cdot 113$

$10,000 = 2^4 \cdot 5^4$

Greatest Common Divisor is 2.

$\dfrac{7006}{10,000} = \dfrac{7006 \div 2}{10,000 \div 2} = \dfrac{3503}{5000}$

49. $n = 0.777\ldots$
$10n = 7.777\ldots$

$10n = 7.777\ldots$
$\underline{-n = 0.777\ldots}$
$9n = 7$

$n = \dfrac{7}{9}$

50. $n = 0.1111\ldots$
$10n = 1.1111\ldots$

$10n = 1.1111\ldots$
$\underline{-n = 0.1111\ldots}$
$9n = 1$

$n = \dfrac{1}{9}$

51. $n = 0.999\ldots$
$10n = 9.999\ldots$

$10n = 9.999\ldots$
$\underline{-n = 0.999\ldots}$
$9n = 9$

$n = 1$

52. $n = 0.\overline{3}\ldots$
$10n = 3.333\ldots$

$10n = 3.3333\ldots$
$\underline{-n = 0.3333\ldots}$
$9n = 3.0$

$n = \dfrac{3}{9}$ or $\dfrac{1}{3}$

53. $n = 0.3636\ldots$
$100n = 36.3636\ldots$

$100n = 36.3636\ldots$
$\underline{-n = 0.3636\ldots}$
$99n = 36$

$n = \dfrac{36}{99}$ or $\dfrac{4}{11}$

54. $n = 0.8181\ldots$
$100n = 81.8181\ldots$

$100n = 81.8181\ldots$
$\underline{-n = 0.8181\ldots}$
$99n = 81$

$n = \dfrac{81}{99}$ or $\dfrac{9}{11}$

55. $n = 0.257257\ldots$
$1000n = 257.257257\ldots$

$1000n = 257.257257\ldots$
$\underline{-n = .257257\ldots}$
$999n = 257$

$n = \dfrac{257}{999}$

56.
$$n = 0.529529\ldots$$
$$1000n = 529.529529\ldots$$

$$1000n = 529.529529\ldots$$
$$\underline{-n = 0.529529\ldots}$$
$$999n = 529$$
$$n = \frac{529}{999}$$

57. $\dfrac{3}{8} \cdot \dfrac{7}{11} = \dfrac{3 \cdot 7}{8 \cdot 11} = \dfrac{21}{88}$

58. $\dfrac{5}{8} \cdot \dfrac{3}{11} = \dfrac{5 \cdot 3}{8 \cdot 11} = \dfrac{15}{88}$

59. $\left(-\dfrac{1}{10}\right)\left(\dfrac{7}{12}\right) = \dfrac{(-1)(7)}{10 \cdot 12} = \dfrac{-7}{120} = -\dfrac{7}{120}$

60. $\left(-\dfrac{1}{8}\right)\left(\dfrac{5}{9}\right) = \dfrac{(-1)(5)}{8 \cdot 9} = \dfrac{-5}{72} = -\dfrac{5}{72}$

61. $\left(-\dfrac{2}{3}\right)\left(-\dfrac{9}{4}\right) = \dfrac{(-2)(-9)}{3 \cdot 4} = \dfrac{18}{12} = \dfrac{3}{2}$

62. $\left(-\dfrac{5}{4}\right)\left(-\dfrac{6}{7}\right) = \dfrac{(-5)(-6)}{4 \cdot 7} = \dfrac{30}{28} = \dfrac{15}{14}$

63. $\left(3\dfrac{3}{4}\right)\left(1\dfrac{3}{5}\right) = \dfrac{15}{4} \cdot \dfrac{8}{5} = \dfrac{120}{20} = \dfrac{6}{1} = 6$

64. $\left(2\dfrac{4}{5}\right)\left(1\dfrac{1}{4}\right) = \dfrac{14}{5} \cdot \dfrac{5}{4} = \dfrac{70}{20} = \dfrac{7}{2}$ or $3\dfrac{1}{2}$

65. $\dfrac{5}{4} \div \dfrac{3}{8} = \dfrac{5}{4} \cdot \dfrac{8}{3} = \dfrac{5 \cdot 8}{4 \cdot 3} = \dfrac{40}{12} = \dfrac{10}{3}$

66. $\dfrac{5}{8} \div \dfrac{4}{3} = \dfrac{5}{8} \cdot \dfrac{3}{4} = \dfrac{5 \cdot 3}{8 \cdot 4} = \dfrac{15}{32}$

67. $-\dfrac{7}{8} \div \dfrac{15}{16} = -\dfrac{7}{8} \cdot \dfrac{16}{15}$

$$= \dfrac{(-7)(16)}{8 \cdot 15}$$
$$= \dfrac{-112}{120}$$
$$= -\dfrac{14}{15}$$

68. $-\dfrac{13}{20} \div \dfrac{4}{5} = -\dfrac{13}{20} \cdot \dfrac{5}{4}$

$$= \dfrac{(-13)(5)}{20 \cdot 4}$$
$$= \dfrac{-65}{80}$$
$$= -\dfrac{65}{80}$$
$$= -\dfrac{13}{16}$$

69. $6\dfrac{3}{5} \div 1\dfrac{1}{10} = \dfrac{33}{5} \div \dfrac{11}{10} = \dfrac{33}{5} \cdot \dfrac{10}{11} = \dfrac{330}{55} = \dfrac{6}{1} = 6$

70. $1\dfrac{3}{4} \div 2\dfrac{5}{8} = \dfrac{7}{4} \div \dfrac{21}{8} = \dfrac{7}{4} \cdot \dfrac{8}{21} = \dfrac{56}{84} = \dfrac{2}{3}$

71. $\dfrac{2}{11} + \dfrac{3}{11} = \dfrac{2+3}{11} = \dfrac{5}{11}$

72. $\dfrac{5}{13} + \dfrac{2}{13} = \dfrac{5+2}{13} = \dfrac{7}{13}$

73. $\dfrac{5}{6} - \dfrac{1}{6} = \dfrac{5-1}{6} = \dfrac{4}{6} = \dfrac{2}{3}$

74. $\dfrac{7}{12} - \dfrac{5}{12} = \dfrac{7-5}{12} = \dfrac{2}{12} = \dfrac{1}{6}$

75. $\dfrac{7}{12} - \left(-\dfrac{1}{12}\right) = \dfrac{7}{12} + \dfrac{1}{12} = \dfrac{7+1}{12} = \dfrac{8}{12} = \dfrac{2}{3}$

76. $\dfrac{5}{16} - \left(-\dfrac{5}{16}\right) = \dfrac{5}{16} + \dfrac{5}{16} = \dfrac{5+5}{16} = \dfrac{10}{16} = \dfrac{5}{8}$

77. $\dfrac{1}{2} + \dfrac{1}{5} = \left(\dfrac{1}{2}\right)\left(\dfrac{5}{5}\right) + \left(\dfrac{1}{5}\right)\left(\dfrac{2}{2}\right)$

$$= \dfrac{5}{10} + \dfrac{2}{10}$$
$$= \dfrac{5+2}{10}$$
$$= \dfrac{7}{10}$$

78. $\frac{1}{3}+\frac{1}{5}=\left(\frac{1}{3}\right)\left(\frac{5}{5}\right)+\left(\frac{1}{5}\right)\left(\frac{3}{3}\right)$

$\qquad =\frac{5}{15}+\frac{3}{15}$

$\qquad =\frac{5+3}{15}$

$\qquad =\frac{8}{15}$

79. $\frac{3}{4}+\frac{3}{20}=\left(\frac{3}{4}\right)\left(\frac{5}{5}\right)+\frac{3}{20}$

$\qquad =\frac{15}{20}+\frac{3}{20}$

$\qquad =\frac{15+3}{20}$

$\qquad =\frac{18}{20}$

$\qquad =\frac{9}{10}$

80. $\frac{2}{5}+\frac{2}{15}=\left(\frac{2}{5}\right)\left(\frac{3}{3}\right)+\frac{2}{15}=\frac{6}{15}+\frac{2}{15}=\frac{6+2}{15}=\frac{8}{15}$

81. $\frac{5}{24}+\frac{7}{30}=\left(\frac{5}{24}\right)\left(\frac{5}{5}\right)+\left(\frac{7}{30}\right)\left(\frac{4}{4}\right)$

$\qquad =\frac{25}{120}+\frac{28}{120}$

$\qquad =\frac{25+28}{120}$

$\qquad =\frac{53}{120}$

82. $\frac{7}{108}+\frac{55}{144}$

$108=2^2\cdot3^3$

$144=2^4\cdot3^2$

Least Common Multiple: $2^4\cdot3^3=432$

$\frac{7}{108}+\frac{55}{144}=\left(\frac{7}{108}\right)\left(\frac{4}{4}\right)+\left(\frac{55}{144}\right)\left(\frac{3}{3}\right)$

$\qquad =\frac{28}{432}+\frac{165}{432}$

$\qquad =\frac{28+165}{432}=\frac{193}{432}$

83. $\frac{13}{18}-\frac{2}{9}=\frac{13}{18}-\frac{2}{9}\left(\frac{2}{2}\right)$

$\qquad =\frac{13}{18}-\frac{4}{18}$

$\qquad =\frac{13-4}{18}$

$\qquad =\frac{9}{18}$

$\qquad =\frac{1}{2}$

84. $\frac{13}{15}-\frac{2}{45}=\left(\frac{13}{15}\right)\left(\frac{3}{3}\right)-\frac{2}{45}=\frac{39}{45}-\frac{2}{45}=\frac{39-2}{45}$

$\qquad =\frac{37}{45}$

85. $\frac{4}{3}-\frac{3}{4}=\frac{4}{3}\left(\frac{4}{4}\right)-\frac{3}{4}\left(\frac{3}{3}\right)$

$\qquad =\frac{16}{12}-\frac{9}{12}$

$\qquad =\frac{16-9}{12}$

$\qquad =\frac{7}{12}$

86. $\frac{3}{2}-\frac{2}{3}=\frac{3}{2}\left(\frac{3}{3}\right)-\frac{2}{3}\left(\frac{2}{2}\right)=\frac{9}{6}-\frac{4}{6}=\frac{9-4}{6}=\frac{5}{6}$

87. $\frac{1}{15}-\frac{27}{50}$

$15=3\cdot5$

$50=2\cdot5^2$

Least Common Multiple is $2\cdot3\cdot5^2=6\cdot25=150$

$\frac{1}{15}\left(\frac{10}{10}\right)-\frac{27}{50}\left(\frac{3}{3}\right)=\frac{10}{150}-\frac{81}{150}$

$\qquad =\frac{10-81}{150}$

$\qquad =-\frac{71}{150}$

88. $\dfrac{4}{15} - \dfrac{1}{6} = \dfrac{4}{15}\left(\dfrac{2}{2}\right) - \dfrac{1}{6}\left(\dfrac{5}{5}\right)$

$\qquad = \dfrac{8}{30} - \dfrac{5}{30}$

$\qquad = \dfrac{8-5}{30}$

$\qquad = \dfrac{3}{30}$

$\qquad = \dfrac{1}{10}$

89. $3\dfrac{3}{4} - 2\dfrac{1}{3} = 3\dfrac{9}{12} - 2\dfrac{4}{12} = 1\dfrac{5}{12}$

90. $3\dfrac{2}{3} - 2\dfrac{1}{2} = 3\dfrac{4}{6} - 2\dfrac{3}{6} = 1\dfrac{1}{6}$

91. $\left(\dfrac{1}{2} - \dfrac{1}{3}\right) \div \dfrac{5}{8} = \left[\left(\dfrac{1}{2}\right)\left(\dfrac{3}{3}\right) - \dfrac{1}{3}\left(\dfrac{2}{2}\right)\right] \div \dfrac{5}{8}$

$\qquad = \left(\dfrac{3}{6} - \dfrac{2}{6}\right) \div \dfrac{5}{8}$

$\qquad = \dfrac{1}{6} \div \dfrac{5}{8}$

$\qquad = \dfrac{1}{6} \cdot \dfrac{8}{5}$

$\qquad = \dfrac{1 \cdot 8}{6 \cdot 5}$

$\qquad = \dfrac{8}{30}$

$\qquad = \dfrac{4}{15}$

92. $\left(\dfrac{1}{2} + \dfrac{1}{4}\right) \div \left(\dfrac{1}{2} + \dfrac{1}{3}\right) = \left(\dfrac{1}{2} \cdot \dfrac{2}{2} + \dfrac{1}{4}\right) \div \left(\dfrac{1}{2} \cdot \dfrac{3}{3} + \dfrac{1}{3} \cdot \dfrac{2}{2}\right)$

$\qquad = \left(\dfrac{2}{4} + \dfrac{1}{4}\right) \div \left(\dfrac{3}{6} + \dfrac{2}{6}\right)$

$\qquad = \dfrac{3}{4} \div \dfrac{5}{6}$

$\qquad = \dfrac{3}{4} \cdot \dfrac{6}{5}$

$\qquad = \dfrac{3 \cdot 6}{4 \cdot 5}$

$\qquad = \dfrac{18}{20}$

$\qquad = \dfrac{9}{10}$

93. $\dfrac{1}{4} + \dfrac{1}{3} = \left(\dfrac{1}{4}\right)\left(\dfrac{3}{3}\right) + \left(\dfrac{1}{3}\right)\left(\dfrac{4}{4}\right)$

$\qquad = \dfrac{3}{12} + \dfrac{4}{12}$

$\qquad = \dfrac{3+4}{12}$

$\qquad = \dfrac{7}{12}$

$\dfrac{7}{12} \div 2 = \dfrac{7}{12} \cdot \dfrac{1}{2} = \dfrac{7}{24}$

94. $\dfrac{2}{3} + \dfrac{5}{6} = \left(\dfrac{2}{3}\right)\left(\dfrac{2}{2}\right) + \dfrac{5}{6}$

$\qquad = \dfrac{4}{6} + \dfrac{5}{6}$

$\qquad = \dfrac{4+5}{6}$

$\qquad = \dfrac{9}{6}$

$\qquad = \dfrac{3}{2}$

$\dfrac{3}{2} \div 2 = \dfrac{3}{2} \cdot \dfrac{1}{2} = \dfrac{3}{4}$

95. $\dfrac{1}{2} + \dfrac{2}{3} = \left(\dfrac{1}{2}\right)\left(\dfrac{3}{3}\right) + \left(\dfrac{2}{3}\right)\left(\dfrac{2}{2}\right)$

$\qquad = \dfrac{3}{6} + \dfrac{4}{6}$

$\qquad = \dfrac{3+4}{6}$

$\qquad = \dfrac{7}{6}$

$\dfrac{7}{6} \div 2 = \dfrac{7}{6} \cdot \dfrac{1}{2} = \dfrac{7}{12}$

96. $\dfrac{3}{5} + \dfrac{2}{3} = \left(\dfrac{3}{5}\right)\left(\dfrac{3}{3}\right) + \left(\dfrac{2}{3}\right)\left(\dfrac{5}{5}\right)$

$\qquad = \dfrac{9}{15} + \dfrac{10}{15}$

$\qquad = \dfrac{9+10}{15}$

$\qquad = \dfrac{19}{15}$

$\dfrac{19}{15} \div 2 = \dfrac{19}{15} \cdot \dfrac{1}{2} = \dfrac{19}{30}$

97. $-\dfrac{2}{3}+\left(-\dfrac{5}{6}\right)=\left(-\dfrac{2}{3}\right)\left(\dfrac{2}{2}\right)-\dfrac{5}{6}$

$\qquad =\dfrac{-4}{6}-\dfrac{5}{6}$

$\qquad =\dfrac{-4-5}{6}$

$\qquad =-\dfrac{9}{6}$

$-\dfrac{9}{6}\div 2=-\dfrac{9}{6}\cdot\dfrac{1}{2}=-\dfrac{9}{12}=-\dfrac{3}{4}$

98. $-4+\left(-\dfrac{7}{2}\right)=(-4)\left(\dfrac{2}{2}\right)-\left(\dfrac{7}{2}\right)$

$\qquad =-\dfrac{8}{2}-\dfrac{7}{2}$

$\qquad =-\dfrac{8+7}{2}$

$\qquad =-\dfrac{15}{2}$

$-\dfrac{15}{2}\div 2=-\dfrac{15}{2}\cdot\dfrac{1}{2}=-\dfrac{15}{4}$

99. $\dfrac{13}{4}+\dfrac{13}{9}=\dfrac{13\cdot 9}{4\cdot 9}+\dfrac{13\cdot 4}{9\cdot 4}$

$\qquad =\dfrac{117}{36}+\dfrac{52}{36}$

$\qquad =\dfrac{117+52}{36}$

$\qquad =\dfrac{169}{36}$

$\dfrac{13}{4}\times\dfrac{13}{9}=\dfrac{13\cdot 13}{4\cdot 9}$

$\qquad =\dfrac{169}{36}$

Both are equal to $\dfrac{169}{36}$

100. $\dfrac{169}{30}+\dfrac{13}{15}=\dfrac{169}{30}+\left(\dfrac{13}{15}\right)\left(\dfrac{2}{2}\right)$

$\qquad =\dfrac{169}{30}+\dfrac{26}{30}$

$\qquad =\dfrac{169+26}{30}$

$\qquad =\dfrac{195}{30}$

$\qquad =\dfrac{39}{6}$

$\qquad =\dfrac{13}{2}$

$\dfrac{169}{30}\div\dfrac{13}{15}=\dfrac{169}{30}\cdot\dfrac{15}{13}$

$\qquad =\dfrac{169\cdot 15}{30\cdot 13}$

$\qquad =\dfrac{169\cdot\overset{1}{\cancel{15}}}{\underset{2}{\cancel{30}}\cdot 13}$

$\qquad =\dfrac{\overset{13}{\cancel{169}}\cdot 1}{2\cdot\underset{1}{\cancel{13}}}$

$\qquad =\dfrac{13\cdot 1}{2\cdot 1}$

$\qquad =\dfrac{13}{2}$

Both are equal to $\dfrac{13}{2}$

101. $\dfrac{86}{192}=\dfrac{43}{96}$

102. $\dfrac{48}{192}=\dfrac{1}{4}$

103. $3\dfrac{3}{10}-2\dfrac{1}{2}=3\dfrac{3}{10}-2\dfrac{5}{10}=2\dfrac{13}{10}-2\dfrac{5}{10}=\dfrac{8}{10}=\dfrac{4}{5}$

104. $4\dfrac{1}{5}-2\dfrac{1}{2}=4\dfrac{2}{10}-2\dfrac{5}{10}=3\dfrac{12}{10}-2\dfrac{5}{10}=1\dfrac{7}{10}$

105. $2\dfrac{4}{5}-1\dfrac{9}{10}=2\dfrac{8}{10}-1\dfrac{9}{10}=1\dfrac{18}{10}-1\dfrac{9}{10}=\dfrac{9}{10}$

106. $4\dfrac{1}{2}-1\dfrac{9}{10}=4\dfrac{5}{10}-1\dfrac{9}{10}=3\dfrac{15}{10}-1\dfrac{9}{10}=2\dfrac{6}{10}=2\dfrac{3}{5}$

107. Find $\dfrac{1}{2}$ of $\dfrac{3}{4}$ or divide $\dfrac{3}{4}$ by 2:

$\dfrac{3}{4}\div 2=\dfrac{3}{4}\cdot\dfrac{1}{2}=\dfrac{3}{8}$ cup

108. Find 3 times $\dfrac{3}{4}$ of a cup:

$3\cdot\dfrac{3}{4}=\dfrac{9}{4}$ cups $=2\dfrac{1}{4}$cups.

109. $2\dfrac{2}{3}\cdot\dfrac{11}{8}=\dfrac{8}{3}\cdot\dfrac{11}{8}=\dfrac{88}{24}=\dfrac{11}{3}$ or $3\dfrac{2}{3}$ cups of water.

110. $2\dfrac{2}{3}\cdot\dfrac{6}{8}=\dfrac{8}{3}\cdot\dfrac{6}{8}=\dfrac{48}{24}=2$ cups of water.

111. $1-\dfrac{5}{12}-\dfrac{1}{4}=\dfrac{12}{12}-\dfrac{5}{12}-\dfrac{3}{12}=\dfrac{4}{12}=\dfrac{1}{3}$ ownership.

112. $1-\dfrac{1}{4}-\dfrac{2}{5}-\dfrac{1}{10}=\dfrac{20}{20}-\dfrac{5}{20}-\dfrac{8}{20}-\dfrac{2}{20}=\dfrac{5}{20}=\dfrac{1}{4}$

113. The total distance is their sum:

$\dfrac{3}{4}+\dfrac{2}{5}=\dfrac{15}{20}+\dfrac{8}{20}=\dfrac{23}{20}$ miles.

The difference is the amount farther:

$\dfrac{3}{4}-\dfrac{2}{5}=\dfrac{15}{20}-\dfrac{8}{20}=\dfrac{7}{20}$ mile.

114. 40 hours at \$12 rate

6 hours at $\left(\dfrac{3}{2}\right)$\$12 rate or $\left(\dfrac{3}{2}\right)$\$12 $=\dfrac{\$36}{2}=\$18$

$40\cdot\$12+6\cdot\$18=\$480+\$108=\$588$

115. $\dfrac{3}{5}$ of the total goes to relatives, so there is $\dfrac{2}{5}$ of the estate left. $\dfrac{1}{4}$ of that $\dfrac{2}{5}$ goes for AIDS research:

$\dfrac{1}{4}\cdot\dfrac{2}{5}=\dfrac{2}{20}=\dfrac{1}{10}$

116. $2\dfrac{3}{8}\cdot 16=\dfrac{19}{8}\cdot\dfrac{16}{1}=\dfrac{304}{8}=38$ miles

117-128. Answers will vary.

129. 1st measure: $\dfrac{1}{4}+\dfrac{1}{4}+\dfrac{1}{8}+\dfrac{1}{8}=\dfrac{2}{8}+\dfrac{2}{8}+\dfrac{1}{8}+\dfrac{1}{8}=\dfrac{6}{8}=\dfrac{3}{4}$

2nd measure: $\dfrac{1}{4}+\dfrac{1}{4}+\dfrac{1}{4}=\dfrac{3}{4}$

3rd measure: $\dfrac{1}{4}+\dfrac{1}{8}+\dfrac{1}{8}+\dfrac{1}{8}+\dfrac{1}{8}=\dfrac{2}{8}+\dfrac{1}{8}+\dfrac{1}{8}+\dfrac{1}{8}+\dfrac{1}{8}=\dfrac{6}{8}=\dfrac{3}{4}$

4th measure: $\dfrac{1}{4}+\dfrac{1}{4}+\dfrac{1}{8}+\dfrac{1}{8}=\dfrac{2}{8}+\dfrac{2}{8}+\dfrac{1}{8}+\dfrac{1}{8}=\dfrac{6}{8}=\dfrac{3}{4}$

say does that   Star-span-gled   Ban-ner   yet   wave O'er the

130. Conjecture: The sums of $\frac{2}{3}$, $\frac{3}{4}$, and $\frac{4}{5}$ will be followed by a sum of $\frac{5}{6}$.

Verifiction: $\dfrac{1}{1\cdot 2}+\dfrac{1}{2\cdot 3}+\dfrac{1}{3\cdot 4}+\dfrac{1}{4\cdot 5}+\dfrac{1}{5\cdot 6}=\dfrac{1}{2}+\dfrac{1}{6}+\dfrac{1}{12}+\dfrac{1}{20}+\dfrac{1}{30}$

$=\dfrac{30}{60}+\dfrac{10}{60}+\dfrac{5}{60}+\dfrac{3}{60}+\dfrac{2}{60}$

$=\dfrac{50}{60}$

$=\dfrac{5}{6}$

131. a. $\dfrac{197}{800} = 0.24625$

b. $\dfrac{4539}{3125} = 1.45248$

c. $\dfrac{7}{6250} = 0.00112$

Check Points 5.4

1. a. $\sqrt{12} = \sqrt{4 \cdot 3} = \sqrt{4} \cdot \sqrt{3} = 2\sqrt{3}$

b. $\sqrt{60} = \sqrt{4 \cdot 15} = \sqrt{4} \cdot \sqrt{15} = 2\sqrt{15}$

c. $\sqrt{55}$ cannot be simplified.

2. a. $\sqrt{3} \cdot \sqrt{10} = \sqrt{3 \cdot 10} = \sqrt{30}$

b. $\sqrt{10} \cdot \sqrt{10} = \sqrt{10 \cdot 10} = \sqrt{100} = 10$

c. $\sqrt{6} \cdot \sqrt{2} = \sqrt{6 \cdot 2} = \sqrt{12} = \sqrt{4} \cdot \sqrt{3} = 2\sqrt{3}$

3. a. $\dfrac{\sqrt{80}}{\sqrt{5}} = \sqrt{\dfrac{80}{5}} = \sqrt{16} = 4$

b. $\dfrac{\sqrt{48}}{\sqrt{6}} = \sqrt{\dfrac{48}{6}} = \sqrt{8} = \sqrt{4} \cdot \sqrt{2} = 2\sqrt{2}$

4. a. $8\sqrt{3} + 10\sqrt{3} = (8 + 10)\sqrt{3} = 18\sqrt{3}$

b. $4\sqrt{13} - 9\sqrt{13} = (4 - 9)\sqrt{13} = -5\sqrt{13}$

c. $7\sqrt{10} + 2\sqrt{10} - \sqrt{10} = (7 + 2 - 1)\sqrt{10} = 8\sqrt{10}$

5. a. $\sqrt{3} + \sqrt{12} = \sqrt{3} + \sqrt{4} \cdot \sqrt{3} = \sqrt{3} + 2\sqrt{3} = 3\sqrt{3}$

b.
$$4\sqrt{8} - 7\sqrt{18}$$
$$= 4\sqrt{4 \cdot 2} - 7\sqrt{9 \cdot 2}$$
$$= 4 \cdot 2\sqrt{2} - 7 \cdot 3\sqrt{2}$$
$$= 8\sqrt{2} - 21\sqrt{2}$$
$$= (8 - 21)\sqrt{2}$$
$$= -13\sqrt{2}$$

6. a. $\dfrac{25}{\sqrt{10}} = \dfrac{25}{\sqrt{10}} \cdot \dfrac{\sqrt{10}}{\sqrt{10}} = \dfrac{25\sqrt{10}}{\sqrt{100}} = \dfrac{25\sqrt{10}}{10} = \dfrac{5\sqrt{10}}{2}$

b. $\sqrt{\dfrac{2}{7}} = \dfrac{\sqrt{2}}{\sqrt{7}} = \dfrac{\sqrt{2}}{\sqrt{7}} \cdot \dfrac{\sqrt{7}}{\sqrt{7}} = \dfrac{\sqrt{14}}{\sqrt{49}} = \dfrac{\sqrt{14}}{7}$

c. $\dfrac{5}{\sqrt{18}} = \dfrac{5}{\sqrt{18}} \cdot \dfrac{\sqrt{2}}{\sqrt{2}} = \dfrac{5\sqrt{2}}{\sqrt{36}} = \dfrac{5\sqrt{2}}{6}$

Exercise Set 5.4

1. $\sqrt{9} = 3$ because $3^2 = 9$.

2. $\sqrt{16} = 4$ because $4^2 = 16$.

3. $\sqrt{25} = 5$ because $5^2 = 25$.

4. $\sqrt{49} = 7$ because $7^2 = 49$.

5. $\sqrt{64} = 8$ because $8^2 = 64$.

6. $\sqrt{100} = 10$ because $10^2 = 100$.

7. $\sqrt{121} = 11$ because $11^2 = 121$.

8. $\sqrt{144} = 12$ because $12^2 = 144$.

9. $\sqrt{169} = 13$ because $13^2 = 169$.

10. $\sqrt{225} = 15$ because $15^2 = 225$.

11. a. $\sqrt{173} \approx 13.2$

b. $\sqrt{173} \approx 13.15$

c. $\sqrt{173} \approx 13.153$

12. a. $\sqrt{3176} \approx 56.4$

b. $\sqrt{3176} \approx 56.36$

c. $\sqrt{3176} \approx 56.356$

13. a. $\sqrt{17,761} \approx 133.3$

  b. $\sqrt{17,761} \approx 133.27$

  c. $\sqrt{17,761} \approx 133.270$

14. a. $\sqrt{779,264} \approx 882.8$

  b. $\sqrt{779,264} \approx 882.76$

  c. $\sqrt{779,264} \approx 882.759$

15. a. $\sqrt{\pi} \approx 1.8$

  b. $\sqrt{\pi} \approx 1.77$

  c. $\sqrt{\pi} \approx 1.772$

16. a. $\sqrt{2\pi} \approx 2.5$

  b. $\sqrt{2\pi} \approx 2.51$

  c. $\sqrt{2\pi} \approx 2.507$

17. $\sqrt{20} = \sqrt{4 \cdot 5} = \sqrt{4} \cdot \sqrt{5} = 2\sqrt{5}$

18. $\sqrt{50} = \sqrt{25 \cdot 2} = \sqrt{25} \cdot \sqrt{2} = 5\sqrt{2}$

19. $\sqrt{80} = \sqrt{16 \cdot 5} = \sqrt{16} \cdot \sqrt{5} = 4\sqrt{5}$

20. $\sqrt{12} = \sqrt{4 \cdot 3} = \sqrt{4} \cdot \sqrt{3} = 2\sqrt{3}$

21. $\sqrt{250} = \sqrt{25 \cdot 10} = \sqrt{25} \cdot \sqrt{10} = 5\sqrt{10}$

22. $\sqrt{192} = \sqrt{64 \cdot 3} = \sqrt{64} \cdot \sqrt{3} = 8\sqrt{3}$

23. $7\sqrt{28} = 7\sqrt{4 \cdot 7}$
$$= 7\sqrt{4} \cdot \sqrt{7}$$
$$= 7 \cdot 2 \cdot \sqrt{7}$$
$$= 14\sqrt{7}$$

24. $3\sqrt{52} = 3\sqrt{4 \cdot 13} = 3\sqrt{4} \cdot \sqrt{13} = 3 \cdot 2 \cdot \sqrt{13} = 6\sqrt{13}$

25. $\sqrt{7} \cdot \sqrt{6} = \sqrt{7 \cdot 6} = \sqrt{42}$

26. $\sqrt{19} \cdot \sqrt{3} = \sqrt{19 \cdot 3} = \sqrt{57}$

27. $\sqrt{6} \cdot \sqrt{6} = \sqrt{6 \cdot 6} = \sqrt{36} = 6$

28. $\sqrt{5} \cdot \sqrt{5} = \sqrt{5 \cdot 5} = \sqrt{25} = 5$

29. $\sqrt{3} \cdot \sqrt{6} = \sqrt{3 \cdot 6}$
$$= \sqrt{18}$$
$$= \sqrt{9 \cdot 2}$$
$$= \sqrt{9} \cdot \sqrt{2}$$
$$= 3\sqrt{2}$$

30. $\sqrt{12} \cdot \sqrt{2} = \sqrt{12 \cdot 2}$
$$= \sqrt{24}$$
$$= \sqrt{4 \cdot 6}$$
$$= \sqrt{4} \cdot \sqrt{6}$$
$$= 2\sqrt{6}$$

31. $\sqrt{2} \cdot \sqrt{26} = \sqrt{2 \cdot 26}$
$$= \sqrt{52}$$
$$= \sqrt{4 \cdot 13}$$
$$= \sqrt{4} \cdot \sqrt{13}$$
$$= 2\sqrt{13}$$

32. $\sqrt{5} \cdot \sqrt{50} = \sqrt{5 \cdot 50}$
$$= \sqrt{250}$$
$$= \sqrt{25 \cdot 10}$$
$$= \sqrt{25} \cdot \sqrt{10}$$
$$= 5\sqrt{10}$$

33. $\dfrac{\sqrt{54}}{\sqrt{6}} = \sqrt{\dfrac{54}{6}} = \sqrt{9} = 3$

34. $\dfrac{\sqrt{75}}{\sqrt{3}} = \sqrt{\dfrac{75}{3}} = \sqrt{25} = 5$

35. $\dfrac{\sqrt{90}}{\sqrt{2}} = \sqrt{\dfrac{90}{2}}$
$$= \sqrt{45}$$
$$= \sqrt{9 \cdot 5}$$
$$= \sqrt{9} \cdot \sqrt{5}$$
$$= 3\sqrt{5}$$

36. $\dfrac{\sqrt{60}}{\sqrt{3}} = \sqrt{\dfrac{60}{3}} = \sqrt{20} = \sqrt{4 \cdot 5} = \sqrt{4} \cdot \sqrt{5} = 2\sqrt{5}$

37. $\dfrac{-\sqrt{96}}{\sqrt{2}} = -\sqrt{\dfrac{96}{2}}$

$\qquad = -\sqrt{48}$

$\qquad = -\sqrt{16 \cdot 3}$

$\qquad = -\sqrt{16} \cdot \sqrt{3}$

$\qquad = -4\sqrt{3}$

38. $\dfrac{-\sqrt{150}}{\sqrt{3}} = -\sqrt{\dfrac{150}{3}}$

$\qquad = -\sqrt{50}$

$\qquad = -\sqrt{25 \cdot 2}$

$\qquad = -\sqrt{25} \cdot \sqrt{2}$

$\qquad = -5\sqrt{2}$

39. $7\sqrt{3} + 6\sqrt{3} = (7+6)\sqrt{3} = 13\sqrt{3}$

40. $8\sqrt{5} + 11\sqrt{5} = (8+11)\sqrt{5} = 19\sqrt{5}$

41. $4\sqrt{13} - 6\sqrt{13} = (4-6)\sqrt{13} = -2\sqrt{13}$

42. $6\sqrt{17} - 8\sqrt{17} = (6-8)\sqrt{17} = -2\sqrt{17}$

43. $\sqrt{5} + \sqrt{5} = 1\sqrt{5} + 1\sqrt{5} = (1+1)\sqrt{5} = 2\sqrt{5}$

44. $\sqrt{3} + \sqrt{3} = 1\sqrt{3} + 1\sqrt{3} = (1+1)\sqrt{3} = 2\sqrt{3}$

45. $4\sqrt{2} - 5\sqrt{2} + 8\sqrt{2} = (4-5+8)\sqrt{2} = 7\sqrt{2}$

46. $6\sqrt{3} + 8\sqrt{3} - 16\sqrt{3} = (6+8-16)\sqrt{3} = -2\sqrt{3}$

47. $\sqrt{5} + \sqrt{20} = 1\sqrt{5} + \sqrt{4} \cdot \sqrt{5}$

$\qquad = 1\sqrt{5} + 2\sqrt{5}$

$\qquad = (1+2)\sqrt{5}$

$\qquad = 3\sqrt{5}$

48. $\sqrt{3} + \sqrt{27} = 1\sqrt{3} + \sqrt{9} \cdot \sqrt{3}$

$\qquad = 1\sqrt{3} + 3\sqrt{3}$

$\qquad = (1+3)\sqrt{3}$

$\qquad = 4\sqrt{3}$

49. $\sqrt{50} - \sqrt{18} = \sqrt{25} \cdot \sqrt{2} - \sqrt{9} \cdot \sqrt{2}$

$\qquad = 5\sqrt{2} - 3\sqrt{2}$

$\qquad = (5-3)\sqrt{2}$

$\qquad = 2\sqrt{2}$

50. $\sqrt{63} - \sqrt{28} = \sqrt{9} \cdot \sqrt{7} - \sqrt{4} \cdot \sqrt{7}$

$\qquad = 3\sqrt{7} - 2\sqrt{7}$

$\qquad = (3-2)\sqrt{7}$

$\qquad = \sqrt{7}$

51. $3\sqrt{18} + 5\sqrt{50} = 3\sqrt{9} \cdot \sqrt{2} + 5\sqrt{25} \cdot \sqrt{2}$

$\qquad = 3 \cdot 3 \cdot \sqrt{2} + 5 \cdot 5\sqrt{2}$

$\qquad = 9\sqrt{2} + 25\sqrt{2}$

$\qquad = (9+25)\sqrt{2}$

$\qquad = 34\sqrt{2}$

52. $4\sqrt{12} + 2\sqrt{75} = 4\sqrt{4} \cdot \sqrt{3} + 2\sqrt{25} \cdot \sqrt{3}$

$\qquad = 4 \cdot 2 \cdot \sqrt{3} + 2 \cdot 5 \cdot \sqrt{3}$

$\qquad = 8\sqrt{3} + 10\sqrt{3}$

$\qquad = (8+10)\sqrt{3}$

$\qquad = 18\sqrt{3}$

53. $\dfrac{1}{4}\sqrt{12} - \dfrac{1}{2}\sqrt{48} = \dfrac{1}{4}\sqrt{4} \cdot \sqrt{3} - \dfrac{1}{2}\sqrt{16} \cdot \sqrt{3}$

$\qquad = \dfrac{1}{4} \cdot 2 \cdot \sqrt{3} - \dfrac{1}{2} \cdot 4 \cdot \sqrt{3}$

$\qquad = \dfrac{1}{2}\sqrt{3} - \dfrac{4}{2}\sqrt{3}$

$\qquad = \left(\dfrac{1}{2} - \dfrac{4}{2}\right)\sqrt{3}$

$\qquad = -\dfrac{3}{2}\sqrt{3}$

54. $\dfrac{1}{5}\sqrt{300} - \dfrac{2}{3}\sqrt{27} = \dfrac{1}{5} \cdot \sqrt{100} \cdot \sqrt{3} - \dfrac{2}{3} \cdot \sqrt{9} \cdot \sqrt{3}$

$\qquad = \dfrac{1}{5} \cdot 10 \cdot \sqrt{3} - \dfrac{2}{3} \cdot 3 \cdot \sqrt{3}$

$\qquad = 2\sqrt{3} - 2\sqrt{3}$

$\qquad = 0$

55. $3\sqrt{75} + 2\sqrt{12} - 2\sqrt{48}$

$= 3 \cdot \sqrt{25} \cdot \sqrt{3} + 2 \cdot \sqrt{4} \cdot \sqrt{3} - 2 \cdot \sqrt{16} \cdot \sqrt{3}$

$= 3 \cdot 5 \cdot \sqrt{3} + 2 \cdot 2 \cdot \sqrt{3} - 2 \cdot 4 \cdot \sqrt{3}$

$= 15\sqrt{3} + 4\sqrt{3} - 8\sqrt{3}$

$= (15 + 4 - 8)\sqrt{3}$

$= 11\sqrt{3}$

56. $2\sqrt{72} + 3\sqrt{50} - \sqrt{128}$

$= 2 \cdot \sqrt{36} \cdot \sqrt{2} + 3 \cdot \sqrt{25} \cdot \sqrt{2} - \sqrt{64} \cdot \sqrt{2}$

$= 2 \cdot 6 \cdot \sqrt{2} + 3 \cdot 5 \cdot \sqrt{2} - 8 \cdot \sqrt{2}$

$= 12\sqrt{2} + 15\sqrt{2} - 8\sqrt{2}$

$= (12 + 15 - 8)\sqrt{2}$

$= 19\sqrt{2}$

57. $\dfrac{5}{\sqrt{3}} = \dfrac{5}{\sqrt{3}} \cdot \dfrac{\sqrt{3}}{\sqrt{3}} = \dfrac{5\sqrt{3}}{\sqrt{9}} = \dfrac{5\sqrt{3}}{3}$

58. $\dfrac{12}{\sqrt{5}} = \dfrac{12}{\sqrt{5}} \cdot \dfrac{\sqrt{5}}{\sqrt{5}} = \dfrac{12\sqrt{5}}{\sqrt{25}} = \dfrac{12\sqrt{5}}{5}$

59. $\dfrac{21}{\sqrt{7}} = \dfrac{21}{\sqrt{7}} \cdot \dfrac{\sqrt{7}}{\sqrt{7}} = \dfrac{21\sqrt{7}}{\sqrt{49}} = \dfrac{21\sqrt{7}}{7} = 3\sqrt{7}$

60. $\dfrac{30}{\sqrt{5}} = \dfrac{30}{\sqrt{5}} \cdot \dfrac{\sqrt{5}}{\sqrt{5}} = \dfrac{30\sqrt{5}}{\sqrt{25}} = \dfrac{30\sqrt{5}}{5} = 6\sqrt{5}$

61. $\dfrac{12}{\sqrt{30}} = \dfrac{12\sqrt{30}}{\sqrt{30}\sqrt{30}}$

$= \dfrac{12\sqrt{30}}{\sqrt{900}}$

$= \dfrac{12\sqrt{30}}{30}$

$= \dfrac{2\sqrt{30}}{5}$

62. $\dfrac{15}{\sqrt{50}} = \dfrac{15}{\sqrt{50}} \cdot \dfrac{\sqrt{2}}{\sqrt{2}} = \dfrac{15\sqrt{2}}{\sqrt{100}} = \dfrac{15\sqrt{2}}{10} = \dfrac{3\sqrt{2}}{2}$

63. $\dfrac{15}{\sqrt{12}} = \dfrac{15}{\sqrt{4 \cdot 3}}$

$= \dfrac{15}{\sqrt{4}\sqrt{3}}$

$= \dfrac{15}{2\sqrt{3}}$

$= \dfrac{15\sqrt{3}}{2\sqrt{3}\sqrt{3}}$

$= \dfrac{15\sqrt{3}}{2\sqrt{9}}$

$= \dfrac{15\sqrt{3}}{2 \cdot 3}$

$= \dfrac{15\sqrt{3}}{6}$

$= \dfrac{5\sqrt{3}}{2}$

64. $\dfrac{13}{\sqrt{40}} = \dfrac{13\sqrt{10}}{\sqrt{40}\sqrt{10}} = \dfrac{13\sqrt{10}}{\sqrt{400}} = \dfrac{13\sqrt{10}}{20}$

65. $\sqrt{\dfrac{2}{5}} = \dfrac{\sqrt{2}}{\sqrt{5}} = \dfrac{\sqrt{2}}{\sqrt{5}} \cdot \dfrac{\sqrt{5}}{\sqrt{5}} = \dfrac{\sqrt{10}}{\sqrt{25}} = \dfrac{\sqrt{10}}{5}$

66. $\sqrt{\dfrac{5}{7}} = \dfrac{\sqrt{5}}{\sqrt{7}} = \dfrac{\sqrt{5}}{\sqrt{7}} \cdot \dfrac{\sqrt{7}}{\sqrt{7}} = \dfrac{\sqrt{35}}{\sqrt{49}} = \dfrac{\sqrt{35}}{7}$

67. $\dfrac{7\sqrt{2 \cdot 2 \cdot 3}}{6} = \dfrac{7 \cdot \sqrt{4} \cdot \sqrt{3}}{6}$

$= \dfrac{7 \cdot 2 \cdot \sqrt{3}}{6}$

$= \dfrac{14 \cdot \sqrt{3}}{6}$

$= \dfrac{7}{3}\sqrt{3}$

68. $s = 4\sqrt{r}$

$s = 4\sqrt{8}$

$s = 4 \cdot \sqrt{4 \cdot 2}$

$s = 4 \cdot 2\sqrt{2}$

$s = 8\sqrt{2}$

$s \approx 11.3$

The greatest speed is about 11.3 mph.

69. $s = 4\sqrt{r}$

$s = 4\sqrt{12}$

$s = 4 \cdot \sqrt{4 \cdot 3}$

$s = 4 \cdot 2\sqrt{3}$

$s = 8\sqrt{3}$

$s \approx 13.9$

The greatest speed is about 13.9 mph.

70. $t = \sqrt{\dfrac{x}{16}}$

$t = \sqrt{\dfrac{320}{16}}$

$t = \sqrt{20}$

$t = \sqrt{4} \cdot \sqrt{5}$

$t = 2\sqrt{5}$

$t \approx 4.5$

It will take about 4.5 seconds.

71. $t = \sqrt{\dfrac{x}{16}}$

$t = \sqrt{\dfrac{640}{16}}$

$t = \sqrt{40}$

$t = \sqrt{4} \cdot \sqrt{10}$

$t = 2\sqrt{10}$

$t \approx 6.3$

It will take about 6.3 seconds.

72. $h = 2.9\sqrt{x} + 20.1$

$h = 2.9\sqrt{48} + 20.1 \approx 40.2$ inches

The formula models the actual median height well.

73. $h = 2.9\sqrt{x} + 20.1$

$h = 2.9\sqrt{60} + 20.1 \approx 42.6$ inches

The formula models the actual median height well.

74. $P = 6.85\sqrt{t} + 19$

$P = 6.85\sqrt{1} + 19 = 25.85\%$ online in 1998.

The formula models the actual data well.

75. $P = 6.85\sqrt{t} + 19$

$P = 6.85\sqrt{4} + 19 = 32.7\%$ online in 2001.

The formula models the actual data well.

76. $P = 6.85\sqrt{t} + 19$

$P = 6.85\sqrt{8} + 19 \approx 38\%$ online in 2005.

77. $P = 6.85\sqrt{t} + 19$

$P = 6.85\sqrt{13} + 19 \approx 44\%$ online in 2010.

78-84. Answers will vary.

85. c is true

$\sqrt{\sqrt{16}} = \sqrt{4} = 2$

86. $\sqrt{2} \approx 1.4$

$\sqrt{2} < 1.5$

87. $-\pi \approx -3.14$

$-\pi > -3.5$

88. $\dfrac{-3.14}{2} = -1.5700$

$-\dfrac{\pi}{2} \approx -1.5708$

$\dfrac{-3.14}{2} > -\dfrac{\pi}{2}$

89. The square root is multiplied by $\sqrt{2}$.

90. $-\sqrt{47} \approx -6.86$

Therefore $-\sqrt{47}$ is between -7 and -6.

91. $\sqrt{2} + \sqrt{\dfrac{1}{2}} = \sqrt{2} + \dfrac{\sqrt{1}}{\sqrt{2}} = \sqrt{2} + \dfrac{\sqrt{1}}{\sqrt{2}} \cdot \dfrac{\sqrt{2}}{\sqrt{2}}$

$= \sqrt{2} + \dfrac{\sqrt{2}}{2} = \dfrac{2\sqrt{2}}{2} + \dfrac{\sqrt{2}}{2}$

$= \dfrac{2\sqrt{2} + \sqrt{2}}{2}$

$= \dfrac{(2+1)\sqrt{2}}{2} = \dfrac{3\sqrt{2}}{2}$

92. $\sqrt{2} - \sqrt{2} = 0$ ($\sqrt{2}$ is irrational, yet 0 is rational)

Check Points 5.5

1. $\left\{ -9,\ -1.3,\ 0,\ 0.\overline{3},\ \dfrac{\pi}{2},\ \sqrt{9},\ \sqrt{10} \right\}$

    a. Natural numbers: $\sqrt{9}$ because $\sqrt{9} = 3$

    b. Whole numbers: 0, $\sqrt{9}$

c. Integers: $-9, 0, \sqrt{9}$

d. Rational numbers: $-9, -1.3, 0, 0.\overline{3}, \sqrt{9}$

e. Irrational numbers: $\frac{\pi}{2}, \sqrt{10}$

f. Real numbers: All numbers in this set.

2. a. Associative property of multiplication

b. Commutative property of addition

c. Distributive property of multiplication over addition

d. Commutative property of multiplication

3. a. Yes, the natural numbers are closed with respect to multiplication.

b. No, the integers are not closed with respect to division. Example: $3 \div 5 = 0.6$ which is not an integer.

Exercise Set 5.5

1. $\left\{-9, -\frac{4}{5}, 0, 0.25, \sqrt{3}, 9.2, \sqrt{100}\right\}$

a. Natural numbers: $\sqrt{100}$ because $\sqrt{100} = 10$

b. Whole numbers: $0, \sqrt{100}$

c. Integers: $-9, 0, \sqrt{100}$

d. Rational numbers: $-9, -\frac{4}{5}, 0, 0.25, 9.2, \sqrt{100}$

e. Irrational numbers: $\sqrt{3}$

f. Real numbers: All numbers in this set.

2. $\{-7, -0.\overline{6}, 0, \sqrt{49}, \sqrt{50}\}$

a. Natural numbers: $\sqrt{49}$ because $\sqrt{49} = 7$

b. Whole numbers: $0, \sqrt{49}$

c. Integers: $-7, 0, \sqrt{49}$

d. Rational numbers: $-7, -0.\overline{6}, 0, \sqrt{49}$

e. Irrational numbers: $\sqrt{50}$

f. Real numbers: All numbers in this set.

3. $\left\{-11, -\frac{5}{6}, 0, 0.75, \sqrt{5}, \pi, \sqrt{64}\right\}$

a. Natural numbers: $\sqrt{64}$ because $\sqrt{64} = 8$

b. Whole numbers: 0 and $\sqrt{64}$

c. Integers: $-11, 0, \sqrt{64}$

d. Rational numbers: $-11, -\frac{5}{6}, 0, 0.75, \sqrt{64}$

e. Irrational numbers: $\sqrt{5}, \pi$

f. Real numbers: All numbers in this set.

4. $\{-5, -0.\overline{3}, 0, \sqrt{2}, \sqrt{4}\}$

a. Natural numbers: $\sqrt{4}$ because $\sqrt{4} = 2$

b. Whole numbers: 0 and $\sqrt{4}$

c. Integers: $-5, 0, \sqrt{4}$

d. Rational numbers: $-5, -0.\overline{3}, 0, \sqrt{4}$

e. Irrational numbers: $\sqrt{2}$

f. Real numbers: All numbers in this set.

5. 0 is the only whole number that is not a natural number.

6. Answers will vary. Possible answer: -1

7. Answers will vary. Possible answer: 0.5

8. Answers will vary. Possible answer: $-\frac{2}{5}$

9. Answers will vary. Possible answer: 7

10. Answers will vary. Possible answer: 5

11. Answers will vary. Possible answer: $\sqrt{3}$

12. Answers will vary. Possible answer: -200

13. $3 + (4 + 5) = 3 + (5 + 4)$

14. $\sqrt{5}\cdot 4 = 4\cdot\sqrt{5}$

15. $9\cdot(6+2) = 9\cdot(2+6)$

16. $(3+7)+9 = 3+(7+9)$

17. $(4\cdot5)\cdot3 = 4\cdot(5\cdot3)$

18. $3\cdot(6+4) = 3\cdot6+3\cdot4$

19. $7\cdot(4+5) = 7\cdot4+7\cdot5$

20. $2\cdot(7+3) = 2\cdot7+2\cdot3$

21. $5(6+\sqrt{2}) = 5\cdot6+5\cdot\sqrt{2} = 30+5\sqrt{2}$

22. $4(3+\sqrt{5}) = 4\cdot3+4\cdot\sqrt{5} = 12+4\sqrt{5}$

23. $\sqrt{7}(3+\sqrt{2}) = \sqrt{7}\cdot3+\sqrt{7}\cdot\sqrt{2} = 3\sqrt{7}+\sqrt{14}$

24. $\sqrt{6}(7+\sqrt{5}) = \sqrt{6}\cdot7+\sqrt{6}\cdot\sqrt{5} = 7\sqrt{6}+\sqrt{30}$

25. $\sqrt{3}(5+\sqrt{3}) = \sqrt{3}\cdot5+\sqrt{3}\cdot\sqrt{3} = 5\sqrt{3}+\sqrt{9}$
$= 5\sqrt{3}+3$

26. $\sqrt{7}(9+\sqrt{7}) = \sqrt{7}\cdot9+\sqrt{7}\cdot\sqrt{7}$
$= 9\sqrt{7}+\sqrt{49}$
$= 9\sqrt{7}+7$

27. $\sqrt{6}(\sqrt{2}+\sqrt{6}) = \sqrt{6}\cdot\sqrt{2}+\sqrt{6}\cdot\sqrt{6}$
$= \sqrt{12}+\sqrt{36}$
$= 2\sqrt{3}+6$

28. $\sqrt{10}(\sqrt{2}+\sqrt{10}) = \sqrt{10}\cdot\sqrt{2}+\sqrt{10}\cdot\sqrt{10}$
$= \sqrt{20}+\sqrt{100}$
$= 2\sqrt{5}+10$

29. $6+(-4) = (-4)+6$
Commutative property of addition.

30. $11\cdot(7+4) = 11\cdot7+11\cdot4$
Distributive property of multiplication over addition.

31. $6+(2+7) = (6+2)+7$
Associative property of addition.

32. $6\cdot(2\cdot3) = 6\cdot(3\cdot2)$
Commutative property of multiplication.

33. $(2+3)+(4+5) = (4+5)+(2+3)$
Commutative property of addition.

34. $7(11\cdot8) = (11\cdot8)\cdot7$
Commutative property of multiplication.

35. $2(-8+6) = -16+12$
Distributive property of multiplication over addition.

36. $-8(3+11) = -24+(-88)$
Distributive property of multiplication over addition.

37. $(2\sqrt{3})\cdot\sqrt{5} = 2(\sqrt{3}\cdot\sqrt{5})$
Associative property of multiplication

38. $\sqrt{2}\pi = \pi\sqrt{2}$
Commutative property of multiplication.

39. Answers will vary.
Example: $1-2 = -1$

40. Answers will vary.
Example: $\dfrac{4}{8} = \dfrac{1}{2}$

41. Answers will vary.
Example: $\dfrac{-2}{8} = -\dfrac{1}{4}$

42. Answers will vary.
Example: $\sqrt{3}-\sqrt{3} = 0$

43. Answers will vary.
Example: $\sqrt{5}\sqrt{5} = \sqrt{25} = 5$

44. Yes; the result is the same if first you put on your right shoe, then put on your left shoe.

45. No; the result is not the same if first you took a shower, then you got undressed.

46. Answers will vary. Possible answer: Put on your socks, then put on your shoes.

47. Answers will vary. Possible answer: First put on left glove, then put on right glove.

48-56. Answers will vary.

57. c is true

58. c is true

Check Points 5.6

1. **a.** $19^0 = 1$

    b. $(3\pi)^0 = 1$

    c. $(-14)^0 = 1$

    d. $-14^0 = -1$

2. **a.** $9^{-2} = \dfrac{1}{9^2} = \dfrac{1}{81}$

    b. $6^{-3} = \dfrac{1}{6^3} = \dfrac{1}{216}$

    c. $12^{-1} = \dfrac{1}{12}$

3. **a.** $7.4 \times 10^9 = 7,400,000,000$

    b. $3.017 \times 10^{-6} = 0.000003017$

4. **a.** $7,410,000,000 = 7.41 \times 10^9$

    b. $0.000000092 = 9.2 \times 10^{-8}$

5. $106.2 \times 10^9 = \left(1.062 \times 10^2\right) \times 10^9 = 1.062 \times 10^{11}$

6. $(1.3 \times 10^7) \times (4 \times 10^{-2}) = (1.3 \times 4) \times (10^7 \times 10^{-2})$
    $$= 5.2 \times 10^{7+(-2)}$$
    $$= 5.2 \times 10^5$$
    $$= 520,000$$

7. $\dfrac{6.9 \times 10^{-8}}{3 \times 10^{-2}} = \left(\dfrac{6.9}{3}\right) \times \left(\dfrac{10^{-8}}{10^{-2}}\right)$
    $$= 2.3 \times 10^{-8-(-2)}$$
    $$= 2.3 \times 10^{-6}$$
    $$= 0.0000023$$

8. **a.** $0.0036 \times 5,200,000$
    $$= 3.6 \times 10^{-3} \times 5.2 \times 10^6$$
    $$= (3.6 \times 5.2) \times (10^{-3} \times 10^6)$$
    $$= 18.72 \times 10^3$$
    $$= 1.872 \times 10 \times 10^3$$
    $$= 1.872 \times 10^4$$

    b. Based on part (a):
    $$0.0036 \times 5,200,000$$
    $$= 1.872 \times 10^4$$
    $$= 18,720$$

9. $\dfrac{3.6 \times 10^9}{2.8 \times 10^8} = \left(\dfrac{3.6}{2.8}\right) \times \left(\dfrac{10^9}{10^8}\right)$
    $$\approx 1.286 \times 10$$
    $$\approx 12.86$$
    $$\approx \$12.86 \text{ per American}$$

Exercise Set 5.6

1. $2^2 \cdot 2^3 = 2^{2+3} = 2^5 = 32$

2. $3^3 \cdot 3^2 = 3^{3+2} = 3^5 = 243$

3. $4 \cdot 4^2 = 4^1 \cdot 4^2 = 4^{1+2} = 4^3 = 64$

4. $5 \cdot 5^2 = 5^1 \cdot 5^2 = 5^{1+2} = 5^3 = 125$

5. $(2^2)^3 = 2^{2 \cdot 3} = 2^6 = 64$

6. $(3^3)^2 = 3^{3 \cdot 2} = 3^6 = 729$

7. $(1^4)^5 = 1^{4 \cdot 5} = 1^{20} = 1$

8. $(1^3)^7 = 1^{3 \cdot 7} = 1^{21} = 1$

9. $\dfrac{4^7}{4^5} = 4^{7-5} = 4^2 = 16$

10. $\dfrac{6^7}{6^5} = 6^{7-5} = 6^2 = 36$

11. $\dfrac{2^8}{2^4} = 2^{8-4} = 2^4 = 16$

12. $\dfrac{3^8}{3^4} = 3^{8-4} = 3^4 = 81$

13. $3^0 = 1$

14. $9^0 = 1$

15. $(-3)^0 = 1$

16. $(-9)^0 = 1$

17. $-3^0 = -1$

18. $-9^0 = -1$

19. $2^{-2} = \dfrac{1}{2^2} = \dfrac{1}{4}$

20. $3^{-2} = \dfrac{1}{3^2} = \dfrac{1}{9}$

21. $4^{-3} = \dfrac{1}{4^3} = \dfrac{1}{64}$

22. $2^{-3} = \dfrac{1}{2^3} = \dfrac{1}{8}$

23. $2^{-5} = \dfrac{1}{2^5} = \dfrac{1}{32}$

24. $2^{-6} = \dfrac{1}{2^6} = \dfrac{1}{64}$

25. $3^4 \cdot 3^{-2} = 3^{4+(-2)} = 3^2 = 9$

26. $2^5 \cdot 2^{-2} = 2^{5+(-2)} = 2^3 = 8$

27. $3^{-3} \cdot 3 = 3^{-3} \cdot 3^1 = 3^{-3+1} = 3^{-2} = \dfrac{1}{3^2} = \dfrac{1}{9}$

28. $2^{-3} \cdot 2 = 2^{-3} \cdot 2^1 = 2^{-3+1} = 2^{-2} = \dfrac{1}{2^2} = \dfrac{1}{4}$

29. $\dfrac{2^3}{2^7} = 2^{3-7} = 2^{-4} = \dfrac{1}{2^4} = \dfrac{1}{16}$

30. $\dfrac{3^4}{3^7} = 3^{4-7} = 3^{-3} = \dfrac{1}{3^3} = \dfrac{1}{27}$

31. $2.7 \times 10^2 = 270$

32. $4.7 \times 10^3 = 4700$

33. $9.12 \times 10^5 = 912{,}000$

34. $8.14 \times 10^4 = 81{,}400$

35. $8 \times 10^7 = 8.0 \times 10^7 = 80{,}000{,}000$

36. $7 \times 10^6 = 7.0 \times 10^6 = 7{,}000{,}000$

37. $1 \times 10^5 = 1.0 \times 10^5 = 100{,}000$

38. $1 \times 10^8 = 1.0 \times 10^8 = 100{,}000{,}000$

39. $7.9 \times 10^{-1} = 0.79$

40. $8.6 \times 10^{-1} = 0.86$

41. $2.15 \times 10^{-2} = 0.0215$

42. $3.14 \times 10^{-2} = 0.0314$

43. $7.86 \times 10^{-4} = 0.000786$

44. $4.63 \times 10^{-5} = 0.0000463$

45. $3.18 \times 10^{-6} = 0.00000318$

46. $5.84 \times 10^{-7} = 0.000000584$

47. $370 = 3.7 \times 10^2$

48. $530 = 5.3 \times 10^2$

49. $3600 = 3.6 \times 10^3$

50. $2700 = 2.7 \times 10^3$

51. $32{,}000 = 3.2 \times 10^4$

52. $64{,}000 = 6.4 \times 10^4$

53. $220{,}000{,}000 = 2.2 \times 10^8$

54. $370{,}000{,}000{,}000 = 3.7 \times 10^{11}$

55. $0.027 = 2.7 \times 10^{-2}$

56. $0.014 = 1.4 \times 10^{-2}$

57. $0.0037 = 3.7 \times 10^{-3}$

58. $0.00083 = 8.3 \times 10^{-4}$

59. $0.00000293 = 2.93 \times 10^{-6}$

60. $0.000000647 = 6.47 \times 10^{-7}$

61. $820 \times 10^5 = \left(8.2 \times 10^2\right) \times 10^5 = 8.2 \times 10^7$

62. $630 \times 10^8 = \left(6.3 \times 10^2\right) \times 10^8 = 6.3 \times 10^{10}$

63. $0.41 \times 10^6 = \left(4.1 \times 10^{-1}\right) \times 10^6 = 4.1 \times 10^5$

64. $0.57 \times 10^9 = \left(5.7 \times 10^{-1}\right) \times 10^9 = 5.7 \times 10^8$

65. $2100 \times 10^{-9} = \left(2.1 \times 10^3\right) \times 10^{-9} = 2.1 \times 10^{-6}$

66. $97,000 \times 10^{-11} = \left(9.7 \times 10^4\right) \times 10^{-11} = 9.7 \times 10^{-7}$

67. $(2 \times 10^3)(3 \times 10^2) = (2 \times 3) \times (10^{3+2})$
$$= 6 \times 10^5$$
$$= 600,000$$

68. $(5 \times 10^2)(4 + 10^4) = (5 \times 4) \times (10^{2+4})$
$$= 20 \times 10^6$$
$$= 2 \times 10 \times 10^6$$
$$= 2 \times 10^7$$
$$= 20,000,000$$

69. $(2 \times 10^9)(3 \times 10^{-5}) = (2 \times 3) \times (10^{9-5})$
$$= 6 \times 10^4$$
$$= 60,000$$

70. $(4 \times 10^8)(2 \times 10^{-4}) = (4 \times 2) \times (10^{8-4})$
$$= 8 \times 10^4$$
$$= 80,000$$

71. $(4.1 \times 10^2)(3 \times 10^{-4}) = (4.1 \times 3) \times (10^{2-4})$
$$= 12.3 \times 10^{-2}$$
$$= 1.23 \times 10 \times 10^{-2}$$
$$= 1.23 \times 10^{-1}$$
$$= 0.123$$

72. $(1.2 \times 10^3)(2 \times 10^{-5}) = (1.2 \times 2) \times (10^{3-5})$
$$= 2.4 \times 10^{-2}$$
$$= 0.024$$

73. $\dfrac{12 \times 10^6}{4 \times 10^2} = \left(\dfrac{12}{4}\right) \times \left(\dfrac{10^6}{10^2}\right)$
$$= 3 \times 10^{6-2}$$
$$= 3 \times 10^4$$
$$= 30,000$$

74. $\dfrac{20 \times 10^{20}}{10 \times 10^{15}} = \left(\dfrac{20}{10}\right) \times \left(\dfrac{10^{20}}{10^{15}}\right)$
$$= 2 \times 10^{20-15}$$
$$= 2 \times 10^5$$
$$= 200,000$$

75. $\dfrac{15 \times 10^4}{5 \times 10^{-2}} = \left(\dfrac{15}{5}\right) \times \left(\dfrac{10^4}{10^{-2}}\right)$
$$= 3 \times 10^{4-(-2)}$$
$$= 3 \times 10^6$$
$$= 3,000,000$$

76. $\dfrac{18 \times 10^2}{9 \times 10^{-3}} = \left(\dfrac{18}{9}\right) \times \left(\dfrac{10^2}{10^{-3}}\right)$
$$= 2 \times 10^{2-(-3)}$$
$$= 2 \times 10^5$$
$$= 200,000$$

77. $\dfrac{6 \times 10^3}{2 \times 10^5} = \left(\dfrac{6}{2}\right) \times \left(\dfrac{10^3}{10^5}\right)$
$$= 3 \times 10^{3-5}$$
$$= 3 \times 10^{-2}$$
$$= 0.03$$

78. $\dfrac{8 \times 10^4}{2 \times 10^7} = \left(\dfrac{8}{2}\right) \times \left(\dfrac{10^4}{10^7}\right)$

$\qquad = 4 \times 10^{4-7}$

$\qquad = 4 \times 10^{-3}$

$\qquad = 0.004$

79. $\dfrac{6.3 \times 10^{-6}}{3 \times 10^{-3}} = \left(\dfrac{6.3}{3}\right) \times \left(\dfrac{10^{-6}}{10^{-3}}\right)$

$\qquad = 2.1 \times 10^{-6-(-3)}$

$\qquad = 2.1 \times 10^{-3}$

$\qquad = 0.0021$

80. $\dfrac{9.6 \times 10^{-7}}{3 \times 10^{-3}} = \left(\dfrac{9.6}{3}\right) \times \left(\dfrac{10^{-7}}{10^{-3}}\right)$

$\qquad = 3.2 \times 10^{-7-(-3)}$

$\qquad = 3.2 \times 10^{-4}$

$\qquad = 0.00032$

81. $(82,000,000)(3,000,000,000)$

$\qquad = (8.2 \times 10^7)(3.0 \times 10^9)$

$\qquad = (8.2 \times 3.0) \times (10^{7+9})$

$\qquad = 24.6 \times 10^{16}$

$\qquad = 2.46 \times 10 \times 10^{16}$

$\qquad = 2.46 \times 10^{17}$

82. $(94,000,000)(6,000,000,000)$

$\qquad = (9.4 \times 10^7)(6.0 \times 10^9)$

$\qquad = (9.4 \times 6.0) \times (10^{7+9})$

$\qquad = 56.4 \times 10^{16}$

$\qquad = 5.64 \times 10 \times 10^{16}$

$\qquad = 5.64 \times 10^{17}$

83. $(0.0005)(6,000,000)$

$\qquad = (5.0 \times 10^{-4})(6.0 \times 10^6)$

$\qquad = (5.0 \times 6.0)(10^{-4+6})$

$\qquad = 30 \times 10^2$

$\qquad = 3 \times 10 \times 10^2$

$\qquad = 3 \times 10^3$

84. $(0.000015)(0.004) = (1.5 \times 10^{-5})(4.0 \times 10^{-3})$

$\qquad\qquad\qquad\qquad = (1.5 \times 4.0) \times (10^{-5-3})$

$\qquad\qquad\qquad\qquad = 6 \times 10^{-8}$

85. $\dfrac{9,500,000}{500} = \dfrac{9.5 \times 10^6}{5 \times 10^2}$

$\qquad\qquad = \left(\dfrac{9.5}{5}\right) \times (10^{6-2})$

$\qquad\qquad = 1.9 \times 10^4$

86. $\dfrac{30,000}{0.0005} = \dfrac{3 \times 10^4}{5 \times 10^{-4}}$

$\qquad\quad = \left(\dfrac{3}{5}\right) \times (10^{4-(-4)})$

$\qquad\quad = 0.6 \times 10^8$

$\qquad\quad = 6 \times 10^{-1} \times 10^8$

$\qquad\quad = 6 \times 10^7$

87. $\dfrac{0.00008}{200} = \dfrac{8 \times 10^{-5}}{2 \times 10^2}$

$\qquad\quad = \left(\dfrac{8}{2}\right) \times (10^{-5-2})$

$\qquad\quad = 4 \times 10^{-7}$

88. $\dfrac{0.0018}{0.0000006} = \dfrac{1.8 \times 10^{-3}}{6 \times 10^{-7}}$

$\qquad\qquad = \left(\dfrac{1.8}{6}\right) \times (10^{-3-(-7)})$

$\qquad\qquad = 0.3 \times 10^4$

$\qquad\qquad = 3 \times 10^{-1} \times 10^4$

$\qquad\qquad = 3 \times 10^3$

89. $\dfrac{480,000,000,000}{0.00012} = \dfrac{4.8 \times 10^{11}}{1.2 \times 10^{-4}}$

$\qquad\qquad\qquad = \left(\dfrac{4.8}{1.2}\right) \times (10^{11-(-4)})$

$\qquad\qquad\qquad = 4 \times 10^{15}$

90. $\dfrac{0.000000096}{16,000} = \dfrac{9.6 \times 10^{-8}}{1.6 \times 10^4}$

$\qquad\qquad\quad = \left(\dfrac{9.6}{1.6}\right) \times (10^{-8-4})$

$\qquad\qquad\quad = 6 \times 10^{-12}$

91. $53.3 \times 10^6 = 5.33 \times 10 \times 10^6 = 5.33 \times 10^7$

92. $70.2 \times 10^6 = 7.02 \times 10 \times 10^6 = 7.02 \times 10^7$

93. $(77.0 - 35.3) \times 10^6$
$= 41.7 \times 10^6$
$= 4.17 \times 10 \times 10^6$
$= 4.17 \times 10^7$

94. $(70.2 - 35.3) \times 10^6$
$= 34.9 \times 10^6$
$= 3.49 \times 10 \times 10^6$
$= 3.49 \times 10^7$

95. 25% of 1.6×10^{12}
$0.25 \times (1.6 \times 10^{12})$
$= (0.25 \times 1.6) \times 10^{12}$
$= 0.4 \times 10^{12}$
$= 4.0 \times 10^{-1} \times 10^{12}$
$= 4.0 \times 10^{11}$
$= \$4 \times 10^{11}$

96. 10% of $205,000,000$
$0.1 \times 2.05 \times 10^8$
$= (0.1 \times 2.05) \times 10^8$
$= 0.205 \times 10^8$
$= 2.05 \times 10^{-1} \times 10^8$
$= 2.05 \times 10^7$ Americans

97. $\dfrac{1.9 \times 10^{12}}{2.8 \times 10^8} = \left(\dfrac{1.9}{2.8}\right) \times \left(\dfrac{10^{12}}{10^8}\right)$
$\approx 0.68 \times 10^4$
$\approx 6.8 \times 10^{-1} \times 10^4$
$\approx 6.8 \times 10^3$
$\approx \$6800$ per American

98. $\dfrac{8 \times 10^{12}}{2.8 \times 10^8} = \left(\dfrac{8}{2.8}\right) \times \left(\dfrac{10^{12}}{10^8}\right)$
$\approx 2.86 \times 10^4$
$\approx \$28,600$ per American

99. $4000 \times 2.8 \times 10^8$
$= 4 \times 10^3 \times 2.8 \times 10^8$
$= (4 \times 2.8) \times (10^3 \times 10^8)$
$= 11.2 \times 10^{11}$
$= 1.12 \times 10 \times 10^{11}$
$= \$1.12 \times 10^{12}$

100. $26 \times 2 \times 10^4$
$= 2.6 \times 10 \times 2 \times 10^4$
$= (2.6 \times 2) \times (10 \times 10^4)$
$= 5.2 \times 10^5$ miles

101. $20,000 \times 5.3 \times 10^{-23}$
$= 2 \times 10^4 \times 5.3 \times 10^{-23}$
$= (2 \times 5.3) \times (10^4 \times 10^{-23})$
$= 10.6 \times 10^{-19}$
$= 1.06 \times 10 \times 10^{-19}$
$= 1.06 \times 10^{-18}$ grams

102. $80,000 \times 1.67 \times 10^{-24}$
$= 8 \times 10^4 \times 1.67 \times 10^{-24}$
$= (8 \times 1.67) \times (10^4 \times 10^{-24})$
$\approx 13.36 \times 10^{-20}$
$\approx 1.336 \times 10 \times 10^{-20}$
$\approx 1.336 \times 10^{-19}$ grams

103-112. Answers will vary.

113. b is true

114. d is true

115. Answers will vary. Possible answer:
$2.0 \times 10^0 = 2.0 \times 1 = 2$
There is no advantage here since $10^0 = 1$.

116. $1 - (2^{-1} + 2^{-2}) = 1 - \left(\dfrac{1}{2} + \dfrac{1}{4}\right)$
$= \dfrac{4}{4} - \left(\dfrac{2}{4} + \dfrac{1}{4}\right)$
$= \dfrac{4}{4} - \dfrac{3}{4} = \dfrac{1}{4}$

Check Points 5.7

1. $100, 100 + 20 = 120, 120 + 20 = 140, 140 + 20 =$
   $160, 160 + 20 = 180, 180 + 20 = 200$
   $100, 120, 140, 160, 180,$ and 200

2. $8, 8 - 3 = 5, 5 - 3 = 2, 2 - 3 = -1, -1 - 3 = -4, -4$
   $- 3 = -7$
   $8, 5, 2, -1, -4,$ and -7

3. $a_n = a_1 + (n-1)d$
   $a_9 = 6 + (9-1)(-5)$
   $\quad = 6 + 8(-5)$
   $\quad = 6 - 40$
   $\quad = -34$

4. **a.** $a_n = a_1 + (n-1)d$ with $a_1 = 159{,}000$ and
   $d = 9700$.
   $a_n = 159{,}000 + (n-1)(9700)$
   $\quad = 159{,}000 + 9700n - 9700$
   $\quad = 9700n + 149{,}300$

   b. $a_n = 9700n + 149{,}300$ with
   $n = 2010 - 1994 = 16$

$a_{16} = 9700(16) + 149{,}300$
$\quad = 304{,}500$
The average cost of a new home is predicted to average about \$304,500 by 2010.

5. $12, 12\left(-\dfrac{1}{2}\right) = -6, -6\left(-\dfrac{1}{2}\right) = 3, 3\left(-\dfrac{1}{2}\right) = -\dfrac{3}{2},$
   $-\dfrac{3}{2}\left(-\dfrac{1}{2}\right) = \dfrac{3}{4}, \dfrac{3}{4}\left(-\dfrac{1}{2}\right) = -\dfrac{3}{8}$

   $12, -6, 3, -\dfrac{3}{2}, \dfrac{3}{4}, -\dfrac{3}{8}$

6. $a_n = a_1 r^{n-1}$ with $a_1 = 5$, $r = -3$, and $n = 7$
   $a_7 = 5(-3)^{7-1} = 5(-3)^6 = 5(729) = 3645$

7. $a_n = a_1 r^{n-1}$ with $a_1 = 3$ and $r = \dfrac{6}{3} = 2$. Thus
   $a_n = 3(2)^{n-1}$
   $a_8 = 3(2)^{8-1} = 3(2)^7 = 3(128) = 384$

Exercise Set 5.7

1. $8, 8 + 2 = 10, 10 + 2 = 12, 12 + 2 = 14, 14 + 2 = 16, 16 + 2 = 18$
   $8, 10, 12, 14, 16,$ and 18

2. $5, 5 + 3 = 8, 8 + 3 = 11, 11 + 3 = 14, 14 + 3 = 17, 17 + 3 = 20$
   $5, 8, 11, 14, 17,$ and 20

3. $200, 200 + 20 = 220, 220 + 20 = 240, 240 + 20 = 260, 260 + 20 = 280, 280 + 20 = 300$
   $200, 220, 240, 260, 280,$ and 300

4. $300, 300 + 50 = 350, 350 + 50 = 400, 400 + 50 = 450, 450 + 50 = 500, 500 + 50 = 550$
   $300, 350, 400, 450, 500,$ and 550

5. $-7, -7 + 4 = -3, -3 + 4 = 1, 1 + 4 = 5, 5 + 4 = 9, 9 + 4 = 13$
   $-7, -3, 1, 5, 9,$ and 13

6. $-8, -8 + 5 = -3, -3 + 5 = 2, 2 + 5 = 7, 7 + 5 = 12, 12 + 5 = 17$
   $-8, -3, 2, 7, 12,$ and 17

7. $-400, -400 + 300 = -100, -100 + 300 = 200, 200 + 300 = 500, 500 + 300 = 800, 800 + 300 = 1100$
   $-400, -100, 200, 500, 800,$ and 1100

8. $-500, -500 + 400 = -100, -100 + 400 = 300, 300 + 400 = 700, 700 + 400 = 1100, 1100 + 400 = 1500$
   $-500, -100, 300, 700, 1100,$ and 1500

9. $7, 7 - 3 = 4, 4 - 3 = 1, 1 - 3 = -2, -2 - 3 = -5, -5 - 3 = -8$
   $7, 4, 1, -2, -5,$ and -8

10. $9, 9 - 5 = 4, 4 - 5 = -1, -1 - 5 = -6, -6 - 5 = -11, -11 - 5 = -16$
    $9, 4, -1, -6, -11,$ and -16

11. $200, 200 - 60 = 140, 140 - 60 = 80, 80 - 60 = 20, 20 - 60 = -40, -40 - 60 = -100$
200, 140, 80, 20, –40, and –100

12. $300, 300 - 90 = 210, 210 - 90 = 120, 120 - 90 = 30, 30 - 90 = -60, -60 - 90 = -150$
300, 210, 120, 30, –60, and –150

13. $\dfrac{5}{2}, \dfrac{5}{2} + \dfrac{1}{2} = \dfrac{6}{2} = 3, \dfrac{6}{2} + \dfrac{1}{2} = \dfrac{7}{2}, \dfrac{7}{2} + \dfrac{1}{2} = \dfrac{8}{2} = 4, \dfrac{8}{2} + \dfrac{1}{2} = \dfrac{9}{2}, \dfrac{9}{2} + \dfrac{1}{2} = \dfrac{10}{2} = 5$
$\dfrac{5}{2}, 3, \dfrac{7}{2}, 4, \dfrac{9}{2},$ and 5

14. $\dfrac{3}{4}, \dfrac{3}{4} + \dfrac{1}{4} = 1, \dfrac{4}{4} + \dfrac{1}{4} = \dfrac{5}{4}, \dfrac{5}{4} + \dfrac{1}{4} = \dfrac{6}{4} = \dfrac{3}{2}, \dfrac{6}{4} + \dfrac{1}{4} = \dfrac{7}{4}, \dfrac{7}{4} + \dfrac{1}{4} = \dfrac{8}{4} = 2$
$\dfrac{3}{4}, 1, \dfrac{5}{4}, \dfrac{3}{2}, \dfrac{7}{4},$ and 2

15. $\dfrac{3}{2}, \dfrac{6}{4} + \dfrac{1}{4} = \dfrac{7}{4}, \dfrac{7}{4} + \dfrac{1}{4} = \dfrac{8}{4} = 2, \dfrac{8}{4} + \dfrac{1}{4} = \dfrac{9}{4}, \dfrac{9}{4} + \dfrac{1}{4} = \dfrac{10}{4} = \dfrac{5}{2}, \dfrac{10}{4} + \dfrac{1}{4} = \dfrac{11}{4}$
$\dfrac{3}{2}, \dfrac{7}{4}, 2, \dfrac{9}{4}, \dfrac{5}{2},$ and $\dfrac{11}{4}$

16. $\dfrac{3}{2}, \dfrac{6}{4} - \dfrac{1}{4} = \dfrac{5}{4}, \dfrac{5}{4} - \dfrac{1}{4} = \dfrac{4}{4} = 1, \dfrac{4}{4} - \dfrac{1}{4} = \dfrac{3}{4}, \dfrac{3}{4} - \dfrac{1}{4} = \dfrac{2}{4} = \dfrac{1}{2}, \dfrac{2}{4} - \dfrac{1}{4} = \dfrac{1}{4}$
$\dfrac{3}{2}, \dfrac{5}{4}, 1, \dfrac{3}{4}, \dfrac{1}{2},$ and $\dfrac{1}{4}$

17. $4.25, 4.25 + 0.3 = 4.55, 4.55 + 0.3 = 4.85, 4.85 + 0.3 = 5.15, 5.15 + 0.3 = 5.45, 5.45 + 0.3 = 5.75$
4.25, 4.55, 4.85, 5.15, 5.45, and 5.75

18. $6.3, 6.3 + 0.25 = 6.55, 6.55 + 0.25 = 6.8, 6.8 + 0.25 = 7.05, 7.05 + 0.25 = 7.3, 7.3 + 0.25 = 7.55$
6.3, 6.55, 6.8, 7.05, 7.3, and 7.55

19. $4.5, 4.5 - 0.75 = 3.75, 3.75 - 0.75 = 3, 3 - 0.75 = 2.25, 2.25 - 0.75 = 1.5, 1.5 - 0.75 = 0.75$
4.5, 3.75, 3, 2.25, 1.5, and 0.75

20. $3.5, 3.5 - 1.75 = 1.75, 1.75 - 1.75 = 0, 0 - 1.75 = -1.75, -1.75 - 1.75 = -3.5, -3.5 - 1.75 = -5.25$
3.5, 1.75, 0, –1.75, –3.5, and –5.25

21. $a_1 = 13, d = 4$
$\begin{aligned} a_6 &= 13 + (6-1)(4) \\ &= 13 + 5(4) \\ &= 13 + 20 \\ &= 33 \end{aligned}$

23. $a_1 = 7, d = 5$
$\begin{aligned} a_{50} &= 7 + (50-1)(5) \\ &= 7 + 49(5) \\ &= 7 + 245 \\ &= 252 \end{aligned}$

22. $a_1 = 9, d = 2$
$\begin{aligned} a_{16} &= 9 + (16-1)(2) \\ &= 9 + 15(2) \\ &= 9 + 30 \\ &= 39 \end{aligned}$

24. $a_1 = 8, d = 6$
$\begin{aligned} a_{60} &= 8 + (60-1)(6) \\ &= 8 + 59(6) \\ &= 8 + 354 \\ &= 362 \end{aligned}$

25. $a_1 = -5, d = 9$

$$a_9 = -5 + (9-1)(9)$$
$$= -5 + 8(9)$$
$$= -5 + 72$$
$$= 67$$

26. $a_1 = -8, d = 10$

$$a_{10} = -8 + (10-1)(10)$$
$$= -8 + 9(10)$$
$$= -8 + 90$$
$$= 82$$

27. $a_1 = -40, d = 5$

$$a_{200} = -40 + (200-1)(5)$$
$$= -40 + 199(5)$$
$$= -40 + 995$$
$$= 955$$

28. $a_1 = -60, d = 5$

$$a_{150} = -60 + (150-1)(5)$$
$$= -60 + 149(5)$$
$$= -60 + 745$$
$$= 685$$

29. $a_1 = -8, d = 10$

$$a_{10} = -8 + (10-1)(10)$$
$$= -8 + 9(10)$$
$$= -8 + 90$$
$$= 82$$

30. $a_1 = 10, d = -6$

$$a_{11} = 10 + (11-1)(-6)$$
$$= 10 + 10(-6)$$
$$= 10 + (-60)$$
$$= -50$$

31. $a_1 = 35, d = -3$

$$a_{60} = 35 + (60-1)(-3)$$
$$= 35 + 59(-3)$$
$$= 35 + (-177)$$
$$= -142$$

32. $a_1 = -32, d = 4$

$$a_{70} = -32 + (70-1)(4)$$
$$= -32 + 69(4)$$
$$= -32 + 276$$
$$= 244$$

33. $a_1 = 12, d = -5$

$$a_{12} = 12 + (12-1)(-5)$$
$$= 12 + 11(-5)$$
$$= 12 + (-55)$$
$$= -43$$

34. $a_1 = -20, d = -4$

$$a_{20} = -20 + (20-1)(-4)$$
$$= -20 + 19(-4)$$
$$= -20 + (-76)$$
$$= -96$$

35. $a_1 = -70, d = -2$

$$a_{90} = -70 + (90-1)(-2)$$
$$= -70 + 89(-2)$$
$$= -70 + (-178)$$
$$= -248$$

36. $a_1 = 106, d = -12$

$$a_{80} = 106 + (80-1)(-12)$$
$$= 106 + 79(-12)$$
$$= 106 + (-948)$$
$$= -842$$

37. $a_1 = 6, d = \dfrac{1}{2}$

$$a_{12} = 6 + (12-1)\left(\frac{1}{2}\right)$$
$$= 6 + 11\left(\frac{1}{2}\right)$$
$$= \frac{12}{2} + \frac{11}{2}$$
$$= \frac{23}{2}$$

38. $a_1 = 8$, $d = \dfrac{1}{4}$

$$a_{14} = 8 + (14-1)\left(\dfrac{1}{4}\right)$$
$$= 8 + 13\left(\dfrac{1}{4}\right)$$
$$= \dfrac{32}{4} + \dfrac{13}{4}$$
$$= \dfrac{45}{4}$$

39. $a_1 = 14$, $d = -0.25$

$$a_{50} = 14 + (50-1)(-0.25)$$
$$= 14 + 49(-0.25)$$
$$= 14 + (-12.25)$$
$$= 1.75$$

40. $a_1 = -12$, $d = -0.5$

$$a_{110} = -12 + (110-1)(-0.5)$$
$$= -12 + 109(-0.5)$$
$$= -12 + (-54.5)$$
$$= -66.5$$

41. $a_n = a_1 + (n-1)d$ with $a_1 = 1$, $d = 4$

$$a_n = 1 + (n-1)4$$
$$= 1 + 4n - 4$$
$$= 4n - 3$$
Thus $a_{20} = 4(20) - 3 = 77$.

42. $a_n = a_1 + (n-1)d$ with $a_1 = 2$, $d = 5$

$$a_n = 2 + (n-1)5$$
$$= 2 + 5n - 5$$
$$= 5n - 3$$
Thus $a_{20} = 5(20) - 3 = 97$.

43. $a_n = a_1 + (n-1)d$ with $a_1 = 7$, $d = -4$

$$a_n = 7 + (n-1)(-4)$$
$$= 7 - 4n + 4$$
$$= -4n + 11$$
Thus $a_{20} = -4(20) + 11 = -69$.

44. $a_n = a_1 + (n-1)d$ with $a_1 = 6$, $d = -5$

$$a_n = 6 + (n-1)(-5)$$
$$= 6 - 5n + 5$$
$$= -5n + 11$$
Thus $a_{20} = -5(20) + 11 = -89$.

45. $a_n = a_1 + (n-1)d$ with $a_1 = 9$, $d = 2$

$$a_n = 9 + (n-1)2$$
$$= 9 + 2n - 2$$
$$= 2n + 7$$
Thus $a_{20} = 2(20) + 7 = 47$.

46. $a_n = a_1 + (n-1)d$ with $a_1 = 6$, $d = 3$

$$a_n = 6 + (n-1)3$$
$$= 6 + 3n - 3$$
$$= 3n + 3$$
Thus $a_{20} = 3(20) + 3 = 63$.

47. $a_n = a_1 + (n-1)d$ with $a_1 = -20$, $d = -4$

$$a_n = -20 + (n-1)(-4)$$
$$= -20 - 4n + 4$$
$$= -4n - 16$$
Thus $a_{20} = -4(20) - 16 = -96$.

48. $a_n = a_1 + (n-1)d$ with $a_1 = -70$, $d = -5$

$$a_n = -70 + (n-1)(-5)$$
$$= -70 - 5n + 5$$
$$= -5n - 65$$
Thus $a_{20} = -5(20) - 65 = -165$.

49. $a_1 = 4$, $r = 2$

$4 \cdot 2 = 8$, $8 \cdot 2 = 16$, $16 \cdot 2 = 32$, $32 \cdot 2 = 64$,
$64 \cdot 2 = 128$
4, 8, 16, 32, 64, 128

50. $a_1 = 2$, $r = 3$

$2 \cdot 3 = 6$, $6 \cdot 3 = 18$, $18 \cdot 3 = 54$, $54 \cdot 3 = 162$,
$162 \cdot 3 = 486$
2, 6, 18, 54, 162, 486

51. $a_1 = 1000$, $r = 1$

1000, $1000 \cdot 1 = 1000$, $1000 \cdot 1 = 1000, \ldots$
1000, 1000, 1000, 1000, 1000, 1000

52. $a_1 = 5000$, $r = 1$

5000, $5000 \cdot 1 = 5000$, $5000 \cdot 1 = 5000, \ldots$
5000, 5000, 5000, 5000, 5000, 5000

53. $a_1 = 3$, $r = -2$

3, $3(-2) = -6$, $-6(-2) = 12$, $12(-2) = -24$, $-24(-2) =$
48, $48(-2) = -96$
3, -6, 12, -24, 48, -96

54. $a_1 = 2$, $r = -3$

2, 2(−3) = −6, −6(−3) = 18, 18(−3) = −54,
−54(−3) = 162, 162(−3) = −486
2, −6, 18, −54, 162, −486

55. $a_1 = 10$, $r = -4$

10, 10(−4) = −40, −40(−4) = 160,
160(−4) = −640, −640(−4) = 2560,
2560(−4) = −10,240
10, −40, 160, −640, 2560, −10,240

56. $a_1 = 20$, $r = -4$

20, 20(−4) = −80, −80(−4) = 320,
320(−4) = −1280, −1280(−4) = 5120,
5120(−4) = −20,480
20, −80, 320, −1280, 5120, −20480

57. $a_1 = 2000$, $r = -1$

2000, 2000(−1) = −2000,
−2000(−1) = 2000, …
2000, −2000, 2000, −2000, 2000, −2000

58. $a_1 = 3000$, $r = -1$

3000, 3000(−1) = −3000, −3000(−1) = 3000, …
3000, −3000, 3000, −3000, 3000, −3000

59. $a_1 = -2$, $r = -3$

−2, −2(−3) = 6, 6(−3) = −18, −18(−3) = 54, 54(−3) =
−162, −162(−3) = 486
−2, 6, −18, 54, −162, 486

60. $a_1 = -4$, $r = -2$

−4, −4(−2) = 8, 8(−2) = −16, −16(−2) = 32,
32(−2) = −64, −64(−2) = 128
−4, 8, −16, 32, −64, 128

61. $a_1 = -6$, $r = -5$

−6, −6(−5) = 30, 30(−5) = −150,
−150(−5) = 750, 750(−5) = −3750,
−3750(−5) = 18,750
−6, 30, −150, 750, −3750, 18750

62. $a_1 = -8$, $r = -5$

−8, −8(−5) = 40, 40(−5) = −200,
−200(−5) = 1000, 1000(−5) = −5000,
−5000(−5) = 25,000
−8, 40, −200, 1000, −5000, 25000

63. $a_1 = \dfrac{1}{4}$, $r = 2$

$\dfrac{1}{4}, \dfrac{1}{4} \cdot 2 = \dfrac{1}{2}, \dfrac{1}{2} \cdot 2 = 1, 1 \cdot 2 = 2, 2 \cdot 2 = 4,$
$4 \cdot 2 = 8$
$\dfrac{1}{4}, \dfrac{1}{2}, 1, 2, 4, 8$

64. $a_1 = \dfrac{1}{2}$, $r = 2$

$\dfrac{1}{2}, \dfrac{1}{2} \cdot 2 = 1, 1 \cdot 2 = 2, 2 \cdot 2 = 4, 4 \cdot 2 = 8, 8 \cdot 2 = 16$
$\dfrac{1}{2}, 1, 2, 4, 8, 16$

65. $a_1 = \dfrac{1}{4}$, $r = \dfrac{1}{2}$

$\dfrac{1}{4}, \dfrac{1}{4} \cdot \dfrac{1}{2} = \dfrac{1}{8}, \dfrac{1}{8} \cdot \dfrac{1}{2} = \dfrac{1}{16}, \dfrac{1}{16} \cdot \dfrac{1}{2} = \dfrac{1}{32},$
$\dfrac{1}{32} \cdot \dfrac{1}{2} = \dfrac{1}{64}, \dfrac{1}{64} \cdot \dfrac{1}{2} = \dfrac{1}{128}$
$\dfrac{1}{4}, \dfrac{1}{8}, \dfrac{1}{16}, \dfrac{1}{32}, \dfrac{1}{64}, \dfrac{1}{128}$

66. $a_1 = \dfrac{1}{5}$, $r = \dfrac{1}{2}$

$\dfrac{1}{5}, \dfrac{1}{5} \cdot \dfrac{1}{2} = \dfrac{1}{10}, \dfrac{1}{10} \cdot \dfrac{1}{2} = \dfrac{1}{20}, \dfrac{1}{20} \cdot \dfrac{1}{2} = \dfrac{1}{40},$
$\dfrac{1}{40} \cdot \dfrac{1}{2} = \dfrac{1}{80}, \dfrac{1}{80} \cdot \dfrac{1}{2} = \dfrac{1}{160}$
$\dfrac{1}{5}, \dfrac{1}{10}, \dfrac{1}{20}, \dfrac{1}{40}, \dfrac{1}{80}, \dfrac{1}{160}$

67. $a_1 = -\dfrac{1}{16}$, $r = -4$

$-\dfrac{1}{16}, -\dfrac{1}{16} \cdot (-4) = \dfrac{1}{4}, \dfrac{1}{4} \cdot (-4) = -1,$
$-1(-4) = 4, 4(-4) = -16, -16(-4) = 64$
$-\dfrac{1}{16}, \dfrac{1}{4}, -1, 4, -16, 64$

68. $a_1 = -\dfrac{1}{8}$, $r = -2$

$-\dfrac{1}{8}, -\dfrac{1}{8}(-2) = \dfrac{1}{4}, \dfrac{1}{4}(-2) = -\dfrac{1}{2}, -\dfrac{1}{2}(-2) = 1,$
$1(-2) = -2, -2(-2) = 4$
$-\dfrac{1}{8}, \dfrac{1}{4}, -\dfrac{1}{2}, 1, -2, 4$

69. $a_1 = 2, r = 0.1$

2, 2(0.1) = 0.2, 0.2(0.1) = 0.02,
0.02(0.1) = 0.002, 0.002(0.1) = 0.0002, 0.0002(0.1)
= 0.00002.
2, 0.2, 0.02, 0.002, 0.0002, 0.00002

70. $a_1 = -1000, r = 0.1$

$-1000, -1000(0.1) = -100, -100(0.1) = -10, -$
$10(0.1) = -1, -1(0.1) = -0.1, -0.1(0.1) = -0.01$
$-1000, -100, -10, -1, -0.1, -0.01$

71. $a_1 = 4, r = 2$

$$a_7 = 4(2)^{7-1}$$
$$= 4(2)^6$$
$$= 4(64)$$
$$= 256$$

72. $a_1 = 4, r = 3$

$$a_5 = 4(3)^{5-1}$$
$$= 4(3)^4$$
$$= 4(81)$$
$$= 324$$

73. $a_1 = 2, r = 3$

$$a_{20} = 2(3)^{20-1}$$
$$= 2(3)^{19}$$
$$= 2,324,522,934$$
$$\approx 2.32 \times 10^9$$

74. $a_1 = 2, r = 2$

$$a_{20} = 2(2)^{20-1}$$
$$= 2(2)^{19}$$
$$= 1,048,576$$

75. $a_1 = 50, r = 1$

$$a_{100} = 50(1)^{100-1}$$
$$= 50(1)^{99}$$
$$= 50$$

76. $a_1 = 60, r = 1$

$$a_{200} = 60(1)^{200-1}$$
$$= 60(1)^{199}$$
$$= 60$$

77. $a_1 = 5, r = -2$

$$a_7 = 5(-2)^{7-1}$$
$$= 5(-2)^6$$
$$= 320$$

78. $a_1 = 4, r = -3$

$$a_4 = 4(-3)^{4-1}$$
$$= 4(-3)^3$$
$$= -108$$

79. $a_1 = 2, r = -1$

$$a_{30} = 2(-1)^{30-1}$$
$$= 2(-1)^{29}$$
$$= -2$$

80. $a_1 = 6, r = -1$

$$a_{40} = 6(-1)^{40-1}$$
$$= 6(-1)^{39}$$
$$= -6$$

81. $a_1 = -2, r = -3$

$$a_6 = -2(-3)^{6-1}$$
$$= -2(-3)^5$$
$$= 486$$

82. $a_1 = -5, r = -2$

$$a_5 = -5(-2)^{5-1}$$
$$= -5(-2)^4$$
$$= -80$$

83. $a_1 = 6, r = \dfrac{1}{2}$

$$a_8 = 6\left(\frac{1}{2}\right)^{8-1}$$
$$= 6\left(\frac{1}{2}\right)^7$$
$$= \frac{6}{128}$$
$$= \frac{3}{64}$$

84. $a_1 = 12, r = \dfrac{1}{2}$

$$a_8 = 12\left(\dfrac{1}{2}\right)^{8-1}$$

$$= 12\left(\dfrac{1}{2}\right)^7$$

$$= \dfrac{12}{128}$$

$$= \dfrac{3}{32}$$

85. $a_1 = 18, r = -\dfrac{1}{3}$

$$a_6 = 18\left(-\dfrac{1}{3}\right)^{6-1}$$

$$= 18\left(-\dfrac{1}{3}\right)^5$$

$$= -\dfrac{18}{243}$$

$$= -\dfrac{2}{27}$$

86. $a_1 = 9, r = -\dfrac{1}{3}$

$$a_4 = 9\left(-\dfrac{1}{3}\right)^{4-1}$$

$$= 9\left(-\dfrac{1}{3}\right)^3$$

$$= -\dfrac{9}{27}$$

$$= -\dfrac{1}{3}$$

87. $a_1 = 1000, r = -\dfrac{1}{2}$

$$a_{40} = 1000\left(-\dfrac{1}{2}\right)^{40-1}$$

$$= 1000\left(-\dfrac{1}{2}\right)^{39}$$

$$\approx -1.82 \times 10^{-9}$$

88. $a_1 = 8000, r = -\dfrac{1}{2}$

$$a_{30} = 8000\left(-\dfrac{1}{2}\right)^{30-1}$$

$$= 8000\left(-\dfrac{1}{2}\right)^{29}$$

$$\approx -0.000014901$$

89. $a_1 = 1,000,000, r = 0.1$

$$a_8 = 1,000,000(0.1)^{8-1}$$

$$= 1,000,000(0.1)^7$$

$$= 0.1$$

90. $a_1 = 40,000, r = 0.1$

$$a_8 = 40,000(0.1)^{8-1}$$

$$= 40,000(0.1)^7$$

$$= 0.004$$

91. $a_n = a_1 r^{n-1}$ with $a_1 = 3$ and $r = \dfrac{12}{3} = 4$. Thus $a_n = 3(4)^{n-1}$

$a_7 = 3(4)^{7-1} = 3(4)^6 = 3(4096) = 12,288$

92. $a_n = a_1 r^{n-1}$ with $a_1 = 3$ and $r = \dfrac{15}{3} = 5$. Thus $a_n = 3(5)^{n-1}$

$a_7 = 3(5)^{7-1} = 3(5)^6 = 3(15,625) = 46,875$

93. $a_n = a_1 r^{n-1}$ with $a_1 = 18$ and $r = \dfrac{6}{18} = \dfrac{1}{3}$. Thus $a_n = 18\left(\dfrac{1}{3}\right)^{n-1}$

$a_7 = 18\left(\dfrac{1}{3}\right)^{7-1} = 18\left(\dfrac{1}{3}\right)^6 = 18\left(\dfrac{1}{729}\right) = \dfrac{18}{729} = \dfrac{2}{81}$

94. $a_n = a_1 r^{n-1}$ with $a_1 = 12$ and $r = \dfrac{6}{12} = \dfrac{1}{2}$. Thus $a_n = 12\left(\dfrac{1}{2}\right)^{n-1}$

$a_7 = 12\left(\dfrac{1}{2}\right)^{7-1} = 12\left(\dfrac{1}{2}\right)^6 = 12\left(\dfrac{1}{64}\right) = \dfrac{12}{64} = \dfrac{3}{16}$

95. $a_n = a_1 r^{n-1}$ with $a_1 = 1.5$ and $r = \dfrac{-3}{1.5} = -2$. Thus $a_n = 1.5(-2)^{n-1}$

$a_7 = 1.5(-2)^{7-1} = 1.5(-2)^6 = 1.5(64) = 96$

96. $a_n = a_1 r^{n-1}$ with $a_1 = 5$ and $r = \dfrac{-1}{5}$. Thus $a_n = 5\left(-\dfrac{1}{5}\right)^{n-1}$

$a_7 = 5\left(-\dfrac{1}{5}\right)^{7-1} = 5\left(-\dfrac{1}{5}\right)^6 = 5\left(\dfrac{1}{15,625}\right) = \dfrac{5}{15,625} = \dfrac{1}{3125}$

97. $a_n = a_1 r^{n-1}$ with $a_1 = 0.0004$ and $r = \dfrac{-0.004}{0.0004} = -10$. Thus $a_n = 0.0004(-10)^{n-1}$

$a_7 = 0.0004(-10)^{7-1} = 0.0004(-10)^6 = 0.0004(1,000,000) = 400$

98. $a_n = a_1 r^{n-1}$ with $a_1 = 0.0007$ and $r = \dfrac{-0.007}{0.0007} = -10$. Thus $a_n = 0.0007(-10)^{n-1}$

$a_7 = 0.0007(-10)^{7-1} = 0.0007(-10)^6 = 0.0007(1,000,000) = 700$

99. The common difference of the arithmetic sequence is 4.
$2 + 4 = 6, 6 + 4 = 10, 10 + 4 = 14,$
$14 + 4 = 18, 18 + 4 = 22$
$2, 6, 10, 14, 18, 22, \ldots$

100. The common difference of the arithmetic sequence is 5.
$3 + 5 = 8, 8 + 5 = 13, 13 + 5 = 18, 18 + 5 = 23, 23 + 5 = 28$
$3, 8, 13, 18, 23, 28, \ldots$

101. The common ratio of the geometric sequence is 3.
$5 \cdot 3 = 15, 15 \cdot 3 = 45, 45 \cdot 3 = 135, \quad 5, 15, 45, 135, 405, 1215, \ldots$
$135 \cdot 3 = 405, 405 \cdot 3 = 1215$

102. The common ratio of the geometric sequence is 2.
$15 \cdot 2 = 30, 30 \cdot 2 = 60, 60 \cdot 2 = 120,$
$120 \cdot 2 = 240, 240 \cdot 2 = 480$
$15, 30, 60, 120, 240, 480, \ldots$

103. The common difference of the arithmetic sequence is 5.
$-7 + 5 = -2, -2 + 5 = 3, 3 + 5 = 8,$
$8 + 5 = 13, 13 + 5 = 18.$
$-7, -2, 3, 8, 13, 18, \ldots$

104. The common difference of the arithmetic sequence is 4.
$-9 + 4 = -5, -5 + 4 = -1, -1 + 4 = 3, 3 + 4 = 7,$
$7 + 4 = 11$
$-9, -5, -1, 3, 7, 11, \ldots$

105. The common ratio of the geometric sequence is $\frac{1}{2}$.

$$3 \cdot \frac{1}{2} = \frac{3}{2}, \frac{3}{2} \cdot \frac{1}{2} = \frac{3}{4}, \frac{3}{4} \cdot \frac{1}{2} = \frac{3}{8}, \frac{3}{8} \cdot \frac{1}{2} = \frac{3}{16}$$

$$\frac{3}{16} \cdot \frac{1}{2} = \frac{3}{32}$$

$$3, \frac{3}{2}, \frac{3}{4}, \frac{3}{8}, \frac{3}{16}, \frac{3}{32}, \dots$$

106. The common ratio of the geometric sequence is $\frac{1}{2}$.

$$6 \cdot \frac{1}{2} = 3, \ 3 \cdot \frac{1}{2} = \frac{3}{2}, \frac{3}{2} \cdot \frac{1}{2} = \frac{3}{4}, \frac{3}{4} \cdot \frac{1}{2} = \frac{3}{8},$$

$$\frac{3}{8} \cdot \frac{1}{2} = \frac{3}{16}$$

$$6, 3, \frac{3}{2}, \frac{3}{4}, \frac{3}{8}, \frac{3}{16}, \dots$$

107. The common difference of the arithmetic sequence is $\frac{1}{2}$.

$$\frac{1}{2} + \frac{1}{2} = 1, \ 1 + \frac{1}{2} = \frac{3}{2}, \frac{3}{2} + \frac{1}{2} = 2, \ 2 + \frac{1}{2} = \frac{5}{2},$$

$$\frac{5}{2} + \frac{1}{2} = 3$$

$$\frac{1}{2}, 1, \frac{3}{2}, 2, \frac{5}{2}, 3, \dots$$

108. The common difference of the arithmetic sequence is $\frac{1}{3}$.

$$\frac{2}{3} + \frac{1}{3} = 1, \ 1 + \frac{1}{3} = \frac{4}{3}, \frac{4}{3} + \frac{1}{3} = \frac{5}{3}, \frac{5}{3} + \frac{1}{3} = 2,$$

$$2 + \frac{1}{3} = \frac{7}{3}$$

$$\frac{2}{3}, 1, \frac{4}{3}, \frac{5}{3}, 2, \frac{7}{3}, \dots$$

109. The common ratio of the geometric sequence is -1.
$7(-1) = -7, \ -7(-1) = 7, \ 7(-1) = -7,$
$-7(-1) = 7, \ 7(-1) = -7$
$7, -7, 7, -7, 7, -7, \dots$

110. The common ratio of the geometric sequence is -1.
$6(-1) = -6, \ -6(-1) = 6, \ 6(-1) = -6, \ -6(-1) = 6, \ 6(-1) = -6$
$6, -6, 6, -6, 6, -6, \dots$

111. The common difference of the arithmetic sequence is -14.
$7 - 14 = -7, \ -7 - 14 = -21, \ -21 - 14 = -35, \ -35 - 14 = -49, \ -49 - 14 = -63$
$7, -7, -21, -35, -49, -63, \dots$

112. The common difference of the arithmetic sequence is -12.
$6 - 12 = -6, -6 - 12 = -18, -18 - 12 = -30,$
$-30 - 12 = -42, 42 - 12 = -54$
$6, -6, -18, -30, -42, -54, \ldots$

113. The common ratio of the geometric sequence is $\sqrt{5}$.
$\sqrt{5} \cdot \sqrt{5} = 5, 5 \cdot \sqrt{5} = 5\sqrt{5}, 5\sqrt{5} \cdot \sqrt{5} = 25,$
$25 \cdot \sqrt{5} = 25\sqrt{5}, 25\sqrt{5} \cdot \sqrt{5} = 125$
$\sqrt{5}, 5, 5\sqrt{5}, 25, 25\sqrt{5}, 125, \ldots$

114. The common ratio of the geometric sequence is $\sqrt{3}$.
$\sqrt{3} \cdot \sqrt{3} = 3, 3 \cdot \sqrt{3} = 3\sqrt{3}, 3\sqrt{3} \cdot \sqrt{3} = 9,$
$9 \cdot \sqrt{3} = 9\sqrt{3}, 9\sqrt{3} \cdot \sqrt{3} = 27$
$\sqrt{3}, 3, 3\sqrt{3}, 9, 9\sqrt{3}, 27, \ldots$

115. a. $a_n = a_1 + (n-1)d$ with $a_1 = 150$ and $d = 1.7$.
$$a_n = 150 + (n-1)(1.7)$$
$$= 150 + 1.7n - 1.7$$
$$= 1.7n + 148.3$$

   b. $a_n = 1.7n + 148.3$ with $n = 2006 - 1969 = 37$
$$a_{37} = 1.7(37) + 148.3 = 211.2$$
The average American will consume about 211.2 pounds of vegetables in 2006.

116. a. $a_n = a_1 + (n-1)d$ with $a_1 = 100$ and $d = 0.9$.
$$a_n = 100 + (n-1)(0.9)$$
$$= 100 + 0.9n - 0.9$$
$$= 0.9n + 99.1$$

   b. $a_n = 0.9n + 99.1$ with $n = 2006 - 1969 = 37$
$$a_{37} = 0.9(37) + 99.1 = 132.4$$
The average American will consume about 132.4 pounds of fruit in 2006.

117. Company A: $a_{10} = 24000 + (10-1)1600 = 38,400$
Company B: $b_{10} = 28000 + (10-1)1000 = 37,000$
Company A will pay \$1400 more in year 10.

118. Company A: $a_{10} = 23000 + (10-1)1200 = 33,800$
Company B: $b_{10} = 26000 + (10-1)800 = 33,200$
Company A will pay \$600 more in year 10.

119. $a_1 = 1, r = 2$
$$a_{15} = 1(2)^{15-1}$$
$$= 2^{14}$$
$$= 16,384$$
On the 15th day you will put aside \$16,384.

120. $a_1 = 1, r = 2$

$a_{30} = 1(2)^{30-1}$

$= 2^{29}$

$= 536,870,912$

On the 30th day you will put aside $536,870,912.

121. $a_7 = \$3,000,000(1.04)^{7-1}$

$\approx \$3,795,957$ salary in year 7.

122. $a_6 = \$30,000(1.05)^{6-1}$

$\approx \$38,288$ salary in year 6.

123. a. $\dfrac{30.15}{29.76} \approx 1.013; \quad \dfrac{30.54}{30.15} \approx 1.013; \quad \dfrac{30.94}{30.54} \approx 1.013; \quad \dfrac{31.34}{30.94} \approx 1.013$

$\dfrac{31.75}{31.34} \approx 1.013; \quad \dfrac{32.16}{31.75} \approx 1.013; \quad \dfrac{32.58}{32.16} \approx 1.013; \quad r \approx 1.013$

b. $a_n = 29.76(1.013)^{n-1}$

c. $a_{11} \approx 29.76(1.013)^{11-1} \approx 33.86$ million in 2000.

The geometric sequence described the actual population very well.

124. a. $\dfrac{17.35}{16.99} \approx 1.021; \quad \dfrac{17.71}{17.35} \approx 1.021; \quad \dfrac{18.08}{17.71} \approx 1.021; \quad \dfrac{18.46}{18.08} \approx 1.021$

$\dfrac{18.85}{18.46} \approx 1.021; \quad \dfrac{19.25}{18.85} \approx 1.021; \quad \dfrac{19.65}{19.25} \approx 1.021; \quad r \approx 1.021$

b. $a_n = 16.99(1.021)^{n-1}$

c. $a_{11} \approx 16.99(1.021)^{11-1} \approx 20.91$ million in 2000.

The geometric sequence described the actual population very well.

125-131. Answers will vary.

132. d is true. The common difference is –4.

5, 1, –3, –7, …

133. d is true.

134. Company A:

$a_1 = 20,000, d = 1000$

$a_6 = 20,000 + (6-1)(1000)$

$= 20,000 + 5000$

$= 25,000$

Company B:

$a_1 = 20,000, r = 1.05$

$$a_6 = 20,000(1.05)^{6-1}$$
$$= 20,000(1.05)^5$$
$$= 25,525.63$$

Company B will pay more in the sixth year.

135. $a_1 = 7721, d = -905$
$$a_{327} = 7721 + (327 - 1)(-905)$$
$$= 7721 - 295,030$$
$$= -287,309$$

136. $a_1 = -3121, d = 698$
$$a_{3126} = -3121 + (3126 - 1)(698)$$
$$= -3121 + 3125(698)$$
$$= -3121 + 2,181,250$$
$$= 2,178,129$$

137. $a_1 = 7721, r = 5$
$$a_{32} = 7721(5)^{32-1}$$
$$= 7721(5)^{31}$$
$$\approx 3.595 \times 10^{25}$$

138. $a_1 = 196,200, r = 0.925$
$$a_{126} = 196,200(0.925)^{126-1}$$
$$\approx 11.4925$$

Chapter 5 Review Exercises

1. 238,632
   2: Yes; The last digit is 2.
   3: Yes; The sum of the digits is 24, which is divisible by 3.
   4: Yes; The last two digits form 32, which is divisible by 4.
   5: No; The last number does not end in 0 or 5.
   6: Yes; The number is divisible by both 2 and 3.
   8: Yes; The last three digits form 632, which is divisible by 8.
   9: No; The sum of the digits is 24, which is not divisible by 9.
   10: No; the last digit is not 0.
   12: Yes; The number is divisible by both 3 and 4.
   The number is divisible by 2, 3, 4, 6, 8, 12.

2. 421,153,470
   2: Yes; The last digit is 0.
   3: Yes; The sum of the digits is 27, which is divisible by 3.
   4: No; The last two digits form 70, which is not divisible by 4.
   5: Yes; The number ends in 0.
   6: Yes; The number is divisible by both 2 and 3.
   8: No; The last three digits form 470, which is not divisible by 8.
   9: Yes; The sum of the digits is 27, which is divisible by 9.
   10: Yes; The number ends in 0.
   12: No; The number is not divisible by both 3 and 4.
   The number is divisible by 2, 3, 5, 6, 9, 10.

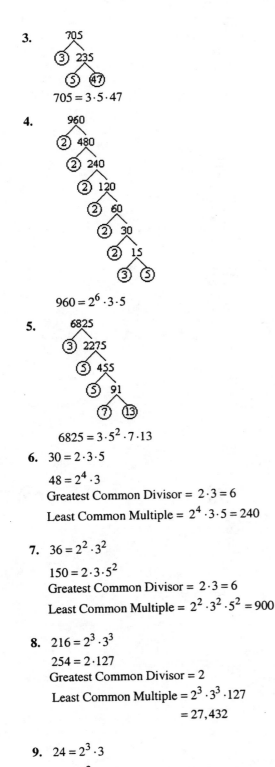

3.

$705 = 3 \cdot 5 \cdot 47$

4.

$960 = 2^6 \cdot 3 \cdot 5$

5.

$6825 = 3 \cdot 5^2 \cdot 7 \cdot 13$

6. $30 = 2 \cdot 3 \cdot 5$

$48 = 2^4 \cdot 3$

Greatest Common Divisor $= 2 \cdot 3 = 6$

Least Common Multiple $= 2^4 \cdot 3 \cdot 5 = 240$

7. $36 = 2^2 \cdot 3^2$

$150 = 2 \cdot 3 \cdot 5^2$

Greatest Common Divisor $= 2 \cdot 3 = 6$

Least Common Multiple $= 2^2 \cdot 3^2 \cdot 5^2 = 900$

8. $216 = 2^3 \cdot 3^3$

$254 = 2 \cdot 127$

Greatest Common Divisor $= 2$

Least Common Multiple $= 2^3 \cdot 3^3 \cdot 127$

$$= 27,432$$

9. $24 = 2^3 \cdot 3$

$60 = 2^2 \cdot 3 \cdot 5$

Greatest Common Divisor $= 2^2 \cdot 3 = 12$

There can be 12 people placed on each team.

10. $42 = 2 \cdot 3 \cdot 7$

$56 = 2^3 \cdot 7$

Least Common Multiple $= 2^3 \cdot 3 \cdot 7 = 168$

$168 \div 60 = 2.8$ or 2 hours and 48 minutes. They will begin again at 11:48 A.M.

11. $-93 < 17$ because -93 is to the left of 17 on the number line.

12. $-2 > -200$ because -2 is to the right of -200 on the number line.

13. $|-860| = 860$ because -860 is 860 units from 0 on the number line.

14. $|53| = 53$ because 53 is 53 units from 0 on the number line.

15. $|0| = 0$ because 0 is 0 units from 0 on the number line.

16. $8 + (-11) = -3$

17. $-6 + (-5) = -11$

18. $-7 - 8 = -7 + (-8) = -15$

19. $-7 - (-8) = -7 + 8 = 1$

20. $(-9)(-11) = 99$

21. $5(-3) = -15$

22. $\dfrac{-36}{-4} = 9$

23. $\dfrac{20}{-5} = -4$

24. $-40 \div 5 \cdot 2 = -8 \cdot 2 = -16$

25. $-6 + (-2) \cdot 5 = -6 + (-10) = -16$

26. $6 - 4(-3 + 2) = 6 - 4(-1) = 6 + 4 = 10$

27. $28 \div (2 - 4^2) = 28 \div (2 - 16)$

$$= 28 \div (-14)$$

$$= -2$$

28. $36 - 24 \div 4 \cdot 3 - 1 = 36 - 6 \cdot 3 - 1$
$$= 36 - 18 - 1$$
$$= 18 - 1$$
$$= 17$$

29. $40 = 2^3 \cdot 5$

$75 = 3 \cdot 5^2$

Greatest Common Divisor is 5.

$$\frac{40}{75} = \frac{40 \div 5}{75 \div 5} = \frac{8}{15}$$

30. $36 = 2^2 \cdot 3^2$

$150 = 2 \cdot 3 \cdot 5^2$

Greatest Common Divisor is $2 \cdot 3$ or 6.

$$\frac{36}{150} = \frac{36 \div 6}{150 \div 6} = \frac{6}{25}$$

31. $165 = 3 \cdot 5 \cdot 11$

$180 = 2^2 \cdot 3^2 \cdot 5$

Greatest Common Divisor is $3 \cdot 5$ or 15.

$$\frac{165}{180} = \frac{165 \div 15}{180 \div 15} = \frac{11}{12}$$

32. $5\frac{9}{11} = \frac{11 \cdot 5 + 9}{11} = \frac{64}{11}$

33. $-3\frac{2}{7} = -\frac{7 \cdot 3 + 2}{7} = -\frac{23}{7}$

34. $\frac{27}{5} = 5\frac{2}{5}$

35. $-\frac{17}{9} = -1\frac{8}{9}$

36. $\frac{4}{5} = 0.8$

$$\begin{array}{r} 0.8 \\ 5)\overline{4.0} \\ \underline{40} \\ 0 \end{array}$$

37. $\frac{3}{7} = 0.\overline{428571}$

$$\begin{array}{r} 0.4285714 \\ 7)\overline{3.0000000} \\ \underline{28} \\ 20 \\ \underline{14} \\ 60 \\ \underline{56} \\ 40 \\ \underline{35} \\ 50 \\ \underline{49} \\ 10 \\ \underline{7} \\ 30 \\ \underline{28} \\ 2 \end{array}$$

38. $\frac{5}{8} = 0.625$

$$\begin{array}{r} 0.625 \\ 8)\overline{5.000} \\ \underline{48} \\ 20 \\ \underline{16} \\ 40 \\ \underline{40} \\ 0 \end{array}$$

39. $\frac{9}{16} = 0.5625$

$$\begin{array}{r} 0.5625 \\ 16)\overline{9.0000} \\ \underline{80} \\ 100 \\ \underline{96} \\ 40 \\ \underline{32} \\ 80 \\ \underline{80} \\ 0 \end{array}$$

40. $0.6 = \frac{6}{10} = \frac{6 \div 2}{10 \div 2} = \frac{3}{5}$

41. $0.68 = \frac{68}{100}$

$68 = 2^2 \cdot 17$

$100 = 2^2 \cdot 5^2$

Greatest Common Divisor is 2^2 or 4.

$$\frac{68 \div 4}{100 \div 4} = \frac{17}{25}$$

42. $0.588 = \dfrac{588}{1000}$

$588 = 2^2 \cdot 3 \cdot 7^2$

$1000 = 2^3 \cdot 5^3$

Greatest Common Divisor is 2^2 or 4.

$\dfrac{588 \div 4}{1000 \div 4} = \dfrac{147}{250}$

43. $0.0084 = \dfrac{84}{10,000}$

$84 = 2^2 \cdot 3 \cdot 7$

$10,000 = 2^4 \cdot 5^4$

Greatest Common Divisor is 2^2 or 4.

$\dfrac{84 \div 4}{10,000 \div 4} = \dfrac{21}{2500}$

44. $n = 0.555\ldots$
$10n = 5.555\ldots$

$10n = 5.555\ldots$
$-\quad n = 0.555\ldots$
$\overline{\quad 9n = 5 \quad}$

$n = \dfrac{5}{9}$

45. $n = 0.3434\ldots$
$100n = 34.3434\ldots$

$100n = 34.3434\ldots$
$-\quad n = 0.3434\ldots$
$\overline{\quad 99n = 34 \quad}$

$n = \dfrac{34}{99}$

46. $n = 0.113113\ldots$
$1000n = 113.113113\ldots$

$1000n = 113.113113\ldots$
$-\quad n = 0.113113\ldots$
$\overline{\quad 999n = 113 \quad}$

$n = \dfrac{113}{999}$

47. $\dfrac{3}{5} \cdot \dfrac{7}{10} = \dfrac{3 \cdot 7}{5 \cdot 10} = \dfrac{21}{50}$

48. $\left(3\dfrac{1}{3}\right)\left(1\dfrac{3}{4}\right) = \dfrac{10}{3} \cdot \dfrac{7}{4} = \dfrac{70}{12} = \dfrac{35}{6}$ or $5\dfrac{5}{6}$

49. $\dfrac{4}{5} \div \dfrac{3}{10} = \dfrac{4}{5} \cdot \dfrac{10}{3} = \dfrac{4 \cdot 10}{5 \cdot 3} = \dfrac{40}{15} = \dfrac{8}{3}$

50. $-1\dfrac{2}{3} \div 6\dfrac{2}{3} = -\dfrac{5}{3} \div \dfrac{20}{3} = -\dfrac{5}{3} \cdot \dfrac{3}{20} = -\dfrac{15}{60} = -\dfrac{1}{4}$

51. $\dfrac{2}{9} + \dfrac{4}{9} = \dfrac{2+4}{9} = \dfrac{6}{9} = \dfrac{2}{3}$

52. $\dfrac{7}{9} + \dfrac{5}{12} = \dfrac{7}{9} \cdot \dfrac{4}{4} + \dfrac{5}{12} \cdot \dfrac{3}{3}$

$= \dfrac{28}{36} + \dfrac{15}{36}$

$= \dfrac{28+15}{36}$

$= \dfrac{43}{36}$

53. $\dfrac{3}{4} - \dfrac{2}{15} = \dfrac{3}{4} \cdot \dfrac{15}{15} - \dfrac{2}{15} \cdot \dfrac{4}{4}$

$= \dfrac{45}{60} - \dfrac{8}{60}$

$= \dfrac{45-8}{60}$

$= \dfrac{37}{60}$

54. $\dfrac{1}{3} + \dfrac{1}{2} \cdot \dfrac{4}{5} = \dfrac{1}{3} + \dfrac{1 \cdot 4}{2 \cdot 5}$

$= \dfrac{1}{3} + \dfrac{4}{10}$

$= \dfrac{1}{3} + \dfrac{2}{5}$

$= \dfrac{1}{3} \cdot \dfrac{5}{5} + \dfrac{2}{5} \cdot \dfrac{3}{3}$

$= \dfrac{5}{15} + \dfrac{6}{15}$

$= \dfrac{11}{15}$

55. $\dfrac{3}{8}\left(\dfrac{1}{2}+\dfrac{1}{3}\right)=\dfrac{3}{8}\left(\dfrac{1}{2}\cdot\dfrac{3}{3}+\dfrac{1}{3}\cdot\dfrac{2}{2}\right)$

$\qquad\qquad = \dfrac{3}{8}\left(\dfrac{3}{6}+\dfrac{2}{6}\right)$

$\qquad\qquad = \dfrac{3}{8}\left(\dfrac{5}{6}\right)$

$\qquad\qquad = \dfrac{15}{48}$

$\qquad\qquad = \dfrac{5}{16}$

56. $\dfrac{1}{7}+\dfrac{1}{8}=\dfrac{1}{7}\cdot\dfrac{8}{8}+\dfrac{1}{8}\cdot\dfrac{7}{7}$

$\qquad\quad = \dfrac{8}{56}+\dfrac{7}{56}$

$\qquad\quad = \dfrac{15}{56}$

$\dfrac{15}{56}\div 2 = \dfrac{15}{56}\cdot\dfrac{1}{2}=\dfrac{15}{112}$

57. $\dfrac{3}{4}+\dfrac{3}{5}=\dfrac{3}{4}\cdot\dfrac{5}{5}+\dfrac{3}{5}\cdot\dfrac{4}{4}$

$\qquad\quad = \dfrac{15}{20}+\dfrac{12}{20}$

$\qquad\quad = \dfrac{27}{20}$

$\dfrac{27}{20}\div 2 = \dfrac{27}{20}\cdot\dfrac{1}{2}=\dfrac{27}{40}$

58. $4\dfrac{1}{2}\cdot\dfrac{15}{6}=\dfrac{9}{2}\cdot\dfrac{15}{6}=\dfrac{135}{12}=\dfrac{45}{4}$ or $11\dfrac{1}{4}$ pounds.

59. $1-\left(\dfrac{1}{4}+\dfrac{1}{3}\right)=1-\left(\dfrac{1}{4}\cdot\dfrac{3}{3}+\dfrac{1}{3}\cdot\dfrac{4}{4}\right)$

$\qquad\qquad\qquad = 1-\left(\dfrac{3}{12}+\dfrac{4}{12}\right)$

$\qquad\qquad\qquad = \dfrac{12}{12}-\dfrac{7}{12}$

$\qquad\qquad\qquad = \dfrac{5}{12}$

At the end of the second day, $\dfrac{5}{12}$ of the tank is filled with gas.

60. $\sqrt{28}=\sqrt{4\cdot 7}=\sqrt{4}\cdot\sqrt{7}=2\sqrt{7}$

61. $\sqrt{72}=\sqrt{36\cdot 2}=\sqrt{36}\cdot\sqrt{2}=6\sqrt{2}$

62. $\sqrt{150}=\sqrt{25\cdot 6}=\sqrt{25}\cdot\sqrt{6}=5\sqrt{6}$

63. $\sqrt{300}=\sqrt{100\cdot 3}=\sqrt{100}\cdot\sqrt{3}=10\sqrt{3}$

64. $\sqrt{6}\cdot\sqrt{8}=\sqrt{6\cdot 8}=\sqrt{48}=\sqrt{16}\cdot\sqrt{3}=4\sqrt{3}$

65. $\sqrt{10}\cdot\sqrt{5}=\sqrt{10\cdot 5}$

$\qquad\qquad = \sqrt{50}$

$\qquad\qquad = \sqrt{25}\cdot\sqrt{2}$

$\qquad\qquad = 5\sqrt{2}$

66. $\dfrac{\sqrt{24}}{\sqrt{2}}=\sqrt{\dfrac{24}{2}}=\sqrt{12}=\sqrt{4}\cdot\sqrt{3}=2\sqrt{3}$

67. $\dfrac{\sqrt{27}}{\sqrt{3}}=\sqrt{\dfrac{27}{3}}=\sqrt{9}=3$

68. $\sqrt{5}+4\sqrt{5}=1\sqrt{5}+4\sqrt{5}=(1+4)\sqrt{5}=5\sqrt{5}$

69. $7\sqrt{11}-13\sqrt{11}=(7-13)\sqrt{11}=-6\sqrt{11}$

70. $\sqrt{50}+\sqrt{8}=\sqrt{25}\cdot\sqrt{2}+\sqrt{4}\cdot\sqrt{2}$

$\qquad\qquad = 5\sqrt{2}+2\sqrt{2}$

$\qquad\qquad = (5+2)\sqrt{2}$

$\qquad\qquad = 7\sqrt{2}$

71. $\sqrt{3}-6\sqrt{27}=\sqrt{3}-6\sqrt{9}\cdot\sqrt{3}$

$\qquad\qquad = \sqrt{3}-6\cdot 3\sqrt{3}$

$\qquad\qquad = 1\sqrt{3}-18\sqrt{3}$

$\qquad\qquad = (1-18)\sqrt{3}$

$\qquad\qquad = -17\sqrt{3}$

72. $2\sqrt{18}+3\sqrt{8}=2\sqrt{9}\cdot\sqrt{2}+3\sqrt{4}\cdot\sqrt{2}$

$\qquad\qquad = 2\cdot 3\cdot\sqrt{2}+3\cdot 2\cdot\sqrt{2}$

$\qquad\qquad = 6\sqrt{2}+6\sqrt{2}$

$\qquad\qquad = (6+6)\sqrt{2}$

$\qquad\qquad = 12\sqrt{2}$

73. $\dfrac{30}{\sqrt{5}}=\dfrac{30}{\sqrt{5}}\cdot\dfrac{\sqrt{5}}{\sqrt{5}}=\dfrac{30\sqrt{5}}{\sqrt{25}}=\dfrac{30\sqrt{5}}{5}=6\sqrt{5}$

74. $\sqrt{\dfrac{2}{3}}=\dfrac{\sqrt{2}}{\sqrt{3}}=\dfrac{\sqrt{2}}{\sqrt{3}}\cdot\dfrac{\sqrt{3}}{\sqrt{3}}=\dfrac{\sqrt{6}}{\sqrt{9}}=\dfrac{\sqrt{6}}{3}$

75. $2\sqrt{5(40)} = 2\sqrt{200} = 2\sqrt{100 \cdot 2}$
$= 2 \cdot 10\sqrt{2} = 20\sqrt{2} \approx 28$ mph

76. $\left\{ -17, -\dfrac{9}{13}, 0, 0.75, \sqrt{2}, \pi, \sqrt{81} \right\}$

   a. Natural numbers:
      $\sqrt{81}$ because $\sqrt{81} = 9$

   b. Whole numbers: $0, \sqrt{81}$

   c. Integers: $-17, 0, \sqrt{81}$

   d. Rational numbers:
      $-17, -\dfrac{9}{13}, 0, 0.75, \sqrt{81}$

   e. Irrational numbers: $\sqrt{2}, \pi$

   f. Real numbers: All numbers in this set.

77. Answers will vary. Example: -3

78. Answers will vary. Example: $\dfrac{1}{2}$

79. Answers will vary: Example: $\sqrt{2}$

80. $3 + 17 = 17 + 3$
Commutative property of addition

81. $(6 \cdot 3) \cdot 9 = 6 \cdot (3 \cdot 9)$
Associative property of multiplication

82. $\sqrt{3}\left(\sqrt{5} + \sqrt{3}\right) = \sqrt{15} + 3$
Distributive property of multiplication over addition.

83. $(6 \cdot 9) \cdot 2 = 2 \cdot (6 \cdot 9)$
Commutative property of multiplication

84. $\sqrt{3}\left(\sqrt{5} + \sqrt{3}\right) = \left(\sqrt{5} + \sqrt{3}\right)\sqrt{3}$
Commutative property of multiplication

85. $(3 \cdot 7) + (4 \cdot 7) = (4 \cdot 7) + (3 \cdot 7)$
Commutative property of addition

86. Answers will vary. Example: $2 \div 6 = \dfrac{1}{3}$

87. Answers will vary. Example: $4 - 5 = -1$

88. $6 \cdot 6^2 = 6^1 \cdot 6^2 = 6^{1+2} = 6^3 = 216$

89. $2^3 \cdot 2^3 = 2^{3+3} = 2^6 = 64$

90. $(2^2)^2 = 2^{2 \cdot 2} = 2^4 = 16$

91. $(3^3)^2 = 3^{3 \cdot 2} = 3^6 = 729$

92. $\dfrac{5^6}{5^4} = 5^{6-4} = 5^2 = 25$

93. $7^0 = 1$

94. $(-7)^0 = 1$

95. $6^{-3} = \dfrac{1}{6^3} = \dfrac{1}{216}$

96. $2^{-4} = \dfrac{1}{2^4} = \dfrac{1}{16}$

97. $\dfrac{7^4}{7^6} = 7^{4-6} = 7^{-2} = \dfrac{1}{7^2} = \dfrac{1}{49}$

98. $3^5 \cdot 3^{-2} = 3^{5-2} = 3^3 = 27$

99. $4.6 \times 10^2 = 460$

100. $3.74 \times 10^4 = 37,400$

101. $2.55 \times 10^{-3} = 0.00255$

102. $7.45 \times 10^{-5} = 0.0000745$

103. $7520 = 7.52 \times 10^3$

104. $3,590,000 = 3.59 \times 10^6$

105. $0.00725 = 7.25 \times 10^{-3}$

106. $0.000000409 = 4.09 \times 10^{-7}$

107. $420 \times 10^{11} = \left(4.2 \times 10^2\right) \times 10^{11} = 4.2 \times 10^{13}$

108. $0.97 \times 10^{-4} = \left(9.7 \times 10^{-1}\right) \times 10^{-4} = 9.7 \times 10^{-5}$

109. $(3 \times 10^7)(1.3 \times 10^{-5}) = (3 \times 1.3) \times 10^{7-5}$

$$= 3.9 \times 10^2$$
$$= 390$$

110. $(5 \times 10^3)(2.3 \times 10^2) = (5 \times 2.3) \times 10^{3+2}$

$$= 11.5 \times 10^5$$
$$= 1.15 \times 10 \times 10^5$$
$$= 1.15 \times 10^6$$
$$= 1,150,000$$

111. $\dfrac{6.9 \times 10^3}{3 \times 10^5} = \left(\dfrac{6.9}{3}\right) \times 10^{3-5}$

$$= 2.3 \times 10^{-2}$$
$$= 0.023$$

112. $\dfrac{2.4 \times 10^{-4}}{6 \times 10^{-6}} = \left(\dfrac{2.4}{6}\right) \times 10^{-4-(-6)}$

$$= 0.4 \times 10^{-4+6}$$
$$= 0.4 \times 10^2$$
$$= 40$$

113. $(60,000)(540,000) = (6.0 \times 10^4)(5.4 \times 10^5)$

$$= (6.0 \times 5.4) \times 10^{4+5}$$
$$= 32.4 \times 10^9$$
$$= 3.24 \times 10 \times 10^9$$
$$= 3.24 \times 10^{10}$$

114. $(91,000)(0.0004) = (9.1 \times 10^4)(4 \times 10^{-4})$

$$= (9.1 \times 4) \times 10^{4-4}$$
$$= 36.4 \times 10^0$$
$$= 3.64 \times 10^1$$

115. $\dfrac{8,400,000}{4000} = \dfrac{8.4 \times 10^6}{4 \times 10^3}$

$$= \left(\dfrac{8.4}{4}\right) \times 10^{6-3}$$
$$= 2.1 \times 10^3$$

116. $\dfrac{0.000003}{0.00000006} = \dfrac{3 \times 10^{-6}}{6 \times 10^{-8}}$

$$= \left(\dfrac{3}{6}\right) \times 10^{-6-(-8)}$$
$$= 0.5 \times 10^2$$
$$= 5 \times 10^{-1} \times 10^2$$
$$= 5 \times 10^1$$

117. $\dfrac{10^9}{10^6} = 10^{9-6} = 10^3 = 1000$ years

118. $(2.8 \times 10^8) \times 150 = (2.8 \times 10^8)(1.5 \times 10^2)$

$$= (2.8 \times 1.5) \times 10^{8+2}$$
$$= \$4.2 \times 10^{10}$$

119. $2 \times 6.1 \times 10^9 = 12.2 \times 10^9$

$$= 1.22 \times 10 \times 10^9$$
$$= 1.22 \times 10^{10}$$

120. $a_1 = 7, d = 4$

$7, 7 + 4 = 11, 11 + 4 = 15, 15 + 4 = 19, 19 + 4 = 23,$
$23 + 4 = 27$
$7, 11, 15, 19, 23, 27$

121. $a_1 = -4, d = -5$

$-4, -4 - 5 = -9, -9 - 5 = -14, -14 - 5 = -19, -19 - 5$
$= -24, -24 - 5 = -29$
$-4, -9, -14, -19, -24, -29$

122. $a_1 = \dfrac{3}{2}, d = -\dfrac{1}{2}$

$\dfrac{3}{2}, \dfrac{3}{2} - \dfrac{1}{2} = \dfrac{2}{2} = 1, \dfrac{2}{2} - \dfrac{1}{2} = \dfrac{1}{2}, \dfrac{1}{2} - \dfrac{1}{2} = 0,$

$0 - \dfrac{1}{2} = -\dfrac{1}{2}, -\dfrac{1}{2} - \dfrac{1}{2} = -1$

$\dfrac{3}{2}, 1, \dfrac{1}{2}, 0, -\dfrac{1}{2}, -1$

123. $a_1 = 5, d = 3$

$a_6 = 5 + (6 - 1)(3)$
$$= 5 + 5(3)$$
$$= 5 + 15$$
$$= 20$$

124. $a_1 = -8, d = -2$

$$a_{12} = -8 + (12-1)(-2)$$
$$= -8 + 11(-2)$$
$$= -8 + (-22)$$
$$= -30$$

125. $a_1 = 14, d = -4$

$$a_{14} = 14 + (14-1)(-4)$$
$$= 14 + 13(-4)$$
$$= 14 + (-52)$$
$$= -38$$

126. $a_n = a_1 + (n-1)d$ with $a_1 = -7, d = 4$

$$a_n = -7 + (n-1)4$$
$$= -7 + 4n - 4$$
$$= 4n - 11$$

Thus $a_{20} = 4(20) - 11 = 69$.

127. $a_n = a_1 + (n-1)d$ with $a_1 = 200, d = -20$

$$a_n = 200 + (n-1)(-20)$$
$$= 200 - 20n + 20$$
$$= -20n + 220$$

Thus $a_{20} = -20(20) + 220 = -180$.

128. $a_1 = 3, r = 2$

$3, 3 \cdot 2 = 6, 6 \cdot 2 = 12, 12 \cdot 2 = 24,$
$24 \cdot 2 = 48, 48 \cdot 2 = 96$
$3, 6, 12, 24, 48, 96$

129. $a_1 = \dfrac{1}{2}, r = \dfrac{1}{2}$

$\dfrac{1}{2}, \dfrac{1}{2} \cdot \dfrac{1}{2} = \dfrac{1}{4}, \dfrac{1}{4} \cdot \dfrac{1}{2} = \dfrac{1}{8}, \dfrac{1}{8} \cdot \dfrac{1}{2} = \dfrac{1}{16},$

$\dfrac{1}{16} \cdot \dfrac{1}{2} = \dfrac{1}{32}, \dfrac{1}{32} \cdot \dfrac{1}{2} = \dfrac{1}{64}$

$\dfrac{1}{2}, \dfrac{1}{4}, \dfrac{1}{8}, \dfrac{1}{16}, \dfrac{1}{32}, \dfrac{1}{64}$

130. $a_1 = 16, r = -\dfrac{1}{2}$

$16, 16\left(-\dfrac{1}{2}\right) = -8, -8\left(-\dfrac{1}{2}\right) = 4, \ 4\left(-\dfrac{1}{2}\right) = -2,$

$-2\left(-\dfrac{1}{2}\right) = 1, 1\left(-\dfrac{1}{2}\right) = -\dfrac{1}{2}$

$16, -8, 4, -2, 1, -\dfrac{1}{2}$

131. $a_1 = 2, r = 3$

$$a_4 = 2(3)^{4-1}$$
$$= 2(3)^3$$
$$= 2(27)$$
$$= 54$$

132. $a_1 = 16, r = \dfrac{1}{2}$

$$a_6 = 16\left(\dfrac{1}{2}\right)^{6-1}$$
$$= 16\left(\dfrac{1}{2}\right)^5$$
$$= \dfrac{16}{32}$$
$$= \dfrac{1}{2}$$

133. $a_1 = -3, r = 2$

$$a_5 = -3(2)^{5-1}$$
$$= -3(2)^4$$
$$= -3(16)$$
$$= -48$$

134. $a_n = a_1 r^{n-1}$ with $a_1 = 1$ and $r = \dfrac{2}{1} = 2$. Thus

$$a_n = 2^{n-1}$$
$$a_8 = 2^{8-1} = 2^7 = 128$$

135. $a_n = a_1 r^{n-1}$ with $a_1 = 100$ and $r = \dfrac{10}{100} = \dfrac{1}{10}$. Thus

$$a_n = 100\left(\dfrac{1}{10}\right)^{n-1}$$
$$a_8 = 100\left(\dfrac{1}{10}\right)^{8-1}$$
$$= 100\left(\dfrac{1}{10}\right)^7$$
$$= \dfrac{100}{10,000,000}$$
$$= \dfrac{1}{100,000}$$

136. The common difference in the arithmetic sequence is 5.
$4 + 5 = 9, 9 + 5 = 14, 14 + 5 = 19,$
$19 + 5 = 24, 24 + 5 = 29$
$4, 9, 14, 19, 24, 29, \ldots$

137. The common ratio in the geometric sequence is 3.
$2 \cdot 3 = 6, 6 \cdot 3 = 18, 18 \cdot 3 = 54, 54 \cdot 3 = 162, 162 \cdot 3$
$= 486$
$2, 6, 18, 54, 162, 486, \ldots$

138. The common ratio in the geometric sequence is $\dfrac{1}{4}$.

$1 \cdot \dfrac{1}{4} = \dfrac{1}{4}, \dfrac{1}{4} \cdot \dfrac{1}{4} = \dfrac{1}{16}, \dfrac{1}{16} \cdot \dfrac{1}{4} = \dfrac{1}{64},$

$\dfrac{1}{64} \cdot \dfrac{1}{4} = \dfrac{1}{256}, \dfrac{1}{256} \cdot \dfrac{1}{4} = \dfrac{1}{1024}$

$1, \dfrac{1}{4}, \dfrac{1}{16}, \dfrac{1}{64}, \dfrac{1}{256}, \dfrac{1}{1024}, \ldots$

139. The common difference in the arithmetic sequence is –7.
$0 - 7 = -7, -7 - 7 = -14, -14 - 7 = -21, -21 - 7 = -28,$
$-28 - 7 = -35$
$0, -7, -14, -21, -28, -35, \ldots$

140. a. $a_n = a_1 + (n-1)d$ with $a_1 = 20$ and $d = 0.52$.
$a_n = 20 + (n-1)(0.52)$
$= 20 + 0.52n - 0.52$
$= 0.52n + 19.48$

b. $a_n = 0.52n + 19.48$ with
$a_{37} = 0.52(111) + 19.48 = 77.2$
It is predicted that white-collar workers will be 77.2% of the labor force by 2010.

141. a. $\dfrac{20.72}{19.96} \approx 1.038; \quad \dfrac{21.51}{20.72} \approx 1.038;$

$\dfrac{22.33}{21.51} \approx 1.038; \quad r \approx 1.038$

b. $a_n = 19.96(1.038)^{n-1}$

c. $n = 2008 - 1997 = 11$.
$a_{11} \approx 19.96(1.038)^{11-1} \approx 28.98$ million in 2008.

Chapter 5 Test

1. 391,248

2: Yes; the last digit is 8.

3: Yes; the sum of the digits is 27, which is divisible by 3.

4: Yes; the last two digits form 48, which is divisible by 4.

5: No; the number does not end in 0 or 5.

6: Yes; the number is divisible by both 2 and 3.

8: Yes; the last three digits form 248, which is divisible by 8.

9: Yes; the sum of the digits is 27, which is divisible by 9.

10: No; the number does not end in 0.

12: Yes; the number is divisible by both 3 and 4.

391, 248 is divisible by 2, 3, 4, 6, 8, 9, 12.

2.

$252 = 2^2 \cdot 3^2 \cdot 7$

3. $48 = 2^4 \cdot 3$
$72 = 2^3 \cdot 3^2$
Greatest Common Divisor $= 2^3 \cdot 3 = 24$
Least Common Multiple $= 2^4 \cdot 3^2 = 144$

4. $-6 - (5 - 12) = -6 - (-7) = -6 + 7 = 1$

5. $(-3)(-4) \div (7 - 10) = (-3)(-4) \div (-3)$
$= 12 \div (-3)$
$= -4$

6. $(6-8)^2 (5-7)^3 = (-2)^2 (-2)^3$
$= 4(-8)$
$= -32$

7. $\dfrac{7}{12} = 0.58\overline{3}$

$$
\begin{array}{r}
0.5833\ldots \\
12\overline{)7.0000} \\
60 \\
\overline{100} \\
96 \\
\overline{40} \\
36 \\
\overline{40} \\
36 \\
\overline{4}
\end{array}
$$

8. $n = 0.6464\ldots$

$100n = 64.6464\ldots$

$100n = 64.6464\ldots$

$\underline{-\quad n = 0.6464\ldots}$

$99n = 64$

$n = \dfrac{64}{99}$

9. $\left(-\dfrac{3}{7}\right) \div \left(-2\dfrac{1}{7}\right) = \left(-\dfrac{3}{7}\right) \div \left(-\dfrac{15}{7}\right)$

$\phantom{\left(-\dfrac{3}{7}\right) \div \left(-2\dfrac{1}{7}\right)} = \left(-\dfrac{3}{7}\right) \cdot \left(-\dfrac{7}{15}\right)$

$\phantom{\left(-\dfrac{3}{7}\right) \div \left(-2\dfrac{1}{7}\right)} = \dfrac{(-3)(-7)}{7 \cdot 15}$

$\phantom{\left(-\dfrac{3}{7}\right) \div \left(-2\dfrac{1}{7}\right)} = \dfrac{21}{105}$

$\phantom{\left(-\dfrac{3}{7}\right) \div \left(-2\dfrac{1}{7}\right)} = \dfrac{1}{5}$

10. $\dfrac{19}{24} - \dfrac{7}{40} = \dfrac{19}{24} \cdot \dfrac{5}{5} - \dfrac{7}{40} \cdot \dfrac{3}{3}$

$\phantom{\dfrac{19}{24} - \dfrac{7}{40}} = \dfrac{95}{120} - \dfrac{21}{120}$

$\phantom{\dfrac{19}{24} - \dfrac{7}{40}} = \dfrac{95 - 21}{120}$

$\phantom{\dfrac{19}{24} - \dfrac{7}{40}} = \dfrac{74}{120}$

$\phantom{\dfrac{19}{24} - \dfrac{7}{40}} = \dfrac{37}{60}$

11. $\dfrac{1}{2} - 8\left(\dfrac{1}{4} + 1\right) = \dfrac{1}{2} - 8\left(\dfrac{5}{4}\right)$

$\phantom{\dfrac{1}{2} - 8\left(\dfrac{1}{4} + 1\right)} = \dfrac{1}{2} - 10$

$\phantom{\dfrac{1}{2} - 8\left(\dfrac{1}{4} + 1\right)} = \dfrac{1}{2} - \dfrac{20}{2}$

$\phantom{\dfrac{1}{2} - 8\left(\dfrac{1}{4} + 1\right)} = -\dfrac{19}{2}$

12. $\dfrac{1}{2} + \dfrac{2}{3} = \dfrac{1}{2} \cdot \dfrac{3}{3} + \dfrac{2}{3} \cdot \dfrac{2}{2}$

$\phantom{\dfrac{1}{2} + \dfrac{2}{3}} = \dfrac{3}{6} + \dfrac{4}{6}$

$\phantom{\dfrac{1}{2} + \dfrac{2}{3}} = \dfrac{7}{6}$

$\dfrac{7}{6} \div 2 = \dfrac{7}{6} \cdot \dfrac{1}{2} = \dfrac{7}{12}$

13. $\sqrt{10} \cdot \sqrt{5} = \sqrt{10 \cdot 5}$

$\phantom{\sqrt{10} \cdot \sqrt{5}} = \sqrt{50}$

$\phantom{\sqrt{10} \cdot \sqrt{5}} = \sqrt{25 \cdot 2}$

$\phantom{\sqrt{10} \cdot \sqrt{5}} = \sqrt{25} \cdot \sqrt{2}$

$\phantom{\sqrt{10} \cdot \sqrt{5}} = 5\sqrt{2}$

14. $\sqrt{50} + \sqrt{32} = \sqrt{25} \cdot \sqrt{2} + \sqrt{16} \cdot \sqrt{2}$

$\phantom{\sqrt{50} + \sqrt{32}} = 5\sqrt{2} + 4\sqrt{2}$

$\phantom{\sqrt{50} + \sqrt{32}} = (5 + 4)\sqrt{2}$

$\phantom{\sqrt{50} + \sqrt{32}} = 9\sqrt{2}$

15. $\dfrac{6}{\sqrt{2}} = \dfrac{6}{\sqrt{2}} \cdot \dfrac{\sqrt{2}}{\sqrt{2}} = \dfrac{6\sqrt{2}}{\sqrt{4}} = \dfrac{6\sqrt{2}}{2} = 3\sqrt{2}$

16. The rational numbers are -7, $-\dfrac{4}{5}$, 0, 0.25, $\sqrt{4}$, $\dfrac{22}{7}$.

17. Commutative property of addition

18. Distributive property of multiplication over addition

19. $3^3 \cdot 3^2 = 3^{3+2} = 3^5 = 243$

20. $\dfrac{4^6}{4^3} = 4^{6-3} = 4^3 = 64$

21. $8^{-2} = \dfrac{1}{8^2} = \dfrac{1}{64}$

22. $(3\times10^8)(2.5\times10^{-5}) = (3\times2.5)\times10^{8-5}$

$$= 7.5\times10^3$$
$$= 7500$$

23. $\dfrac{49,000}{0.007} = \dfrac{4.9\times10^4}{7\times10^{-3}}$

$$= \left(\dfrac{4.9}{7}\right)\times10^{4-(-3)}$$
$$= 0.7\times10^7$$
$$= 7\times10^{-1}\times10^7$$
$$= 7\times10^6$$

24. $\dfrac{3\times10^{10}}{7.5\times10^9} = \left(\dfrac{3}{7.5}\right)\times\left(\dfrac{10^{10}}{10^9}\right) = 0.4\times10 = 4$

25. $a_1 = 1, d = -5$

$1, 1-5 = -4, -4-5 = -9,$
$-9-5 = -14, -14-5 = -19,$
$-19-5 = -24$
$1, -4, -9, -14, -19, -24$

26. $a_1 = -2, d = 3$

$a_9 = -2+(9-1)(3)$
$\quad = -2+8(3)$
$\quad = -2+24$
$\quad = 22$

27. $a_1 = 16, r = \dfrac{1}{2}$

$16, 16\cdot\dfrac{1}{2} = 8, 8\cdot\dfrac{1}{2} = 4, 4\cdot\dfrac{1}{2} = 2, 2\cdot\dfrac{1}{2} = 1, 1\cdot\dfrac{1}{2} = \dfrac{1}{2}$

$16, 8, 4, 2, 1, \dfrac{1}{2}$

28. $a_1 = 5, r = 2$

$a_7 = 5(2)^{7-1}$
$\quad = 5(2)^6$
$\quad = 5(64)$
$\quad = 320$

Chapter 6
Algebra: Equations and Inequalities

Check Points 6.1

1. $6x + 9 = 6 \cdot 12 + 9 = 72 + 9 = 81$

2. $x^2 + 4x - 7 = (-5)^2 + 4(-5) - 7 = 25 - 20 - 7 = -2$

3. $-3x^2 + 4xy - y^2 = -3(5)^2 + 4(5)(6) - (6)^2$
   $= -3 \cdot 25 + 120 - 36$
   $= -75 + 120 - 36$
   $= 9$

4. Using $0.6(220 - a)$
   $0.6(220 - 40) = 0.6(180) = 108$
   Using $132 - 0.6a$
   $132 - 0.6(40) = 132 - 24 = 108$

5. a. $4y + 15y = (4 + 15)y = 19y$

   b. $7x - 20x = (7 - 20)x = -13x$

   c. $y + 99y = (1 + 99)y = 100y$

   d. $5x^2 - 15x^2 = (5 - 15)x^2 = -10x^2$

6. a. $8x + 7 + 10x + 3$
      $= 8x + 10x + 7 + 3$
      $= 18x + 10$

   b. $9x + 6y + 15 - 3x - 20y - 16$
      $= 9x - 3x + 6y - 20y + 15 - 16$
      $= 6x - 14y - 1$

7. $7(2x - 3) - 11x = 7 \cdot 2x - 7 \cdot 3 - 11x$
   $= 14x - 21 - 11x$
   $= 3x - 21$

8. $7x - (15x + 2y - 1) = 7x - 15x - 2y + 1$
   $= -8x - 2y + 1$

9. $P = 0.72x^2 + 9.4x + 783$
   $P = 0.72(40)^2 + 9.4(40) + 783$
   $P = 0.72(1600) + 9.4(40) + 783$
   $P = 1152 + 376 + 783$
   $P = 2311$
   The formula models the data quite well.

Exercise Set 6.1

1. $5x + 7 = 5 \cdot 4 + 7 = 20 + 7 = 27$

2. $9x + 6 = 9 \cdot 5 + 6 = 45 + 6 = 51$

3. $-7x - 5 = -7(-4) - 5 = 28 - 5 = 23$

4. $-6x - 13 = -6(-3) - 13 = 18 - 13 = 5$

5. $x^2 + 4 = 5^2 + 4 = 25 + 4 = 29$

6. $x^2 + 9 = 3^2 + 9 = 9 + 9 = 18$

7. $x^2 - 6 = (-2)^2 - 6 = 4 - 6 = -2$

8. $x^2 - 11 = (-3)^2 - 11 = 9 - 11 = -2$

9. $x^2 + 4x = (10)^2 + 4 \cdot 10 = 100 + 40 = 140$

10. $x^2 + 6x = 9^2 + 6 \cdot 9 = 81 + 54 = 135$

11. $8x^2 + 17 = 8(5)^2 + 17$
    $= 8(25) + 17$
    $= 200 + 17$
    $= 217$

12. $7x^2 + 25 = 7(3)^2 + 25$
    $= 7(9) + 25$
    $= 63 + 25$
    $= 88$

13. $x^2 - 5x = (-11)^2 - 5(-11)$
    $= 121 + 55$
    $= 176$

14. $x^2 - 8x = (-5)^2 - 8(-5) = 25 + 40 = 65$

15. $x^2 + 5x - 6 = 4^2 + 5 \cdot 4 - 6$
    $= 16 + 20 - 6$
    $= 30$

16. $x^2 + 7x - 4 = 6^2 + 7 \cdot 6 - 4 = 36 + 42 - 4 = 74$

17. $2x^2 - 5x - 6 = 2(-3)^2 - 5(-3) - 6$
    $= 2(9) - 5(-3) - 6$
    $= 18 + 15 - 6$
    $= 27$

18. $3x^2 - 4x - 9 = 3(-5)^2 - 4(-5) - 9$
$$= 3(25) - 4(-5) - 9$$
$$= 75 + 20 - 9$$
$$= 86$$

19. $-5x^2 - 4x - 11 = -5(-1)^2 - 4(-1) - 11$
$$= -5(1) - 4(-1) - 11$$
$$= -5 + 4 - 11$$
$$= -12$$

20. $-6x^2 - 11x - 17 = -6(-2)^2 - 11(-2) - 17$
$$= -6(4) - 11(-2) - 17$$
$$= -24 + 22 - 17$$
$$= -19$$

21. $4xy = 4(-3)(-1) = 12$

22. $6xy = 6(-4)(-1) = 24$

23. $x^2 - 4xy + y^2 = (-1)^2 - 4(-1)(-3) + (-3)^2$
$$= 1 - 4(-1)(-3) + 9$$
$$= 1 - 12 + 9$$
$$= -2$$

24. $x^2 - 6xy + y^2 = (-2)^2 - 6(-2)(-1) + (-1)^2$
$$= 4 - 6(-2)(-1) + 1$$
$$= 4 - 12 + 1$$
$$= -7$$

25. $3x^2 + 2xy + 5y^2 = 3(2)^2 + 2(2)(3) + 5(3)^2$
$$= 3(4) + 2(2)(3) + 5(9)$$
$$= 12 + 12 + 45$$
$$= 69$$

26. $4x^2 + 3xy + 2y^2 = 4(3)^2 + 3(3)(2) + 2(2)^2$
$$= 4(9) + 3(3)(2) + 2(4)$$
$$= 36 + 18 + 8$$
$$= 62$$

27. $-x^2 - 4xy + 3y^2$
$$= -(-1)^2 - 4(-1)(-2) + 3(-2)^2$$
$$= -(1) - 4(-1)(-2) + 3(4)$$
$$= -1 - 8 + 12$$
$$= 3$$

28. $-x^2 - 3xy + 4y^2 = -(-3)^2 - 3(-3)(-1) + 4(-1)^2$
$$= -(9) - 3(-3)(-1) + 4(1)$$
$$= -9 - 9 + 4$$
$$= -14$$

29. $x^3 - 5x^2 + 2 = (-4)^3 - 5(-4)^2 + 2$
$$= -64 - 5(16) + 2$$
$$= -64 - 80 + 2$$
$$= -142$$

30. $x^3 - 4x^2 + 3 = (-5)^3 - 4(-5)^2 + 3$
$$= -125 - 4(25) + 3$$
$$= -125 - 100 + 3$$
$$= -222$$

31. $3(x + 5) = 3 \cdot x + 3 \cdot 5 = 3x + 15$

32. $4(x + 6) = 4 \cdot x + 4 \cdot 6 = 4x + 24$

33. $8(2x + 3) = 8 \cdot 2x + 8 \cdot 3 = 16x + 24$

34. $9(2x + 5) = 9 \cdot 2x + 9 \cdot 5 = 18x + 45$

35. $\frac{1}{3}(12 + 6r) = \frac{1}{3} \cdot 12 + \frac{1}{3} \cdot 6r = 4 + 2r$

36. $\frac{1}{4}(12 + 8r) = \frac{1}{4} \cdot 12 + \frac{1}{4} \cdot 8r = 3 + 2r$

37. $5(x + y) = 5 \cdot x + 5 \cdot y = 5x + 5y$

38. $7(x + y) = 7 \cdot x + 7 \cdot y = 7x + 7y$

39. $3(x - 2) = 3 \cdot x - 3 \cdot 2 = 3x - 6$

40. $4(x - 5) = 4 \cdot x - 4 \cdot 5 = 4x - 20$

41. $2(4x - 5) = 2 \cdot 4x - 2 \cdot 5 = 8x - 10$

42. $6(3x - 2) = 6 \cdot 3x - 6 \cdot 2 = 18x - 12$

43. $-4(2x - 3) = -4(2x) - 4(-3) = -8x + 12$

44. $-3(4x - 5) = -3(4x) - 3(-5) = -12x + 15$

45. $-3(-2x + 4) = -3(-2x) - 3(4) = 6x - 12$

46. $-4(-3x + 2) = -4(-3x) - 4(2) = 12x - 8$

47. $7x + 10x = (7 + 10)x = 17x$

48. $5x + 13x = (5 + 13)x = 18x$

49. $11x - 3x = (11 - 3)x = 8x$

50. $14x - 5x = (14 - 5)x = 9x$

51. $x + 9x = 1x + 9x = (1 + 9)x = 10x$

52. $x + 12x = 1x + 12x = (1 + 12)x = 13x$

53. $5y - 7y = (5 - 7)y = -2y$

54. $8y - 11y = (8 - 11)y = -3y$

55. $-5y + y = -5y + 1y = (-5 + 1)y = -4y$

56. $-6y + y = -6y + 1y = (-6 + 1)y = -5y$

57. $2x^2 + 5x^2 = (2 + 5)x^2 = 7x^2$

58. $4x^2 + 6x^2 = (4 + 6)x^2 = 10x^2$

59. $5x^2 - 8x^2 = (5 - 8)x^2 = -3x^2$

60. $7x^2 - 10x^2 = (7 - 10)x^2 = -3x^2$

61. $5x - 3 + 6x = 5x + 6x - 3 = 11x - 3$

62. $8x - 7 + 10x = 8x + 10x - 7 = 18x - 7$

63. $11y + 12 - 3y - 2 = 11y - 3y + 12 - 2$
$= 8y + 10$

64. $13y + 15 - 2y - 11 = 13y - 2y + 15 - 11 = 11y + 4$

65. $3x + 10y + 12 + 7x - 2y - 14$
$= 3x + 7x + 10y - 2y + 12 - 14$
$= 10x + 8y - 2$

66. $5x + 7y + 13 - 2x - 3y - 15$
$= 5x - 2x + 7y - 3y + 13 - 15$
$= 3x + 4y - 2$

67. $5(3x + 4) - 4 = 5(3x) + 5(4) - 4$
$= 15x + 20 - 4$
$= 15x + 16$

68. $2(5x + 4) - 3 = 2(5x) + 2(4) - 3$
$= 10x + 8 - 3$
$= 10x + 5$

69. $5(3x - 2) + 12x = 5(3x) + 5(-2) + 12x$
$= 15x - 10 + 12x$
$= 27x - 10$

70. $2(5x - 1) + 14x = 2(5x) + 2(-1) + 14x$
$= 10x - 2 + 14x$
$= 24x - 2$

71. $7(3y - 5) + 2(4y + 3)$
$= 7(3y) + 7(-5) + 2(4y) + 2(3)$
$= 21y - 35 + 8y + 6$
$= 29y - 29$

72. $4(2y - 6) + 3(5y + 10)$
$= 4(2y) + 4(-6) + 3(5y) + 3(10)$
$= 8y - 24 + 15y + 30$
$= 23y + 6$

73. $4x - (7x - 12y - 2)$
$= 4x - 7x + 12y + 2$
$= -3x + 12y + 2$

74. $5x - (9x - 17y - 3)$
$= 5x - 9x + 17y + 3$
$= -4x + 17y + 3$

75. $5(3y - 2) - (7y + 2)$
$= 15y - 10 - 7y - 2$
$= 8y - 12$

76. $4(5y - 3) - (6y + 3)$
$= 20y - 12 - 6y - 3$
$= 14y - 15$

77. $W = 1.5x + 7$
$= 1.5(4) + 7$
$= 6 + 7$
$= 13$ pounds
The point on the graph is (4, 13).

78. $W = 1.5x + 7$
$= 1.5(6) + 7$
$= 9 + 7$
$= 16$ pounds
The point on the graph is (6, 16).

79. $E = 0.18t + 71$
$= 0.18(40) + 71$
$= 78.2$ years in 1990
78.2 years is close to the actual life expectancy of 78.8.

$E = 0.18t + 71$
$= 0.18(50) + 71$
$= 80$ years in 2000

80 years is close to the actual life expectancy of 79.5.

80. $E = 0.16t + 65$
$\quad = 0.16(40) + 65$
$\quad = 71.4$ years in 1990

71.4 years is close to the actual life expectancy of 71.8.

$E = 0.16t + 65$
$\quad = 0.16(50) + 65$
$\quad = 73$ years in 2000

73 years is close to the actual life expectancy of 74.1.

81. $N = 0.12x^3 - x^2 + 3x + 15$
$N = 0.12(10)^3 - (10)^2 + 3(10) + 15 = 65$

65,000 surgeries is close to the 63,000 performed in 2002.

82. $N = 0.12x^3 - x^2 + 3x + 15$
$N = 0.12(2)^3 - (2)^2 + 3(2) + 15 = 17.96 \approx 18$

18,000 surgeries is off by about 12.5% from the 16,000 performed in 1994.

83-90. Answers will vary.

91. d is true.

92. c is true.

93. $\dfrac{0.5x + 5000}{x}$

    a. $x = 100$

      $\dfrac{0.5(100) + 5000}{100} = \$50.50$

      $x = 1000$

      $\dfrac{0.5(1000) + 5000}{1000} = \$5.50$

      $x = 10,000$

      $\dfrac{0.5(10,000) + 5000}{10,000} = \$1$

    b. No; the business must produce at least 10,000 clocks each week to be competitive.

94. $N = -0.239x^3 + 5.288x^2 + 33.28x + 503.47$ serves as the best model for 2001.

Year	x value	1st formula	2nd formula	3rd formula
2001	16	1457	1439	1411

95. $N = -0.239x^3 + 5.288x^2 + 33.28x + 503.47$ serves as the best model for the period shown.

Year	x value	1st formula	2nd formula	3rd formula
1985	0	505	485	503
1990	5	803	817	772
1995	10	1100	1119	1126
1997	12	1219	1230	1251
1998	13	1279	1284	1305
1999	14	1338	1337	1350
2000	15	1398	1389	1386
2001	16	1457	1439	1411

Check Points 6.2

1.
$$x - 5 = 12$$
$$x - 5 + 5 = 12 + 5$$
$$x = 17$$
The solution set is $\{17\}$.

2.
$$x + 11 = -4$$
$$x + 11 - 11 = -4 - 11$$
$$x = -15$$
The solution set is $\{-15\}$.

3.
$$\frac{x}{3} = 12$$
$$3 \cdot \frac{x}{3} = 3 \cdot 12$$
$$x = 36$$
The solution set is $\{36\}$.

4.
$$-4x = 84$$
$$\frac{-4x}{-4} = \frac{84}{-4}$$
$$x = -21$$
The solution set is $\{-21\}$.

5.
$$4x + 5 = 29$$
$$4x + 5 - 5 = 29 - 5$$
$$4x = 24$$
$$\frac{4x}{4} = \frac{24}{4}$$
$$x = 6$$

Check:
$$4x + 5 = 29$$
$$4(6) + 5 = 29$$
$$24 + 5 = 29$$
$$29 = 29$$
The solution set is $\{6\}$.

6.
$$6(x - 3) + 7x = -57$$
$$6x - 18 + 7x = -57$$
$$13x - 18 = -57$$
$$13x - 18 + 18 = -57 + 18$$
$$13x = -39$$
$$\frac{13x}{13} = \frac{-39}{13}$$
$$x = -3$$
The solution set is $\{-3\}$.

7.
$$2x + 9 = 8x - 3$$
$$2x + 9 - 8x = 8x - 3 - 8x$$
$$-6x + 9 = -3$$
$$-6x + 9 - 9 = -3 - 9$$
$$-6x = -12$$
$$\frac{-6x}{-6} = \frac{-12}{-6}$$
$$x = 2$$
The solution set is $\{2\}$.

8.
$$4(2x + 1) - 29 = 3(2x - 5)$$
$$8x + 4 - 29 = 6x - 15$$
$$8x - 25 = 6x - 15$$
$$8x - 25 - 6x = 6x - 15 - 6x$$
$$2x - 25 = -15$$
$$2x - 25 + 25 = -15 + 25$$
$$2x = 10$$
$$\frac{2x}{2} = \frac{10}{2}$$
$$x = 5$$
The solution set is $\{5\}$.

9.
$$\frac{x}{4} = \frac{2x}{3} + \frac{5}{6}$$
$$12 \cdot \frac{x}{4} = 12 \cdot \left(\frac{2x}{3} + \frac{5}{6}\right)$$
$$12 \cdot \frac{x}{4} = 12 \cdot \frac{2x}{3} + 12 \cdot \frac{5}{6}$$
$$3 \cdot x = 4 \cdot 2x + 2 \cdot 5$$
$$3x = 8x + 10$$
$$3x - 8x = 8x + 10 - 8x$$
$$-5x = 10$$
$$\frac{-5x}{-5} = \frac{10}{-5}$$
$$x = -2$$
The solution set is $\{-2\}$.

10.
$$W = 0.3x + 46.6$$
$$55.9 = 0.3x + 46.6$$
$$55.9 - 46.6 = 0.3x + 46.6 - 46.6$$
$$9.3 = 0.3x$$
$$\frac{9.3}{0.3} = \frac{0.3x}{0.3}$$
$$31 = x$$
The formula indicates that we will average 55.9 hours of work per week 31 years after 1980, or in 2011.

11.
$$4x + 9y = 27$$
$$4x - 4x + 9y = -4x + 27$$
$$9y = -4x + 27$$
$$\frac{9y}{9} = \frac{-4x + 27}{9}$$
$$y = \frac{-4x + 27}{9}$$
$$y = \frac{-4x}{9} + \frac{27}{9}$$
$$y = -\frac{4}{9}x + 3$$

12.
$$T = D + pm$$
$$T - D = D - D + pm$$
$$T - D = pm$$
$$\frac{T - D}{p} = \frac{pm}{p}$$
$$\frac{T - D}{p} = m$$

13.
$$3x + 7 = 3(x + 1)$$
$$3x + 7 = 3x + 3$$
$$3x + 7 - 3x = 3x + 3 - 3x$$
$$7 = 3$$
There is no solution, $\varnothing$.

14.
$$3(x - 1) + 9 = 8x + 6 - 5x$$
$$3x - 3 + 9 = 8x + 6 - 5x$$
$$3x + 6 = 3x + 6$$
$$3x + 6 - 3x = 3x + 6 - 3x$$
$$6 = 6$$
True for all real numbers.

Exercise Set 6.2

1.
$$x - 7 = 3$$
$$x - 7 + 7 = 3 + 7$$
$$x = 10$$
The solution set is $\{10\}$.

2.
$$x - 3 = -17$$
$$x - 3 + 3 = -17 + 3$$
$$x = -14$$
The solution set is $\{-14\}$.

3.
$$x + 5 = -12$$
$$x + 5 - 5 = -12 - 5$$
$$x = -17$$
The solution set is $\{-17\}$.

4.
$$x + 12 = -14$$
$$x + 12 - 12 = -14 - 12$$
$$x = -26$$
The solution set is $\{-26\}$.

5.
$$\frac{x}{3} = 4$$
$$3\left(\frac{x}{3}\right) = 3(4)$$
$$x = 12$$
The solution set is $\{12\}$.

6.
$$\frac{x}{5} = 3$$
$$5\left(\frac{x}{5}\right) = 5(3)$$
$$x = 15$$
The solution set is $\{15\}$.

7. $5x = 45$

$\dfrac{5x}{5} = \dfrac{45}{5}$

$x = 9$

The solution set is $\{9\}$.

8. $6x = 18$

$\dfrac{6x}{6} = \dfrac{18}{6}$

$x = 3$

The solution set is $\{3\}$.

9. $8x = -24$

$\dfrac{8x}{8} = \dfrac{-24}{8}$

$x = -3$

The solution set is $\{-3\}$.

10. $5x = -25$

$\dfrac{5x}{5} = \dfrac{-25}{5}$

$x = -5$

The solution set is $\{-5\}$.

11. $-8x = 2$

$\dfrac{-8x}{-8} = \dfrac{2}{-8}$

$x = -\dfrac{1}{4}$

The solution set is $\left\{-\dfrac{1}{4}\right\}$.

12. $-6x = 3$

$\dfrac{-6x}{-6} = \dfrac{3}{-6}$

$x = -\dfrac{1}{2}$

The solution set is $\left\{-\dfrac{1}{2}\right\}$.

13. $5x + 3 = 18$

$5x + 3 - 3 = 18 - 3$

$5x = 15$

$\dfrac{5x}{5} = \dfrac{15}{5}$

$x = 3$

The solution set is $\{3\}$.

14. $3x + 8 = 50$

$3x + 8 - 8 = 50 - 8$

$3x = 42$

$\dfrac{3x}{3} = \dfrac{42}{3}$

$x = 14$

The solution set is $\{14\}$.

15. $6x - 3 = 63$

$6x - 3 + 3 = 63 + 3$

$6x = 66$

$\dfrac{6x}{6} = \dfrac{66}{6}$

$x = 11$

The solution set is $\{11\}$.

16. $5x - 8 = 72$

$5x - 8 + 8 = 72 + 8$

$5x = 80$

$\dfrac{5x}{5} = \dfrac{80}{5}$

$x = 16$

The solution set is $\{16\}$.

17. $4x - 14 = -82$

$4x - 14 + 14 = -82 + 14$

$4x = -68$

$\dfrac{4x}{4} = \dfrac{-68}{4}$

$x = -17$

The solution set is $\{-17\}$.

18. $9x - 14 = -77$

$9x - 14 + 14 = -77 + 14$

$9x = -63$

$\dfrac{9x}{9} = \dfrac{-63}{9}$

$x = -7$

The solution set is $\{-7\}$.

19. $14 - 5x = -41$

$14 - 5x - 14 = -41 - 14$

$-5x = -55$

$\dfrac{-5x}{-5} = \dfrac{-55}{-5}$

$x = 11$

The solution set is $\{11\}$.

20.
$$25 - 6x = -83$$
$$25 - 6x - 25 = -83 - 25$$
$$-6x = -108$$
$$\frac{-6x}{-6} = \frac{-108}{-6}$$
$$x = 18$$
The solution set is $\{18\}$.

21.
$$9(5x - 2) = 45$$
$$45x - 18 = 45$$
$$45x - 18 + 18 = 45 + 18$$
$$45x = 63$$
$$\frac{45x}{45} = \frac{63}{45}$$
$$x = \frac{7}{5}$$
The solution set is $\left\{\frac{7}{5}\right\}$.

22.
$$10(3x + 2) = 70$$
$$30x + 20 = 70$$
$$30x + 20 - 20 = 70 - 20$$
$$30x = 50$$
$$\frac{30x}{30} = \frac{50}{30}$$
$$x = \frac{5}{3}$$
The solution set is $\left\{\frac{5}{3}\right\}$.

23.
$$5x - (2x - 10) = 35$$
$$5x - 2x + 10 = 35$$
$$3x + 10 = 35$$
$$3x + 10 - 10 = 35 - 10$$
$$3x = 25$$
$$\frac{3x}{3} = \frac{25}{3}$$
$$x = \frac{25}{3}$$
The solution set is $\left\{\frac{25}{3}\right\}$.

24.
$$11x - (6x - 5) = 40$$
$$11x - 6x + 5 = 40$$
$$5x + 5 = 40$$
$$5x + 5 - 5 = 40 - 5$$
$$5x = 35$$
$$\frac{5x}{5} = \frac{35}{5}$$
$$x = 7$$
The solution set is $\{7\}$.

25.
$$3x + 5 = 2x + 13$$
$$3x + 5 - 5 = 2x + 13 - 5$$
$$3x = 2x + 8$$
$$3x - 2x = 2x + 8 - 2x$$
$$x = 8$$
The solution set is $\{8\}$.

26.
$$2x - 7 = 6 + x$$
$$2x - 7 + 7 = 6 + x + 7$$
$$2x = x + 13$$
$$2x - x = x + 13 - x$$
$$x = 13$$
The solution set is $\{13\}$.

27.
$$8x - 2 = 7x - 5$$
$$8x - 2 + 2 = 7x - 5 + 2$$
$$8x = 7x - 3$$
$$8x - 7x = 7x - 3 - 7x$$
$$x = -3$$
The solution set is $\{-3\}$.

28.
$$13x + 14 = -5 + 12x$$
$$13x + 14 - 14 = -5 + 12x - 14$$
$$13x = 12x - 19$$
$$13x - 12x = 12x - 19 - 12x$$
$$x = -19$$
The solution set is $\{-19\}$.

29.
$$7x + 4 = x + 16$$
$$7x + 4 - 4 = x + 16 - 4$$
$$7x = x + 12$$
$$7x - x = x + 12 - x$$
$$6x = 12$$
$$\frac{6x}{6} = \frac{12}{6}$$
$$x = 2$$
The solution set is $\{2\}$.

30.
$$8x+1 = x+43$$
$$8x+1-1 = x+43-1$$
$$8x = x+42$$
$$8x-x = x+42-x$$
$$7x = 42$$
$$\frac{7x}{7} = \frac{42}{7}$$
$$x = 6$$
The solution set is $\{6\}$.

31.
$$8y-3 = 11y+9$$
$$8y-3+3 = 11y+9+3$$
$$8y = 11y+12$$
$$8y-11y = 11y+12-11y$$
$$-3y = 12$$
$$\frac{-3y}{-3} = \frac{12}{-3}$$
$$y = -4$$
The solution set is $\{-4\}$.

32.
$$5y-2 = 9y+2$$
$$5y-2+2 = 9y+2+2$$
$$5y = 9y+4$$
$$5y-9y = 9y+4-9y$$
$$-4y = 4$$
$$\frac{-4y}{-4} = \frac{4}{-4}$$
$$y = -1$$
The solution set is $\{-1\}$.

33.
$$2(4-3x) = 2(2x+5)$$
$$8-6x = 4x+10$$
$$8-6x-8 = 4x+10-8$$
$$-6x = 4x+2$$
$$-6x-4x = 4x+2-4x$$
$$-10x = 2$$
$$\frac{-10x}{-10} = \frac{2}{-10}$$
$$x = -\frac{1}{5}$$
The solution set is $\left\{-\frac{1}{5}\right\}$.

34.
$$3(5-x) = 4(2x+1)$$
$$15-3x = 8x+4$$
$$15-3x-15 = 8x+4-15$$
$$-3x = 8x-11$$
$$-3x-8x = 8x-11-8x$$
$$\frac{-11x}{-11} = \frac{-11}{-11}$$
$$x = 1$$
The solution set is $\{1\}$.

35.
$$8(y+2) = 2(3y+4)$$
$$8y+16 = 6y+8$$
$$8y+16-16 = 6y+8-16$$
$$8y = 6y-8$$
$$8y-6y = 6y-8-6y$$
$$2y = -8$$
$$\frac{2y}{2} = \frac{-8}{2}$$
$$y = -4$$
The solution set is $\{-4\}$.

36.
$$3(3y-1) = 4(3+3y)$$
$$9y-3 = 12+12y$$
$$9y-3+3 = 12+12y+3$$
$$9y = 12y-15$$
$$9y-12y = 12y-15-12y$$
$$-3y = 15$$
$$\frac{-3y}{-3} = \frac{15}{-3}$$
$$y = -5$$
The solution set is $\{-5\}$.

37.
$$3(x+1) = 7(x-2)-3$$
$$3x+3 = 7x-14-3$$
$$3x+3 = 7x-17$$
$$3x+3-3 = 7x-17-3$$
$$3x = 7x-20$$
$$3x-7x = 7x-20-7x$$
$$-4x = -20$$
$$\frac{-4x}{-4} = \frac{-20}{-4}$$
$$x = 5$$
The solution set is $\{5\}$.

38. $5x - 4(x+9) = 2x - 3$
$5x - 4x - 36 = 2x - 3$
$x - 36 = 2x - 3$
$x - 36 + 36 = 2x - 3 + 36$
$x = 2x + 33$
$x - 2x = 2x + 33 - 2x$
$-x = 33$
$\dfrac{-x}{-1} = \dfrac{33}{-1}$
$x = -33$
The solution set is $\{-33\}$.

39. $5(2x - 8) - 2 = 5(x - 3) + 3$
$10x - 40 - 2 = 5x - 15 + 3$
$10x - 42 = 5x - 12$
$10x - 42 + 42 = 5x - 12 + 42$
$10x = 5x + 30$
$10x - 5x = 5x + 30 - 5x$
$5x = 30$
$\dfrac{5x}{5} = \dfrac{30}{5}$
$x = 6$
The solution set is $\{6\}$.

40. $7(3x - 2) + 5 = 6(2x - 1) + 24$
$21x - 14 + 5 = 12x - 6 + 24$
$21x - 9 = 12x + 18$
$21x - 9 + 9 = 12x + 18 + 9$
$21x = 12x + 27$
$21x - 12x = 12x + 27 - 12x$
$9x = 27$
$\dfrac{9x}{9} = \dfrac{27}{9}$
$x = 3$
The solution set is $\{3\}$.

41. $5(x - 2) - 2(2x + 1) = 2 + 5x$
$5x - 10 - 4x - 2 = 2 + 5x$
$x - 12 = 2 + 5x$
$x - 12 + 12 = 2 + 5x + 12$
$x = 14 + 5x$
$x - 5x = 14 + 5x - 5x$
$-4x = 14$
$\dfrac{-4x}{-4} = \dfrac{14}{-4}$
$x = -\dfrac{7}{2}$
The solution set is $\left\{ -\dfrac{7}{2} \right\}$.

42. $2(5x + 4) + 3(2x + 11) = 4x - 19$
$10x + 8 + 6x + 33 = 4x - 19$
$16x + 41 = 4x - 19$
$16x + 41 - 41 = 4x - 19 - 41$
$16x = 4x - 60$
$16x - 4x = 4x - 60 - 4x$
$12x = -60$
$\dfrac{12x}{12} = \dfrac{-60}{12}$
$x = -5$
The solution set is $\{-5\}$.

43. $\dfrac{x}{3} + \dfrac{x}{2} = \dfrac{5}{6}$
$6\left(\dfrac{x}{3} + \dfrac{x}{2} \right) = 6\left(\dfrac{5}{6} \right)$
$6\left(\dfrac{x}{3} \right) + 6\left(\dfrac{x}{2} \right) = 6\left(\dfrac{5}{6} \right)$
$2x + 3x = 5$
$5x = 5$
$\dfrac{5x}{5} = \dfrac{5}{5}$
$x = 1$
The solution set is $\{1\}$.

44. $\dfrac{x}{4} - 1 = \dfrac{x}{5}$
$20\left(\dfrac{x}{4} - 1 \right) = 20\left(\dfrac{x}{5} \right)$
$20 \cdot \dfrac{x}{4} - 20 \cdot 1 = 20 \cdot \dfrac{x}{5}$
$5x - 20 = 4x$
$5x - 20 + 20 = 4x + 20$
$5x = 4x + 20$
$5x - 4x = 4x + 20 - 4x$
$x = 20$
The solution set is $\{20\}$.

45.
$$\frac{x}{2} = 20 - \frac{x}{3}$$
$$6\left(\frac{x}{2}\right) = 6\left(20 - \frac{x}{3}\right)$$
$$6\left(\frac{x}{2}\right) = 6(20) - 6\left(\frac{x}{3}\right)$$
$$3x = 120 - 2x$$
$$3x + 2x = 120 - 2x + 2x$$
$$5x = 120$$
$$\frac{5x}{5} = \frac{120}{5}$$
$$x = 24$$
The solution set is $\{24\}$.

46.
$$\frac{x}{5} - \frac{1}{2} = \frac{x}{6}$$
$$30\left(\frac{x}{5} - \frac{1}{2}\right) = 30\left(\frac{x}{6}\right)$$
$$30 \cdot \frac{x}{5} - 30 \cdot \frac{1}{2} = 30 \cdot \frac{x}{6}$$
$$6x - 15 = 5x$$
$$6x - 15 + 15 = 5x + 15$$
$$6x = 5x + 15$$
$$6x - 5x = 5x + 15 - 5x$$
$$x = 15$$
The solution set is $\{15\}$.

47.
$$\frac{3y}{4} - 3 = \frac{y}{2} + 2$$
$$4\left(\frac{3y}{4} - 3\right) = 4\left(\frac{y}{2} + 2\right)$$
$$4 \cdot \frac{3y}{4} - 4 \cdot 3 = 4 \cdot \frac{y}{2} + 4 \cdot 2$$
$$3y - 12 = 2y + 8$$
$$3y - 12 + 12 = 2y + 8 + 12$$
$$3y = 2y + 20$$
$$3y - 2y = 2y + 20 - 2y$$
$$y = 20$$
The solution set is $\{20\}$.

48.
$$y + \frac{1}{2} = 1 - \frac{y}{3}$$
$$6\left(y + \frac{1}{2}\right) = 6\left(1 - \frac{y}{3}\right)$$
$$6 \cdot y + 6 \cdot \frac{1}{2} = 6 \cdot 1 - 6 \cdot \frac{y}{3}$$
$$6y + 3 = 6 - 2y$$
$$6y + 3 - 3 = 6 - 2y - 3$$
$$6y = 3 - 2y$$
$$6y + 2y = 3 - 2y + 2y$$
$$8y = 3$$
$$\frac{8y}{8} = \frac{3}{8}$$
$$y = \frac{3}{8}$$
The solution set is $\left\{\frac{3}{8}\right\}$.

49.
$$\frac{3x}{5} - x = \frac{x}{10} - \frac{5}{2}$$
$$10\left(\frac{3x}{5} - x\right) = 10\left(\frac{x}{10} - \frac{5}{2}\right)$$
$$10\left(\frac{3x}{5}\right) - 10(x) = 10\left(\frac{x}{10}\right) - 10\left(\frac{5}{2}\right)$$
$$6x - 10x = x - 25$$
$$-4x = x - 25$$
$$-4x - x = x - 25 - x$$
$$-5x = -25$$
$$\frac{-5x}{-5} = \frac{-25}{-5}$$
$$x = 5$$
The solution set is $\{5\}$.

50.
$$2x - \frac{2x}{7} = \frac{x}{2} + \frac{17}{2}$$

$$14\left(2x - \frac{2x}{7}\right) = 14\left(\frac{x}{2} + \frac{17}{2}\right)$$

$$14 \cdot 2x - 14 \cdot \frac{2x}{7} = 14 \cdot \frac{x}{2} + 14 \cdot \frac{17}{2}$$

$$28x - 4x = 7x + 119$$

$$24x = 7x + 119$$

$$24x - 7x = 7x + 119 - 7x$$

$$17x = 119$$

$$\frac{17x}{17} = \frac{119}{17}$$

$$x = 7$$

The solution set is $\{7\}$.

51.
$$3x + y = 6$$
$$3x + y - 3x = -3x + 6$$
$$y = -3x + 6$$

52.
$$5x + y = 7$$
$$5x + y - 5x = -5x + 7$$
$$y = -5x + 7$$

53.
$$x + 2y = 6$$
$$x + 2y - x = -x + 6$$
$$2y = -x + 6$$
$$\frac{2y}{2} = \frac{-x + 6}{2}$$
$$y = -\frac{x}{2} + \frac{6}{2}$$
$$y = -\frac{1}{2}x + 3$$

54.
$$x + 4y = 8$$
$$x + 4y - x = -x + 8$$
$$4y = -x + 8$$
$$\frac{4y}{4} = \frac{-x}{4} + \frac{8}{4}$$
$$y = -\frac{1}{4}x + 2$$

55.
$$2x + 6y = 12$$
$$2x + 6y - 2x = -2x + 12$$
$$6y = -2x + 12$$
$$\frac{6y}{6} = \frac{-2x + 12}{6}$$
$$y = \frac{-2x}{6} + \frac{12}{6}$$
$$y = -\frac{1}{3}x + 2$$

56.
$$3x + 9y = 18$$
$$3x + 9y - 3x = -3x + 18$$
$$9y = -3x + 18$$
$$\frac{9y}{9} = \frac{-3x + 18}{9}$$
$$y = \frac{-3x}{9} + \frac{18}{9}$$
$$y = -\frac{1}{3}x + 2$$

57.
$$-2x + 4y = 0$$
$$-2x + 4y + 2x = 0 + 2x$$
$$4y = 2x$$
$$\frac{4y}{4} = \frac{2x}{4}$$
$$y = \frac{1}{2}x$$

58.
$$-3x + 9y = 0$$
$$-3x + 9y + 3x = 0 + 3x$$
$$9y = 3x$$
$$\frac{9y}{9} = \frac{3x}{9}$$
$$y = \frac{1}{3}x$$

59.
$$2x - 3y = 5$$
$$2x - 3y - 2x = -2x + 5$$
$$-3y = -2x + 5$$
$$\frac{-3y}{-3} = \frac{-2x + 5}{-3}$$
$$y = \frac{-2x}{-3} + \frac{5}{-3}$$
$$y = \frac{2}{3}x - \frac{5}{3}$$

60.
$$9x - 4y = 7$$
$$9x - 4y - 9x = -9x + 7$$
$$-4y = -9x + 7$$
$$\frac{-4y}{-4} = \frac{-9x + 7}{-4}$$
$$y = \frac{-9x}{-4} + \frac{7}{-4}$$
$$y = \frac{9}{4}x - \frac{7}{4}$$

61. $A = LW$ for L

$$\frac{A}{W} = \frac{LW}{W}$$

$$\frac{A}{W} = L \text{ or } L = \frac{A}{W}$$

62. $D = RT$ for R

$$\frac{D}{T} = \frac{RT}{T}$$

$$\frac{D}{T} = R \text{ or } R = \frac{D}{T}$$

63. $A = \frac{1}{2}bh$ for b

$$2(A) = 2\left(\frac{1}{2}bh\right)$$

$$2A = bh$$

$$\frac{2A}{h} = \frac{bh}{h}$$

$$\frac{2A}{h} = b \text{ or } b = \frac{2A}{h}$$

64. $V = \frac{1}{3}Bh$ for B

$$3(V) = 3\left(\frac{1}{3}Bh\right)$$

$$3V = Bh$$

$$\frac{3V}{h} = \frac{Bh}{h}$$

$$\frac{3V}{h} = B \text{ or } B = \frac{3V}{h}$$

65. $I = Prt$ for P

$$\frac{I}{rt} = \frac{Prt}{rt}$$

$$\frac{I}{rt} = P \text{ or } P = \frac{I}{rt}$$

66. $C = 2\pi r$ for r

$$\frac{C}{2\pi} = \frac{2\pi r}{2\pi}$$

$$\frac{C}{2\pi} = r \text{ or } r = \frac{C}{2\pi}$$

67. $E = mc^2$ for m

$$\frac{E}{c^2} = \frac{mc^2}{c^2}$$

$$\frac{E}{c^2} = m \text{ or } m = \frac{E}{c^2}$$

68. $V = \pi r^2 h$ for h

$$\frac{V}{\pi r^2} = \frac{\pi r^2 h}{\pi r^2}$$

$$\frac{V}{\pi r^2} = h \text{ or } h = \frac{V}{\pi r^2}$$

69. $y = mx + b$ for m

$$y - b = mx + b - b$$

$$y - b = mx$$

$$\frac{y-b}{x} = \frac{mx}{x}$$

$$\frac{y-b}{x} = m \text{ or } m = \frac{y-b}{x}$$

70. $P = C + MC$ for M

$$P - C = C + MC - C$$

$$P - C = MC$$

$$\frac{P-C}{C} = \frac{MC}{C}$$

$$\frac{P-C}{C} = M \text{ or } M = \frac{P-C}{C}$$

71. $A = \frac{1}{2}(a + b)$ for a

$$2 \cdot A = 2 \cdot \frac{1}{2}(a+b)$$

$$2A = a + b$$

$$2A - b = a + b - b$$

$$2A - b = a \text{ or } a = 2A - b$$

72. $A = \frac{1}{2}(a + b)$ for b

$$2 \cdot A = 2 \cdot \frac{1}{2}(a+b)$$

$$2A = a + b$$

$$2A - a = a + b - a$$

$$2A - a = b \text{ or } b = 2A - a$$

73. $S = P + Prt$ for r

$$S - P = P + Prt - P$$

$$S - P = Prt$$

$$\frac{S-P}{Pt} = \frac{Prt}{Pt}$$

$$\frac{S-P}{Pt} = r \text{ or } r = \frac{S-P}{Pt}$$

74. $S = P + Prt$ for t

$$S - P = P + Prt - P$$

$$S - P = Prt$$

$$\frac{S-P}{Pr} = \frac{Prt}{Pr}$$

$$\frac{S-P}{Pr} = t \text{ or } t = \frac{S-P}{Pr}$$

75. $10x - 2(4 + 5x) = -8$

$$10x - 8 - 10x = -8$$

$$-8 = -8 \text{ True}$$

True for all real numbers.

76. $9x - 3(-5 + 3x) = 15$

$$9x + 15 - 9x = 15$$

$$15 = 15 \text{ True}$$

True for all real numbers.

77. $10x - 2(4 + 5x) = 8$

$$10x - 8 - 10x = 8$$

$$-8 = 8 \text{ False}$$

There is no solution, $\varnothing$.

78. $9x - 3(-5 + 3x) = -15$

$$9x + 15 - 9x = -15$$

$$15 = -15 \text{ False}$$

There is no solution, $\varnothing$.

79. $2(3x + 4) - 4 = 9x + 4 - 3x$

$$6x + 8 - 4 = 9x + 4 - 3x$$

$$6x + 4 = 6x + 4$$

$$6x + 4 - 6x = 6x + 4 - 6x$$

$$4 = 4 \text{ True}$$

True for all real numbers.

80. $3(x - 4) - 5 = -2x + 5x - 9$

$$3(x - 4) - 5 = -2x + 5x - 9$$

$$3x - 12 - 5 = -2x + 5x - 9$$

$$3x - 17 = 3x - 9$$

$$3x - 17 - 3x = 3x - 9 - 3x$$

$$-17 = -9 \text{ False}$$

There is no solution, $\varnothing$.

81. $F = 10(x - 65) + 50$

$$250 = 10(x - 65) + 50$$

$$250 = 10x - 650 + 50$$

$$250 = 10x - 600$$

$$250 + 600 = 10x - 600 + 600$$

$$850 = 10x$$

$$\frac{850}{10} = \frac{10x}{10}$$

$$85 = x$$

The speed was 85 mph.

82. $F = 10(x - 65) + 50$

$$400 = 10(x - 65) + 50$$

$$400 = 10x - 650 + 50$$

$$400 = 10x - 600$$

$$400 + 600 = 10x - 600 + 600$$

$$1000 = 10x$$

$$\frac{1000}{10} = \frac{10x}{10}$$

$$100 = x$$

The speed was 100 mph.

83. $\dfrac{c}{2} + 80 = 2F$

$$\frac{c}{2} + 80 = 2 \cdot 70$$

$$\frac{c}{2} + 80 = 140$$

$$\frac{c}{2} + 80 - 80 = 140 - 80$$

$$\frac{c}{2} = 60$$

$$2 \cdot \frac{c}{2} = 2 \cdot 60$$

$$c = 120 \text{ chirps per minute}$$

84.
$$\frac{c}{2} + 80 = 2F$$
$$\frac{c}{2} + 80 = 2 \cdot 80$$
$$\frac{c}{2} + 80 = 160$$
$$\frac{c}{2} + 80 - 80 = 160 - 80$$
$$\frac{c}{2} = 80$$
$$2 \cdot \frac{c}{2} = 2 \cdot 80$$
$$c = 160 \text{ chirps per minute}$$

85.
$$p = 15 + \frac{5d}{11}$$
$$201 = 15 + \frac{5d}{11}$$
$$201 - 15 = 15 + \frac{5d}{11} - 15$$
$$186 = \frac{5d}{11}$$
$$\frac{11}{5} \cdot 186 = \frac{11}{5} \cdot \frac{5d}{11}$$
$$409.2 = d$$
$$d = 409.2 \text{ feet}$$

86.
$$p = 15 + \frac{5d}{11}$$
$$20 = 15 + \frac{5d}{11}$$
$$20 - 15 = 15 + \frac{5d}{11} - 15$$
$$5 = \frac{5d}{11}$$
$$\frac{11}{5} \cdot 5 = \frac{11}{5} \cdot \frac{5d}{11}$$
$$11 = d$$
$$d = 11 \text{ feet}$$

87.
$$R = 143 - 0.65A$$
$$117 = 143 - 0.65A$$
$$117 - 143 = 143 - 0.65A - 143$$
$$-26 = -0.65A$$
$$\frac{-26}{-0.65} = \frac{-0.65A}{-0.65}$$
$$40 = A$$

The woman is 40 years old.
The point on the graph is (40, 117).

88.
$$R = 165 - 0.75A$$
$$147 = 165 - 0.75A$$
$$147 - 165 = 165 - 0.75A - 165$$
$$-18 = -0.75A$$
$$\frac{-18}{-0.75} = \frac{-0.75A}{-0.75}$$
$$24 = A$$

The man is 24 years old.
The point on the graph is (24, 147).

89.
$$D = \frac{10}{9}N + \frac{53}{9}$$
$$10 = \frac{10}{9}N + \frac{53}{9}$$
$$9(10) = 9\left(\frac{10}{9}N + \frac{53}{9}\right)$$
$$90 = 10N + 53$$
$$37 = 10N$$
$$3.7 = N$$
$$N = 3.7$$

The solution is shown as point (3.7, 10).

90.
$$D = \frac{1}{9}N + \frac{26}{9}$$
$$3.5 = \frac{1}{9}N + \frac{26}{9}$$
$$9(3.5) = 9\left(\frac{1}{9}N + \frac{26}{9}\right)$$
$$31.5 = N + 26$$
$$5.5 = N$$
$$N = 5.5$$

The solution is shown as point (5.5, 3.5).

91.
$$N = -1.4t + 14.7$$
$$3 = -1.4t + 14.7$$
$$10(3) = 10(-1.4t + 14.7)$$
$$30 = -14t + 147$$
$$14t + 30 = 147$$
$$14t = 117$$
$$t = 8\frac{5}{14}$$
$$t \approx 8$$

The number of welfare patients will be reduced to 3 million approximately 8 years after 1994, or 2002.

92.
$$N = -1.4t + 14.7$$
$$0 = -1.4t + 14.7$$
$$10(0) = 10(-1.4t + 14.7)$$
$$0 = -14t + 147$$
$$14t = 147$$
$$t = 10\tfrac{1}{2}$$
$$t \approx 11$$
The number of welfare patients will be reduced to 0 approximately 11 years after 1994, or during 2005. Explanations will vary.

93-102. Answers will vary.

103. c is true

104. Possible answers:
$$6x = 25 + x$$
$$2(x + 3) = 16$$
$$-x + 9 = x - 1$$

105. Answers will vary.

106. Yes: Her height is slightly over 5 feet tall.
$$f = 0.432h - 10.44$$
$$16 = 0.432h - 10.44$$
$$26.44 = 0.432h$$
$$61.2 \approx h$$

Check Points 6.3

1. Let x = the number.
$$6x - 4 = 68$$
$$6x - 4 + 4 = 68 + 4$$
$$6x = 72$$
$$\frac{6x}{6} = \frac{72}{6}$$
$$x = 12$$

2. Let x = miles traveled.
$$125 + 0.20x = 335$$
$$125 + 0.20x - 125 = 335 - 125$$
$$0.20x = 210$$
$$\frac{0.20x}{0.20} = \frac{210}{0.20}$$
$$x = 1050 \text{ miles}$$
You can travel 1050 miles in one week for $335.

3. Let x = the number of *Saturday Night Fever* albums sold (in millions).
Let $x + 5$ = the number of *Jagged Little Pill* albums sold (in millions).
$$x + x + 5 = 27$$
$$2x + 5 = 27$$
$$2x + 5 - 5 = 27 - 5$$
$$2x = 22$$
$$\frac{2x}{2} = \frac{22}{2}$$
$$x = 11$$
$$x + 5 = 16$$
11 million *Saturday Night Fever* albums and 16 million *Jagged Little Pill* albums have been sold.

4. Let x = the number years until total costs for solar heating and electric heating will be the same.

$$\overbrace{29,700 + 150x}^{\text{solar heating}} = \overbrace{5000 + 1100x}^{\text{electric heating}}$$
$$29,700 + 150x - 29,700 = 5000 + 1100x - 29,700$$
$$150x = 1100x - 24,700$$
$$150x - 1100x = 1100x - 24,700 - 1100x$$
$$-950x = -24,700$$
$$\frac{-950x}{-950} = \frac{-24,700}{-950}$$
$$x = 26 \text{ years}$$

$$\begin{aligned}
\text{Cost for solar heating} &= \$29,700 + \$150x \\
&= \$29,700 + \$150(26) \\
&= \$29,700 + \$3900 \\
&= \$33,600
\end{aligned}$$

$$\begin{aligned}
\text{Cost for electric heating} &= \$5000 + \$1100x \\
&= \$5000 + \$1100(26) \\
&= \$5000 + \$28,600 \\
&= \$33,600
\end{aligned}$$

Exercise Set 6.3

1. $x + 9$

2. $x + 13$

3. $20 - x$

4. $x - 13$

5. $8 - 5x$

6. $6x - 14$

7. $\dfrac{15}{x}$

8. $\dfrac{x}{15}$

9. $2x + 20$

10. $2(x + 20)$

11. $7x - 30$

12. $\dfrac{12}{x} - 3x$

13. $4(x + 12)$

14. $5(x - 6)$

15. $\begin{aligned} x + 40 &= 450 \\ x + 40 - 40 &= 450 - 40 \\ x &= 410 \end{aligned}$
The number is 410.

16. $\begin{aligned} x + 29 &= 54 \\ x + 29 - 29 &= 54 - 29 \\ x &= 25 \end{aligned}$
The number is 25.

17. $\begin{aligned} x - 13 &= 123 \\ x - 13 + 13 &= 123 + 13 \\ x &= 136 \end{aligned}$
The number is 136.

18. $\begin{aligned} x - 14 &= 28 \\ x - 14 + 14 &= 28 + 14 \\ x &= 42 \end{aligned}$
The number is 42.

19. $\begin{aligned} 7x &= 91 \\ \dfrac{7x}{7} &= \dfrac{91}{7} \\ x &= 13 \end{aligned}$
The number is 13.

20. $\begin{aligned} 8x &= 184 \\ \dfrac{8x}{8} &= \dfrac{184}{8} \\ x &= 23 \end{aligned}$
The number is 23.

21. $\begin{aligned} \dfrac{x}{18} &= 6 \\ 18 \cdot \dfrac{x}{18} &= 18 \cdot 6 \\ x &= 108 \end{aligned}$
The number is 108.

22. $\begin{aligned} \dfrac{x}{13} &= 9 \\ 13 \cdot \dfrac{x}{13} &= 13 \cdot 9 \\ x &= 117 \end{aligned}$
The number is 117.

23. $\begin{aligned} 4 + 2x &= 36 \\ 4 + 2x - 4 &= 36 - 4 \\ 2x &= 32 \\ \dfrac{2x}{2} &= \dfrac{32}{2} \\ x &= 16 \end{aligned}$
The number is 16.

24. $\begin{aligned} 5 + 3x &= 29 \\ 5 + 3x - 5 &= 29 - 5 \\ 3x &= 24 \\ \dfrac{3x}{3} &= \dfrac{24}{3} \\ x &= 8 \end{aligned}$
The number is 8.

25. $\begin{aligned} 5x - 7 &= 123 \\ 5x - 7 + 7 &= 123 + 7 \\ 5x &= 130 \\ \dfrac{5x}{5} &= \dfrac{130}{5} \\ x &= 26 \end{aligned}$
The number is 26.

26. $\begin{aligned} 6x - 8 &= 184 \\ 6x - 8 + 8 &= 184 + 8 \\ 6x &= 192 \\ \dfrac{6x}{6} &= \dfrac{192}{6} \\ x &= 32 \end{aligned}$
The number is 32.

27. $\begin{aligned} x + 5 &= 2x \\ x + 5 - x &= 2x - x \\ 5 &= x \end{aligned}$
The number is 5.

28.
$$x + 12 = 4x$$
$$x + 12 - x = 4x - x$$
$$12 = 3x$$
$$\frac{12}{3} = \frac{3x}{3}$$
$$4 = x$$
The number is 4.

29.
$$2(4 + x) = 36$$
$$8 + 2x = 36$$
$$8 + 2x - 8 = 36 - 8$$
$$2x = 28$$
$$\frac{2x}{2} = \frac{28}{2}$$
$$x = 14$$
The number is 14.

30.
$$3(5 + x) = 48$$
$$15 + 3x = 48$$
$$15 + 3x - 15 = 48 - 15$$
$$3x = 33$$
$$\frac{3x}{3} = \frac{33}{3}$$
$$x = 11$$
The number is 11.

31.
$$9x = 3x + 30$$
$$9x - 3x = 3x + 30 - 3x$$
$$6x = 30$$
$$\frac{6x}{6} = \frac{30}{6}$$
$$x = 5$$
The number is 5.

32.
$$4x + 5 = x + 35$$
$$4x + 5 - 5 = x + 35 - 5$$
$$4x = x + 30$$
$$4x - x = x + 30 - x$$
$$3x = 30$$
$$\frac{3x}{3} = \frac{30}{3}$$
$$x = 10$$
The number is 10.

33.
$$\frac{3x}{5} + 4 = 34$$
$$\frac{3x}{5} + 4 - 4 = 34 - 4$$
$$\frac{3x}{5} = 30$$
$$\frac{5}{3} \cdot \frac{3x}{5} = \frac{5}{3} \cdot 30$$
$$x = 50$$
The number is 50.

34.
$$\frac{3x}{4} - 3 = 9$$
$$\frac{3x}{4} - 3 + 3 = 9 + 3$$
$$\frac{3x}{4} = 12$$
$$\frac{4}{3} \cdot \frac{3x}{4} = \frac{4}{3} \cdot 12$$
$$x = 16$$
The number is 16.

35. Let x = number of miles.
$$200 + 0.15x = 320$$
$$200 + 0.15x - 200 = 320 - 200$$
$$0.15x = 120$$
$$\frac{0.15x}{0.15} = \frac{120}{0.15}$$
$$x = 800$$
You can travel 800 miles in one week for \$320.

36. Let x = number of miles.
$$180 + 0.25x = 395$$
$$180 + 0.25x - 180 = 395 - 180$$
$$0.25x = 215$$
$$\frac{0.25x}{0.25} = \frac{215}{0.25}$$
$$x = 860$$
You can travel 860 miles in one week for \$395.

37. Let x = number of years since 1990.
$$28 + 0.6x = 37$$
$$28 + 0.6x - 28 = 37 - 28$$
$$0.6x = 9$$
$$\frac{0.6x}{0.6} = \frac{9}{0.6}$$
$$x = 15$$
$$1990 + 15 = 2005$$
37% of babies will be born out of wedlock in 2005.

38. Let x = number of years since 1990.

$$28 + 0.6x = 40$$
$$28 + 0.6x - 28 = 40 - 28$$
$$0.6x = 12$$
$$\frac{0.6x}{0.6} = \frac{12}{0.6}$$
$$x = 20$$

$1990 + 20 = 2010$

40% of babies will be born out of wedlock in 2010.

39. Let x = the number (in thousands) of births per day. Then $521 - x$ = the number (in thousands) of deaths per day.

$$x - (521 - x) = 229$$
$$x - 521 + x = 229$$
$$2x - 521 = 229$$
$$2x = 750$$
$$x = 375$$

The number of births per day is 375,000.

$521 - x = 521 - 375 = 146$

Thus, the number of deaths per day is 146,000.

40. Let x = the population (in millions) of China in 2001.
Then $2310 - x$ = the population (in millions) of India in 2001.

$$x - (2310 - x) = 260$$
$$x - 2310 + x = 260$$
$$2x - 2310 = 260$$
$$2x = 2570$$
$$x = 1285$$

The population of China was 1285 million in 2001.

$2310 - x = 2310 - 1285 = 1025$

Thus, the population of India was 1025 million in 2001.

41. Let x = cost (in billions) of Hurricane Hugo, then $x + 5.5$ = cost (in billions) of the Northridge earthquake and $x + 13$ = cost (in billions) of Hurricane Andrew.

$$x + x + 5.5 + x + 13 = 39.5$$
$$3x + 18.5 = 39.5$$
$$3x + 18.5 - 18.5 = 39.5 - 18.5$$
$$3x = 21$$
$$\frac{3x}{3} = \frac{21}{3}$$
$$x = 7$$
$$x + 5.5 = 12.5$$
$$x + 13 = 20$$

Hurricane Hugo, the Northridge earthquake, and

Hurricane Andrew cost $7, $12.5, and $20 billion respectively.

42. Let x = the average hours wasted by motorists in Los Angeles.
Then $139 - x$ = the average hours wasted by motorists in Miami.

$$x = 2(139 - x) - 32$$
$$x = 278 - 2x - 32$$
$$x = -2x + 246$$
$$2x + x = 246$$
$$3x = 246$$
$$x = 82$$

Los Angeles motorists waste an average of 82 hours stuck in traffic.

$139 - x = 139 - 82 = 57$

Thus, Miami motorists waste an average of 57 hours stuck in traffic.

43. Let x = number of hours of labor

$$63 + 35x = 448$$
$$63 + 35x - 63 = 448 - 63$$
$$35x = 385$$
$$\frac{35x}{35} = \frac{385}{35}$$
$$x = 11$$

The shop took 11 hours to repair the car.

44. Let x = number of hours of labor

$$532 + 63x = 1603$$
$$532 + 63x - 532 = 1603 - 532$$
$$63x = 1071$$
$$63x = 1071$$
$$\frac{63x}{63} = \frac{1071}{63}$$
$$x = 17$$

It took 17 hours to repair the yacht.

45. Let x = the number of minutes at which the costs of the two plans are the same.

$$\overset{\text{Plan A}}{\overbrace{15 + 0.08x}} = \overset{\text{Plan B}}{\overbrace{3 + 0.12x}}$$
$$15 + 0.08x - 15 = 3 + 0.12x - 15$$
$$0.08x = 0.12x - 12$$
$$0.08x - 0.12x = 0.12x - 12 - 0.12x$$
$$-0.04x = -12$$
$$\frac{-0.04x}{-0.04} = \frac{-12}{-0.04}$$
$$x = 300$$

The two plans are the same at 300 minutes.

46. Let x = the amount of merchandise at which the costs of the two plans are the same.

$$\overbrace{300+0.70x}^{\text{Plan A}} = \overbrace{40+0.90x}^{\text{Plan B}}$$

$$300+0.70x-300 = 40+0.90x-300$$

$$0.70x = 0.90x-260$$

$$0.70x-0.90x = 0.90x-260-0.90x$$

$$-0.20x = -260$$

$$\frac{-0.20x}{-0.20} = \frac{-260}{-0.20}$$

$$x = 1300$$

The two plans are the same at $1300 of merchandise.

$$\overbrace{300+0.70x}^{\text{Plan A}} = \overbrace{40+0.90x}^{\text{Plan B}}$$

$$300+0.70(1300) = 40+0.90(1300)$$

$$300+910 = 40+1170$$

$$1210 = 1210$$

$1300 worth of merchandise will cost $1210 under both plans.

47. Let x = the number of bus trips in the month.
Cost with coupon book: $21+0.50x$
Cost without coupon book: $1.25x$

$$21+0.50x = 1.25x$$

$$21+0.50x-21 = 1.25x-21$$

$$0.50x = 1.25x-21$$

$$0.50x-1.25x = 1.25x-21-1.25x$$

$$-0.75x = -21$$

$$\frac{-0.75x}{-0.75} = \frac{-21}{-0.75}$$

$$x = 28$$

The monthly costs are the same after 28 bus trips.

48. Let x = the number of bridge crossings in the month.
Cost with coupon book: $21+1.00x$
Cost without coupon book: $2.50x$

$$21+1.00x = 2.50x$$

$$21+1.00x-21 = 2.50x-21$$

$$1.00x = 2.50x-21$$

$$1.00x-2.50x = 2.50x-21-2.50x$$

$$-1.50x = -21$$

$$\frac{-1.50x}{-1.50} = \frac{-21}{-1.50}$$

$$x = 14$$

The bridge must be crossed 14 times for the costs to be the same.

49. Let x = the height of the bookcase, then
$3x$ = the length of the bookcase.
Note that the bookcase requires 3 vertical, and 4 horizontal boards.

$$3(x)+4(3x) = 60$$

$$3x+12x = 60$$

$$15x = 60$$

$$\frac{15x}{15} = \frac{60}{15}$$

$$x = 4$$

$$3x = 12$$

The length is 12 feet and the height is 4 feet.

50-53. Answers will vary.

54. Let x = number of inches over 5 feet.

$$100+5x = 135$$

$$100+5x-100 = 135-100$$

$$5x = 35$$

$$\frac{5x}{5} = \frac{35}{5}$$

$$x = 7$$

The height that corresponds to 135 pounds is $5'7''$.

55. Let x = number of minutes after first minute.

$$0.55+0.40x = 6.95$$

$$0.55+0.40x-0.55 = 6.95-0.55$$

$$0.40x = 6.40$$

$$\frac{0.40x}{0.40} = \frac{6.40}{0.40}$$

$$x = 16$$

The call was 16 minutes plus the first minute, or 17 minutes long.

56. Let x = total number of Americans who suffer spinal cord injuries yearly.

$$0.22x = 1760$$

$$\frac{0.22x}{0.22} = \frac{1760}{0.22}$$

$$x = 8000$$

There are 8000 Americans who suffer spinal cord injuries each year.
Violence: $0.16 \times 8000 = 1280$
Vehicular Accidents: $0.45 \times 8000 = 3600$
Sports Injuries: $0.13 \times 8000 = 1040$
Other: $0.04 \times 8000 = 320$

57. Let x = current age of woman, then

$3x$ = current age of "uncle."

$$2(x+20) = 3x+20$$
$$2x+40 = 3x+20$$
$$2x+40-2x = 3x+20-2x$$
$$40 = x+20$$
$$40-20 = x+20-20$$
$$20 = x$$
$$60 = 3x$$

The woman is 20 years and the "uncle" is 60 years.

58. Let x = number of problems solved correctly, then

$26 - x$ = number of problems done incorrectly

$$0.08x = 0.05(26-x)$$
$$0.08x = 1.30 - 0.05x$$
$$0.08x + 0.05x = 1.30 - 0.05x + 0.05x$$
$$0.13x = 1.30$$
$$\frac{0.13x}{0.13} = \frac{1.30}{0.13}$$
$$x = 10$$

There were 10 problems solved correctly.

Check Points 6.4

1. $\dfrac{160}{180} = \dfrac{160 \div 20}{180 \div 20} = \dfrac{8}{9}$ or $8:9$

2. a. $\dfrac{10}{x} = \dfrac{2}{3}$

$$10 \cdot 3 = 2x$$
$$30 = 2x$$
$$\frac{30}{2} = \frac{2x}{2}$$
$$15 = x$$

The solution set is $\{15\}$

b. $\dfrac{11}{910-x} = \dfrac{2}{x}$

$$11x = 2(910-x)$$
$$11x = 1820 - 2x$$
$$11x + 2x = 1820 - 2x + 2x$$
$$13x = 1820$$
$$\frac{13x}{13} = \frac{1820}{13}$$
$$x = 140$$

The solution set is $\{140\}$

3. Let x = tax on a $112,500 house.

$$\frac{\$600}{\$45,000} = \frac{\$x}{\$112,500}$$
$$\frac{600}{45,000} = \frac{x}{112,500}$$
$$(600)(112,500) = 45,000x$$
$$67,500,000 = 45,000x$$
$$\frac{67,500,000}{45,000} = \frac{45,000x}{45,000}$$
$$1500 = x$$

The tax on the $112,500 house is $1500.

4. Let x = the number of deer in the refuge.

$$\frac{120 \text{ tagged deer}}{x} = \frac{25 \text{ tagged deer in sample}}{150 \text{ deer in sample}}$$
$$\frac{120}{x} = \frac{25}{150}$$
$$25x = (120)(150)$$
$$25x = 18,000$$
$$\frac{25x}{25} = \frac{18,000}{25}$$
$$x = 720$$

There are approximately 720 deer in the refuge.

5. Let x = the pressure (in pounds per square inch) at 330 feet below the surface.

$$\frac{25 \text{ pounds per square inch}}{60 \text{ feet}} = \frac{x}{330 \text{ feet}}$$
$$\frac{25}{60} = \frac{x}{330}$$
$$(25)(330) = 60x$$
$$8250 = 60x$$
$$\frac{8250}{60} = \frac{60x}{60}$$
$$137.5 = x$$

The pressure at 330 feet is 137.5 pounds per square inch.

6. Let x = the distance (in feet) required to stop a car traveling at 100 mph.

$$\frac{200 \text{ feet}}{60^2 \text{ miles per hour}} = \frac{x}{100^2 \text{ miles per hour}}$$

$$\frac{200}{60^2} = \frac{x}{100^2}$$

$$\frac{200}{3600} = \frac{x}{10,000}$$

$$(200)(10,000) = 3600x$$

$$2,000,000 = 3600x$$

$$\frac{2,000,000}{3600} = \frac{3600x}{3600}$$

$$556 \approx x$$

Approximately 556 feet are needed to stop at 100 mph.

7. Let x = pounds per square inch when the volume is 22 cubic inches.

$$\frac{8 \text{ cubic inches}}{\underbrace{x}_{\substack{\text{corresponds to} \\ \text{22 cubic inches}}}} = \frac{22 \text{ cubic inches}}{\underbrace{12 \text{ pounds per square inch}}_{\substack{\text{corresponds to} \\ \text{8 cubic inches}}}}$$

$$\frac{8}{x} = \frac{22}{12}$$

$$(8)(12) = 22x$$

$$96 = 22x$$

$$\frac{96}{22} = \frac{22x}{22}$$

$$4.36 \approx x$$

The pressure is about 4.36 pounds per square inch.

Exercise Set 6.4

1. $\dfrac{24}{48} = \dfrac{24 \div 24}{48 \div 24} = \dfrac{1}{2}$

2. $\dfrac{14}{49} = \dfrac{14 \div 7}{49 \div 7} = \dfrac{2}{7}$

3. $\dfrac{48}{20} = \dfrac{48 \div 4}{20 \div 4} = \dfrac{12}{5}$

4. $\dfrac{24}{15} = \dfrac{24 \div 3}{15 \div 3} = \dfrac{8}{5}$

5. $\dfrac{27}{36} = \dfrac{27 \div 9}{36 \div 9} = \dfrac{3}{4}$

6. $\dfrac{25}{40} = \dfrac{25 \div 5}{40 \div 5} = \dfrac{5}{8}$

7. $\dfrac{20}{10} = \dfrac{20 \div 10}{10 \div 10} = \dfrac{2}{1}$ or 2:1

8. $\dfrac{10}{20} = \dfrac{10 \div 10}{20 \div 10} = \dfrac{1}{2}$ or 1:2

9. $\dfrac{10}{10 + 20} = \dfrac{10}{30} = \dfrac{10 \div 10}{30 \div 10} = \dfrac{1}{3}$ or 1:3

10. $\dfrac{20}{10 + 20} = \dfrac{20}{30} = \dfrac{20 \div 10}{30 \div 10} = \dfrac{2}{3}$ or 2:3

11. $\dfrac{24}{x} = \dfrac{12}{7}$

$$12x = 24 \cdot 7$$
$$12x = 168$$
$$\frac{12x}{12} = \frac{168}{12}$$
$$x = 14$$

12. $\dfrac{56}{x} = \dfrac{8}{7}$

$$8x = 56 \cdot 7$$
$$8x = 392$$
$$\frac{8x}{8} = \frac{392}{8}$$
$$x = 49$$

13. $\dfrac{x}{6} = \dfrac{18}{4}$

$$4x = 6 \cdot 18$$
$$4x = 108$$
$$\frac{4x}{4} = \frac{108}{4}$$
$$x = 27$$

14. $\dfrac{x}{32} = \dfrac{3}{24}$

$$24x = 3 \cdot 32$$
$$24x = 96$$
$$\frac{24x}{24} = \frac{96}{24}$$
$$x = 4$$

15. $\dfrac{x}{3} = -\dfrac{3}{4}$

$$4x = 3(-3)$$
$$4x = -9$$
$$\frac{4x}{4} = \frac{-9}{4}$$
$$x = -\frac{9}{4}$$

16. $\dfrac{x}{2} = -\dfrac{1}{5}$

$5x = 2(-1)$

$5x = -2$

$\dfrac{5x}{5} = \dfrac{-2}{5}$

$x = -\dfrac{2}{5}$

17. $\dfrac{-3}{8} = \dfrac{x}{40}$

$8x = -3(40)$

$8x = -120$

$\dfrac{8x}{8} = \dfrac{-120}{8}$

$x = -15$

18. $\dfrac{-3}{8} = \dfrac{6}{x}$

$-3x = 8 \cdot 6$

$-3x = 48$

$\dfrac{-3x}{-3} = \dfrac{48}{-3}$

$x = -16$

19. $\dfrac{x-2}{5} = \dfrac{3}{10}$

$10(x-2) = 3 \cdot 5$

$10x - 20 = 15$

$10x - 20 + 20 = 15 + 20$

$10x = 35$

$\dfrac{10x}{10} = \dfrac{35}{10}$

$x = \dfrac{7}{2}$

20. $\dfrac{x+4}{8} = \dfrac{3}{16}$

$16(x+4) = 8 \cdot 3$

$16x + 64 = 24$

$16x + 64 - 64 = 24 - 64$

$16x = -40$

$\dfrac{16x}{16} = \dfrac{-40}{16}$

$x = -2.5$

21. $\dfrac{y+10}{10} = \dfrac{y-2}{4}$

$4(y+10) = 10(y-2)$

$4y + 40 = 10y - 20$

$4y + 40 - 40 = 10y - 20 - 40$

$4y = 10y - 60$

$4y - 10y = 10y - 60 - 10y$

$-6y = -60$

$\dfrac{-6y}{-6} = \dfrac{-60}{-6}$

$y = 10$

22. $\dfrac{2}{y-5} = \dfrac{3}{y+6}$

$2(y+6) = 3(y-5)$

$2y + 12 = 3y - 15$

$2y + 12 - 2y = 3y - 15 - 2y$

$12 = y - 15$

$12 + 15 = y - 15 + 15$

$27 = y$ or $y = 27$

23. Possible Answer:

$\dfrac{80}{170} = \dfrac{80 \div 10}{170 \div 10} = \dfrac{8}{17}$ or $8{:}17$

24. Possible Answer:

$\dfrac{105}{220} = \dfrac{105 \div 5}{220 \div 5} = \dfrac{21}{44}$ or $21{:}44$

25. Let x = tax.

$\dfrac{725}{65,000} = \dfrac{x}{100,000}$

$65,000x = 725 \cdot 100,000$

$65,000x = 72,500,000$

$\dfrac{65,000x}{65,000} = \dfrac{72,500,000}{65,000}$

$x \approx 1115.38$

The tax on a property with an assessed value of $100,000 is $1115.38.

26. Let x = maintenance bill.

$$\frac{x}{4800} = \frac{45,000}{180,000}$$

$$180,000x = 4800 \cdot 45,000$$

$$180,000x = 216,000,000$$

$$\frac{180,000x}{180,000} = \frac{216,000,000}{180,000}$$

$$x = 1200$$

The maintenance bill for a store that is 4800 square feet is $1200.

27. Let x = total number of fur seal pups in this rookery.

$$\frac{218}{900} = \frac{4963}{x}$$

$$218x = 900 \cdot 4963$$

$$218x = 4,466,700$$

$$\frac{218x}{218} = \frac{4,466,700}{218}$$

$$x \approx 20,489$$

There were an estimated 20,489 fur seal pups in this rookery.

28. Let x = number of bass in the lake.

$$\frac{27}{108} = \frac{50}{x}$$

$$27x = 108 \cdot 50$$

$$27x = 5400$$

$$\frac{27x}{27} = \frac{5400}{27}$$

$$x = 200$$

There are approximately 200 bass in the lake.

29. Let x = amount to pay in monthly child support.

$$\frac{1}{40} = \frac{x}{38,000}$$

$$1 \cdot 38,000 = 40x$$

$$\frac{38,000}{40} = \frac{40x}{40}$$

$$950 = x$$

The father should pay $950 each month.

30. Let x = moon weight.

$$\frac{55}{8.8} = \frac{90}{x}$$

$$55x = 8.8(90)$$

$$55x = 792$$

$$\frac{55x}{55} = \frac{792}{55}$$

$$x = 14.4$$

A person who weighs 90 kilograms on earth will weigh 14.4 kilograms on the moon.

31. Let x = height of the critter.

$$\frac{67}{10} = \frac{x}{23}$$

$$10x = 67 \cdot 23$$

$$10x = 1541$$

$$\frac{10x}{10} = \frac{1541}{10}$$

$$x = 154.1$$

The critter was 154.1 inches tall or about 12 ft 10 in.

32. Let x = length of mustache.

$$\frac{8}{2} = \frac{x}{17}$$

$$2x = 8 \cdot 17$$

$$2x = 136$$

$$\frac{2x}{2} = \frac{136}{2}$$

$$x = 68$$

His mustache was 68 inches long.

33. Let x = speed of Blackbird.

$$\frac{1502.2}{2.03} = \frac{x}{3.3}$$

$$2.03x = 1502.2(3.3)$$

$$2.03x = 4957.26$$

$$\frac{2.03x}{2.03} = \frac{4957.26}{2.03}$$

$$x = 2442$$

The Blackbird's speed is 2442 mph.

34. Let x = revolutions.

$$\frac{135}{3} = \frac{x}{2.4}$$
$$3x = 135(2.4)$$
$$3x = 324$$
$$\frac{3x}{3} = \frac{324}{3}$$
$$x = 108$$

The record made 108 revolutions.

35. Let x = Mr. Wadlow's weight.

$$\frac{x}{(107)^3} = \frac{170}{(70)^3}$$
$$\frac{x}{1,225,043} = \frac{170}{343,000}$$
$$343,000x = 1,225,043 \cdot 170$$
$$343,000x = 208,257,310$$
$$\frac{343,000x}{343,000} = \frac{208,257,310}{343,000}$$
$$x \approx 607$$

Robert Wadlow's weight was about 607 pounds.

36. Let x = feet the object will fall in 7 seconds.

$$\frac{144}{3^2} = \frac{x}{7^2}$$
$$\frac{144}{9} = \frac{x}{49}$$
$$144 \cdot 49 = 9x$$
$$7056 = 9x$$
$$\frac{7056}{9} = \frac{9x}{9}$$
$$784 = x$$

The object will fall 784 feet.

37. Let x = hours it takes to get to campus averaging 60 mph.

$$\frac{20}{x} = \frac{60}{1.5}$$
$$20 \cdot 1.5 = 60x$$
$$30 = 60x$$
$$\frac{30}{60} = \frac{60x}{60}$$
$$0.5 = x$$

At a rate of 60 mph, it takes 0.5 hours, or 30 minutes, to drive to campus.

38. Let x = the pounds that can be supported by a 5-foot 2-by-4.

$$\frac{10}{x} = \frac{5}{500}$$
$$10 \cdot 500 = 5x$$
$$5000 = 5x$$
$$\frac{5000}{5} = \frac{5x}{5}$$
$$1000 = x$$

A 5-foot 2-by-4 can support 1000 pounds.

39. Let x = pressure when the volume is 40 cubic centimeters.

$$\frac{32}{x} = \frac{40}{8}$$
$$40x = 32(8)$$
$$40x = 256$$
$$\frac{40x}{40} = \frac{256}{40}$$
$$x = 6.4$$

The pressure is 6.4 pounds.

40. Let x = current when the resistance is 16 ohms.

$$\frac{20}{16} = \frac{x}{5}$$
$$16x = 5 \cdot 20$$
$$16x = 100$$
$$\frac{16x}{16} = \frac{100}{16}$$
$$x = 6.25$$

The current is 6.25 amperes.

41-46. Answers will vary.

47. $\dfrac{\text{front}}{\text{rear}} = \dfrac{5}{1}$

$$\frac{60}{x} = \frac{5}{1} \quad \text{or} \quad \frac{y}{20} = \frac{5}{1}$$
$$5x = 60 \qquad\qquad 1y = 5 \cdot 20$$
$$x = 12 \qquad\qquad y = 100$$

Replace the rear sprocket with one that has 12 teeth or replace the front sprocket with one that has 100 teeth.

48. Let x = age of friend if dog.

$$\frac{7}{56} = \frac{x}{44}$$

$$56x = 7 \cdot 44$$

$$56x = 308$$

$$\frac{56x}{56} = \frac{308}{56}$$

$$x = 5.5$$

The friend would be 5.5 years old if the friend was a dog.

49. Let p = the initial pressure and
Let x = the pressure after the wind velocity doubles
Let v = the initial wind velocity, then
  $2v$ = double the wind velocity

$$\frac{p}{v^2} = \frac{x}{(2v)^2}$$

$$\frac{p}{v^2} = \frac{x}{4v^2}$$

$$v^2 \cdot x = p \cdot 4v^2$$

$$\frac{v^2 \cdot x}{v^2} = \frac{p \cdot 4v^2}{v^2}$$

$$x = 4p$$

If the wind velocity doubles, the pressure quadruples.

50. Let x_{15} = the light intensity at 15 inches and
Let x_{30} = the light intensity at 30 inches.

$$\frac{x_{15}}{30^2} = \frac{x_{30}}{15^2}$$

$$\frac{x_{15}}{900} = \frac{x_{30}}{225}$$

$$225x_{15} = 900x_{30}$$

$$\frac{225x_{15}}{225} = \frac{900x_{30}}{225}$$

$$x_{15} = 4x_{30}$$

$$\frac{x_{15}}{4} = \frac{4x_{30}}{4}$$

$$\frac{1}{4}x_{15} = x_{30}$$

The illumination at 30 inches is one-forth of the original intensity.

Check Points 6.5

1. a. $x < 4$

b. $x \geq -2$

c. $-4 \leq x < 1$

2.
$$5x - 3 \leq 17$$
$$5x - 3 + 3 \leq 17 + 3$$
$$5x \leq 20$$
$$\frac{5x}{5} \leq \frac{20}{5}$$
$$x \leq 4$$
$$\{x \mid x \leq 4\}$$

3. a.
$$\frac{1}{4}x < 2$$
$$4 \cdot \frac{1}{4}x < 4 \cdot 2$$
$$x < 8$$
$$\{x \mid x < 8\}$$

b.
$$-6x < 18$$
$$\frac{-6x}{-6} > \frac{18}{-6}$$
$$x > -3$$
$$\{x \mid x > -3\}$$

4.
$$7x - 3 > 13x + 33$$
$$7x - 3 + 3 > 13x + 33 + 3$$
$$7x > 13x + 36$$
$$7x - 13x > 13x + 36 - 13x$$
$$-6x > 36$$
$$\frac{-6x}{-6} < \frac{36}{-6}$$
$$x < -6$$
$$\{x \mid x < -6\}$$

5. $2(x-3)-1 \le 3(x+2)-14$

$2x-6-1 \le 3x+6-14$

$2x-7 \le 3x-8$

$2x-7+7 \le 3x-8+7$

$2x \le 3x-1$

$2x-3x \le 3x-1-3x$

$-x \le -1$

$\dfrac{-x}{-1} \ge \dfrac{-1}{-1}$

$x \ge 1$

$\{x \mid x \ge 1\}$

6. Let x = your grade on the final exam.

$\dfrac{82+74+78+x+x}{5} \ge 80$

$\dfrac{234+2x}{5} \ge 80$

$5\left(\dfrac{234+2x}{5}\right) \ge 5(80)$

$234+2x \ge 400$

$234+2x-234 \ge 400-234$

$2x \ge 166$

$\dfrac{2x}{2} \ge \dfrac{166}{2}$

$x \ge 83$

You need at least an 83 on the final to get a B in the course.

Exercise Set 6.5

1. $x > 6$

2. $x > -2$

3. $x < -4$

4. $x < 0$

5. $x \ge -3$

6. $x \ge -5$

7. $x \le 4$

8. $x \le 7$

9. $-2 < x \le 5$

10. $-3 \le x < 7$

11. $-1 < x < 4$

12. $-7 \le x \le 0$

13. $x-3 > 2$

$x-3+3 > 2+3$

$x > 5$

$\{x \mid x > 5\}$

14. $x+1 < 5$

$x+1-1 < 5-1$

$x < 4$

$\{x \mid x < 4\}$

15. $x+4 \le 9$

$x+4-4 \le 9-4$

$x \le 5$

$\{x \mid x \le 5\}$

16. $x-5 \ge 1$

$x-5+5 \ge 1+5$

$x \ge 6$

$\{x \mid x \ge 6\}$

17. $x-3 < 0$

$x-3+3 < 0+3$

$x < 3$

$\{x \mid x < 3\}$

18.
$$x + 4 \geq 0$$
$$x + 4 - 4 \geq 0 - 4$$
$$x \geq -4$$
$$\{x \mid x \geq -4\}$$

19.
$$4x < 20$$
$$\frac{4x}{4} < \frac{20}{4}$$
$$x < 5$$
$$\{x \mid x < 5\}$$

20.
$$6x \geq 18$$
$$\frac{6x}{6} \geq \frac{18}{6}$$
$$x \geq 3$$
$$\{x \mid x \geq 3\}$$

21.
$$3x \geq -15$$
$$\frac{3x}{3} \geq \frac{-15}{3}$$
$$x \geq -5$$
$$\{x \mid x \geq -5\}$$

22.
$$7x < -21$$
$$\frac{7x}{7} < \frac{-21}{7}$$
$$x < -3$$
$$\{x \mid x < -3\}$$

23.
$$2x - 3 > 7$$
$$2x - 3 + 3 > 7 + 3$$
$$2x > 10$$
$$\frac{2x}{2} > \frac{10}{2}$$
$$x > 5$$
$$\{x \mid x > 5\}$$

24.
$$3x + 2 \leq 14$$
$$3x + 2 - 2 \leq 14 - 2$$
$$3x \leq 12$$
$$\frac{3x}{3} \leq \frac{12}{3}$$
$$x \leq 4$$
$$\{x \mid x \leq 4\}$$

25.
$$3x + 3 < 18$$
$$3x + 3 - 3 < 18 - 3$$
$$3x < 15$$
$$\frac{3x}{3} < \frac{15}{3}$$
$$x < 5$$
$$\{x \mid x < 5\}$$

26.
$$8x - 4 > 12$$
$$8x - 4 + 4 > 12 + 4$$
$$8x > 16$$
$$\frac{8x}{8} > \frac{16}{8}$$
$$x > 2$$
$$\{x \mid x > 2\}$$

27.
$$\frac{1}{2}x < 4$$
$$2 \cdot \frac{1}{2}x < 2 \cdot 4$$
$$x < 8$$
$$\{x \mid x < 8\}$$

28.
$$\frac{1}{2}x > 3$$
$$2 \cdot \frac{1}{2}x > 2 \cdot 3$$
$$x > 6$$
$$\{x \mid x > 6\}$$

29. $\dfrac{x}{3} > -2$

$3 \cdot \dfrac{x}{3} > 3 \cdot (-2)$

$x > -6$

$\{x \mid x > -6\}$

30. $\dfrac{x}{4} < -1$

$4 \cdot \dfrac{x}{4} < 4 \cdot (-1)$

$x < -4$

$\{x \mid x < -4\}$

31. $-3x < 15$

$\dfrac{-3x}{-3} > \dfrac{15}{-3}$

$x > -5$

$\{x \mid x > -5\}$

32. $-7x > 21$

$\dfrac{-7x}{-7} < \dfrac{21}{-7}$

$x < -3$

$\{x \mid x < -3\}$

33. $-3x \geq -15$

$\dfrac{-3x}{-3} \leq \dfrac{-15}{-3}$

$x \leq 5$

$\{x \mid x \leq 5\}$

34. $-7x \leq -21$

$\dfrac{-7x}{-7} \geq \dfrac{-21}{-7}$

$x \geq 3$

$\{x \mid x \geq 3\}$

35. $3x + 4 \leq 2x + 7$

$3x + 4 - 4 \leq 2x + 7 - 4$

$3x \leq 2x + 3$

$3x - 2x \leq 2x + 3 - 2x$

$x \leq 3$

$\{x \mid x \leq 3\}$

36. $2x + 9 \leq x + 2$

$2x + 9 - 9 \leq x + 2 - 9$

$2x \leq x - 7$

$2x - x \leq x - 7 - x$

$x \leq -7$

$\{x \mid x \leq -7\}$

37. $5x - 9 < 4x + 7$

$5x - 9 + 9 < 4x + 7 + 9$

$5x < 4x + 16$

$5x - 4x < 4x + 16 - 4x$

$x < 16$

$\{x \mid x < 16\}$

38. $3x - 8 < 2x + 11$

$3x - 8 + 8 < 2x + 11 + 8$

$3x < 2x + 19$

$3x - 2x < 2x + 19 - 2x$

$x < 19$

$\{x \mid x < 19\}$

39. $-2x - 3 < 3$

$-2x - 3 + 3 < 3 + 3$

$-2x < 6$

$\dfrac{-2x}{-2} > \dfrac{6}{-2}$

$x > -3$

$\{x \mid x > -3\}$

40.
$$14 - 3x > 5$$
$$14 - 3x - 14 > 5 - 14$$
$$-3x > -9$$
$$\frac{-3x}{-3} < \frac{-9}{-3}$$
$$x < 3$$
$$\{x \mid x < 3\}$$

41.
$$3 - 7x \le 17$$
$$3 - 7x - 3 \le 17 - 3$$
$$-7x \le 14$$
$$\frac{-7x}{-7} \ge \frac{14}{-7}$$
$$x \ge -2$$
$$\{x \mid x \ge -2\}$$

42.
$$5 - 3x \ge 20$$
$$5 - 3x - 5 \ge 20 - 5$$
$$-3x \ge 15$$
$$\frac{-3x}{-3} \le \frac{15}{-3}$$
$$x \le -5$$
$$\{x \mid x \le -5\}$$

43.
$$-x < 4$$
$$\frac{-x}{-1} > \frac{4}{-1}$$
$$x > -4$$
$$\{x \mid x > -4\}$$

44.
$$-x > -3$$
$$\frac{-x}{-1} < \frac{-3}{-1}$$
$$x < 3$$
$$\{x \mid x < 3\}$$

45.
$$5 - x \le 1$$
$$5 - x - 5 \le 1 - 5$$
$$-x \le -4$$
$$\frac{-x}{-1} \ge \frac{-4}{-1}$$
$$x \ge 4$$
$$\{x \mid x \ge 4\}$$

46.
$$3 - x \ge -3$$
$$3 - x - 3 \ge -3 - 3$$
$$-x \ge -6$$
$$\frac{-x}{-1} \le \frac{-6}{-1}$$
$$x \le 6$$
$$\{x \mid x \le 6\}$$

47.
$$2x - 5 > -x + 6$$
$$2x - 5 + 5 > -x + 6 + 5$$
$$2x > -x + 11$$
$$2x + x > -x + 11 + x$$
$$3x > 11$$
$$\frac{3x}{3} > \frac{11}{3}$$
$$x > \frac{11}{3}$$
$$\left\{ x \mid x > \frac{11}{3} \right\}$$

48.
$$6x - 2 \ge 4x + 6$$
$$6x - 2 + 2 \ge 4x + 6 + 2$$
$$6x > 4x + 8$$
$$6x - 4x \ge 4x + 8 - 4x$$
$$2x \ge 8$$
$$\frac{2x}{2} \ge \frac{8}{2}$$
$$x \ge 4$$
$$\{x \mid x \ge 4\}$$

49.
$$2x-5 < 5x-11$$
$$2x-5+5 < 5x-11+5$$
$$2x < 5x-6$$
$$2x-5x < 5x-6-5x$$
$$-3x < -6$$
$$\frac{-3x}{-3} > \frac{-6}{-3}$$
$$x > 2$$
$$\{x \mid x > 2\}$$

50.
$$4x-7 > 9x-2$$
$$4x-7+7 > 9x-2+7$$
$$4x > 9x+5$$
$$4x-9x > 9x+5-9x$$
$$-5x > 5$$
$$\frac{-5x}{-5} < \frac{5}{-5}$$
$$x < -1$$
$$\{x \mid x < -1\}$$

51.
$$3(x+1)-5 < 2x+1$$
$$3x+3-5 < 2x+1$$
$$3x-2 < 2x+1$$
$$3x-2+2 < 2x+1+2$$
$$3x < 2x+3$$
$$3x-2x < 2x+3-2x$$
$$x < 3$$
$$\{x \mid x < 3\}$$

52.
$$4(x+1)+2 \geq 3x+6$$
$$4x+4+2 \geq 3x+6$$
$$4x+6 \geq 3x+6$$
$$4x+6-6 \geq 3x+6-6$$
$$4x \geq 3x$$
$$4x-3x \geq 3x-3x$$
$$x \geq 0$$
$$\{x \mid x \geq 0\}$$

53.
$$8x+3 > 3(2x+1)-x+5$$
$$8x+3 > 6x+3-x+5$$
$$8x+3 > 5x+8$$
$$8x+3-3 > 5x+8-3$$
$$8x > 5x+5$$
$$8x-5x > 5x+5-5x$$
$$3x > 5$$
$$\frac{3x}{3} > \frac{5}{3}$$
$$x > \frac{5}{3}$$
$$\left\{x \mid x > \frac{5}{3}\right\}$$

54.
$$7-2(x-4) < 5(1-2x)$$
$$7-2x+8 < 5-10x$$
$$15-2x < 5-10x$$
$$15-2x-15 < 5-10x-15$$
$$-2x < -10-10x$$
$$-2x+10x < -10-10x+10x$$
$$8x < -10$$
$$\frac{8x}{8} < \frac{-10}{8}$$
$$x < -\frac{5}{4}$$
$$\left\{x \mid x < -\frac{5}{4}\right\}$$

55. Denmark, the Netherlands, and Norway.

56. Denmark and the Netherlands.

57. Japan and Mexico.

58. Spain, Japan, and Mexico.

59. The Netherlands, Norway, Canada, and the United States.

60. Spain and Japan.

61. a. $\dfrac{88+78+86+100}{4} = \dfrac{352}{4} = 88$

The average is 88. An A is not possible.

b. $\dfrac{88+78+86+x}{4} \geq 80$

$\dfrac{252+x}{4} \geq 80$

$4 \cdot \dfrac{252+x}{4} \geq 80 \cdot 4$

$252+x \geq 320$

$252+x-252 \geq 320-252$

$x \geq 68$

You must get at least 68 on the final to earn a B in the course.

62. a. $\dfrac{86+88+x}{3} \geq 90$

$\dfrac{174+x}{3} \geq 90$

$3 \cdot \dfrac{174+x}{3} \geq 3 \cdot 90$

$174+x \geq 270$

$174+x-174 \geq 270-174$

$x \geq 96$

You must get at least 96 on the final to earn an A in the course.

b. $\dfrac{86+88+x}{3} < 80$

$\dfrac{174+x}{3} < 80$

$3 \cdot \dfrac{174+x}{3} < 80 \cdot 3$

$174+x < 240$

$174+x-174 < 240-174$

$x < 66$

If you get less than a 66 on the final you will lose your B in the course.

63. $N = 550-9x; \quad N < 370$

$550-9x < 370$

$550-9x-550 < 370-550$

$-9x < -180$

$\dfrac{-9x}{-9} > \dfrac{-180}{-9}$

$x > 20$

20 years after 1988 is 2008. According to the model, there will be 370 billion cigarettes consumed in 2008 and less than 370 billion from 2009 onward.

64. $N = 550-9x; \quad N < 325$

$550-9x < 325$

$550-9x-550 < 325-550$

$-9x < -225$

$\dfrac{-9x}{-9} > \dfrac{-225}{-9}$

$x > 25$

25 years after 1988 is 2013. According to the model, there will be 325 billion cigarettes consumed in 2013 and less than 325 billion from 2014 onward.

65. Let x = number of miles driven.

$80+0.25x \leq 400$

$80+0.25x-80 \leq 400-80$

$0.25x \leq 320$

$\dfrac{0.25x}{0.25} \leq \dfrac{320}{0.25}$

$x \leq 1280$

You can drive at most 1280 miles.

66. Let x = number of miles driven.

$60+0.50x \leq 600$

$60+0.50x-60 \leq 600-60$

$0.50x \leq 540$

$\dfrac{0.50x}{0.50} \leq \dfrac{540}{0.50}$

$x \leq 1080$

You can drive at most 1080 miles.

67. Let x = number of cement bags.

$245+95x \leq 3000$

$245+95x-245 \leq 3000-245$

$95x \leq 2755$

$\dfrac{95x}{95} \leq \dfrac{2755}{95}$

$x \leq 29$

At most 29 bags can be safely lifted.

68. Let x = number of cement bags.
$$265 + 65x \le 2800$$
$$265 + 65x - 265 \le 2800 - 265$$
$$65x \le 2535$$
$$\frac{65x}{65} \le \frac{2535}{65}$$
$$x \le 39$$
At most 39 bags can be safely lifted.

69-73. Answers will vary.

74. Let x = number of miles driven.
Basic: 260
Continental: $80 + 0.25x$
$$260 < 80 + 0.25x$$
$$260 - 80 < 80 + 0.25x - 80$$
$$180 < 0.25x$$
$$\frac{180}{0.25} < \frac{0.25x}{0.25}$$
$$720 < x \text{ or } x > 720$$
The miles driven must exceed 720 for Basic Rental to be a better deal than Continental.

75. Let x = the number of packages produced
$$5.50x > 3000 + 3.00x$$
$$5.50x - 3.00x > 3000$$
$$2.5x > 3000$$
$$2.5x > 3000$$
$$\frac{2.5x}{2.5} > \frac{3000}{2.5}$$
$$x > 1200$$
The number of packages produced must exceed 1200 for the company to generate a profit.

Check Points 6.6

1. $(x+5)(x+6) = x \cdot x + x \cdot 6 + 5 \cdot x + 5 \cdot 6$
$$= x^2 + 6x + 5x + 30$$
$$= x^2 + 11x + 30$$

2. $(7x+5)(4x-3) = 7x \cdot 4x + 7x(-3) + 5 \cdot 4x + 5(-3)$
$$= 28x^2 - 21x + 20x - 15$$
$$= 28x^2 - x - 15$$

3. $x^2 + 5x + 6 = (x+2)(x+3)$

4. $x^2 + 3x - 10 = (x+5)(x-2)$

5. $5x^2 - 14x + 8 = (5x-4)(x-2)$

6. $6y^2 + 19y - 7 = (3y-1)(2y+7)$

7. $(x+6)(x-3) = 0$
$$x+6 = 0 \quad \text{or} \quad x-3 = 0$$
$$x = -6 \qquad x = 3$$
The solution set is $\{-6, 3\}$.

8. $\qquad x^2 - 6x = 16$
$$x^2 - 6x - 16 = 16 - 16$$
$$x^2 - 6x - 16 = 0$$
$$(x+2)(x-8) = 0$$
$$x+2 = 0 \quad \text{or} \quad x-8 = 0$$
$$x = -2 \qquad x = 8$$
The solution set is $\{-2, 8\}$.

9. $\qquad 2x^2 + 7x - 4 = 0$
$$(2x-1)(x+4) = 0$$
$$2x-1 = 0 \quad \text{or} \quad x+4 = 0$$
$$2x = 1 \qquad x = -4$$
$$x = \frac{1}{2}$$
The solution set is $\left\{-4, \frac{1}{2}\right\}$.

10. $8x^2 + 2x - 1 = 0$
$$x = \frac{-b \pm \sqrt{b^2 - 4ac}}{2a}$$
$$x = \frac{-(2) \pm \sqrt{(2)^2 - 4(8)(-1)}}{2(8)}$$
$$x = \frac{-2 \pm \sqrt{4+32}}{16}$$
$$x = \frac{-2 \pm \sqrt{36}}{16}$$
$$x = \frac{-2 \pm 6}{16}$$
$$x = \frac{-2+6}{16} \quad \text{or} \quad x = \frac{-2-6}{16}$$
$$x = \frac{4}{16} \qquad x = \frac{-8}{16}$$
$$x = \frac{1}{4} \qquad x = -\frac{1}{2}$$
The solution set is $\left\{-\frac{1}{2}, \frac{1}{4}\right\}$.

Chapter 6: Algebra: Equations and Inequalities

11.
$$2x^2 = 6x - 1$$
$$2x^2 - 6x + 1 = 0$$
$$x = \frac{-b \pm \sqrt{b^2 - 4ac}}{2a}$$
$$x = \frac{-(-6) \pm \sqrt{(-6)^2 - 4(2)(1)}}{2(2)}$$
$$x = \frac{6 \pm \sqrt{36 - 8}}{4}$$
$$x = \frac{6 \pm \sqrt{28}}{4}$$
$$x = \frac{6 \pm 2\sqrt{7}}{4}$$
$$x = \frac{2(3 \pm \sqrt{7})}{4}$$
$$x = \frac{3 \pm \sqrt{7}}{2}$$
$$x = \frac{3 + \sqrt{7}}{2} \quad \text{or} \quad x = \frac{3 - \sqrt{7}}{2}$$
The solution set is $\left\{ \frac{3 + \sqrt{7}}{2}, \frac{3 - \sqrt{7}}{2} \right\}$.

Exercise Set 6.6

1. $(x+3)(x+5) = x^2 + 5x + 3x + 15$
$$= x^2 + 8x + 15$$

2. $(x+7)(x+2) = x^2 + 2x + 7x + 14$
$$= x^2 + 9x + 14$$

3. $(x-5)(x+3) = x^2 + 3x - 5x - 15$
$$= x^2 - 2x - 15$$

4. $(x-1)(x+2) = x^2 + 2x - 1x - 2$
$$= x^2 + x - 2$$

5. $(2x-1)(x+2) = 2x^2 + 4x - 1x - 2$
$$= 2x^2 + 3x - 2$$

6. $(2x-5)(x+3) = 2x^2 + 6x - 5x - 15$
$$= 2x^2 + x - 15$$

7. $(3x-7)(4x-5) = 12x^2 - 15x - 28x + 35$
$$= 12x^2 - 43x + 35$$

8. $(2x-9)(7x-4) = 14x^2 - 8x - 63x + 36$
$$= 14x^2 - 71x + 36$$

9. $x^2 + 5x + 6 = (x+2)(x+3)$
Check: $(x+2)(x+3)$
$$= x^2 + 3x + 2x + 6$$
$$= x^2 + 5x + 6$$

10. $x^2 + 8x + 15 = (x+3)(x+5)$
Check: $(x+3)(x+5)$
$$= x^2 + 5x + 3x + 15$$
$$= x^2 + 8x + 15$$

11. $x^2 - 2x - 15 = (x-5)(x+3)$
Check: $(x-5)(x+3)$
$$= x^2 + 3x - 5x - 15$$
$$= x^2 - 2x - 15$$

12. $x^2 - 4x - 5 = (x-5)(x+1)$
Check: $(x-5)(x+1)$
$$= x^2 + x - 5x - 5$$
$$= x^2 - 4x - 5$$

13. $x^2 - 8x + 15 = (x-3)(x-5)$
Check: $(x-3)(x-5)$
$$= x^2 - 5x - 3x + 15$$
$$= x^2 - 8x + 15$$

14. $x^2 - 14x + 45 = (x-9)(x-5)$
Check: $(x-9)(x-5)$
$$= x^2 - 5x - 9x + 45$$
$$= x^2 - 14x + 45$$

15. $x^2 - 9x - 36 = (x-12)(x+3)$
Check: $(x-12)(x+3)$
$$= x^2 + 3x - 12x - 36$$
$$= x^2 - 9x - 36$$

16. $x^2 - x - 90 = (x-10)(x+9)$
Check: $(x-10)(x+9)$
$$= x^2 + 9x - 10x - 90$$
$$= x^2 - x - 90$$

17. $x^2 - 8x + 32$ is prime.

18. $x^2 - 9x + 81$ is prime.

19. $x^2 + 17x + 16 = (x + 16)(x + 1)$

Check: $(x + 16)(x + 1)$
$$= x^2 + x + 16x + 16$$
$$= x^2 + 17x + 16$$

20. $x^2 - 7x - 44 = (x - 11)(x + 4)$

Check: $(x - 11)(x + 4)$
$$= x^2 + 4x - 11x - 44$$
$$= x^2 - 7x - 44$$

21. $2x^2 + 7x + 3 = (2x + 1)(x + 3)$

Check: $(2x + 1)(x + 3)$
$$= 2x^2 + 6x + x + 3$$
$$= 2x^2 + 7x + 3$$

22. $3x^2 + 7x + 2 = (3x + 1)(x + 2)$

Check: $(3x + 1)(x + 2)$
$$= 3x^2 + 6x + x + 3$$
$$= 3x^2 + 7x + 2$$

23. $2x^2 - 17x + 30 = (2x - 5)(x - 6)$

Check: $(2x - 5)(x - 6)$
$$= 2x^2 - 12x - 5x + 30$$
$$= 2x^2 - 17x + 30$$

24. $5x^2 - 13x + 6 = (5x - 3)(x - 2)$

Check: $(5x - 3)(x - 2)$
$$= 5x^2 - 10x - 3x + 6$$
$$= 5x^2 - 13x + 6$$

25. $3x^2 - x - 2 = (3x + 2)(x - 1)$

Check: $(3x + 2)(x - 1)$
$$= 3x^2 - 3x + 2x - 2$$
$$= 3x^2 - x - 2$$

26. $2x^2 + 5x - 3 = (2x - 1)(x + 3)$

Check: $(2x - 1)(x + 3)$
$$= 2x^2 + 6x - x - 3$$
$$= 2x^2 + 5x - 3$$

27. $3x^2 - 25x - 28 = (3x - 28)(x + 1)$

Check: $(3x - 28)(x + 1)$
$$= 3x^2 + 3x - 28x - 28$$
$$= 3x^2 - 25x - 28$$

28. $3x^2 - 2x - 5 = (3x - 5)(x + 1)$

Check: $(3x - 5)(x + 1)$
$$= 3x^2 + 3x - 5x - 5$$
$$= 3x^2 - 2x - 5$$

29. $6x^2 - 11x + 4 = (2x - 1)(3x - 4)$

Check: $(2x - 1)(3x - 4)$
$$= 6x^2 - 8x - 3x + 4$$
$$= 6x^2 - 11x + 4$$

30. $6x^2 - 17x + 12 = (3x - 4)(2x - 3)$

Check: $(3x - 4)(2x - 3)$
$$= 6x^2 - 9x - 8x + 12$$
$$= 6x^2 - 17x + 12$$

31. $4x^2 + 16x + 15 = (2x + 5)(2x + 3)$

Check: $(2x + 5)(2x + 3)$
$$= 4x^2 + 6x + 10x + 15$$
$$= 4x^2 + 16x + 15$$

32. $8x^2 + 33x + 4 = (8x + 1)(x + 4)$

Check: $(8x + 1)(x + 4)$
$$= 8x^2 + 32x + x + 4$$
$$= 8x^2 + 33x + 4$$

33. $(x - 8)(x + 3) = 0$
$$x - 8 = 0 \quad \text{or} \quad x + 3 = 0$$
$$x = 8 \qquad\qquad x = -3$$
The solution set is $\{-3, 8\}$.

34. $(x + 11)(x - 5) = 0$
$$x + 11 = 0 \quad \text{or} \quad x - 5 = 0$$
$$x = -11 \qquad\qquad x = 5$$
The solution set is $\{-11, 5\}$.

35. $(4x + 5)(x - 2) = 0$
$$4x + 5 = 0 \quad \text{or} \quad x - 2 = 0$$
$$4x = -5 \qquad\qquad x = 2$$
$$x = -\frac{5}{4}$$
The solution set is $\left\{-\frac{5}{4}, 2\right\}$.

36. $(x+9)(3x-1)=0$

$x+9=0$ or $3x-1=0$

$\qquad x=-9 \qquad\qquad 3x=1$

$$x=\frac{1}{3}$$

The solution set is $\left\{-9,\frac{1}{3}\right\}$.

37. $x^2+8x+15=0$

$(x+5)(x+3)=0$

$x+5=0$ or $x+3=0$

$\qquad x=-5 \qquad\qquad x=-3$

The solution set is $\{-5,-3\}$.

38. $x^2+5x+6=0$

$(x+3)(x+2)=0$

$x+3=0$ or $x+2=0$

$\qquad x=-3 \qquad\qquad x=-2$

The solution set is $\{-3,-2\}$.

39. $x^2-2x-15=0$

$(x-5)(x+3)=0$

$x-5=0$ or $x+3=0$

$\qquad x=5 \qquad\qquad x=-3$

The solution set is $\{-3,5\}$.

40. $x^2+x-42=0$

$(x+7)(x-6)=0$

$x+7=0$ or $x-6=0$

$\qquad x=-7 \qquad\qquad x=6$

The solution set is $\{-7,6\}$.

41. $x^2-4x=21$

$x^2-4x-21=0$

$(x+3)(x-7)=0$

$x+3=0$ or $x-7=0$

$\qquad x=-3 \qquad\qquad x=7$

The solution set is $\{-3,7\}$.

42. $x^2+7x=18$

$x^2+7x-18=0$

$(x+9)(x-2)=0$

$x+9=0$ or $x-2=0$

$\qquad x=-9 \qquad\qquad x=2$

The solution set is $\{-9,2\}$.

43. $x^2+9x=-8$

$x^2+9x+8=0$

$(x+8)(x+1)=0$

$x+8=0$ or $x+1=0$

$\qquad x=-8 \qquad\qquad x=-1$

The solution set is $\{-8,-1\}$.

44. $x^2-11x=-10$

$x^2-11x+10=0$

$(x-1)(x-10)=0$

$x-1=0$ or $x-10=0$

$\qquad x=1 \qquad\qquad x=10$

The solution set is $\{1,10\}$.

45. $x^2-12x=-36$

$x^2-12x+36=0$

$(x-6)(x-6)=0$

$x-6=0$ or $x-6=0$

$\qquad x=6 \qquad\qquad x=6$

The solution set is $\{6\}$.

46. $x^2-14x=-49$

$x^2-14x+49=0$

$(x-7)(x-7)=0$

$x-7=0$ or $x-7=0$

$\qquad x=7 \qquad\qquad x=7$

The solution set is $\{7\}$.

47. $2x^2=7x+4$

$2x^2-7x-4=0$

$(2x+1)(x-4)=0$

$2x+1=0$ or $x-4=0$

$\qquad 2x=-1 \qquad\qquad x=4$

$$x=-\frac{1}{2}$$

The solution set is $\left\{-\frac{1}{2},4\right\}$.

48. $3x^2=x+4$

$3x^2-x-4=0$

$(3x-4)(x+1)=0$

$3x-4=0$ or $x+1=0$

$\qquad 3x=4 \qquad\qquad x=-1$

$$x=\frac{4}{3}$$

The solution set is $\left\{-1,\frac{4}{3}\right\}$.

49. $5x^2 + x = 18$

$5x^2 + x - 18 = 0$

$(5x - 9)(x + 2) = 0$

$5x - 9 = 0$ or $x + 2 = 0$

$5x = 9$ $x = -2$

$x = \dfrac{9}{5}$

The solution set is $\left\{-2, \dfrac{9}{5}\right\}$.

50. $\qquad 3x^2 - 4x = 15$

$3x^2 - 4x - 15 = 0$

$(3x + 5)(x - 3) = 0$

$3x + 5 = 0$ or $x - 3 = 0$

$3x = -5$ $x = 3$

$x = -\dfrac{5}{3}$

The solution set is $\left\{-\dfrac{5}{3}, 3\right\}$.

51. $\quad x(6x + 23) + 7 = 0$

$6x^2 + 23x + 7 = 0$

$(2x + 7)(3x + 1) = 0$

$2x + 7 = 0$ or $3x + 1 = 0$

$2x = -7$ $3x = -1$

$x = -\dfrac{7}{2}$ $x = -\dfrac{1}{3}$

The solution set is $\left\{-\dfrac{7}{2}, -\dfrac{1}{3}\right\}$.

52. $\quad x(6x + 13) + 6 = 0$

$6x^2 + 13x + 6 = 0$

$(3x + 2)(2x + 3) = 0$

$3x + 2 = 0$ or $2x + 3 = 0$

$3x = -2$ $2x = -3$

$x = -\dfrac{2}{3}$ $x = -\dfrac{3}{2}$

The solution set is $\left\{-\dfrac{2}{3}, -\dfrac{3}{2}\right\}$.

53. $x^2 + 8x + 15 = 0$

$x = \dfrac{-b \pm \sqrt{b^2 - 4ac}}{2a}$

$x = \dfrac{-8 \pm \sqrt{8^2 - 4(1)(15)}}{2(1)}$

$x = \dfrac{-8 \pm \sqrt{4}}{2}$

$x = \dfrac{-8 \pm 2}{2}$

$x = \dfrac{-8 - 2}{2}$ or $x = \dfrac{-8 + 2}{2}$

$x = -5$ $x = -3$

The solution set is $\{-5, -3\}$.

54. $x^2 + 8x + 12 = 0$

$x = \dfrac{-b \pm \sqrt{b^2 - 4ac}}{2a}$

$x = \dfrac{-8 \pm \sqrt{8^2 - 4(1)(12)}}{2(1)}$

$x = \dfrac{-8 \pm \sqrt{16}}{2}$

$x = \dfrac{-8 \pm 4}{2}$

$x = \dfrac{-8 - 4}{2}$ or $x = \dfrac{-8 + 4}{2}$

$x = -6$ $x = -2$

The solution set is $\{-6, -2\}$.

55. $x^2 + 5x + 3 = 0$

$x = \dfrac{-b \pm \sqrt{b^2 - 4ac}}{2a}$

$x = \dfrac{-5 \pm \sqrt{5^2 - 4(1)(3)}}{2(1)}$

$x = \dfrac{-5 \pm \sqrt{13}}{2}$

The solution set is $\left\{\dfrac{-5 - \sqrt{13}}{2}, \dfrac{-5 + \sqrt{13}}{2}\right\}$.

56. $x^2 + 5x + 2 = 0$

$$x = \frac{-b \pm \sqrt{b^2 - 4ac}}{2a}$$

$$x = \frac{-5 \pm \sqrt{5^2 - 4(1)(2)}}{2(1)}$$

$$x = \frac{-5 \pm \sqrt{17}}{2}$$

The solution set is $\left\{ \dfrac{-5 - \sqrt{17}}{2}, \dfrac{-5 + \sqrt{17}}{2} \right\}$.

57. $\quad x^2 + 4x = 6$

$x^2 + 4x - 6 = 0$

$$x = \frac{-b \pm \sqrt{b^2 - 4ac}}{2a}$$

$$x = \frac{-4 \pm \sqrt{4^2 - 4(1)(-6)}}{2(1)}$$

$$x = \frac{-4 \pm \sqrt{40}}{2}$$

$$x = \frac{-4 \pm 2\sqrt{10}}{2}$$

$x = -2 \pm \sqrt{10}$

The solution set is $\left\{ -2 - \sqrt{10},\ -2 + \sqrt{10} \right\}$.

58. $\quad x^2 + 2x = 4$

$x^2 + 2x - 4 = 0$

$$x = \frac{-b \pm \sqrt{b^2 - 4ac}}{2a}$$

$$x = \frac{-2 \pm \sqrt{2^2 - 4(1)(-4)}}{2(1)}$$

$$x = \frac{-2 \pm \sqrt{20}}{2}$$

$$x = \frac{-2 \pm 2\sqrt{5}}{2}$$

$x = -1 \pm \sqrt{5}$

The solution set is $\left\{ -1 - \sqrt{5},\ -1 + \sqrt{5} \right\}$.

59. $x^2 + 4x - 7 = 0$

$$x = \frac{-b \pm \sqrt{b^2 - 4ac}}{2a}$$

$$x = \frac{-4 \pm \sqrt{4^2 - 4(1)(-7)}}{2(1)}$$

$$x = \frac{-4 \pm \sqrt{44}}{2}$$

$$x = \frac{-4 \pm 2\sqrt{11}}{2}$$

$x = -2 \pm \sqrt{11}$

The solution set is $\left\{ -2 - \sqrt{11},\ -2 + \sqrt{11} \right\}$.

60. $x^2 + 4x + 1 = 0$

$$x = \frac{-b \pm \sqrt{b^2 - 4ac}}{2a}$$

$$x = \frac{-4 \pm \sqrt{4^2 - 4(1)(1)}}{2(1)}$$

$$x = \frac{-4 \pm \sqrt{12}}{2}$$

$$x = \frac{-4 \pm 2\sqrt{3}}{2}$$

$x = -2 \pm \sqrt{3}$

The solution set is $\left\{ -2 - \sqrt{3},\ -2 + \sqrt{3} \right\}$.

61. $\qquad x^2 - 3x = 18$

$x^2 - 3x - 18 = 0$

$$x = \frac{-b \pm \sqrt{b^2 - 4ac}}{2a}$$

$$x = \frac{-(-3) \pm \sqrt{(-3)^2 - 4(1)(-18)}}{2(1)}$$

$$x = \frac{3 \pm \sqrt{81}}{2}$$

$$x = \frac{3 \pm 9}{2}$$

$$x = \frac{3 - 9}{2} \quad \text{or} \quad x = \frac{3 + 9}{2}$$

$x = -3 \qquad\qquad x = 6$

The solution set is $\{-3, 6\}$.

62.
$$x^2 - 3x = 10$$
$$x^2 - 3x - 10 = 0$$
$$x = \frac{-b \pm \sqrt{b^2 - 4ac}}{2a}$$
$$x = \frac{-(-3) \pm \sqrt{(-3)^2 - 4(1)(-10)}}{2(1)}$$
$$x = \frac{3 \pm \sqrt{49}}{2}$$
$$x = \frac{3 \pm 7}{2}$$
$$x = \frac{3 - 7}{2} \quad \text{or} \quad x = \frac{3 + 7}{2}$$
$$x = -2 \qquad\qquad x = 5$$
The solution set is $\{-2, 5\}$.

63.
$$6x^2 - 5x - 6 = 0$$
$$x = \frac{-b \pm \sqrt{b^2 - 4ac}}{2a}$$
$$x = \frac{-(-5) \pm \sqrt{(-5)^2 - 4(6)(-6)}}{2(6)}$$
$$x = \frac{5 \pm \sqrt{169}}{12}$$
$$x = \frac{5 \pm 13}{12}$$
$$x = \frac{5 + 13}{12} \quad \text{or} \quad x = \frac{5 - 13}{12}$$
$$x = \frac{18}{12} \qquad\qquad x = \frac{-8}{12}$$
$$x = \frac{3}{2} \qquad\qquad x = -\frac{2}{3}$$
The solution set is $\left\{\frac{3}{2}, \ -\frac{2}{3}\right\}$.

64.
$$9x^2 - 12x - 5 = 0$$
$$x = \frac{-b \pm \sqrt{b^2 - 4ac}}{2a}$$
$$x = \frac{-(-12) \pm \sqrt{(-12)^2 - 4(9)(-5)}}{2(9)}$$
$$x = \frac{12 \pm \sqrt{324}}{18}$$
$$x = \frac{12 \pm 18}{18}$$
$$x = \frac{12 - 18}{18} \quad \text{or} \quad x = \frac{12 + 18}{18}$$
$$x = -\frac{1}{3} \qquad\qquad x = \frac{5}{3}$$
The solution set is $\left\{-\frac{1}{3}, \frac{5}{3}\right\}$.

65.
$$x^2 - 2x - 10 = 0$$
$$x = \frac{-b \pm \sqrt{b^2 - 4ac}}{2a}$$
$$x = \frac{-(-2) \pm \sqrt{(-2)^2 - 4(1)(-10)}}{2(1)}$$
$$x = \frac{2 \pm \sqrt{44}}{2}$$
$$x = \frac{2 \pm 2\sqrt{11}}{2}$$
$$x = 1 \pm \sqrt{11}$$
The solution set is $\left\{1 - \sqrt{11}, \ 1 + \sqrt{11}\right\}$.

66.
$$x^2 + 6x - 10 = 0$$
$$x = \frac{-b \pm \sqrt{b^2 - 4ac}}{2a}$$
$$x = \frac{-6 \pm \sqrt{6^2 - 4(1)(-10)}}{2(1)}$$
$$x = \frac{-6 \pm \sqrt{76}}{2}$$
$$x = \frac{-6 \pm 2\sqrt{19}}{2}$$
$$x = -3 \pm \sqrt{19}$$
The solution set is $\left\{-3 - \sqrt{19}, \ -3 + \sqrt{19}\right\}$.

67.
$$x^2 - x = 14$$
$$x^2 - x - 14 = 0$$
$$x = \frac{-b \pm \sqrt{b^2 - 4ac}}{2a}$$
$$x = \frac{-(-1) \pm \sqrt{(-1)^2 - 4(1)(-14)}}{2(1)}$$
$$x = \frac{1 \pm \sqrt{57}}{2}$$

The solution set is $\left\{ \dfrac{1 - \sqrt{57}}{2}, \ \dfrac{1 + \sqrt{57}}{2} \right\}$.

68.
$$x^2 - 5x = 10$$
$$x^2 - 5x - 10 = 0$$
$$x = \frac{-b \pm \sqrt{b^2 - 4ac}}{2a}$$
$$x = \frac{-(-5) \pm \sqrt{(-5)^2 - 4(1)(-10)}}{2(1)}$$
$$x = \frac{5 \pm \sqrt{65}}{2}$$

The solution set is $\left\{ \dfrac{5 - \sqrt{65}}{2}, \ \dfrac{5 + \sqrt{65}}{2} \right\}$.

69. $6x^2 + 6x + 1 = 0$
$$x = \frac{-b \pm \sqrt{b^2 - 4ac}}{2a}$$
$$x = \frac{-6 \pm \sqrt{6^2 - 4(6)(1)}}{2(6)}$$
$$x = \frac{-6 \pm \sqrt{12}}{12}$$
$$x = \frac{-6 \pm 2\sqrt{3}}{12}$$
$$x = \frac{-3 \pm \sqrt{3}}{6}$$

The solution set is $\left\{ \dfrac{-3 - \sqrt{3}}{6}, \ \dfrac{-3 + \sqrt{3}}{6} \right\}$.

70.
$$3x^2 = 5x - 1$$
$$3x^2 - 5x + 1 = 0$$
$$x = \frac{-b \pm \sqrt{b^2 - 4ac}}{2a}$$
$$x = \frac{-(-5) \pm \sqrt{(-5)^2 - 4(3)(1)}}{2(3)}$$
$$x = \frac{5 \pm \sqrt{13}}{6}$$

The solution set is $\left\{ \dfrac{5 - \sqrt{13}}{6}, \ \dfrac{5 + \sqrt{13}}{6} \right\}$.

71.
$$4x^2 = 12x - 9$$
$$4x^2 - 12x + 9 = 0$$
$$x = \frac{-b \pm \sqrt{b^2 - 4ac}}{2a}$$
$$x = \frac{-(-12) \pm \sqrt{(-12)^2 - 4(4)(9)}}{2(4)}$$
$$x = \frac{12 \pm \sqrt{0}}{8}$$
$$x = \frac{12}{8} = \frac{3}{2}$$

The solution set is $\left\{ \dfrac{3}{2} \right\}$.

72. $9x^2 + 6x + 1 = 0$
$$x = \frac{-b \pm \sqrt{b^2 - 4ac}}{2a}$$
$$x = \frac{-6 \pm \sqrt{6^2 - 4(9)(1)}}{2(9)}$$
$$x = \frac{-6 \pm \sqrt{0}}{18}$$
$$x = -\frac{6}{18} = -\frac{1}{3}$$

The solution set is $\left\{ -\dfrac{1}{3} \right\}$.

73. $N = \dfrac{t^2 - t}{2}$

$36 = \dfrac{t^2 - t}{2}$

$72 = t^2 - t$

$0 = t^2 - t - 72$

$0 = (t+8)(t-9)$

$t + 8 = 0 \quad$ or $\quad t - 9 = 0$

$\quad t = -8 \qquad\qquad t = 9$

Thus, the league has 9 teams.

74. $N = \dfrac{t^2 - t}{2}$

$45 = \dfrac{t^2 - t}{2}$

$90 = t^2 - t$

$0 = t^2 - t - 90$

$0 = (t+9)(t-10)$

$t + 9 = 0 \quad$ or $\quad t - 10 = 0$

$\quad t = -9 \qquad\qquad t = 10$

Thus, the league has 10 teams.

75. $P = 0.0021x^2 - 0.286x + 16.28$

$20 = 0.0021x^2 - 0.286x + 16.28$

$0 = 0.0021x^2 - 0.286x - 3.72$

$x = \dfrac{-b \pm \sqrt{b^2 - 4ac}}{2a}$

$x = \dfrac{-(-0.286) \pm \sqrt{(-0.286)^2 - 4(0.0021)(-3.72)}}{2(0.0021)}$

$x = -12 \quad$ or $\quad x \approx 148$

20% of the U.S. population will be foreign-born 148 years after 1900, or in 2048.

76. $P = 0.0021x^2 - 0.286x + 16.28$

$25 = 0.0021x^2 - 0.286x + 16.28$

$0 = 0.0021x^2 - 0.286x - 8.72$

$x = \dfrac{-b \pm \sqrt{b^2 - 4ac}}{2a}$

$x = \dfrac{-(-0.286) \pm \sqrt{(-0.286)^2 - 4(0.0021)(-8.72)}}{2(0.0021)}$

$x = -26 \quad$ or $\quad x \approx 162$

25% of the U.S. population will be foreign-born 162 years after 1900, or in 2062.

77. $N = 0.013x^2 - 1.19x + 28.24$, for $N = 3$

$3 = 0.013x^2 - 1.19x + 28.24$

$0 = 0.013x^2 - 1.19x + 28.24 - 3$

$0 = 0.013x^2 - 1.19x + 25.24$

$x = \dfrac{-b \pm \sqrt{b^2 - 4ac}}{2a}$

$x = \dfrac{-(-1.19) \pm \sqrt{(-1.19)^2 - 4(0.013)(25.24)}}{2(0.013)}$

$x = \dfrac{1.19 \pm \sqrt{0.10362}}{0.026}$

$x \approx \dfrac{1.19 \pm 0.3219}{0.026}$

$x \approx \dfrac{1.19 + 0.3219}{0.026} \quad$ or $\quad x \approx \dfrac{1.19 - 0.3219}{0.026}$

$x \approx \dfrac{1.5119}{0.026} \qquad\qquad x \approx \dfrac{0.8681}{0.026}$

$x \approx 58 \qquad\qquad\qquad x \approx 33$

33-year-olds and 58-year-olds are expected to be involved in 3 fatal crashes per 100 million miles driven. The formula models the data quite well.

78. $N = 0.013x^2 - 1.19x + 28.24$, for $N = 10$

$10 = 0.013x^2 - 1.19x + 28.24$

$0 = 0.013x^2 - 1.19x + 28.24 - 10$

$0 = 0.013x^2 - 1.19x + 18.24$

$x = \dfrac{-b \pm \sqrt{b^2 - 4ac}}{2a}$

$x = \dfrac{-(-1.19) \pm \sqrt{(-1.19)^2 - 4(0.013)(18.24)}}{2(0.013)}$

$x = \dfrac{1.19 \pm \sqrt{0.46762}}{0.026}$

$x \approx \dfrac{1.19 \pm 0.684}{0.026}$

$x \approx \dfrac{1.19 + 0.684}{0.026}$ or $x \approx \dfrac{1.19 - 0.684}{0.026}$

$x \approx \dfrac{1.874}{0.026}$ $x \approx \dfrac{0.506}{0.026}$

$x \approx 72$ $x \approx 19$

19-year-olds and 72-year-olds are expected to be involved in 10 fatal crashes per 100 million miles driven. The formula does not model the data well for these values.

79-83. Answers will vary.

84. If $b^2 - 4ac$ is negative, there are no real solutions because the square root of a negative number is not real. If $b^2 - 4ac = 0$, then there is one rational solution. If $b^2 - 4ac$ is a positive perfect square, then there are two rational solutions. If $b^2 - 4ac$ is positive, but not a perfect square, then there are two irrational solutions.

85. $x^2 + bx + 15$

$(x + 3)(x + 5) = x^2 + 8x + 15$

$(x + 1)(x + 15) = x^2 + 16x + 15$

Therefore, $b = 8, 16$.

86. $x^2 + 4x + b$

$(x + 3)(x + 1) = x^2 + 4x + 3$

$(x + 2)(x + 2) = x^2 + 4x + 4$

Therefore, $b = 3, 4$.

87. $x^{2n} + 20x^n + 99 = (x^n + 11)(x^n + 9)$

88. $h = -16t^2 + 64t + 80$, the water level is $h = 0$

$0 = -16t^2 + 64t + 80$

$0 = -16(t^2 - 4t - 5)$

$0 = -16(t - 5)(t + 1)$

$t - 5 = 0$ or $t + 1 = 0$

$t = 5$ $t = -1$ (Disregard)

It will reach the water in 5 seconds.

Chapter 6 Review Exercises

1. $6x + 9 = 6 \cdot 4 + 9 = 24 + 9 = 33$

2. $4x^2 - 3x + 2 = 4 \cdot 5^2 - 3 \cdot 5 + 2$
$= 4 \cdot 25 - 3 \cdot 5 + 2$
$= 100 - 15 + 2$
$= 87$

3. $7x^2 + 4x - 5 = 7(-2)^2 + 4(-2) - 5$
$= 7(4) + 4(-2) - 5$
$= 28 - 8 - 5$
$= 15$

4. $7x + 9 - 12 - x = 7x - x + 9 - 12$
$= 6x - 3$

5. $6(5x + 3) - 20 = 6 \cdot 5x + 6 \cdot 3 - 20$
$= 30x + 18 - 20$
$= 30x - 2$

6. $4(7x - 1) + 11x = 28x - 4 + 11x$
$= 39x - 4$

7. $9x = 9 \cdot 15 = 135$
You can stay in the sun 135 minutes without burning with a number 9 spf lotion.

8. $x - 0.25x = 2400 - 0.25(2400)$
$= 2400 - 600$
$= 1800$
The computer's discount price is $1800.

9. $x = 2005 - 1995 = 10$
$N = 1.2x^2 + 15.2x + 181.4$
$N = 1.2(10)^2 + 15.2(10) + 181.4$
$N = 120 + 152 + 181.4$
$N = 453.4$
The formula suggests that $453.4 billion will be spent in 2005. The formula models the graph quite well.

10.
$$4x+9=33$$
$$4x+9-9=33-9$$
$$4x=24$$
$$\frac{4x}{4}=\frac{24}{4}$$
$$x=6$$
The solution set is $\{6\}$.

11. $5x-3=x+5$
$$5x-3+3=x+5+3$$
$$5x=x+8$$
$$5x-x=x+8-x$$
$$4x=8$$
$$\frac{4x}{4}=\frac{8}{4}$$
$$x=2$$
The solution set is $\{2\}$.

12.
$$3(x+4)=5x-12$$
$$3x+12=5x-12$$
$$3x+12-12=5x-12-12$$
$$3x=5x-24$$
$$3x-5x=5x-24-5x$$
$$-2x=-24$$
$$\frac{-2x}{-2}=\frac{-24}{-2}$$
$$x=12$$
The solution set is $\{12\}$.

13. $2(x-2)+3(x+5)=2x-2$
$$2x-4+3x+15=2x-2$$
$$5x+11=2x-2$$
$$5x+11-11=2x-2-11$$
$$5x=2x-13$$
$$5x-2x=2x-13-2x$$
$$3x=-13$$
$$\frac{3x}{3}=\frac{-13}{3}$$
$$x=-\frac{13}{3}$$
The solution set is $\left\{-\frac{13}{3}\right\}$.

14.
$$\frac{2x}{3}=\frac{x}{6}+1$$
$$6\left(\frac{2x}{3}\right)=6\left(\frac{x}{6}+1\right)$$
$$4x=x+6$$
$$4x-x=x+6-x$$
$$3x=6$$
$$\frac{3x}{3}=\frac{6}{3}$$
$$x=2$$
The solution set is $\{2\}$.

15.
$$3x+y=9$$
$$3x+y-3x=-3x+9$$
$$y=-3x+9$$

16. $4x+2y=16$
$$4x+2y-4x=-4x+16$$
$$2y=-4x+16$$
$$\frac{2y}{2}=\frac{-4x+16}{2}$$
$$y=\frac{-4x}{2}+\frac{16}{2}$$
$$y=-2x+8$$

17. $D=RT$, for T
$$\frac{D}{R}=\frac{RT}{R}$$
$$\frac{D}{R}=T \text{ or } T=\frac{D}{R}$$

18. $P=2l+2w$ for w
$$P-2l=2l+2w-2l$$
$$P-2l=2w$$
$$\frac{P-2l}{2}=\frac{2w}{2}$$
$$\frac{P-2l}{2}=w \text{ or } w=\frac{P-2l}{2}$$

19. $A=\frac{1}{2}bh$ for h
$$2\cdot A=2\cdot\frac{1}{2}bh$$
$$2A=bh$$
$$\frac{2A}{b}=\frac{bh}{b}$$
$$\frac{2A}{b}=h \text{ or } h=\frac{2A}{b}$$

20.
$$A = \frac{B+C}{2} \text{ for } B$$
$$2 \cdot A = 2 \cdot \frac{B+C}{2}$$
$$2A = B+C$$
$$2A - C = B + C - C$$
$$2A - C = B \text{ or } B = 2A - C$$

21.
$$y = 420x + 720$$
$$4080 = 420x + 720$$
$$4080 - 720 = 420x + 720 - 720$$
$$3360 = 420x$$
$$\frac{3360}{420} = \frac{420x}{420}$$
$$8 = x$$
Losses amounted to $4080 million in 1997 (8 years after 1989).

22. $17 - 9x$

23. $3x - 7$

24. $5x + 8$

25. $\frac{6}{x} + 3x$

26.
$$17 - 4x = 5$$
$$17 - 4x - 17 = 5 - 17$$
$$-4x = -12$$
$$\frac{-4x}{-4} = \frac{-12}{-4}$$
$$x = 3$$
The number is 3.

27.
$$5x + 2 = x + 22$$
$$5x + 2 - 2 = x + 22 - 2$$
$$5x = x + 20$$
$$5x - x = x + 20 - x$$
$$4x = 20$$
$$\frac{4x}{4} = \frac{20}{4}$$
$$x = 5$$
The number is 5.

28.
$$7x - 1 = 5x + 9$$
$$7x - 1 + 1 = 5x + 9 + 1$$
$$7x = 5x + 10$$
$$7x - 5x = 5x + 10 - 5x$$
$$2x = 10$$
$$\frac{2x}{2} = \frac{10}{2}$$
$$x = 5$$
The number is 5.

29.
$$8(x - 5) = 56$$
$$8x - 40 = 56$$
$$8x - 40 + 40 = 56 + 40$$
$$8x = 96$$
$$\frac{8x}{8} = \frac{96}{8}$$
$$x = 12$$
The number is 12.

30. Let x = the years after 2000.
$$567 + 15x = 702$$
$$567 + 15x - 567 = 702 - 567$$
$$15x = 135$$
$$\frac{15x}{15} = \frac{135}{15}$$
$$x = 9$$
The average weekly salary will reach $702 nine years after 2000 or in 2009.

31. Let x = the yearly average salary for a preschool teacher, then
$x + 22{,}870$ = the yearly average salary for a fitness trainer.
$$x + x + 22{,}870 = 79{,}030$$
$$2x + 22{,}870 = 79{,}030$$
$$2x + 22{,}870 - 22{,}870 = 79{,}030 - 22{,}870$$
$$2x = 56{,}160$$
$$\frac{2x}{2} = \frac{56{,}160}{2}$$
$$x = 28{,}080$$
$$x + 22{,}870 = 50{,}950$$
The yearly average salary is $28,080 for a preschool teacher and $50,950 for a fitness trainer.

32. Let x = the number of unhealthy air days in New York City, then
$3x + 48$ = the number of unhealthy air days in Los Angeles.
$$x + 3x + 48 = 268$$
$$4x + 48 = 268$$
$$4x + 48 - 48 = 268 - 48$$
$$4x = 220$$
$$\frac{4x}{4} = \frac{220}{4}$$
$$x = 55$$
$$3x + 48 = 213$$
New York City averages 55 unhealthy air days and Los Angeles averages 213.

33. Let x = the number of minutes at which the costs of the two plans are the same.
$$\overbrace{15 + 0.05x}^{\text{first plan}} = \overbrace{5 + 0.07x}^{\text{other plan}}$$
$$15 + 0.05x - 15 = 5 + 0.07x - 15$$
$$0.05x = 0.07x - 10$$
$$0.05x - 0.07x = 0.07x - 10 - 0.07x$$
$$-0.02x = -10$$
$$\frac{-0.02x}{-0.02} = \frac{-10}{-0.02}$$
$$x = 500$$
The two plans are the same at 500 minutes.

34. a. $\dfrac{30}{22} = \dfrac{30 \div 2}{22 \div 2} = \dfrac{15}{11}$ or $15{:}11$

b. $\dfrac{16 + 10}{18} = \dfrac{26}{18} = \dfrac{26 \div 2}{18 \div 2} = \dfrac{13}{9}$ or $13{:}9$

35. $\dfrac{3}{x} = \dfrac{15}{25}$
$$3 \cdot 25 = x \cdot 15$$
$$75 = 15x$$
$$\frac{75}{15} = \frac{15x}{15}$$
$$5 = x$$
The solution set is $\{5\}$.

36. $\dfrac{-7}{5} = \dfrac{91}{x}$
$$-7 \cdot x = 5 \cdot 91$$
$$-7x = 455$$
$$\frac{-7x}{-7} = \frac{455}{-7}$$
$$x = -65$$
The solution set is $\{-65\}$.

37. $\dfrac{x + 2}{3} = \dfrac{4}{5}$
$$5(x + 2) = 3 \cdot 4$$
$$5x + 10 = 12$$
$$5x + 10 - 10 = 12 - 10$$
$$5x = 2$$
$$\frac{5x}{5} = \frac{2}{5}$$
$$x = \frac{2}{5}$$
The solution set is $\left\{\dfrac{2}{5}\right\}$.

38. $\dfrac{5}{x + 7} = \dfrac{3}{x + 3}$
$$5(x + 3) = 3(x + 7)$$
$$5x + 15 = 3x + 21$$
$$5x + 15 - 15 = 3x + 21 - 15$$
$$5x = 3x + 6$$
$$5x - 3x = 3x + 6 - 3x$$
$$2x = 6$$
$$\frac{2x}{2} = \frac{6}{2}$$
$$x = 3$$
The solution set is $\{3\}$.

39. Let x = number of teachers
$$\frac{3}{50} = \frac{x}{5400}$$
$$50 \cdot x = 3 \cdot 5400$$
$$50x = 16{,}200$$
$$\frac{50x}{50} = \frac{16{,}200}{50}$$
$$x = 324$$
There should be 324 teachers for 5400 students.

40. Let x = number of trout in lake

$$\frac{32}{82} = \frac{112}{x}$$

$$32x = 82 \cdot 112$$

$$32x = 9184$$

$$\frac{32x}{32} = \frac{9184}{32}$$

$$x = 287$$

There are 287 trout in the lake.

41. Let x = the dollar amount of the electric bill.

$$\frac{1400}{98} = \frac{2200}{x}$$

$$1400 \cdot x = 98 \cdot 2200$$

$$1400x = 215,600$$

$$\frac{1400x}{1400} = \frac{215,600}{1400}$$

$$x = 154$$

The electric bill is $154.

42. Let x = feet the object will fall in 10 seconds.

$$\frac{144}{3^2} = \frac{x}{10^2}$$

$$\frac{144}{9} = \frac{x}{100}$$

$$144 \cdot 100 = 9x$$

$$14,400 = 9x$$

$$\frac{14,400}{9} = \frac{9x}{9}$$

$$1600 = x$$

The object will fall 1600 feet in 10 seconds.

43. Let x = hours needed when driving 40 mph.

$$\frac{50}{x} = \frac{40}{4}$$

$$50 \cdot 4 = 40x$$

$$200 = 40x$$

$$\frac{200}{40} = \frac{40x}{40}$$

$$5 = x$$

At a rate of 40 mph, it will take 5 hours.

44.

$$2x - 5 < 3$$

$$2x - 5 + 5 < 3 + 5$$

$$2x < 8$$

$$\frac{2x}{2} < \frac{8}{2}$$

$$x < 4$$

$$\{x \mid x < 4\}$$

45.

$$\frac{x}{2} > -4$$

$$2 \cdot \frac{x}{2} > 2(-4)$$

$$x > -8$$

$$\{x \mid x > -8\}$$

46.

$$3 - 5x \le 18$$

$$3 - 5x - 3 \le 18 - 3$$

$$-5x \le 15$$

$$\frac{-5x}{-5} \ge \frac{15}{-5}$$

$$x \ge -3$$

$$\{x \mid x \ge -3\}$$

47.

$$4x + 6 < 5x$$

$$4x + 6 - 6 < 5x - 6$$

$$4x < 5x - 6$$

$$4x - 5x < 5x - 6 - 5x$$

$$-x < -6$$

$$\frac{-x}{-1} > \frac{-6}{-1}$$

$$x > 6$$

$$\{x \mid x > 6\}$$

48.
$$6x - 10 \geq 2(x + 3)$$
$$6x - 10 + 10 \geq 2x + 6 + 10$$
$$6x \geq 2x + 16$$
$$6x - 2x \geq 2x + 16 - 2x$$
$$4x \geq 16$$
$$\frac{4x}{4} \geq \frac{16}{4}$$
$$x \geq 4$$
$$\{x \mid x \geq 4\}$$

49.
$$4x + 3(2x - 7) \leq x - 3$$
$$4x + 6x - 21 \leq x - 3$$
$$10x - 21 \leq x - 3$$
$$10x - 21 + 21 \leq x - 3 + 21$$
$$10x \leq x + 18$$
$$10x - x \leq x + 18 - x$$
$$9x \leq 18$$
$$\frac{9x}{9} \leq \frac{18}{9}$$
$$x \leq 2$$
$$\{x \mid x \leq 2\}$$

50. Let x = score on third test.
$$\frac{42 + 74 + x}{3} \geq 60$$
$$\frac{116 + x}{3} \geq 60$$
$$3 \cdot \frac{116 + x}{3} \geq 3 \cdot 60$$
$$116 + x \geq 180$$
$$116 + x - 116 \geq 180 - 116$$
$$x \geq 64$$
The score on the third test must be at least 64.

51. $(x + 9)(x - 5) = x^2 - 5x + 9x - 45$
$$= x^2 + 4x - 45$$

52. $(4x - 7)(3x + 2) = 12x^2 + 8x - 21x - 14$
$$= 12x^2 - 13x - 14$$

53. $x^2 - x - 12 = (x - 4)(x + 3)$

54. $x^2 - 8x + 15 = (x - 5)(x - 3)$

55. $x^2 + 2x + 3$ is prime.

56. $3x^2 - 17x + 10 = (3x - 2)(x - 5)$

57. $6x^2 - 11x - 10 = (3x + 2)(2x - 5)$

58. $3x^2 - 6x - 5$ is prime.

59. $x^2 + 5x - 14 = 0$
$$(x + 7)(x - 2) = 0$$
$$x + 7 = 0 \quad \text{or} \quad x - 2 = 0$$
$$x = -7 \qquad x = 2$$
The solution set is $\{-7, 2\}$.

60.
$$x^2 - 4x = 32$$
$$x^2 - 4x - 32 = 0$$
$$(x - 8)(x + 4) = 0$$
$$x - 8 = 0 \quad \text{or} \quad x + 4 = 0$$
$$x = 8 \qquad x = -4$$
The solution set is $\{-4, 8\}$.

61.
$$2x^2 + 15x - 8 = 0$$
$$(2x - 1)(x + 8) = 0$$
$$2x - 1 = 0 \quad \text{or} \quad x + 8 = 0$$
$$2x = 1 \qquad x = -8$$
$$x = \frac{1}{2}$$
The solution set is $\left\{-8, \frac{1}{2}\right\}$.

62.
$$3x^2 = -21x - 30$$
$$3x^2 + 21x + 30 = 0$$
$$(3x + 6)(x + 5) = 0$$
$$3x + 6 = 0 \quad \text{or} \quad x + 5 = 0$$
$$3x = -6 \qquad x = -5$$
$$x = -2$$
The solution set is $\{-5, -2\}$.

63. $x^2 - 4x + 3 = 0$

$$x = \frac{-b \pm \sqrt{b^2 - 4ac}}{2a}$$

$$x = \frac{-(-4) \pm \sqrt{(-4)^2 - 4(1)(3)}}{2(1)}$$

$$x = \frac{4 \pm \sqrt{4}}{2}$$

$$x = \frac{4 \pm 2}{2}$$

$$x = \frac{4 - 2}{2} \quad \text{or} \quad x = \frac{4 + 2}{2}$$

$$x = 1 \qquad\qquad x = 3$$

The solution set is $\{1, 3\}$.

64. $x^2 - 5x = 4$

$x^2 - 5x - 4 = 0$

$$x = \frac{-b \pm \sqrt{b^2 - 4ac}}{2a}$$

$$x = \frac{-(-5) \pm \sqrt{(-5)^2 - 4(1)(-4)}}{2(1)}$$

$$x = \frac{5 \pm \sqrt{41}}{2}$$

The solution set is $\left\{ \dfrac{5 - \sqrt{41}}{2}, \dfrac{5 + \sqrt{41}}{2} \right\}$.

65. $2x^2 + 5x - 3 = 0$

$$x = \frac{-b \pm \sqrt{b^2 - 4ac}}{2a}$$

$$x = \frac{-5 \pm \sqrt{5^2 - 4(2)(-3)}}{2(2)}$$

$$x = \frac{-5 \pm \sqrt{49}}{4}$$

$$x = \frac{-5 \pm 7}{4}$$

$$x = \frac{-5 + 7}{4} \quad \text{or} \quad x = \frac{-5 - 7}{4}$$

$$x = \frac{1}{2} \qquad\qquad x = -3$$

The solution set is $\left\{ -3, \dfrac{1}{2} \right\}$.

66. $3x^2 - 6x = 5$

$3x^2 - 6x - 5 = 0$

$$x = \frac{-b \pm \sqrt{b^2 - 4ac}}{2a}$$

$$x = \frac{-(-6) \pm \sqrt{(-6)^2 - 4(3)(-5)}}{2(3)}$$

$$x = \frac{6 \pm \sqrt{96}}{6}$$

$$x = \frac{6 \pm 4\sqrt{6}}{6}$$

$$x = \frac{3 \pm 2\sqrt{6}}{3}$$

The solution set is $\left\{ \dfrac{3 - 2\sqrt{6}}{3}, \dfrac{3 + 2\sqrt{6}}{3} \right\}$.

67. $P = -10x^2 + 475x + 3500$

$P = -10(3)^2 + 475(3) + 3500$

$P = -90 + 1425 + 3500$

$P = 4835$

Three years after the program is in effect, the alligator population will be 4835.

This is represented by the point (3, 4835).

68. $P = -10x^2 + 475x + 3500$

$7250 = -10x^2 + 475x + 3500$

$0 = -10x^2 + 475x - 3750$

$$\frac{0}{-5} = \frac{-10x^2}{-5} + \frac{475x}{-5} - \frac{3750}{-5}$$

$0 = 2x^2 - 95x + 750$

$0 = (x - 10)(2x - 75)$

$x - 10 = 0 \quad \text{or} \quad 2x - 75 = 0$

$x = 10 \qquad\qquad 2x = 75$

$\qquad\qquad\qquad\qquad x = 37.5$

Since $0 \le x \le 12$, the population will reach 7250 after the program is in effect for 10 years.

Chapter 6 Test

1. Evaluate $5x^2 - 7x - 2$ when $x = -3$.
$$5x^2 - 7x - 2 = 5(-3)^2 - 7(-3) - 2$$
$$= 5(9) - 7(-3) - 2$$
$$= 45 + 21 - 2$$
$$= 64$$

2. $5(3x-2) + 7x = 5 \cdot 3x + 5(-2) + 7x$
$$= 15x - 10 + 7x$$
$$= 15x + 7x - 10$$
$$= 22x - 10$$

3. $t = 1994 - 1984 = 10$
$$S = 91t + 164$$
$$S = 91(10) + 164$$
$$S = 910 + 164$$
$$S = 1074$$
The annual salary in 1994 was $1074 thousand or $1,074,000.

4. $8x - 5(x-2) = x + 26$
$$8x - 5x + 10 = x + 26$$
$$3x + 10 = x + 26$$
$$3x + 10 - 10 = x + 26 - 10$$
$$3x = x + 16$$
$$3x - x = x + 16 - x$$
$$2x = 16$$
$$\frac{2x}{2} = \frac{16}{2}$$
$$x = 8$$
The solution set is $\{8\}$.

5. $3(2x-4) = 9 - 3(x+1)$
$$6x - 12 = 9 - 3x - 3$$
$$6x - 12 = 6 - 3x$$
$$6x - 12 + 12 = 6 - 3x + 12$$
$$6x = -3x + 18$$
$$6x + 3x = -3x + 18 + 3x$$
$$9x = 18$$
$$\frac{9x}{9} = \frac{18}{9}$$
$$x = 2$$
The solution set is $\{2\}$.

6. Solve when $N = 142$
$$N = 3.5x + 58$$
$$142 = 3.5x + 58$$
$$142 - 58 = 3.5x + 58 - 58$$
$$84 = 3.5x$$
$$\frac{84}{3.5} = \frac{3.5x}{3.5}$$
$$24 = x$$
The average mortgage loan will be $142 thousand in 2004.

7. $2x + 4y = 8$
$$2x + 4y - 2x = -2x + 8$$
$$4y = -2x + 8$$
$$\frac{4y}{4} = \frac{-2x+8}{4}$$
$$y = \frac{-2x}{4} + \frac{8}{4}$$
$$y = -\frac{1}{2}x + 2$$

8. $L = \dfrac{P - 2W}{2}$
$$2 \cdot L = 2 \cdot \frac{P-2W}{2}$$
$$2L = P - 2W$$
$$2L + 2W = P - 2W + 2W$$
$$2L + 2W = P \text{ or } P = 2L + 2W$$

9. Let $x =$ the number.
$$5x - 9 = 310$$
$$5x - 9 + 9 = 310 + 9$$
$$5x = 319$$
$$\frac{5x}{5} = \frac{319}{5}$$
$$x = 63.8$$
The number is 63.8.

10. Let x = Buchanan's age the time he took office, then
$x + 4$ = Reagan's age the time he took office.
$$x + x + 4 = 134$$
$$2x + 4 = 134$$
$$2x + 4 - 4 = 134 - 4$$
$$2x = 130$$
$$\frac{2x}{2} = \frac{130}{2}$$
$$x = 65$$
$$x + 4 = 69$$
At the time they took office, Buchanan was 65 and Reagan was 69.

11. Let x = the number of minutes
$$15 + 0.05x = 45$$
$$15 + 0.05x - 15 = 45 - 15$$
$$0.05x = 30$$
$$\frac{0.05x}{0.05} = \frac{30}{0.05}$$
$$x = 600$$
You can talk for 600 minutes, or 10 hours.

12. $\dfrac{10}{15 + 10} = \dfrac{10}{25} = \dfrac{10 \div 5}{25 \div 5} = \dfrac{2}{5}$ or $2 : 5$

13. $\dfrac{5}{8} = \dfrac{x}{12}$
$$8 \cdot x = 5 \cdot 12$$
$$8x = 60$$
$$\frac{8x}{8} = \frac{60}{8}$$
$$x = 7.5$$
The solution set is $\{7.5\}$.

14. $\dfrac{x + 5}{8} = \dfrac{x + 2}{5}$
$$5(x + 5) = 8(x + 2)$$
$$5x + 25 = 8x + 16$$
$$5x + 25 - 25 = 8x + 16 - 25$$
$$5x = 8x - 9$$
$$5x - 8x = 8x - 9 - 8x$$
$$-3x = -9$$
$$\frac{-3x}{-3} = \frac{-9}{-3}$$
$$x = 3$$
The solution set is $\{3\}$.

15. Let x = number of elk in the park.
$$\frac{5}{150} = \frac{200}{x}$$
$$5x = 150 \cdot 200$$
$$5x = 30,000$$
$$\frac{5x}{5} = \frac{30,000}{5}$$
$$x = 6000$$
There are 6000 elk in the park.

16. Let x = pressure.
$$\frac{25}{60} = \frac{x}{330}$$
$$60x = 25 \cdot 330$$
$$60x = 8250$$
$$\frac{60x}{60} = \frac{8250}{60}$$
$$x = 137.5$$
The pressure will be 137.5 pounds per square inch.

17. Let x = the current when the resistance is 5 ohms.
$$\frac{5}{x} = \frac{4}{42}$$
$$4x = 5(42)$$
$$4x = 210$$
$$\frac{4x}{4} = \frac{210}{4}$$
$$x = 52.5$$
The current will be 52.5 amperes when the resistance is 5 ohms.

18. $$6 - 9x \geq 33$$
$$6 - 9x - 6 \geq 33 - 6$$
$$-9x \geq 27$$
$$\frac{-9x}{-9} \leq \frac{27}{-9}$$
$$x \leq -3$$
$$\{x \mid x \leq -3\}$$

19.
$$4x - 2 > 2(x + 6)$$
$$4x - 2 > 2x + 12$$
$$4x - 2 + 2 > 2x + 12 + 2$$
$$4x > 2x + 14$$
$$4x - 2x > 2x + 14 - 2x$$
$$2x > 14$$
$$\frac{2x}{2} > \frac{14}{2}$$
$$x > 7$$
$$\{x \mid x > 7\}$$

20. Let x = grade on 4th examination.
$$\frac{76 + 80 + 72 + x}{4} \geq 80$$
$$\frac{228 + x}{4} \geq 80$$
$$4 \cdot \frac{228 + x}{4} \geq 80 \cdot 4$$
$$228 + x \geq 320$$
$$228 + x - 228 \geq 320 - 228$$
$$x \geq 92$$
The student must earn at least a 92 to receive a B.

21. $(2x - 5)(3x + 4) = 6x^2 + 8x - 15x - 20$
$$= 6x^2 - 7x - 20$$

22. $2x^2 - 9x + 10 = (2x - 5)(x - 2)$

23.
$$x^2 + 5x = 36$$
$$x^2 + 5x - 36 = 0$$
$$(x + 9)(x - 4) = 0$$
$$x + 9 = 0 \quad \text{or} \quad x - 4 = 0$$
$$x = -9 \qquad x = 4$$
The solution set is $\{-9, 4\}$.

24.
$$2x^2 + 4x = -1$$
$$2x^2 + 4x + 1 = 0$$
$$x = \frac{-b \pm \sqrt{b^2 - 4ac}}{2a}$$
$$x = \frac{-4 \pm \sqrt{4^2 - 4(2)(1)}}{2(2)}$$
$$x = \frac{-4 \pm \sqrt{8}}{4}$$
$$x = \frac{-4 \pm 2\sqrt{2}}{4}$$
$$x = \frac{-2 \pm \sqrt{2}}{2}$$

The solution set is $\left\{ \dfrac{-2 - \sqrt{2}}{2}, \dfrac{-2 + \sqrt{2}}{2} \right\}$.

Chapter 7
Algebra: Graphs, Functions, and Linear Systems

Check Points 7.1

1.

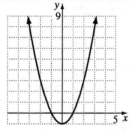

2.

x	$y = x^2 - 1$	(x, y)
-3	$y = (-3)^2 - 1 = 9 - 1 = 8$	$(-3, 8)$
-2	$y = (-2)^2 - 1 = 4 - 1 = 3$	$(-2, 3)$
-1	$y = (-1)^2 - 1 = 1 - 1 = 0$	$(-1, 0)$
0	$y = (0)^2 - 1 = 0 - 1 = -1$	$(0, -1)$
1	$y = (1)^2 - 1 = 1 - 1 = 0$	$(1, 0)$
2	$y = (2)^2 - 1 = 4 - 1 = 3$	$(2, 3)$
3	$y = (3)^2 - 1 = 9 - 1 = 8$	$(3, 8)$

3. **a.**

Without the coupon book

x	$y = 2x$	(x, y)
0	$y = 2(0) = 0$	$(0, 0)$
2	$y = 2(2) = 4$	$(2, 4)$
4	$y = 2(4) = 8$	$(4, 8)$
6	$y = 2(6) = 12$	$(6, 12)$
8	$y = 2(8) = 16$	$(8, 16)$
10	$y = 2(10) = 20$	$(10, 20)$
12	$y = 2(12) = 24$	$(12, 24)$

With the coupon book

x	$y = 10 + x$	(x, y)
0	$y = 10 + 0 = 10$	$(0, 10)$
2	$y = 10 + 2 = 12$	$(2, 12)$
4	$y = 10 + 4 = 14$	$(4, 14)$
6	$y = 10 + 6 = 16$	$(6, 16)$
8	$y = 10 + 8 = 18$	$(8, 18)$
10	$y = 10 + 10 = 20$	$(10, 20)$
12	$y = 10 + 12 = 22$	$(12, 22)$

b.

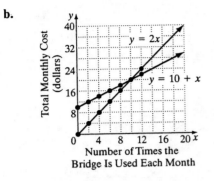

c. The graphs intersect at $(10, 20)$. This means that if the bridge is used ten times in a month, the total monthly cost is $20 with or without the coupon book.

4. a. We can express $y = -0.05x^2 + 4.2x - 26$ in function notation by replacing y by $f(x)$. The formula in function notation is $f(x) = -0.05x^2 + 4.2x - 26$

b.
$$f(x) = -0.05x^2 + 4.2x - 26$$
$$f(20) = -0.05(20)^2 + 4.2(20) - 26$$
$$= -20 + 84 - 26$$
$$= 38$$

c. We see that $f(20) = 38$, so 38% of 20-year-old coffee drinkers become irritable if they do not have coffee at their regular time.

5.

x	$f(x) = 2x$	(x, y) or $(x, f(x))$
-2	$f(-2) = 2(-2) = -4$	$(-2, -4)$
-1	$f(-1) = 2(-1) = -2$	$(-1, -2)$
0	$f(0) = 2(0) = 0$	$(0, 0)$
1	$f(1) = 2(1) = 2$	$(1, 2)$
2	$f(2) = 2(2) = 4$	$(2, 4)$

x	$g(x) = 2x - 3$	(x, y) or $(x, f(x))$
-2	$g(-2) = 2(-2) - 3 = -7$	$(-2, -7)$
-1	$g(-1) = 2(-1) - 3 = -5$	$(-1, -5)$
0	$g(0) = 2(0) - 3 = -3$	$(0, -3)$
1	$g(1) = 2(1) - 3 = -1$	$(1, -1)$
2	$g(2) = 2(2) - 3 = 1$	$(2, 1)$

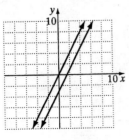

The graph of g is the graph of f shifted vertically down 3 units.

6. a. y is a function of x.

b. y is a function of x.

    c. *y* is not a function of *x*. Two values of *y* correspond to an *x*-value.

7. To find $f(10)$, locate 10 on the *x*-axis. Follow that value up to the graph, then look to the *y*-axis to find the corresponding *y*-coordinate. A reasonable estimate of the *y*-coordinate is 16. Thus $f(10) \approx 16$.

Exercise Set 7.1

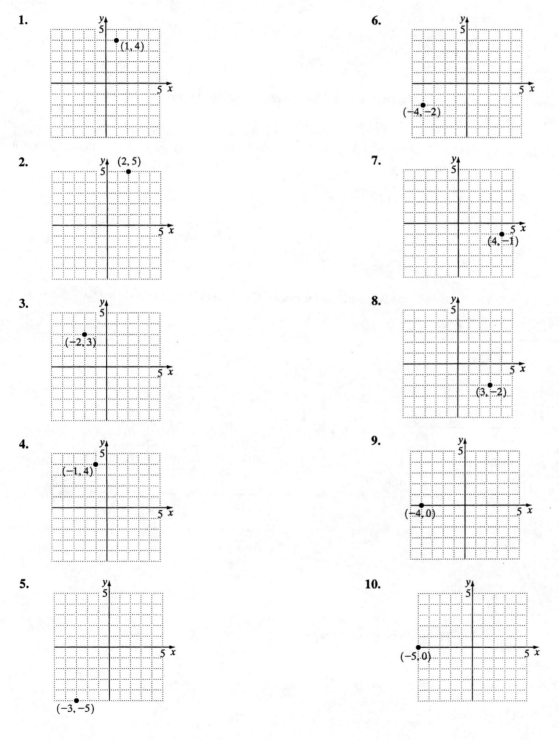

11.

12.

13.

14.

15.

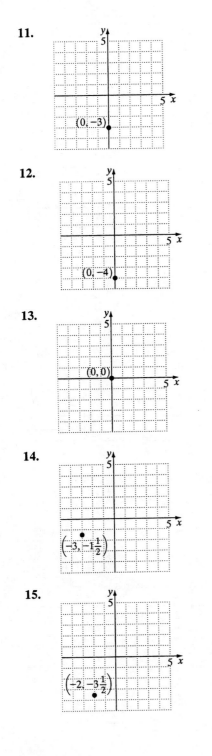

16.

17.

18.

19.

20.

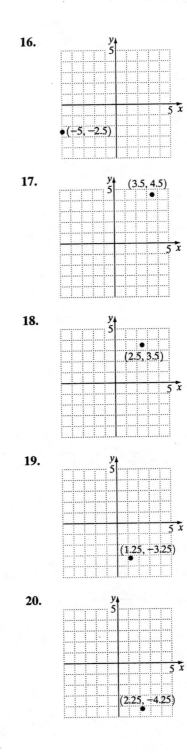

21.

x	-3	-2	-1	0	1	2	3
$y = x^2 - 2$	7	2	-1	-2	-1	2	7

22.

x	-3	-2	-1	0	1	2	3
$y = x^2 + 2$	11	6	3	2	3	6	11

23.

x	-3	-2	-1	0	1	2	3
$y = x - 2$	-5	-4	-3	-2	-1	0	1

24.

x	-3	-2	-1	0	1	2	3
$y = x + 2$	-1	0	1	2	3	4	5

25.

x	-3	-2	-1	0	1	2	3
$y = 2x + 1$	-5	-3	-1	1	3	5	7

26.

x	-3	-2	-1	0	1	2	3
$y = 2x - 4$	-10	-8	-6	-4	-2	0	2

27.

x	-3	-2	-1	0	1	2	3
$y = -\frac{1}{2}x$	$\frac{3}{2}$	1	$\frac{1}{2}$	0	$-\frac{1}{2}$	-1	$-\frac{3}{2}$

28.

x	-3	-2	-1	0	1	2	3
$y = \frac{-1}{2}x + 2$	$\frac{7}{2}$	3	$\frac{5}{2}$	2	$\frac{3}{2}$	1	$\frac{1}{2}$

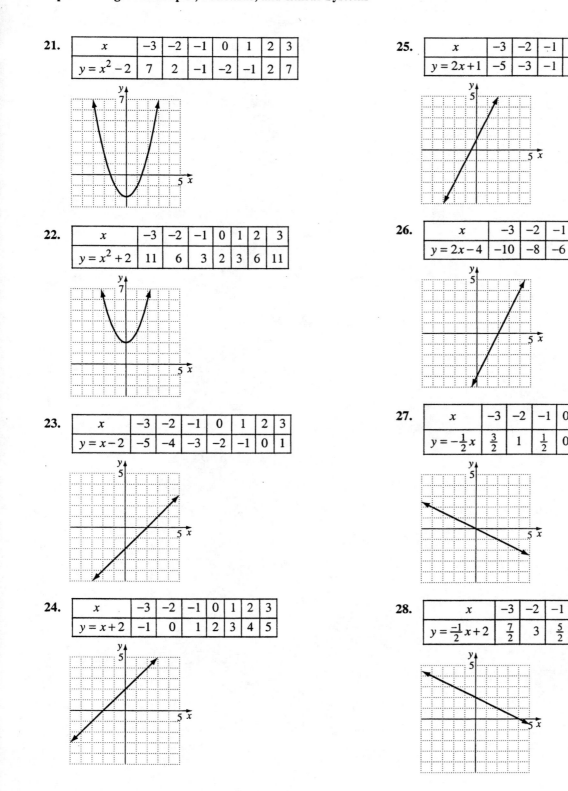

29.

x	-3	-2	-1	0	1	2	3
$y = x^3$	-27	-8	-1	0	1	8	27

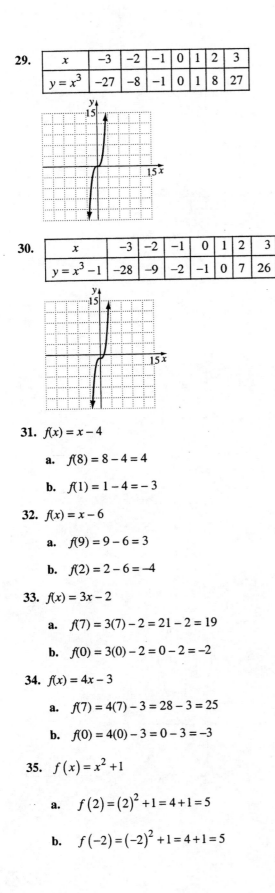

30.

x	-3	-2	-1	0	1	2	3
$y = x^3 - 1$	-28	-9	-2	-1	0	7	26

31. $f(x) = x - 4$

   a. $f(8) = 8 - 4 = 4$

   b. $f(1) = 1 - 4 = -3$

32. $f(x) = x - 6$

   a. $f(9) = 9 - 6 = 3$

   b. $f(2) = 2 - 6 = -4$

33. $f(x) = 3x - 2$

   a. $f(7) = 3(7) - 2 = 21 - 2 = 19$

   b. $f(0) = 3(0) - 2 = 0 - 2 = -2$

34. $f(x) = 4x - 3$

   a. $f(7) = 4(7) - 3 = 28 - 3 = 25$

   b. $f(0) = 4(0) - 3 = 0 - 3 = -3$

35. $f(x) = x^2 + 1$

   a. $f(2) = (2)^2 + 1 = 4 + 1 = 5$

   b. $f(-2) = (-2)^2 + 1 = 4 + 1 = 5$

36. $f(x) = x^2 + 4$

   a. $f(3) = (3)^2 + 4 = 9 + 4 = 13$

   b. $f(-3) = (-3)^2 + 4 = 9 + 4 = 13$

37. $f(x) = 3x^2 + 5$

   a. $f(4) = 3(4)^2 + 5$
$$= 3(16) + 5$$
$$= 48 + 5$$
$$= 53$$

   b. $f(-1) = 3(-1)^2 + 5 = 3 + 5 = 8$

38. $f(x) = 2x^2 - 4$

   a. $f(5) = 2(5)^2 - 4$
$$= 2(25) - 4$$
$$= 50 - 4$$
$$= 46$$

   b. $f(-1) = 2(-1)^2 - 4 = 2 - 4 = -2$

39. $f(x) = 2x^2 + 3x - 1$

   a. $f(3) = 2(3)^2 + 3(3) - 1$
$$= 2(9) + 9 - 1$$
$$= 18 + 9 - 1$$
$$= 26$$

   b. $f(-4) = 2(-4)^2 + 3(-4) - 1$
$$= 2(16) - 12 - 1$$
$$= 32 - 12 - 1$$
$$= 19$$

40. $f(x) = 3x^2 + 4x - 2$

   a. $f(2) = 3(2)^2 + 4(2) - 2$
$$= 3(4) + 8 - 2$$
$$= 12 + 8 - 2$$
$$= 18$$

   b. $f(-1) = 3(-1)^2 + 4(-1) - 2 = 3 - 4 - 2 = -3$

41.

x	$f(x) = x^2 - 1$
–2	3
–1	0
0	–1
1	0
2	3

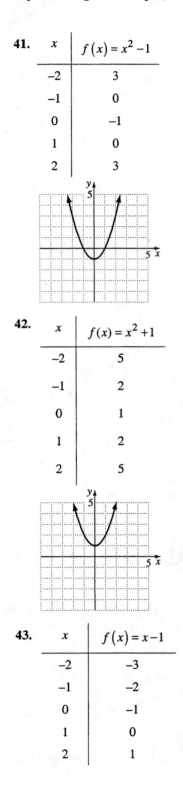

42.

x	$f(x) = x^2 + 1$
–2	5
–1	2
0	1
1	2
2	5

43.

x	$f(x) = x - 1$
–2	–3
–1	–2
0	–1
1	0
2	1

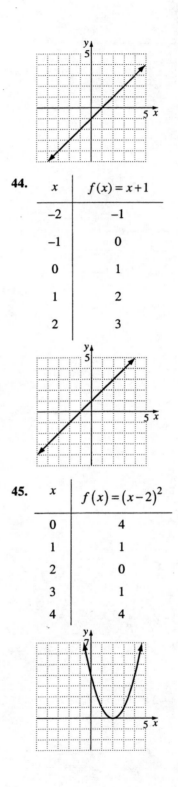

44.

x	$f(x) = x + 1$
–2	–1
–1	0
0	1
1	2
2	3

45.

x	$f(x) = (x - 2)^2$
0	4
1	1
2	0
3	1
4	4

46.

x	$f(x) = (x+1)^2$
−3	4
−2	1
−1	0
0	1
1	4

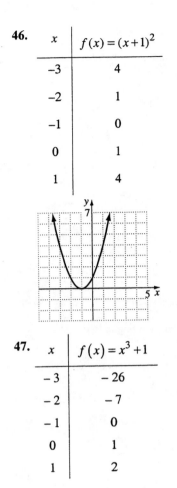

47.

x	$f(x) = x^3 + 1$
−3	−26
−2	−7
−1	0
0	1
1	2

48.

x	$f(x) = (x+1)^3$
−3	−8
−2	−1
−1	0
0	1
1	8

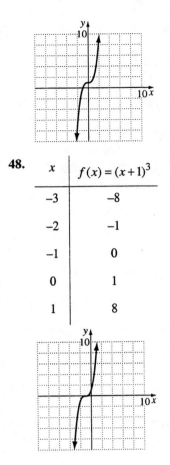

49. y is a function of x.

50. y is a function of x.

51. y is a function of x.

52. y is not a function of x. All values of y correspond to an x-value.

53. y is not a function of x. Two values of y correspond to an x-value.

54. y is not a function of x. Two values of y correspond to an x-value.

55. y is a function of x.

56. y is not a function of x. Two values of y correspond to an x-value.

57. A (2, 7); The ball is 7 feet above the ground when it is 2 yards from the quarterback.

58. B (28, 7); The ball is 7 feet above the ground when it is 28 yards from the quarterback.

59. C (6, 9.25)

60. D (24, 9.5)

61. The maximum height is 12 feet. It reaches this maximum when it is 15 yards from the quarterback.

62. The football is 5 feet above the ground when it is caught. This occurs 30 yards from the quarterback.

63. $f(20) = 0.76(20) + 171.4 = 186.6$
At age 20 an average American man's cholesterol level is expected to be 186.6.

64. $f(50) = 0.76(50) + 171.4 = 209.4$
At age 50 an average American man's cholesterol level is expected to be 209.4.

65. $f(4) = -\frac{1}{2}(4)^2 + 4(4) + 19 = -8 + 16 + 19 = 27$
In 1994, 27 million people received food stamps.

66. $f(0) = -\frac{1}{2}(0)^2 + 4(0) + 19 = 0 + 0 + 19 = 19$ and $f(8) = -\frac{1}{2}(8)^2 + 4(8) + 19 = -32 + 32 + 19 = 19$;
In 1990 and 1998, 19 million people received food stamps.

67. (4, 27); This is the highest point on the graph. It represents when the most food stamps were given out after 1990.

68. (0, 19) (8, 19); The number of food stamp recipients increased from 1990 to 1994 and then began to decrease.

69. $f(1970) \approx 4$; In 1970, there were about 4 divorces per thousand persons ages 15 older.

70. $f(2001) \approx 4$; In 2001, there were about 4 divorces per thousand persons ages 15 older.

71. For $1940 \le x \le 1970$, the rate reached a maximum of about 4 divorces per thousand in 1945 and 1970.

72. In about 1978 the divorce rate was approximately 5.3 per thousand persons ages 15 older.

73. f is a function of x because it's graph passes the vertical line test.

74. The divorce rate increased from 1890 to 1945, with a sharp increase between 1930 and 1945. There was also a sharp increase between 1960 and 1978. The divorce rate decreased from 1945 to 1960 and has been decreasing since 1978.

75. a.

x	$f(x) = 0.1x^2 - 0.4 + 0.6$
0	0.6
1	0.3
2	0.2
3	0.3
4	0.6
5	1.1

b. 0.3 ppm corresponds to 1 and 3. To avoid unsafe air, runners should exercise between 1 and 3 hours after 9 A.M., which means between 10 A.M. and 12 P.M.

76-82. Answers will vary.

83. a. $f(x) = -\dfrac{x}{2}$ if x is even.

b. $f(x) = \dfrac{x+1}{2}$ if x is odd.

c. $f(20) + f(40) + f(65)$

$= \left(-\dfrac{20}{2}\right) + \left(-\dfrac{40}{2}\right) + \left(\dfrac{65+1}{2}\right)$

$= 3$

84. It is more realistic to graph each formula using only the points shown rather than connecting them with lines because the number of times the Bridge is used each month is not continuous.

Check Points 7.2

1. Find the x-intercept by setting $y = 0$

$2x + 3(0) = 6$

$2x = 6$

$x = 3$; resulting point $(3, 0)$

Find the y-intercept by setting $x = 0$

$2(0) + 3y = 6$

$3y = 6$

$y = 2$; resulting point $(0, 2)$

Find a checkpoint by substituting any value.

$2(1) + 3y = 6$

$2 + 3y = 6$

$3y = 4$

$y = \dfrac{4}{3}$; resulting point $\left(1, \dfrac{4}{3}\right)$

2. a. $m = \dfrac{-2-4}{-4-(-3)} = \dfrac{-6}{-1} = 6$

b. $m = \dfrac{5-(-2)}{-1-4} = \dfrac{7}{-5} = -\dfrac{7}{5}$

3. Step 1. Plot the y-intercept of $(0, 1)$

Step 2. Obtain a second point using the slope m.

$m = \dfrac{3}{5} = \dfrac{\text{Rise}}{\text{Run}}$

Starting from the y-intercept move up 3 units and move 5 units to the right. This puts the second point at $(3, 6)$.

Step 3. Draw the line through the two points.

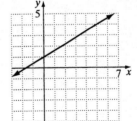

4. Solve for y.

$$3x + 4y = 0$$

$$4y = -3x + 0$$

$$\frac{4y}{4} = \frac{-3x}{4} + \frac{0}{4}$$

$$y = \frac{-3}{4}x + 0$$

$m = \frac{-3}{4}$ and the y-intercept is $(0, 0)$

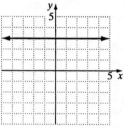

5. Draw horizontal line that intersects the y-axis at 3.

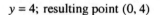

6. Draw vertical line that intersects the x-axis at -2.

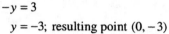

7. Find the slope using the points $(1995, 10)$ and $(2010, 12)$.

$$m = \frac{12 - 10}{2010 - 1995} = \frac{2}{15} \approx 0.13$$

This means that every 15 years the number of men living alone increases by 2 million.
Alternatively it means that every year the number of men living alone increases by 0.13 million or 130,000.

Exercise Set 7.2

1. Find the x-intercept by setting $y = 0$

$$x - y = 3$$

$$x - 0 = 3$$

$$x = 3; \text{ resulting point } (3, 0)$$

Find the y-intercept by setting $x = 0$

$$0 - y = 3$$

$$-y = 3$$

$$y = -3; \text{ resulting point } (0, -3)$$

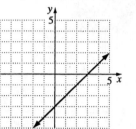

2. Find the x-intercept by setting $y = 0$

$$x + y = 4$$

$$x + 0 = 4$$

$$x = 4; \text{ resulting point } (4, 0)$$

Find the y-intercept by setting $x = 0$

$$0 + y = 4$$

$$y = 4; \text{ resulting point } (0, 4)$$

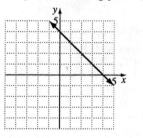

3. Find the *x*-intercept by setting $y = 0$
$$3x - 4(0) = 12$$
$$3x = 12$$
$$x = 4;\text{ resulting point } (4, 0)$$
Find the *y*-intercept by setting $x = 0$
$$3(0) - 4y = 12$$
$$-4y = 12$$
$$y = -3;\text{ resulting point } (0, -3)$$

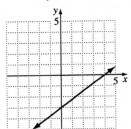

4. Find the *x*-intercept by setting $y = 0$
$$2x - 5(0) = 10$$
$$2x = 10$$
$$x = 5;\text{ resulting point } (5, 0)$$
Find the *y*-intercept by setting $x = 0$
$$2(0) - 5y = 10$$
$$-5y = 10$$
$$y = -2;\text{ resulting point } (0, -2)$$

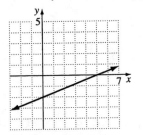

5. Find the *x*-intercept by setting $y = 0$
$$2x + 0 = 6$$
$$2x = 6$$
$$x = 3;\text{ resulting point } (3, 0)$$
Find the *y*-intercept by setting $x = 0$
$$2(0) + y = 6$$
$$y = 6;\text{ resulting point } (0, 6)$$

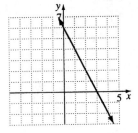

6. Find the *x*-intercept by setting $y = 0$
$$x + 3(0) = 6$$
$$x = 6;\text{ resulting point } (6, 0)$$
Find the *y*-intercept by setting $x = 0$
$$0 + 3y = 6$$
$$3y = 6$$
$$y = 2;\text{ resulting point } (0, 2)$$

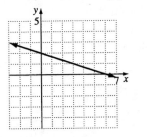

7. Find the *x*-intercept by setting $y = 0$
$$5x = 3(0) - 15$$
$$5x = -15$$
$$x = -3;\text{ resulting point } (-3, 0)$$
Find the *y*-intercept by setting $x = 0$
$$5(0) = 3y - 15$$
$$0 = 3y - 15$$
$$-3y = -15$$
$$y = 5;\text{ resulting point } (0, 5)$$

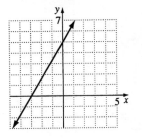

8. Find the *x*-intercept by setting $y = 0$

$$3x = 2(0) + 6$$

$$3x = 6$$

$$x = 2; \text{ resulting point } (2, 0)$$

Find the *y*-intercept by setting $x = 0$

$$3(0) = 2y + 6$$

$$0 = 2y + 6$$

$$-2y = 6$$

$$y = -3; \text{ resulting point } (0, -3)$$

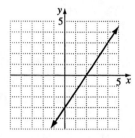

9. $m = \dfrac{5-6}{3-2} = \dfrac{-1}{1} = -1$; line falls.

10. $m = \dfrac{4-2}{3-4} = \dfrac{2}{-1} = -2$; line falls.

11. $m = \dfrac{2-1}{2-(-2)} = \dfrac{1}{4}$; line rises.

12. $m = \dfrac{4-3}{2-(-1)} = \dfrac{1}{3}$; line rises.

13. $m = \dfrac{-1-4}{-1-(-2)} = \dfrac{-5}{1} = -5$; line falls.

14. $m = \dfrac{-2-(-4)}{4-6} = \dfrac{2}{-2} = -1$; line falls.

15. $m = \dfrac{-2-3}{5-5} = \dfrac{-5}{0}$;
Slope undefined. Line is vertical.

16. $m = \dfrac{5-(-4)}{3-3} = \dfrac{9}{0}$;
Slope undefined. Line is vertical.

17. $m = \dfrac{8-0}{0-2} = \dfrac{8}{-2} = -4$; line falls.

18. $m = \dfrac{-9-0}{0-3} = \dfrac{-9}{-3} = 3$; line rises.

19. $m = \dfrac{1-1}{-2-5} = \dfrac{0}{-7} = 0$; line is horizontal.

20. $m = \dfrac{3-3}{1-(-2)} = \dfrac{0}{3} = 0$; line is horizontal.

21. $y = 2x + 3$
Slope: 2, *y*-intercept: 3
Plot point (0, 3) and second point using
$$m = \dfrac{2}{1} = \dfrac{\text{rise}}{\text{run}}$$

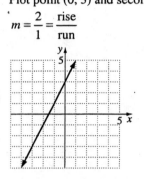

22. $y = 2x + 1$
Slope: 2, *y*-intercept: 1
Plot point (0, 1) and second point using
$$m = \dfrac{2}{1} = \dfrac{\text{rise}}{\text{run}}$$

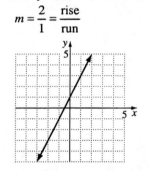

23. $y = -2x + 4$
Slope: -2, *y*-intercept: 4
Plot point (0, 4) and second point using
$$m = \dfrac{-2}{1} = \dfrac{\text{rise}}{\text{run}}$$

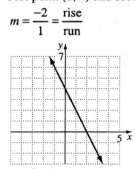

24. $y = -2x + 3$
Slope: -2, y-intercept: 3
Plot point $(0, 3)$ and second point using

$$m = \frac{-2}{1} = \frac{\text{rise}}{\text{run}}$$

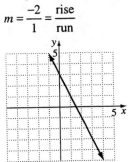

25. $y = \frac{1}{2}x + 3$

Slope: $\frac{1}{2}$, y-intercept: 3

Plot point $(0, 3)$ and second point using

$$m = \frac{1}{2} = \frac{\text{rise}}{\text{run}}.$$

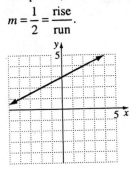

26. $y = \frac{1}{2}x + 2$

Slope: $\frac{1}{2}$, y-intercept: 2

Plot point $(0, 2)$ and second point using

$$m = \frac{1}{2} = \frac{\text{rise}}{\text{run}}.$$

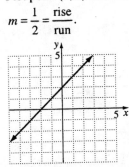

27. $f(x) = \frac{2}{3}x - 4$

Slope: $\frac{2}{3}$, y-intercept: -4

Plot point $(0, -4)$ and second point using

$$m = \frac{2}{3} = \frac{\text{rise}}{\text{run}}.$$

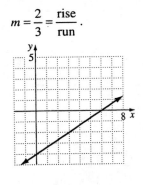

28. $f(x) = \frac{3}{4}x - 5$

Slope: $\frac{3}{4}$, y-intercept: -5

Plot point $(0, -5)$ and second point using

$$m = \frac{3}{4} = \frac{\text{rise}}{\text{run}}.$$

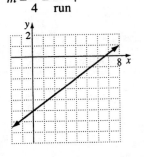

29. $y = -\frac{3}{4}x + 4$

Slope: $-\frac{3}{4}$, y-intercept: 4

Plot point $(0, 4)$ and second point using

$$m = \frac{-3}{4} = \frac{\text{rise}}{\text{run}}.$$

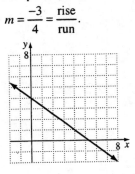

30. $y = -\dfrac{2}{3}x + 5$

Slope: $-\dfrac{2}{3}$, y-intercept: 5

Plot point $(0, 5)$ and second point using

$m = \dfrac{-2}{3} = \dfrac{\text{rise}}{\text{run}}$.

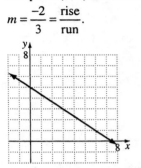

31. $f(x) = -\dfrac{5}{3}x$ or $f(x) = -\dfrac{5}{3}x + 0$

Slope: $-\dfrac{5}{3}$, y-intercept: 0

Plot point $(0, 0)$ and second point using

$m = \dfrac{-5}{3} = \dfrac{\text{rise}}{\text{run}}$.

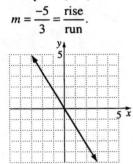

32. $f(x) = -\dfrac{4}{3}x$ or $f(x) = -\dfrac{4}{3}x + 0$

Slope: $-\dfrac{4}{3}$, y-intercept: 0

Plot point $(0, 0)$ and second point using

$m = \dfrac{-4}{3} = \dfrac{\text{rise}}{\text{run}}$.

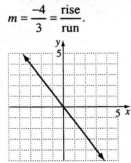

33. a. $3x + y = 0$

$y = -3x$ or $y = -3x + 0$

b. Slope $= -3$
y-intercept $= 0$

c.

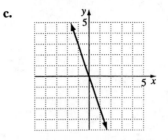

34. a. $2x + y = 0$

$y = -2x$ or $y = -2x + 0$

b. Slope $= -2$
y-intercept $= 0$

c.

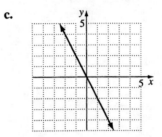

35. a. $3y = 4x$

$y = \dfrac{4}{3}x$ or $y = \dfrac{4}{3}x + 0$

b. Slope $= \dfrac{4}{3}$

y-intercept $= 0$

c.

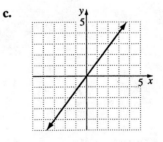

36. a. $4y = 5x$

$y = \dfrac{5}{4}x$ or $y = \dfrac{5}{4}x + 0$

b. Slope $= \dfrac{5}{4}$

y-intercept $= 0$

c.

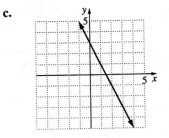

37. a. $2x + y = 3$

$y = -2x + 3$

b. Slope $= -2$

y-intercept $= 3$

c.

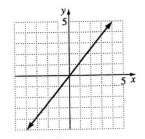

38. a. $3x + y = 4$

$y = -3x + 4$

b. Slope $= -3$

y-intercept $= 4$

c.

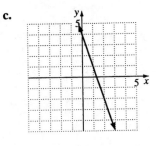

39. a. $7x + 2y = 14$

$2y = -7x + 14$

$y = -\dfrac{7}{2}x + 7$

b. Slope $= -\dfrac{7}{2}$

y-intercept $= 7$

c.

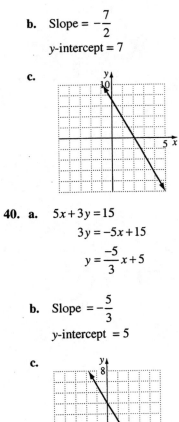

40. a. $5x + 3y = 15$

$3y = -5x + 15$

$y = \dfrac{-5}{3}x + 5$

b. Slope $= -\dfrac{5}{3}$

y-intercept $= 5$

c.

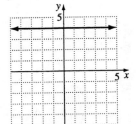

41. $y = 4$

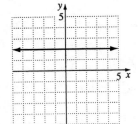

42. $y = 2$

43. $y = -2$

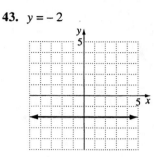

46. $x = 4$

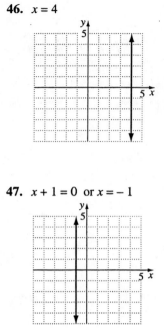

44. $y = -3$

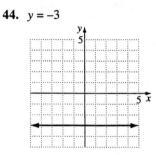

47. $x + 1 = 0$ or $x = -1$

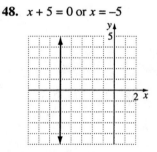

45. $x = 2$

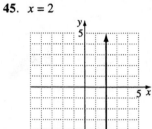

48. $x + 5 = 0$ or $x = -5$

49. $m = \dfrac{1500 - 1000}{2001 - 1999} = \dfrac{500}{2} = 250$

The amount spent online per U.S. online household increased $250 per year from 1999 to 2001.

50. $m = \dfrac{3900 - 1500}{2004 - 2001} = \dfrac{2400}{3} = 800$

The amount spent online per U.S. online household is expected to increase $800 per year from 2001 to 2004.

51. $m = \dfrac{-286 - 50}{2010 - 2001} = \dfrac{-336}{9} \approx -37.33$

The federal budget surplus is expected to decrease $37.33 billion per year from 2001 through 2010.

52. $m = \dfrac{1200 - 200}{2010 - 2001} = \dfrac{1000}{9} \approx 111.11$

The federal budget surplus is expected to increase $111.11 billion per year from 2001 through 2010.

53. a. The y-intercept is 24. This represents an average retail prescription cost of $24 in 1991.

    b. $m = \dfrac{38-24}{7-0} = \dfrac{14}{7} = 2$; The cost increased at a rate of $2 per year from 1991 to 2000.

    c. $y = 2x + 24$

    d. Since 2005 is 14 years after 1991, let $x = 14$.
        $y = 2(14) + 24 = 28 + 24 = 52$; The expected average cost will be $52 in 2005.

54. a. The y-intercept is $(0, 22)$. The 0 represents 0 years after 1995. Thus, in 1995 there were 22 thousand movie screens.

    b. $m = \dfrac{38-22}{4-0} = \dfrac{16}{4} = \dfrac{4}{1} = 4$; The number of movie screens is increasing at a rate of 4 thousand per year.

    c. $y = 4x + 22$

    d. Since 2005 is 10 years after 1995, let $x = 10$.
        $y = 4(10) + 22 = 62$; It's predicted that there will be 62 thousand movie screens in 2005.

55-63. Answers will vary.

64. Let A be the coefficient of x and let B be the coefficient of y, giving the equation $Ax + By = 10$.
The coordinates of the x-intercept are $(5, 0)$. The coordinates of the y-intercept are $(0, 2)$
Substitute the coordinates of the intercepts into the equation:

x-intercept: $(5, 0)$ y-intercept: $(0, 2)$

$$Ax + By = 10 \qquad\qquad Ax + By = 10$$
$$A(5) + B(0) = 10 \qquad A(0) + B(2) = 10$$
$$5A = 10 \qquad\qquad\qquad 2B = 10$$
$$A = 2 \qquad\qquad\qquad\quad B = 5$$

Thus the equation is $2x + 5y = 10$

65. Let A be the coefficient of x and let B be the coefficient of y, giving the equation $Ax + By = 12$.
The coordinates of the x-intercept are $(-2, 0)$. The coordinates of the y-intercept are $(0, 4)$
Substitute the coordinates of the intercepts into the equation:

x-intercept: $(-2, 0)$ y-intercept: $(0, 4)$

$$Ax + By = 12 \qquad\qquad Ax + By = 12$$
$$A(-2) + B(0) = 12 \qquad A(0) + B(4) = 12$$
$$-2A = 12 \qquad\qquad\qquad 4B = 12$$
$$A = -6 \qquad\qquad\qquad\quad B = 3$$

Thus the equation is $-6x + 3y = 10$

66. $m = 2$

67. $m = -3$

68. $m = -\dfrac{1}{2}$

69. $m = \dfrac{3}{4}$

Check Points 7.3

1. $f(x) = 0.4x^2 - 36x + 1000$

$$f(30) = 0.4(30)^2 - 36(30) + 1000$$
$$= 0.4(900) - 36(30) + 1000$$
$$= 360 - 1080 + 1000$$
$$= 280$$

Thus $f(30) = 280$ which indicates that 30-year-olds have 280 accidents per 50 million miles driven.

2. a. The coefficient, a, of x^2 is 1. Since $a > 0$, the parabola opens up.

b.

x	$y = x^2 - 6x + 8$	(x, y)
0	$y = (0)^2 - 6(0) + 8 = 8$	$(0, 8)$
1	$y = (1)^2 - 6(1) + 8 = 3$	$(1, 3)$
2	$y = (2)^2 - 6(2) + 8 = 0$	$(2, 0)$
3	$y = (3)^2 - 6(3) + 8 = -1$	$(3, -1)$
4	$y = (4)^2 - 6(4) + 8 = 0$	$(4, 0)$
5	$y = (5)^2 - 6(5) + 8 = 3$	$(5, 3)$
6	$y = (6)^2 - 6(6) + 8 = 8$	$(6, 8)$

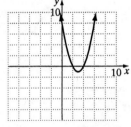

3. Replace y with 0 and solve the equation for x by factoring.

$$x^2 - 6x + 8 = 0$$
$$(x - 4)(x - 2) = 0$$
$$x - 4 = 0 \quad \text{or} \quad x - 2 = 0$$
$$x = 4 \qquad\qquad x = 2$$

Thus the x-intercepts are 4 and 2, which are located at the points $(4, 0)$ and $(2, 0)$.

4. Replace x with 0 and solve the equation for y.

$$y = x^2 - 6x + 8$$
$$y = (0)^2 - 6(0) + 8$$
$$y = 8$$

Thus the y-intercept is 8, which is located at the point $(0, 8)$.

5. In the equation $y = x^2 - 6x + 8$, $a = 1$ and $b = -6$.

   x-coordinate of vertex $= \dfrac{-b}{2a} = \dfrac{-(-6)}{2(1)} = \dfrac{6}{2} = 3$

   To find the y-coordinate of the vertex, substitute 3 for x in $y = x^2 - 6x + 8$, and evaluate.

   y-coordinate of vertex $= (3)^2 - 6(3) + 8 = 9 - 18 + 8 = -1$

   Thus, the vertex is the point $(3, -1)$.

6. Step 1. Since $a > 0$, the parabola opens upward $(a = 1)$.

   Step 2. Find the vertex given $a = 1$ and $b = 6$.

   x-coordinate of vertex $= \dfrac{-b}{2a} = \dfrac{-6}{2(1)} = \dfrac{-6}{2} = -3$

   y-coordinate of vertex $= (-3)^2 + 6(-3) + 5 = 9 - 18 + 5 = -4$

   Thus, the vertex is the point $(-3, -4)$.

   Step 3. Replace y with 0 and solve the equation for x by factoring.

   $x^2 + 6x + 5 = 0$

   $(x + 5)(x + 1) = 0$

   $x + 5 = 0 \quad$ or $\quad x + 1 = 0$

   $x = -5 \qquad\qquad x = -1$

   Thus the x-intercepts are -5 and -1, , which are located at the points $(-5, 0)$ and $(-1, 0)$.

   Step 4. Replace x with 0 and solve the equation for y.

   $y = x^2 + 6x + 5$

   $y = (0)^2 + 6(0) + 5$

   $y = 5$

   Thus the y-intercept is 5, which is located at the point $(0, 5)$.

   Steps 5 and 6.   Plot the intercepts at the vertex. Connect these points with a smooth curve.

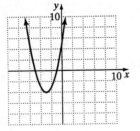

7. Step 1. Since $a < 0$, the parabola opens downward $(a = -1)$.

   Step 2. Find the vertex given $a = -1$ and $b = -2$.

   x-coordinate of vertex $= \dfrac{-b}{2a} = \dfrac{-(-2)}{2(-1)} = \dfrac{2}{-2} = -1$

   y-coordinate of vertex $= -(-1)^2 - 2(-1) + 5 = -1 + 2 + 5 = 6$

   Thus, the vertex is the point $(-1, 6)$.

Step 3. Replace y with 0 and solve for x by using the quadratic formula ($a = -1$, $b = -2$, and $c = 5$).

$$x = \frac{-b \pm \sqrt{b^2 - 4ac}}{2a} = \frac{-(-2) \pm \sqrt{(-2)^2 - 4(-1)(5)}}{2(-1)} = \frac{2 \pm \sqrt{24}}{-2}$$

$$x = \frac{2 + \sqrt{24}}{-2} \approx -3.4 \quad \text{or} \quad x = \frac{2 - \sqrt{24}}{-2} \approx 1.4$$

Thus the points are $(-3.4, 0)$ and $(1.4, 0)$.

Step 4. Replace x with 0 and solve the equation for y.

$$y = -x^2 - 2x + 5$$
$$y = -(0)^2 - 2(0) + 5$$
$$y = 5$$

Thus the y-intercept is 5, which is located at the point $(0, 5)$.

Steps 5 and 6. Plot the intercepts at the vertex. Connect these points with a smooth curve.

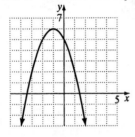

8. In the equation $y = -0.5x^2 + 4x + 19$, $a = -0.5$ and $b = 4$.

x-coordinate of vertex $= \dfrac{-b}{2a} = \dfrac{-4}{2(-0.5)} = 4$

To find the y-coordinate of the vertex, substitute 4 for x in $y = -0.5x^2 + 4x + 19$, and evaluate.

y-coordinate of vertex $= -0.5(4)^2 + 4(4) + 19 = -8 + 16 + 19 = 27$

Thus, the vertex is the point $(4, 27)$. This represents that the number of people receiving food reached a maximum of 27 million in 1994, 4 years after 1990.

Exercise Set 7.3

1. $y = x^2 - 4x + 3$

   $a = 1 > 0$; the parabola opens upward.

2. $y = x^2 - 6x + 5$

   $a = 1 > 0$; the parabola opens upward.

3. $f(x) = -2x^2 + x + 6$

   $a = -2 < 0$; the parabola opens downward.

4. $f(x) = -2x^2 - 4x + 6$

   $a = -2 < 0$; the parabola opens downward.

5. $y = x^2 - 4x + 3$

   Replace y with 0.

$$0 = x^2 - 4x + 3$$
$$0 = (x - 3)(x - 1)$$
$$x - 3 = 0 \text{ or } x - 1 = 0$$
$$x = 3 \qquad x = 1$$

The x-intercepts are 3 and 1. The parabola passes through $(3, 0)$ and $(1, 0)$.

6. $y = x^2 - 6x + 5$

Replace y with 0.

$$0 = x^2 - 6x + 5$$
$$0 = (x - 5)(x - 1)$$
$$x - 5 = 0 \quad \text{or} \quad x - 1 = 0$$
$$x = 5 \qquad x = 1$$

The x-intercepts are 5 and 1. The parabola passes through $(5, 0)$ and $(1, 0)$.

7. $y = -x^2 + 8x - 12$

Replace y with 0.

$$0 = -x^2 + 8x - 12 \text{ or } x^2 - 8x + 12 = 0$$
$$(x - 6)(x - 2) = 0$$
$$x - 6 = 0 \text{ or } x - 2 = 0$$
$$x = 6 \qquad x = 2$$

The x-intercepts are 6 and 2. The parabola passes through $(6, 0)$ and $(2, 0)$.

8. $y = -x^2 - 2x + 3$

Replace y with 0.

$$0 = -x^2 - 2x + 3 \quad \text{or} \quad x^2 + 2x - 3 = 0$$
$$(x + 3)(x - 1) = 0$$
$$x + 3 = 0 \quad \text{or} \quad x - 1 = 0$$
$$x = -3 \qquad x = 1$$

The x-intercepts are -3 and 1. The parabola passes through $(-3, 0)$ and $(1, 0)$.

9. $f(x) = x^2 + 2x - 4$

Replace $f(x)$ with 0.

$$0 = x^2 + 2x - 4$$
$$x = \frac{-b \pm \sqrt{b^2 - 4ac}}{2a} = \frac{-2 \pm \sqrt{2^2 - 4(1)(-4)}}{2(1)} = \frac{-2 \pm \sqrt{20}}{2} = -1 \pm \sqrt{5}$$
$$x \approx -3.2 \quad x \approx 1.2$$

The x-intercepts are approximately -3.2 and 1.2. The parabola passes through $(-3.2, 0)$ and $(1.2, 0)$.

10. $f(x) = x^2 + 8x + 14$

Replace $f(x)$ with 0.

$$0 = x^2 + 8x + 14$$
$$x = \frac{-b \pm \sqrt{b^2 - 4ac}}{2a} = \frac{-8 \pm \sqrt{8^2 - 4(1)(14)}}{2(1)}$$

$$= \frac{-8 \pm \sqrt{8}}{2}$$

$$= -4 \pm \sqrt{2}$$

$$x \approx -5.4 \quad x \approx -2.6$$

The x-intercepts are approximately
–5.4 and –2.6. The parabola passes through
$(-5.4, 0)$ and $(-2.6, 0)$.

11. $y = x^2 - 4x + 3$

Replace x with 0.

$y = 0^2 - 4(0) + 3 = 3$

The y-intercept is 3. The parabola passes through $(0, 3)$.

12. $y = x^2 - 6x + 5$

Replace x with 0.

$y = (0)^2 - 6(0) + 5 = 5$

The y-intercept is 5. The parabola passes through $(0, 5)$.

13. $y = -x^2 + 8x - 12$

Replace x with 0.

$y = -(0)^2 + 8(0) - 12 = -12$

The y-intercept is – 12. The parabola passes through $(0, -12)$.

14. $y = -x^2 - 2x + 3$

Replace x with 0.

$y = -(0)^2 - 2(0) + 3 = 3$

The y-intercept is 3. The parabola passes through $(0, 3)$.

15. $y = x^2 + 2x - 4$

Replace x with 0.

$y = (0)^2 + 2(0) - 4 = -4$

The y-intercept is – 4. The parabola passes through $(0, -4)$.

16. $y = x^2 + 8x + 14$

Replace x with 0.

$y = (0)^2 + 8(0) + 14 = 14$

The y-intercept is 14. The parabola passes through $(0, 14)$.

17. $f(x) = x^2 + 6x$

Replace x with 0.

$f(0) = (0)^2 + 6(0) = 0.$

The y-intercept is 0. The parabola passes through $(0, 0)$.

18. $f(x) = x^2 + 8x$

Replace x with 0.

$f(0) = (0)^2 + 8(0) = 0$

The y-intercept is 0. The parabola passes through $(0, 0)$.

19. Because $y = x^2 - 4x + 3$, a (the coefficient of x^2) is 1 and b (the coefficient of x) is -4.
    The x-coordinate of the vertex is:

    $$x = \frac{-b}{2a} = \frac{-(-4)}{2(1)} = \frac{4}{2} = 2$$

    Substitute 2 for x in the equation of the function to find the y-coordinate of the vertex.

    $$y = (2)^2 - 4(2) + 3 = 4 - 8 + 3 = -1$$

    The y-coordinate of the vertex is -1.
    The vertex is at $(2, -1)$ and is a minimum.

20. Because $y = x^2 - 6x + 5$, a (the coefficient of x^2) is 1 and b (the coefficient of x) is -6. The

    x-coordinate of the vertex is $x = \frac{-b}{2a} = -\frac{(-6)}{2(1)} = \frac{6}{2} = 3$.

    Substitute 3 for x in the equation of the function to find the y-coordinate of the vertex.

    $$y = (3)^2 - 6(3) + 5 = 9 - 18 + 5 = -4.$$

    The y-coordinate of the vertex is -4. The vertex is at $(3, -4)$ and is a minimum.

21. Because $y = 2x^2 + 4x - 6$, a (the coefficient of x^2) is 2 and b (the coefficient of x) is 4. The x-coordinate of the vertex
    is:

    $$x = \frac{-b}{2a} = \frac{-4}{2(2)} = \frac{-4}{4} = -1$$

    Substitute -1 for x in the equation of the function to find the y-coordinate of the vertex.

    $$y = 2(-1)^2 + 4(-1) - 6 = 2 - 4 - 6$$
    $$= -8$$

    The y-coordinate of the vertex is -8.
    The vertex is at $(-1, -8)$ and is a minimum.

22. Because $y = -2x^2 - 4x - 2$, a (the coefficient of x^2) is -2 and b (the coefficient of x) is -4. The

    x-coordinate of the vertex is $x = \frac{-b}{2a} = \frac{-(-4)}{2(-2)} = \frac{4}{(-4)} = -1$.

    Substitute -1 for x in the equation of the function to find the y-coordinate of the vertex.

    $$y = -2(-1)^2 - 4(-1) - 2 = -2 + 4 - 2 = 0.$$

    The y-coordinate of the vertex is 0. The vertex is at $(-1, 0)$ and is a maximum.

23. Because $f(x) = x^2 + 6x$, a, (the coefficient of x^2) is 1 and b (the coefficient of x) is 6. The x-coordinate of the vertex
    is:

    $$x = \frac{-b}{2a} = \frac{-6}{2(1)} = -3$$

    Substitute -3 for x in the equation of the function to find the y-coordinate of the vertex.

    $$f(-3) = (-3)^2 + 6(-3) = 9 - 18 = -9$$

    The y-coordinate of the vertex is -9. The vertex is at $(-3, -9)$ and is a minimum.

24. Because $f(x) = x^2 + 8x$, a (the coefficient of x^2) is 1 and b (the coefficient of x) is 8. The

x-coordinate of the vertex is $x = \dfrac{-b}{2a} = \dfrac{-8}{2(1)} = \dfrac{-8}{2} = -4$.

Substitute -4 for x in the equation of the function to find the y-coordinate of the vertex.

$f(-4) = (-4)^2 + 8(-4) = 16 - 32 = -16$.

The y-coordinate of the vertex is -16. The vertex is at $(-4, -16)$ and is a minimum.

25. $y = x^2 + 8x + 7$

The parabola opens upward because $a > 0$.

$x = \dfrac{-b}{2a} = \dfrac{-8}{2(1)} = -4$

$y = (-4)^2 + 6(-4) + 5 = -3$

The vertex is at $(-4, -3)$.

Find the x-intercepts.

$0 = x^2 + 8x + 7$

$0 = (x + 7)(x + 1)$

$x + 7 = 0$ or $x + 1 = 0$

$x = -7$ $x = -1$

The parabola passes through $(-7, 0)$, and $(-1, 0)$.

Find the y-intercept.

$y = 0^2 + 8(0) + 7$

$y = 7$

The parabola passes through $(0, 7)$.

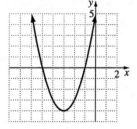

26. $y = x^2 + 10x + 9$

The parabola opens upward because $a > 0$.

$x = \dfrac{-b}{2a} = \dfrac{-10}{2(1)} = -5$

$y = (-5)^2 + 4(-5) + 9 = 14$

The vertex is at $(-5, 14)$.

Find the x-intercepts.

$0 = x^2 + 10x + 9$

$0 = (x + 9)(x + 1)$

$x + 9 = 0$ or $x + 1 = 0$

$x = -9$ $x = -1$

The parabola passes through $(-9, 0)$ and $(-1, 0)$.

Find the y-intercept.

$y = (0)^2 + 10(0) + 9$

$y = 9$

The parabola passes through $(0, 9)$.

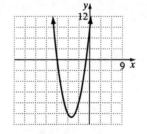

27. $y = x^2 - 2x - 8$

The parabola opens upward because $a > 0$.

$x = \dfrac{-b}{2a} = \dfrac{-(-2)}{2(1)} = 1$

$y = (1)^2 - 2(1) - 8 = -9$

The vertex is at $(1, -9)$.
Find the x-intercepts.

$0 = x^2 - 2x - 8$

$0 = (x + 2)(x - 4)$

$x + 2 = 0$ or $x - 4 = 0$

     $x = -2$ $x = 4$

The parabola passes through $(-2, 0)$, and $(4, 0)$.
Find the y-intercept.

$y = 0^2 - 2 \cdot 0 - 8$

$y = -8$

The parabola passes through $(0, -8)$.

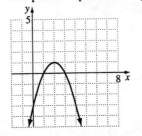

28. $y = x^2 + 4x - 5$

The parabola opens upward because $a > 0$.

$x = \dfrac{-b}{2a} = \dfrac{-4}{2(1)} = -2$

$y = (-2)^2 + 4(-2) - 5 = -9$

The vertex is at $(-2, -9)$.
Find the x-intercepts.

$0 = x^2 + 4x - 5$

$0 = (x + 5)(x - 1)$

$x + 5 = 0$ or $x - 1 = 0$

     $x = -5$ $x = 1$

The parabola passes through $(-5, 0)$ and $(1, 0)$.
Find the y-intercept.

$y = 0^2 + 4 \cdot 0 - 5$

$y = -5$

The parabola passes through $(0, -5)$.

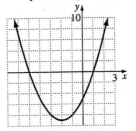

29. $y = -x^2 + 4x - 3$

The parabola opens downward because $a < 0$.

$x = \dfrac{-b}{2a} = \dfrac{-4}{2(-1)} = 2$

$y = -2^2 + 4 \cdot 2 - 3 = 1$

The vertex is at $(2, 1)$.
Find the x-intercepts.

$0 = -x^2 + 4x - 3$ or $x^2 - 4x + 3 = 0$

$(x - 1)(x - 3) = 0$

$x - 1 = 0$ or $x - 3 = 0$

     $x = 1$ $x = 3$

The parabola passes through $(1, 0)$ and $(3, 0)$.
Find the y-intercept.

$y = -0^2 + 4 \cdot 0 - 3$

$y = -3$

The parabola passes through $(0, -3)$.

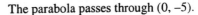

30. $y = -x^2 + 2x + 3$

The parabola opens downward because $a < 0$.

$x = \dfrac{-b}{2a} = \dfrac{-2}{2(-1)} = 1$

$y = -(1)^2 + 2(1) + 3 = 4$

The vertex is at $(1, 4)$.
Find the x-intercepts.

$0 = -x^2 + 2x + 3$

$0 = x^2 - 2x - 3$

$0 = (x + 1)(x - 3)$

$x+1=0$ or $x-3=0$

$x=-1$ $x=3$

The parabola passes through (-1, 0) and (3, 0).
Find the y-intercept.

$y=-x^2+2x+3$

$y=-(0)^2+4(0)+3$

$y=3$

The parabola passes through (0, 3).

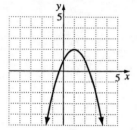

31. $y=x^2-1$

The parabola opens upward because $a>0$.

$x=\dfrac{-b}{2a}=\dfrac{-0}{2(1)}=0$

$y=0^2-1=-1$

The vertex is at $(0,-1)$.
Find the x-intercepts.

$0=x^2-1$

$0=(x+1)(x-1)$

$x+1=0$ or $x-1=0$

$x=-1$ $x=1$

The parabola passes through
$(-1, 0)$, and $(1, 0)$.
Find the y-intercept.

$y=0^2-1$

$y=-1$

The parabola passes through $(0,-1)$.

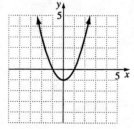

32. $y=x^2-4$

The parabola opens upward because $a>0$.

$x=\dfrac{-b}{2a}=\dfrac{-0}{2(1)}=0$

$y=0^2-4=-4$

The vertex is at $(0,-4)$.
Find the x-intercepts.

$0=x^2-4$

$0=(x+2)(x-2)$

$x+2=0$ or $x-2=0$

$x=-2$ $x=2$

The parabola passes through $(-2, 0)$ and $(2, 0)$.
Find the y-intercept.

$y=0^2-4$

$y=-4$

The parabola passes through $(0,-4)$.

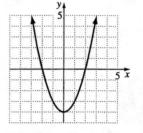

33. $f(x)=x^2+2x+1$

The parabola opens upward because $a>0$.

$x=\dfrac{-b}{2a}=\dfrac{-2}{2(1)}=-1$

$f(-1)=(-1)^2+2(-1)+1=0$

The vertex is $(-1, 0)$.
Find the x-intercept.

$0=x^2+2x+1$

$0=(x+1)(x+1)$

$x+1=0$

$x=-1$

The parabola passes through $(-1, 0)$.
Find the y-intercept.

$f(0)=0^2+2\cdot0+1$

$f(0)=1$

The parabola passes through (0, 1).

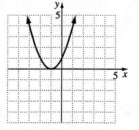

34. $f(x) = x^2 - 2x + 1$

The parabola opens upward because $a > 0$.

$$x = \frac{-b}{2a} = \frac{-(-2)}{2(1)} = 1$$

$$f(1) = 1^2 - 2 \cdot 1 + 1 = 0$$

The vertex is at $(1, 0)$.

Find the x-intercept.

$$0 = x^2 - 2x + 1$$

$$0 = (x-1)(x-1)$$

$$x - 1 = 0$$

$$x = 1$$

The parabola passes through $(1, 0)$.

Find the y-intercept.

$$f(0) = 0^2 - 2 \cdot 0 + 1$$

$$f(0) = 1$$

The parabola passes through $(0, 1)$.

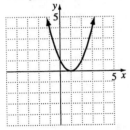

35. $f(x) = -2x^2 + 4x + 5$

The parabola opens downward because $a < 0$.

$$x = \frac{-b}{2a} = \frac{-4}{2(-2)} = 1$$

$$y = f(1) = -2(1)^2 + 4(1) + 5 = 7$$

The vertex is at $(1, 7)$.

Find the x-intercepts.

$$0 = -2x^2 + 4x + 5$$

$$x = \frac{-4 \pm \sqrt{4^2 - 4(-2)(5)}}{2(-2)}$$

$$x \approx -0.9 \text{ or } x \approx 2.9$$

The parabola passes through the approximate points $(-0.9, 0)$ and $(2.9, 0)$.

Find the y-intercept.

$$y = f(0) = -2(0)^2 + 4(0) + 5$$

$$y = f(0) = 5$$

The parabola passes through $(0, 5)$.

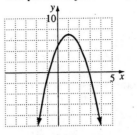

36. $f(x) = -3x^2 + 6x - 2$

The parabola opens downward because $a < 0$.

$$x = \frac{-b}{2a} = \frac{-6}{2(-3)} = 1$$

$$y = f(1) = -3(1)^2 + 6(1) - 2 = 1$$

The vertex is at $(1, 1)$.

Find the x-intercepts.

$$0 = -3x^2 + 6x - 2$$

$$x = \frac{-6 \pm \sqrt{6^2 - 4(-3)(-2)}}{2(-3)}$$

$$x \approx 0.4 \text{ or } x \approx 1.6$$

The parabola passes through the approximate points $(0.4, 0)$ and $(1.6, 0)$.

Find the y-intercept.

$$y = f(0) = -3(0)^2 + 6(0) - 2$$

$$y = f(0) = -2$$

The parabola passes through $(0, -2)$.

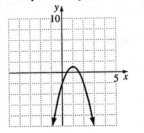

37. $f(50) = 0.036(50)^2 - 2.8(50) + 58.14$
$$= 90 - 140 + 58.14 = 8.14$$
There are 8.14 deaths per year per thousand people among 50-year-olds.

38. $f(40) = 0.036(40)^2 - 2.8(40) + 58.14$
$$= 57.6 - 112 + 58.14 = 3.74$$
There are 3.74 deaths per year per thousand people among 40-year-olds.

39. $(50, 8.14)$

40. $(40, 3.74)$

41. 57-year-olds

42. 47-year-olds

43. In the function $y = -16x^2 + 200x + 4$, $a = -16$ and $b = 200$.

x-coordinate of vertex $= \dfrac{-b}{2a} = \dfrac{-200}{2(-16)} = 6.25$;   y-coordinate of vertex $= -16(6.25)^2 + 200(6.25) + 4 = 629$

The vertex $(6.25, 629)$ represents that after 6.25 seconds the firework reaches its greatest height of 629 feet.

44. In the function $y = -0.025x^2 + x + 5$, $a = -0.025$ and $b = 1$.

x-coordinate of vertex $= \dfrac{-b}{2a} = \dfrac{-1}{2(-0.025)} = 20$;   y-coordinate of vertex $= -0.025(20)^2 + (20) + 5 = 15$

The vertex $(20, 15)$ represents that after 20 yards the football reaches it's greatest height of 15 feet.

45. In the function $y = -0.01x^2 + 0.8x$, $a = -0.01$ and $b = 0.8$.

x-coordinate of vertex $= \dfrac{-b}{2a} = \dfrac{-0.8}{2(-0.01)} = 40$;   y-coordinate of vertex $= -0.01(40)^2 + 0.8(40) = 16$

The vertex $(40, 16)$ represents that 40 trees should be planted per acre to reach the maximun possible yield of 16 bushels of avocados per tree.

46. $A(x) = x(120 - 2x) = 120x - 2x^2$, thus $a = -2$ and $b = 120$.

x-coordinate of vertex $= \dfrac{-b}{2a} = \dfrac{-120}{2(-2)} = 30$

The optimal width is 30 feet and therefore, the optimal length is $120 - 2(30)$ or 60 feet.

The maximum area is $A(30) = 30\big[120 - 2(30)\big] = 1800$ square feet.

47-54. Answers will vary.

55. There are two x-intercepts because the vertex is above the x-axis and the parabola opens downward $(a < 0)$.

56. There is only one x-intercept because the vertex on the x-axis. The vertex is the x-intercept.

57. There are no x-intercepts because the vertex is above the x-axis and the parabola opens upward $(a > 0)$.

58. We must find a, b, and c for $y = ax^2 + bx + c$. The y-intercept of -21 indicates that $c = -21$.

The x-intercepts of 3 and 7 indicate that the function can be factored into the form $y = a(x-3)(x-7)$.

Multiplying gives; $y = a(x-3)(x-7)$

$$y = a(x^2 - 10x + 21)$$
$$y = ax^2 - 10ax + 21a$$

Since $c = -21$ and $c = 21a$, then $21a = -21$. Therefore $a = -1$.

Thus by substitution; $y = ax^2 - 10ax + 21a$

$$y = (-1)x^2 - 10(-1)x + 21(-1)$$
$$y = -x^2 + 10x - 21$$

Check Points 7.4

1.

x	$f(x) = 3^x$
-3	$f(-3) = 3^{-3} = \dfrac{1}{27}$
-2	$f(-2) = 3^{-2} = \dfrac{1}{9}$
-1	$f(-1) = 3^{-1} = \dfrac{1}{3}$
0	$f(0) = 3^0 = 1$
1	$f(1) = 3^1 = 3$
2	$f(2) = 3^2 = 9$
3	$f(3) = 3^3 = 27$

2.

x	$f(x) = \left(\dfrac{1}{3}\right)^x$
-3	$f(-3) = \left(\dfrac{1}{3}\right)^{-3} = 27$
-2	$f(-2) = \left(\dfrac{1}{3}\right)^{-2} = 9$
-1	$f(-1) = \left(\dfrac{1}{3}\right)^{-1} = 3$
0	$f(0) = \left(\dfrac{1}{3}\right)^{0} = 1$
1	$f(1) = \left(\dfrac{1}{3}\right)^{1} = \dfrac{1}{3}$
2	$f(2) = \left(\dfrac{1}{3}\right)^{2} = \dfrac{1}{9}$
3	$f(3) = \left(\dfrac{1}{3}\right)^{3} = \dfrac{1}{27}$

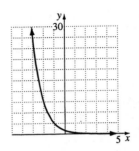

3. $f(60) = 13.49(0.967)^{60} - 1 \approx 0.8 \approx 1$. Thus one 0-ring is expected to fail at $60°\text{F}$.

4. $f(90) = 1000(0.5)^{\left(\frac{90}{30}\right)} = 125$. After 90 years, 125 kilograms of cesium-137 will be in the atmosphere. Because this exceeds 100, the Chernobyl area will still be unsafe in 2076.

5. $f(50) = 6e^{0.013(50)} \approx 11.49$. This indicates that world population in 2050 will be approximately 11.49 billion.

Exercise Set 7.4

1.

x	-2	-1	0	1	2
$f(x) = 3^x$	$\dfrac{1}{9}$	$\dfrac{1}{3}$	1	3	9

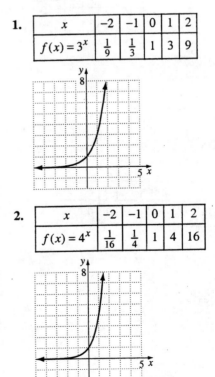

2.

x	-2	-1	0	1	2
$f(x) = 4^x$	$\dfrac{1}{16}$	$\dfrac{1}{4}$	1	4	16

3.

x	−2	−1	0	1	2
$f(x) = 2^{x+1}$	$\frac{1}{2}$	1	2	4	8

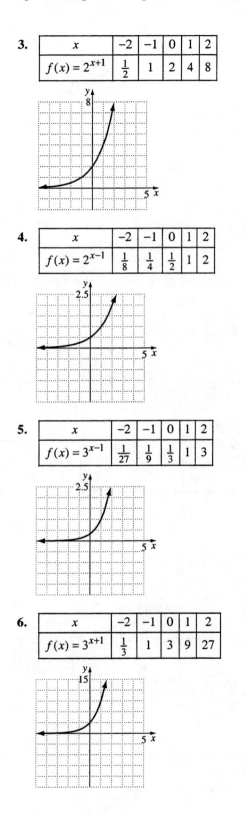

4.

x	−2	−1	0	1	2
$f(x) = 2^{x-1}$	$\frac{1}{8}$	$\frac{1}{4}$	$\frac{1}{2}$	1	2

5.

x	−2	−1	0	1	2
$f(x) = 3^{x-1}$	$\frac{1}{27}$	$\frac{1}{9}$	$\frac{1}{3}$	1	3

6.

x	−2	−1	0	1	2
$f(x) = 3^{x+1}$	$\frac{1}{3}$	1	3	9	27

7.

x	−2	−1	0	1	2
$f(x) = \left(\frac{1}{3}\right)^{x}$	9	3	1	$\frac{1}{3}$	$\frac{1}{9}$

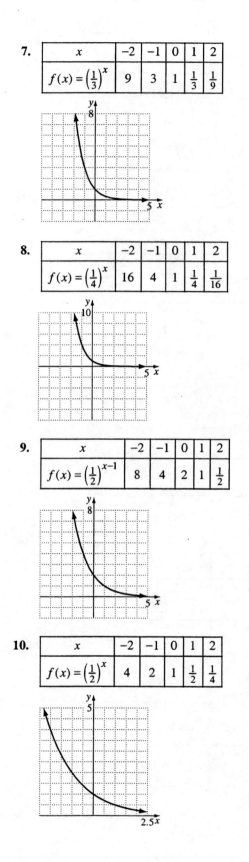

8.

x	−2	−1	0	1	2
$f(x) = \left(\frac{1}{4}\right)^{x}$	16	4	1	$\frac{1}{4}$	$\frac{1}{16}$

9.

x	−2	−1	0	1	2
$f(x) = \left(\frac{1}{2}\right)^{x-1}$	8	4	2	1	$\frac{1}{2}$

10.

x	−2	−1	0	1	2
$f(x) = \left(\frac{1}{2}\right)^{x}$	4	2	1	$\frac{1}{2}$	$\frac{1}{4}$

11. $f(x) = 574(1.026)^x$

   a. $f(0) = 574(1.026)^0 = 574$ million

   b. $f(27) = 574(1.026)^{27} \approx 1147.9$ million or 1.1 billion

   c. $2028 - 1974 = 54$
   $f(54) = 574(1.026)^{54} \approx 2295.5$ million or 2.3 billion

   d. $2055 - 1974 = 81$
   $f(81) = 574(1.026)^{81} \approx 4590.4$ million or 4.6 billion

   e. Every 27 years, India's population about doubles.

12. $y = 6(351,512)^{0.17} \approx 53\%$

13. $S = 65,000(1+0.06)^{10} \approx \$116,405.10$

14. $S = 110,000(1+0.03)^5 \approx \$127,520.15$

15. a. $f(x) = 0.08e^{0.47x}$
   $f(9) = 0.08e^{0.47(9)} \approx 5.5$ million
   It models the data quite well.

   b. The highest 20% is represented by groups 9 and 10. Thus, divide their sum by the sum of all ten groups.
   $$\frac{5.5+9.6}{0.2+0.2+0.3+0.4+0.7+1.3+2.2+3.5+5.5+9.6}$$
   $$= \frac{15.1}{23.9} \approx .6318$$

   The top 20% of players earn about 63% of all major-league pay

16. a. $f(x) = 80e^{-0.5x} + 20$
   $f(0) = 80e^{-0.5(0)} + 20 = 100$
   100% of the information is remembered at the moment it is first learned.

   b. $f(1) = 80e^{-0.5(1)} + 20 \approx 68.52$
   After 1 week, 68.52% of information is remembered.

   c. $f(4) = 80e^{-0.5(4)} + 20 \approx 30.83$
   After 4 weeks, 30.83% of information is remembered.

   d. $f(52) = 80e^{-0.5(52)} + 20 \approx 20$
   After 52 weeks, 20% of information is remembered.

17. $f(30) = \dfrac{90}{1+270e^{-0.122(30)}} \approx 11.3\%$
   About 11.3% of 30-year-olds have some coronary heart disease.

18. $f(70) = \dfrac{90}{1+270e^{-0.122(70)}} \approx 85.5\%$
   About 85.5% of 70-year-olds have some coronary heart disease.

19-23. Answers will vary.

24. $a \leftrightarrow y = \left(\dfrac{1}{3}\right)^x$

   $b \leftrightarrow y = \left(\dfrac{1}{5}\right)^x$

   $c \leftrightarrow y = 5^x$

   $d \leftrightarrow y = 3^x$

   c and d have the form of $y = b^x$ where $b > 1$, a and b have the form of $y = b^x$ where $b < 1$.
   For every positive value of x
   $\left(\dfrac{1}{5}\right)^x < \left(\dfrac{1}{3}\right)^x < 3^x < 5^x$, and since for positive values of x the values of y are as follows:
   $y_b < y_a < y_d < y_c$.
   Therefore $b \leftrightarrow \left(\dfrac{1}{5}\right)^x$

   $a \leftrightarrow \left(\dfrac{1}{3}\right)^x$

   $d \leftrightarrow 3^x$

   $c \leftrightarrow 5^x$

Check Points 7.5

1. Replace x with -4 and y with 3.

$$x+2y=2 \qquad\qquad x-2y=6$$
$$-4+2(3)=2 \qquad -4-2(3)=6$$
$$-4+6=2 \qquad\qquad -4-6=6$$
$$2=2 \text{ true} \qquad -10=6 \text{ false}$$

The pair $(-4,3)$ does not satisfy both equations. Therefore it is not a solution of the system.

2.

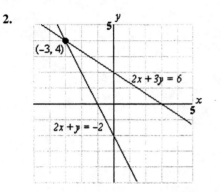

Check coordinates of intersection:

$$2x+3y=6 \qquad\qquad 2x+y=-2$$
$$2(-3)+3(4)=6 \qquad 2(-3)+(4)=-2$$
$$-6+12=6 \qquad\qquad -6+2=-2$$
$$6=6, \text{ true} \qquad -2=-2, \text{ true}$$

The solution set is $\{(-3,4)\}$.

3. **Step 1.** Solve one of the equations for one variable: $y=3x-7$

Step 2. Substitute into the other equation:
$$5x-2y=8$$

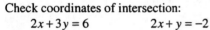

$$5x-2\overbrace{(3x-7)}^{y}=8$$

Step 3. Solve: $5x-2(3x-7)=8$
$$5x-6x+14=8$$
$$-x+14=8$$
$$-x=-6$$
$$x=6$$

Step 4. Back-substitute the obtained value into the equation from step 1:
$$y=3x-7$$
$$y=3(6)-7$$
$$y=11$$

Step 5. Check $(6, 11)$ in both equations:
$$y=3x-7 \qquad\qquad 5x-2y=8$$
$$11=3(6)-7 \qquad 5(6)-2(11)=8$$
$$11=11, \text{ true} \qquad\qquad 8=8, \text{ true}$$

The solution set is $\{(6,11)\}$.

4. Step 1. Solve one of the equations for one variable:
$$x - y = 3$$
$$x = y + 3$$

Step 2. Substitute into the other equation:
$$3x + 2y = -1$$
$$3\overbrace{(y+3)}^{x} + 2y = -1$$

Step 3. Solve: $3(y+3) + 2y = -1$
$$3y + 9 + 2y = -1$$
$$5y + 9 = -1$$
$$5y = -10$$
$$y = -2$$

Step 4. Back-substitute the obtained value into the equation from step 1:
$$x = y + 3$$
$$x = -2 + 3$$
$$x = 1$$

Step 5. Check $(1, -2)$ in both equations:
$$x - y = 3 \qquad 3x + 2y = -1$$
$$1 - (-2) = 3 \qquad 3(1) + 2(-2) = -1$$
$$3 = 3, \text{ true} \qquad -1 = -1, \text{ true}$$
The solution set is $\{(1, -2)\}$.

5.
$$2x - 5y = 26$$
$$-2x + 9y = -42$$
$$\overline{4y = -16}$$
$$y = -4$$
Substitute into either equation:
$$2x - 5\overbrace{(-4)}^{y} = 26$$
$$2x + 20 = 26$$
$$2x = 6$$
$$x = 3$$
Check:
$$2(3) - 5(-4) = 26 \qquad -2(3) + 9(-4) = -42$$
$$6 + 20 = 26 \qquad -6 - 36 = -42$$
$$26 = 26 \text{ true} \qquad -42 = -42 \text{ true}$$
The solution set is $\{(3, -4)\}$.

6. Rewrite one or both equations:
$$4x + 5y = 3 \xrightarrow{\text{No change}} 4x + 5y = 3$$
$$2x - 3y = 7 \xrightarrow{\text{Mult. by } -2} -4x + 6y = -14$$
$$\overline{11y = -11}$$
$$y = -1$$
Back-substitute into either equation:
$$4x + 5y = 3$$
$$4x + 5(-1) = 3$$
$$4x - 5 = 3$$
$$4x = 8$$
$$x = 2$$
Checking confirms the solution set is $\{(2, -1)\}$.

7. Rewrite both equations in the form $Ax + By = C$:
$$3x = 2 - 4y \quad \rightarrow \quad 3x + 4y = 2$$
$$5y = -1 - 2x \quad \rightarrow \quad 2x + 5y = -1$$
Rewrite with opposite coefficients, then add and solve:
$$3x + 4y = 2 \xrightarrow{\text{Mult. by } 2} 6x + 8y = 4$$
$$2x + 5y = -1 \xrightarrow{\text{Mult. by } -3} -6x - 15y = 3$$
$$\overline{-7y = 7}$$
$$y = -1$$

Back-substitute into either equation:
$$3x = 2 - 4y$$
$$3x = 2 - 4(-1)$$
$$3x = 6$$
$$x = 2$$
Checking confirms the solution set is $\{(2, -1)\}$.

8. Rewrite with a pair of opposite coefficients, then add:
$$x + 2y = 4 \xrightarrow{\text{Mult. by } -3} -3x - 6y = -12$$
$$3x + 6y = 13 \xrightarrow{\text{No change}} 3x + 6y = 13$$
$$\overline{0 = 1}$$

The statement $0 = 1$ is false which indicates that the system has no solution. The solution set is the empty set, $\varnothing$.

9. Substitute $4x-4$ for y in the other equation:

$$8x-2\overset{\overbrace{\hspace{1.2em}}^{y}}{(4x-4)}=8$$
$$8x-8x+8=8$$
$$8=8$$

The statement $8 = 8$ is true which indicates that the system has infinitely many solutions. The solution set is $\{(x,y)\,|\,y=4x-4\}$ or $\{(x,y)\,|\,8x-2y=8\}$.

10. Step 1. Use variables to represent the unknown quantities:
Let x represent calories in a Quarter Pounder.
Let y represent calories in a Whopper with cheese.

Step 2. Write a system of equations:
$$2x+3y=2607$$
$$x+y=1009$$

Step 3. Solve and answer:

$$2x+3y=2607 \xrightarrow{\text{No change}} 2x+3y=\ \ 2607$$
$$x+y=1009 \xrightarrow{\text{Mult. by }-2} -2x-2y=-2018$$
$$y=589$$

$$x+y=1009$$
$$x+589=1009$$
$$x=420$$

Therefore a Quarter Pounder contains 420 calories and a Whopper with cheese contains 589 calories.

Step 4. Checking confirms the proposed answers:

$$2x+3y=2607 \qquad\qquad x+y=1009$$
$$2(420)+3(589)=2607 \qquad 420+589=1009$$
$$840+1767=2607 \qquad\qquad 1009=1009,\ \text{true}$$
$$2607=2607,\ \text{true}$$

Exercise Set 7.5

1. Replace x with 2 and y with 3.

$$x+3y=11 \qquad\qquad x-5y=-13$$
$$2+3(3)=11 \qquad\quad 2-5(3)=13$$
$$2+9=11 \qquad\qquad\ 2-15=13$$
$$11=11,\ \text{true} \qquad 13=13,\ \text{true}$$

The pair (2, 3) is a solution of the system.

2. Replace x with -3 and y with 5.

$$9x+7y=8 \qquad\qquad 8x-9y=-69$$
$$9(-3)+7(5)=8 \qquad 8(-3)-9(5)=-69$$
$$-27+35=8 \qquad\qquad -24-45=-69$$
$$8=8,\ \text{true} \qquad\qquad -69=-69,\ \text{true}$$

The pair $(-3, 5)$ is a solution of the system.

3. Replace x with 2 and y with 5.

$$2x+3y=17$$
$$2(2)+3(5)=17$$
$$4+15=17$$
$$19=17,\ \text{false.}$$

The pair (2, 5) is not a solution of the system.

4. Replace x with 8 and y with 5.

$$5x-4y=20 \qquad\qquad 3y=2x+1$$
$$5(8)-4(5)=20 \qquad 3(5)=2(8)+1$$
$$40-20=20 \qquad\qquad 15=16+1$$
$$20=20,\ \text{true} \qquad\ 15=17,\ \text{false}$$

The pair (8, 5) is not a solution of the system.

5.

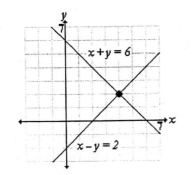

Check coordinates of intersection:
$x + y = 6 \qquad x - y = 2$
$4 + 2 = 6 \qquad 4 - 2 = 2$
$\quad 6 = 6, \text{ true} \qquad 2 = 2, \text{ true}$
The solution set is $\{(4, 2)\}$.

6.

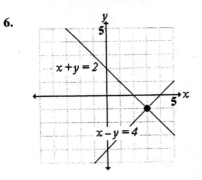

Check coordinates of intersection:
$x + y = 2 \qquad\qquad x - y = 4$
$3 + (-1) = 2 \qquad 3 - (-1) = 4$
$\quad 2 = 2, \text{ true} \qquad\quad 4 = 4, \text{ true}$
The solution set is $\{(3, -1)\}$.

7.

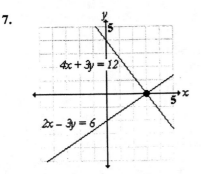

Check coordinates of intersection:
$2x - 3y = 6 \qquad\qquad 4x + 3y = 12$
$2(3) - 3(0) = 6 \qquad 4(3) + (0) = 12$
$\quad 6 = 6, \text{ true} \qquad\quad 12 = 12, \text{ true}$
The solution set is $\{(3, 0)\}$.

8.

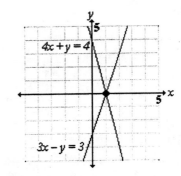

Check coordinates of intersection:
$4x + y = 4 \qquad\qquad 3x - y = 3$
$4(1) + 0 = 4 \qquad 3(1) - (0) = 3$
$\quad 4 = 4, \text{ true} \qquad\quad 3 = 3, \text{ true}$
The solution set is $\{(1, 0)\}$.

9.

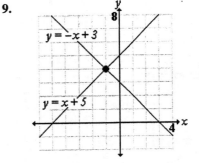

Check coordinates of intersection:
$y = x + 5 \qquad y = -x + 3$
$4 = -1 + 5 \qquad 4 = -(-1) + 3$
$4 = 4, \text{ true} \qquad 4 = 4, \text{ true}$
The solution set is $\{(-1, 4)\}$.

10.

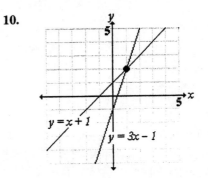

Check coordinates of intersection:
$y = x + 1 \qquad y = 3x - 1$
$2 = 1 + 1 \qquad 2 = 3(1) - 1$
$2 = 2, \text{ true} \qquad 2 = 2, \text{ true}$
The solution set is $\{(1, 2)\}$.

11.

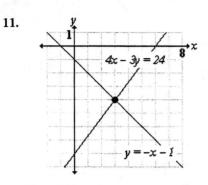

Check coordinates of intersection:

$$y = -x - 1 \qquad\qquad 4x - 3y = 24$$
$$-4 = -(3) - 1 \qquad 4(3) - 3(-4) = 24$$
$$-4 = -4, \text{ true} \qquad\qquad 24 = 24, \text{ true}$$

The solution set is $\{(3, -4)\}$.

12.

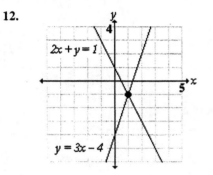

Check coordinates of intersection:

$$y = 3x - 4 \qquad\qquad 2x + y = 1$$
$$-1 = 3(1) - 4 \qquad 2(1) + (-1) = 1$$
$$-1 = -1, \text{ true} \qquad\qquad 1 = 1, \text{ true}$$

The solution set is $\{(1, -1)\}$.

13. $y = 3x \qquad x + y = 4$
$$x + 3x = 4$$
$$4x = 4$$
$$x = 1$$
$$y = 3(1) = 3$$
The proposed solution is $(1, 3)$
Check: $3 = 3(1) \qquad 1 + 3 = 4$
$\qquad\qquad 3 = 3, \text{ true} \qquad 4 = 4, \text{ true}$
The pair $(1, 3)$ satisfies both equations.
The system's solution set is $\{(1, 3)\}$.

14. $y = 2x \qquad\quad x + y = 6$
$$x + 2x = 6$$
$$3x = 6$$
$$x = 2$$
$$y = 2(2) = 4$$
The proposed solution is $(2, 4)$.

Check: $4 = 2(2) \qquad 2 + 4 = 6$
$\qquad\qquad 4 = 4, \text{ true} \qquad 6 = 6, \text{ true}$
The pair $(2, 4)$ satisfies both equations.
The system's solution set is $\{(2, 4)\}$.

15. $y = 2x - 9 \qquad x + 3y = 8$
$$x + 3(2x - 9) = 8$$
$$x + 6x - 27 = 8$$
$$7x = 35$$
$$x = 5$$
$$y = 2(5) - 9 = 1$$
The proposed solution is $(5, 1)$.
Check:
$$1 = 2(5) - 9 \quad 5 + 3(1) = 8$$
$$1 = 10 - 9 \qquad\quad 5 + 3 = 8$$
$$1 = 1, \text{ true} \qquad\quad 8 = 8, \text{ true}$$
The pair $(5, 1)$ satisfies both equations.
The system's solution set is $\{(5, 1)\}$.

16. $y = 2x + 7 \qquad\qquad 2x - 3y = -13$
$$2x - 3(2x + 7) = -13$$
$$2x - 6x - 21 = -13$$
$$-4x = 8$$
$$x = -2$$
$$y = 2(-2) + 7 = -4 + 7 = 3$$
The proposed solution is $(-2, 3)$.
Check:
$$2(-2) - 3(3) = -13 \qquad\quad 3 = 2(-2) + 7$$
$$-4 - 9 = -13 \qquad\qquad 3 = -4 + 7$$
$$-13 = -13, \text{ true} \quad 3 = 3, \text{ true}$$
The pair $(-2, 3)$ satisfies both equations.
The system's solution set is $\{(-2, 3)\}$.

17. $x + 3y = 5$
$$x = 5 - 3y \qquad 4x + 5y = 13$$
$$4(5 - 3y) + 5y = 13$$
$$20 - 12y + 5y = 13$$
$$20 - 7y = 13$$
$$-7y = -7$$
$$y = 1$$
$$x = 5 - 3(1) = 2$$
The proposed solution is $(2, 1)$.
Check:
$$2 + 3(1) = 5 \qquad\quad 4(2) + 5(1) = 13$$
$$5 = 5, \text{ true} \qquad\qquad 8 + 5 = 13$$
$$\qquad\qquad\qquad\qquad 13 = 13, \text{ true}$$
The pair $(2, 1)$ satisfies both equations.
The system's solution set is $\{(2, 1)\}$.

18. Substitute $2x+7$ for y into $2x-y=-15$

$$2x-\overbrace{(2x+7)}^{y}=-15$$
$$2x-2x-7=-15$$
$$-7=-15,\text{ false}$$

The system's solution set is $\varnothing$.

19. $2x-y=-5$
$y=2x+5 \quad x+5y=14$
$x+5(2x+5)=14$
$x+10x+25=14$
$\qquad 11x=-11$
$\qquad\quad x=-1$
$y=2(-1)+5=-2+5=3$
The proposed solution is $(-1, 3)$.
Check:
$2(-1)-3=-5 \qquad -1+5(3)=14$
$\quad -2-3=-5 \qquad\quad -1+15=14$
$\qquad -5=-5,\text{ true} \qquad 14=14,\text{ true}$
The pair $(-1, 3)$ satisfies both equations.
The system's solution set is $\{(-1, 3)\}$.

20. $x-4y=0$
$x=4y \qquad\qquad 2x+3y=11$
$2(4y)+3y=11$
$\quad 8y+3y=11$
$\qquad 11y=11$
$\qquad\quad y=1$
$x=4(1)=4$
The proposed solution is $(4, 1)$.
Check:
$4-4(1)=0 \qquad 2(4)+3(1)=11$
$\quad 0=0,\text{ true} \qquad 8+3=11$
$\qquad\qquad\qquad\qquad 11=11,\text{ true}$
The pair $(4, 1)$ satisfies both equations.
The system's solution set is $\{(4, 1)\}$.

21. $2x-y=3$
$y=2x-3 \qquad 5x-2y=10$
$5x-2(2x-3)=10$
$\quad 5x-4x+6=10$
$\qquad\qquad x=4$
$y=2(4)-3=8-3=5$
The proposed solution is $(4, 5)$.
Check:
$2(4)-5=3 \qquad 5(4)-2(5)=10$
$\quad 8-5=3 \qquad\quad 20-10=10$
$\qquad 3=3,\text{ true} \qquad 10=10,\text{ true}$
The pair $(4, 5)$ satisfies both equations.
The system's solution set is $\{(4, 5)\}$.

22. $-x+3y=10$
$x=3y-10 \qquad\qquad 2x+8y=-6$
$2(3y-10)+8y=-6$
$\quad 6y-20+8y=-6$
$\qquad\qquad 14y=14$
$\qquad\qquad\quad y=1$
$x=3(1)-10=-7$
The proposed solution is $(-7, 1)$.
Check:
$-(-7)+3(1)=10 \qquad 2(-7)+8(1)=-6$
$\quad 7+3=10 \qquad\qquad -14+8=-6$
$\qquad 10=10,\text{ true} \qquad -6=-6,\text{ true}$
The pair $(-7, 1)$ satisfies both equations.
The system's solution set is $\{(-7, 1)\}$.

23. $x+8y=6$
$x=6-8y \qquad 2x+4y=-3$
$2(6-8y)+4y=-3$
$\quad 12-16y+4y=-3$
$\qquad\quad -12y=-15$
$$\frac{-12y}{-12}=\frac{-15}{-12}$$
$$y=\frac{15}{12}=\frac{5}{4}$$
$x=6-8\left(\frac{5}{4}\right)=6-10=-4$

The proposed solution is $\left(-4,\dfrac{5}{4}\right)$.

Check:
$-4+8\left(\dfrac{5}{4}\right)=6 \quad 2(-4)+4\left(\dfrac{5}{4}\right)=-3$
$\quad -4+10=6 \qquad\qquad -8+5=-3$
$\qquad 6=6,\text{ true} \qquad\qquad -3=-3,\text{ true}$

The pair $\left(-4,\dfrac{5}{4}\right)$ satisfies both equations.

The system's solution set is $\left\{\left(-4,\dfrac{5}{4}\right)\right\}$.

24. $-4x+y=-11$
$y=-11+4x \qquad 2x-3y=5$
$2x-3(-11+4x)=5$
$\quad 2x+33-12x=5$
$\qquad\qquad -10x=-28$
$$x=\frac{28}{10}$$
$$x=\frac{14}{5}$$

$$y = -11 + 4\left(\frac{14}{5}\right) = \frac{-55}{5} + \frac{56}{5} = \frac{1}{5}$$

The proposed solution is $\left(\frac{14}{5}, \frac{1}{5}\right)$.

Check:

$$-4\left(\frac{14}{5}\right) + \left(\frac{1}{5}\right) = -11 \qquad 2\left(\frac{14}{5}\right) - 3\left(\frac{1}{5}\right) = 5$$

$$\frac{-56}{5} + \frac{1}{5} = -11 \qquad\qquad \frac{28}{5} - \frac{3}{5} = 5$$

$$\frac{-55}{5} = -11 \qquad\qquad\qquad \frac{25}{5} = 5$$

$$-11 = -11, \text{true} \qquad\qquad\qquad 5 = 5, \text{true}$$

The pair $\left(\frac{14}{5}, \frac{1}{5}\right)$ satisfies both equations.

The system's solution set is $\left\{\left(\frac{14}{5}, \frac{1}{5}\right)\right\}$.

25.
$$\begin{aligned} x + y &= 1 \\ x - y &= 3 \\ \hline 2x &= 4 \\ x &= 2 \end{aligned}$$
$$x + y = 1$$
$$2 + y = 1$$
$$y = -1$$
Check: $2 + (-1) = 1 \quad 2 - (-1) = 3$
$$1 = 1, \text{true} \qquad 3 = 3, \text{ true}$$
The solution set is $\{(2, -1)\}$.

26.
$$\begin{aligned} x + y &= 6 \\ x - y &= -2 \\ \hline 2x &= 4 \\ x &= 2 \end{aligned}$$
$$x + y = 6$$
$$2 + y = 6$$
$$y = 4$$
Check: $2 + 4 = 6 \qquad 2 - 4 = -2$
$$6 = 6, \text{true} \qquad -2 = -2, \text{true}$$
The solution set is $\{(2, 4)\}$.

27.
$$\begin{aligned} 2x + 3y &= 6 \\ 2x - 3y &= 6 \\ \hline 4x &= 12 \\ x &= 3 \end{aligned}$$
$$2x + 3y = 6$$
$$2 \cdot 3 + 3y = 6$$
$$6 + 3y = 6$$
$$3y = 0$$
$$y = 0$$
Check:
$$\cdot 2(3) + 3(0) = 6 \qquad 2(3) - 3(0) = 6$$
$$6 + 0 = 6 \qquad\qquad 6 - 0 = 6$$
$$6 = 6, \text{true} \qquad\qquad 6 = 6, \text{true}$$
The solution set is $\{(3, 0)\}$.

28.
$$\begin{aligned} 3x + 2y &= 14 \\ 3x - 2y &= 10 \\ \hline 6x &= 24 \\ x &= 4 \end{aligned}$$
$$3x + 2y = 14$$
$$3 \cdot 4 + 2y = 14$$
$$12 + 2y = 14$$
$$2y = 2$$
$$y = 1$$
Check:
$$3(4) + 2(1) = 14 \qquad 3(4) - 2(1) = 10$$
$$12 + 2 = 14 \qquad\qquad 12 - 2 = 10$$
$$14 = 14, \text{true} \qquad\qquad 10 = 10, \text{true}$$
The solution set is $\{(4, 1)\}$.

29.
$$\begin{array}{llll} x + 2y = 2 & \text{Mult. by 3.} & 3x + 6y = 6 \\ -4x + 3y = 25 & \text{Mult. by} -2. & 8x - 6y = -50 \\ & & \hline \\ & & 11x = -44 \\ & & x = -4 \end{array}$$
$$x + 2y = 2$$
$$-4 + 2y = 2$$
$$2y = 6$$
$$y = 3$$
Check:
$$-4 + 2(3) = 2 \qquad -4(-4) + 3(3) = 25$$
$$-4 + 6 = 2 \qquad\qquad 16 + 9 = 25$$
$$2 = 2, \text{true} \qquad\qquad 25 = 25, \text{ true}$$
The solution set is $\{(-4, 3)\}$.

30. $2x - 7y = 2$ No change. $2x - 7y = 2$

$3x + y = -20$ Mult. by 7. $\underline{21x + 7y = -140}$

$23x = -138$

$x = -\frac{138}{23}$

$x = -6$

$3x + y = -20$

$3(-6) + y = -20$

$-18 + y = -20$

$y = -2$

Check:

$2(-6) - 7(-2) = 2 \qquad 3(-6) + (-2) = -20$

$-12 + 14 = 2 \qquad\qquad -18 - 2 = -20$

$2 = 2, \text{true} \qquad\qquad -20 = -20, \text{true}$

The solution set is $\{(-6, -2)\}$.

31. $4x + 3y = 15$ Mult. by 5. $20x + 15y = 75$

$2x - 5y = 1$ Mult. by 3. $\underline{6x - 15y = 3}$

$26x = 78$

$x = 3$

$4x + 3y = 15$

$4 \cdot 3 + 3y = 15$

$12 + 3y = 15$

$3y = 3$

$y = 1$

Check:

$4(3) + 3(1) = 15 \qquad 2(3) - 5(1) = 1$

$12 + 3 = 15 \qquad\qquad 6 - 5 = 1$

$15 = 15, \text{true} \qquad 1 = 1, \text{true}$

The solution set is $\{(3, 1)\}$.

32. $3x - 7y = 13$ Mult. by 5. $15x - 35y = 65$

$6x + 5y = 7$ Mult. by 7. $\underline{42x + 35y = 49}$

$57x = 114$

$x = \frac{114}{57}$

$x = 2$

$6x + 5y = 7$

$6 \cdot 2 + 5y = 7$

$12 + 5y = 7$

$5y = -5$

$y = -1$

Check:

$3x - 7y = 13 \qquad\qquad 6x + 5y = 7$

$3(2) - 7(-1) = 13 \qquad 6(2) + 5(-1) = 7$

$6 + 7 = 13 \qquad\qquad 12 - 5 = 7$

$13 = 13, \text{true} \qquad\qquad 7 = 7, \text{true}$

The solution set is $\{(2, -1)\}$.

33. $3x - 4y = 11$ Mult. by 3. $9x - 12y = 33$

$2x + 3y = -4$ Mult. by 4. $\underline{8x + 12y = -16}$

$17x = 17$

$x = 1$

$2x + 3y = -4$

$2 \cdot 1 + 3y = -4$

$2 + 3y = -4$

$3y = -6$

$y = -2$

Check:

$3(1) - 4(-2) = 11$

$3 + 8 = 11$

$11 = 11, \text{true}$

$2(1) + 3(-2) = -4$

$2 - 6 = -4$

$-4 = -4, \text{true}$

The solution set is $\{(1, -2)\}$.

34. $2x + 3y = -16$ Mult. by 10. $20x + 30y = -160$
$5x - 10y = 30$ Mult. by 3. $\underline{15x - 30y = \ \ 90}$
$$35x \qquad = -70$$
$$x \qquad = \tfrac{-70}{35}$$
$$x \qquad = -2$$

$$2x + 3y = -16$$
$$2(-2) + 3y = -16$$
$$-4 + 3y = -16$$
$$3y = -12$$
$$y = -4$$
Check:
$$2(-2) + 3(-4) = -16$$
$$-4 - 12 = -16$$
$$-16 = -16, \text{true}$$
$$5(-2) - 10(-4) = 30$$
$$-10 + 40 = 30$$
$$30 = 30, \text{true}$$
The solution set is $\{(-2, -4)\}$.

35. $2x = 3y - 4$ Rearrange and Mult. by 3. $6x - 9y = -12$
$-6x + 12y = 6$ No change. $\underline{-6x + 12y = 6}$
$$3y = -6$$
$$y = -2$$

$$2x = 3y - 4$$
$$2x = 3(-2) - 4$$
$$2x = -6 - 4$$
$$2x = -10$$
$$x = -5$$
Check:
$$2(-5) = 3(-2) - 4 \qquad -6(-5) + 12(-2) = 6$$
$$-10 = -6 - 4 \qquad\qquad 30 - 24 = 6$$
$$-10 = -10, \text{true} \qquad\quad 6 = 6, \text{true}$$
The solution set is $\{(-5, -2)\}$.

36. $5x = 4y - 8$ Rearrange and Mult. by 7. $35x - 28y = -56$
$3x + 7y = 14$ Mult. by 4. $\underline{12x + 28y = 56}$
$$47x = 0$$
$$x = 0$$

$$5x = 4y - 8$$
$$5 \cdot 0 = 4y - 8$$
$$0 = 4y - 8$$
$$8 = 4y$$
$$2 = y$$

Check:
$$5(0) = 4(2) - 8 \qquad 3(0) + 7(2) = 14$$
$$0 = 8 - 8 \qquad\qquad 0 + 14 = 14$$
$$0 = 0, \text{true} \qquad\quad 14 = 14, \text{true}$$
The solution set is $\{(0, 2)\}$.

37. $x = 9 - 2y \quad x + 2y = 13$
$$(9 - 2y) + 2y = 13$$
$$9 = 13 \quad \text{false}$$
The system has no solution.
The solution set is the empty set, $\varnothing$.

38. $y = 2 - 3x \qquad\qquad 6x + 2y = 7$
$$6x + 2(2 - 3x) = 7$$
$$6x + 4 - 6x = 7$$
$$4 = 7 \text{ false}$$
The system has no solution.
The solution set is the empty set, $\varnothing$.

39. $y = 3x - 5 \quad 21x - 35 = 7y$
$$21x - 35 = 7(3x - 5)$$
$$21x - 35 = 21x - 35$$
$$21x - 21x = 35 - 35$$
$$0 = 0, \text{true}$$
The system has infinitely many solutions.
The solution set is $\{(x, y) | y = 3x - 5\}$.

40. $y = 3x - 4 \qquad\qquad 9x - 3y = 12$
$$9x - 3(3x - 4) = 12$$
$$9x - 9x + 12 = 12$$
$$12 = 12, \text{true}$$
The system has infinitely many solutions.
The solution set is $\{(x, y) | y = 3x - 4\}$.

41. $3x - 2y = -5$ No change. $3x - 2y = -5$
$4x + y = 8$ Mult. by 2. $\underline{8x + 2y = 16}$
$$11x = 11$$
$$x = 1$$

$$4x + y = 8$$
$$4(1) + y = 8$$
$$y = 4$$
Check:
$$3(1) - 2(4) = -5 \qquad 4(1) + (4) = 8$$
$$3 - 8 = -5 \qquad\qquad 4 + 4 = 8$$
$$-5 = -5, \text{true} \qquad 8 = 8, \text{true}$$
The solution set is $\{(1, 4)\}$.

42.

$2x+5y=-4$ No change. $2x+5y=-4$

$3x-\;y=11$ Multiply by 5. $\underline{15x-5y=55}$

$$17x\quad\;\;=51$$
$$x=\frac{51}{17}$$
$$x=3$$

$3x-y=11$

$3(3)-y=11$

$9-y=11$

$y=-2$

Check:

$2(3)+5(-2)=-4$ $3(3)-(-2)=11$

$6-10=-4$ $9+2=11$

$-4=-4$ true $11=11$ true

The solution set is $\{(3,-2)\}$.

43. $x+3y=2$

$x=2-3y$ $3x+9y=6$

$3(2-3y)+9y=6$

$6-9y+9y=6$

$6=6$ true

The system has infinitely many solutions.

The solution set is $\left\{(x,y)\,|\,x+3y=2\right\}$.

44. $4x-2y=2$ No change. $4x-2y=2$

$2x-\;y=1$ Mult. by -2. $\underline{-4x+2y=-2}$

$$0=0\ \text{true}$$

The system has infinitely many solutions.

The solution set is $\left\{(x,\;y)\,|\,4x-2y=2\right\}$.

45. $x+y=7$

$\underline{x-y=-1}$

$2x=6$

$x=3$

$y=7-x=7-3=4$

The numbers are 3 and 4.

46. $x+y=2$

$\underline{x-y=8}$

$2x=10$

$x=5$

$y=2-x$

$y=2-5=-3$

The numbers are -3 and 5.

47. $3x-y=1$ Multiply by 2. $6x-2y=2$

$x+2y=12$ No change. $\underline{x+2y=12}$

$$7x=14$$
$$x=2$$

$3x-y=1$

$3(2)-y=1$

$-y=-5$

$y=5$

The numbers are 2 and 5.

48. $3x+2y=8$ No change. $3x+2y=8$

$2x-\;y=3$ Multiply by 2. $\underline{4x-2y=6}$

$$7x=14$$
$$x=2$$

$2x-y=3$

$y=2x-3$

$y=2(2)-3$

$y=1$

The numbers are 2 and 1.

49. Let x represent calories in a pan pizza.

Let y represent calories in a beef burrito.

$x+2y=1980$ $\xrightarrow{\text{Mult. by }-2}$ $-2x-4y=-3960$

$2x+y=2670$ $\xrightarrow{\text{No change}}$ $\underline{2x\;+y=\;2670}$

$$-3y=-1290$$
$$y=430$$

$x+2y=1980$

$x+2(430)=1980$

$x+860=1980$

$x=1120$

A pan pizza has 1120 calories and a beef burrito has 430 calories.

50. Let x represent calories in a Kung Pao chicken.
Let y represent calories in a Big Mac.

$$x + 2y = 2620 \xrightarrow{\text{Mult. by } -2} -2x - 4y = -5240$$
$$2x + y = 3740 \xrightarrow{\text{No change}} \underline{2x + y = 3740}$$
$$-3y = -1500$$
$$y = 500$$

$$x + 2y = 2620$$
$$x + 2(500) = 2620$$
$$x + 1000 = 2620$$
$$x = 1620$$

A Kung Pao chicken has 1620 calories and a Big Mac has 500 calories.

51. Substitute $-0.4x + 28$ for y in the equation $0.07x + y = 15$:

$$0.07x + \overbrace{(-0.4x + 28)}^{y} = 15$$
$$0.07x - 0.4x + 28 = 15$$
$$-0.33x + 28 = 15$$
$$-0.33x = -13$$
$$x \approx 39.39 \text{ years}$$

When $x \approx 39.39,$ $y \approx -0.4(39.39) + 28$
$y \approx 12.24$ car accident deaths per 100,000

Using the other equation, $y \approx 15 - 0.07(39.39)$
$y \approx 12.24$ gunfire deaths per 100,000

In 39 years after 1965, or 2004, there will be about 12.24 deaths per 100,000 from car accidents and from gunfire. This is represented by the point (2004, 12.24).

52. Substitute $0.57x + 20$ for M in the equation $M = -0.57x + 80.$:

$$\overbrace{(0.57x + 20)}^{M} = -0.57x + 80$$
$$1.14x = 60$$
$$x \approx 52.63 \text{ years}$$

In about 53 years after 1994, or 2047, carbonated and noncarbonated beverages will have equal market shares.

53. Let x represent the number of years after 1985.
Let y represent the average weekly earnings of a high school graduate.

This question seeks to find the year in which the average college graduate earns twice as much as a high school graduate. Thus the average college graduate's earnings will be $2y$.

College graduate's earnings will be: $2y = 508 + 25x$
High school graduate's earnings will be: $y = 345 + 9x$

Substitute $345 + 9x$ for y in the equation $2y = 508 + 25x$:

$$2\overbrace{(345 + 9x)}^{y} = 508 + 25x$$
$$690 + 18x = 508 + 25x$$
$$182 = 7x$$
$$x = 26 \text{ years}$$

When $x = 26,$ $y = 345 + 9(26)$ and $2y = 508 + 25(26)$
$y = \$579$ $2y = \$1158$

In 26 years after 1985, or 2011, average college graduate's earnings will be $1158 per week and the average high school graduate will earn $579 per week.

54. Let x represent the number of years after 1985.
Let y represent the average weekly earnings of people with less than four years of high school.

This question seeks to find the year in which the average college graduate earns three times as much as a person with less than four years of high school. Thus the average college graduate's earnings will be $3y$.

College graduate's earnings will be: $3y = 508 + 25x$

Earnings of people with less than four years of high school will be: $y = 270 + 4x$

Substitute $270 + 4x$ for y in the equation $3y = 508 + 25x$:

$3(\overbrace{270 + 4x}^{y}) = 508 + 25x$

$810 + 12x = 508 + 25x$

$302 = 13x$

$x \approx 23$ years

When $x \approx 23$, $y \approx 270 + 4(23)$ and $3y \approx 508 + 25(23)$

$y \approx \$362$ $3y \approx \$1083$

In 23 years after 1985, or 2008, average college graduate's earnings will be $\$1083$ per week and the average person with less than four years of high school will earn $\$362$ per week.

55-66. Answers will vary.

67. Let x be the number of people downstairs and y the number of people upstairs.

$x + 1 = y - 1$ $x = y - 2$

$2x = y + 1$ $2(y - 2) = y + 1$

$2y - 4 = y + 1$

$y = 5$

$x = 5 - 2$

$x = 3$

There are 3 people downstairs and 5 people upstairs.

Check Points 7.6

1. To graph $2x - 4y \geq 8$, begin by graphing $2x - 4y = 8$ with a solid line because $\geq$ includes equality.

x-intercept:	y-intercept:	test point $(0, 0)$:
$2x - 4(0) = 8$	$2(0) - 4y = 8$	$2x - 4y \geq 8$
$2x = 8$	$-4y = 8$	$2(0) - 4(0) \geq 8$
$x = 4$	$y = -2$	$0 \geq 8$, false

Since the test point makes the inequality <u>false</u>, shade the half-plane not containing test point $(0, 0)$.

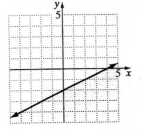

2. To graph $y > -\frac{3}{4}x$, begin by graphing $y = -\frac{3}{4}x$ with a dashed line because $>$ does not include equality.

test point $(1, 1)$:

$y > -\frac{3}{4}x$

$1 > -\frac{3}{4} \cdot 1$

$1 > -\frac{3}{4}$, true

Since the test point makes the inequality <u>true</u>, shade the half-plane <u>containing</u> test point (1, 1).

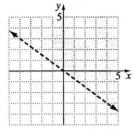

3. To graph $x + 2y > 4$, begin by graphing $x + 2y = 4$ with a dashed line because > does not include equality.

   <u>test point (0, 0):</u>

   $x + 2y > 4$

   $0 > 4$

   $0 + 2(0) > 4$, false

   Since the test point makes the inequality <u>false</u>, shade the half-plane <u>not containing</u> test point (0, 0).
   To graph $2x - 3y \leq -6$, begin by graphing $2x - 3y = -6$ with a solid line because $\leq$ does include equality.

   <u>test point (0, 0):</u>

   $2x - 3y \leq -6$

   $0 - 0 \leq -6$

   $0 \leq -6$, false

   Since the test point makes the inequality <u>false</u>, shade the half-plane <u>not containing</u> test point (0, 0).
   The graph shows the intersection of the two half-planes.

   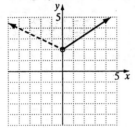

4. To graph $x < 3$, begin by graphing $x = 3$ with a dashed line because < does not include equality.
   The graph of $x < 3$ is the half-plane to the left of the dashed line.
   To graph $y \geq -1$, begin by graphing $y = -1$ with a solid line because $\geq$ does include equality.
   The graph of $y \geq -1$ is the half-plane above the solid line.
   The graph shows the intersection of the two half-planes.

   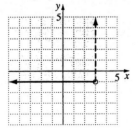

5. **a.** Another point in the target zone is (30, 140). This means that a pulse rate of 140 beats per minute is within the target zone for a 30-year-old person engaged in aerobic exercise.

    b. The pair (30, 140) makes each inequality of the system true.

$$2a + 3p \geq 450 \qquad\qquad a + p \leq 190$$
$$2(30) + 3(140) \geq 450 \qquad 30 + 140 \leq 190$$
$$60 + 420 \geq 450 \qquad\qquad 170 \leq 190, \text{ true}$$
$$480 \geq 450, \text{ true}$$

Exercise Set 7.6

1. To graph $x + y \geq 2$, begin by graphing $x + y = 2$ with a solid line because $\geq$ includes equality.

    test point (0, 0):

    $x + y \geq 2$

    $0 + 0 \geq 2$

    $0 \geq 2$, false

    Since the test point makes the inequality <u>false</u>, shade the half-plane <u>not containing</u> test point (0, 0).

    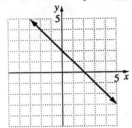

2. To graph $x - y \leq 1$, begin by graphing $x - y = 1$ with a solid line because $\leq$ includes equality.

    test point (0, 0):

    $x - y \leq 1$

    $0 - 0 \leq 1$

    $0 \leq 1$, true

    Since the test point makes the inequality <u>true</u>, shade the half-plane <u>containing</u> test point (0, 0).

    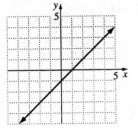

3. To graph $3x - y \geq 6$, begin by graphing $3x - y = 6$ with a solid line because $\geq$ includes equality.

    test point (0, 0):

    $3x - y \geq 6$

    $3(0) - 0 \geq 6$

    $0 \geq 6$, false

    Since the test point makes the inequality <u>false</u>, shade the half-plane <u>not containing</u> test point (0, 0).

    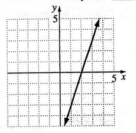

4. To graph $3x + y \leq 3$, begin by graphing $3x + y = 3$ with a solid line because $\leq$ includes equality.

    test point (0, 0):

    $3x + y \leq 3$

    $3(0) + 0 \leq 3$

    $0 \leq 3$, true

    Since the test point makes the inequality <u>true</u>, shade the half-plane <u>containing</u> test point (0, 0).

    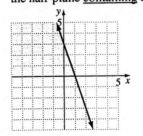

5. To graph $2x + 3y > 12$, begin by graphing
$2x + 3y = 12$ with a dashed line because $>$ does not
include equality.

   test point (0, 0):

$$2x + 3y > 12$$
$$2(0) + 3(0) > 12$$
$$0 > 12, \text{ false}$$

Since the test point makes the inequality <u>false</u>,
shade the half-plane <u>not containing</u> test point (0, 0).

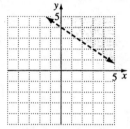

6. To graph $2x - 5y < 10$, begin by graphing
$2x - 5y = 10$ with a dashed line because $<$ does not
include equality.

   test point (0, 0):

$$2x - 5y < 10$$
$$2(0) - 5(0) < 10$$
$$0 < 10, \text{ true}$$

Since the test point makes the inequality <u>true</u>, shade
the half-plane <u>containing</u> test point (0, 0).

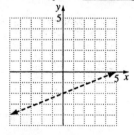

7. To graph $5x + 3y \leq -15$, begin by graphing
$5x + 3y = -15$ with a solid line because $\leq$ includes
equality.

   test point (0, 0):

$$5x + 3y \leq -15$$
$$5(0) + 3(0) \leq -15$$
$$0 \leq -15, \text{ false}$$

Since the test point makes the inequality <u>false</u>,

shade the half-plane <u>not containing</u> test point (0, 0).

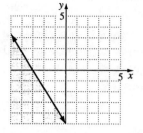

8. To graph $3x + 4y \leq -12$, begin by graphing
$3x + 4y = -12$ with a solid line because $\leq$ includes
equality.

   test point (0, 0):

$$3x + 4y \leq -12$$
$$3(0) + 4(0) \leq -12$$
$$0 \leq -12, \text{ false}$$

Since the test point makes the inequality <u>false</u>,
shade the half-plane <u>not containing</u> test point (0, 0).

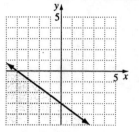

9. To graph $2y - 3x > 6$, begin by graphing
$2y - 3x = 6$ with a dashed line because $>$ does not
include equality.

   test point (0, 0):

$$2y - 3x > 6$$
$$2(0) - 3(0) > 6$$
$$0 > 6, \text{ false}$$

Since the test point makes the inequality <u>false</u>,
shade the half-plane <u>not containing</u> test point (0, 0).

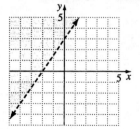

10. To graph $2y - x > 4$, begin by graphing $2y - x = 4$ with a dashed line because $>$ does not include equality.

test point (0, 0):

$2y - x > 4$

$2(0) - 0 > 4$

$0 > 4$, false

Since the test point makes the inequality <u>false</u>, shade the half-plane <u>not containing</u> test point (0, 0).

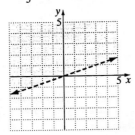

11. To graph $y > \frac{1}{3}x$, begin by graphing $y = \frac{1}{3}x$ as a dashed line passing through the origin with a slope of $\frac{1}{3}$, then shade above the line.

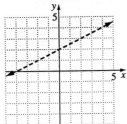

12. To graph $y > \frac{1}{4}x$, begin by graphing $y = \frac{1}{4}x$ as a dashed line passing through the origin with a slope of $\frac{1}{4}$, then shade above the line.

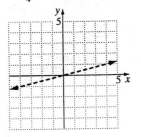

13. To graph $y \le 3x + 2$, begin by graphing $y = 3x + 2$ as a solid line passing through (0, 2) with a slope of

$\frac{3}{1}$, then shade below the line.

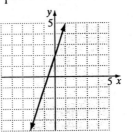

14. To graph $y \le 2x - 1$, begin by graphing $y = 2x - 1$ as a solid line passing through $(0, -1)$ with a slope of $\frac{2}{1}$, then shade below the line.

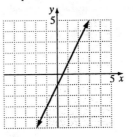

15. To graph $y < -\frac{1}{4}x$, begin by graphing $y = -\frac{1}{4}x$ as a dashed line passing through the origin with a slope of $-\frac{1}{4}$, then shade below the line.

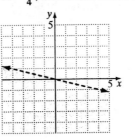

16. To graph $y < -\frac{1}{3}x$, begin by graphing $y = -\frac{1}{3}x$ as a dashed line passing through the origin with a slope of $-\frac{1}{3}$, then shade below the line.

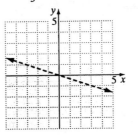

17. To graph $x \le 2$, begin by graphing $x = 2$ as a solid vertical line passing through $x = 2$, then shade to the left of the line.

18. To graph $x \le -4$, begin by graphing $x = -4$ as a solid vertical line passing through $x = -4$, then shade to the left of the line.

19. To graph $y > -4$, begin by graphing $y = -4$ as a dashed horizontal line passing through $y = -4$, then shade above the line.

20. To graph $y > -2$, begin by graphing $y = -2$ as a dashed horizontal line passing through $y = -2$, then shade above the line.

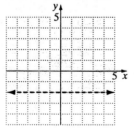

21. To graph $y \ge 0$, begin by graphing $y = 0$ as a solid horizontal line passing through $y = 0$, then shade above the line.

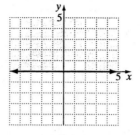

22. To graph $x \ge 0$, begin by graphing $x = 0$ as a solid horizontal line passing through $x = 0$, then shade to the right of the line.

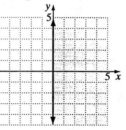

23. $3x + 6y \le 6$
$2x + y \le 8$

Graph $3x + 6y = 6$ as a solid line.
If $x = 0$, then $y = 1$ and if $y = 0$, then $x = 2$.
Because (0, 0) makes the inequality true, shade the half-plane containing (0, 0).
Graph $2x + y = 8$ as a solid line.
If $x = 0$, then $y = 8$ and if $y = 0$, then $x = 4$.
Because (0, 0) makes the inequality true, shade the half-plane containing (0, 0).

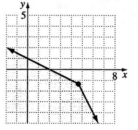

24. $x - y \geq 4$

$x + y \leq 6$

Graph $x - y = 4$ as a solid line.
If $x = 0$, then $y = -4$ and if $y = 0$, then $x = 4$.
Because $(0, 0)$ makes the inequality false, shade the half-plane not containing $(0, 0)$.
Graph $x + y = 6$ as a solid line.
If $x = 0$, then $y = 6$ and if $y = 0$, then $x = 6$.
Because $(0, 0)$ makes the inequality true, shade the half-plane containing $(0, 0)$.

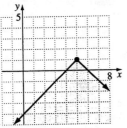

25. $2x + y < 3$

$x - y > 2$

Graph $2x + y = 3$ as a dashed line.

If $x = 0$, then $y = 3$ and if $y = 0$, then $x = \dfrac{3}{2}$.

Because $(0, 0)$ makes the inequality true, shade the half-plane containing $(0, 0)$.
Graph $x - y = 2$ as a dashed line.
If $x = 0$, then $y = -2$ and if $y = 0$, then $x = 2$.
Because $(0, 0)$ makes the inequality false, shade the half-plane not containing $(0, 0)$.

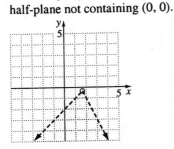

26. $x + y < 4$

$4x - 2y < 6$

Graph $x + y = 4$ as a dashed line.
If $x = 0$, then $y = 4$ and if $y = 0$, then $x = 4$.
Because $(0, 0)$ makes the inequality true, shade the half-plane containing $(0, 0)$.
Graph $4x - 2y = 6$ as a dashed line.

If $x = 0$, then $y = -3$ and if $y = 0$, then $x = \dfrac{3}{2}$.

Because $(0, 0)$ makes the inequality true, shade the

half-plane containing $(0, 0)$.

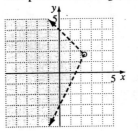

27. $2x + y < 4$

$x - y > 4$

Graph $2x + y = 4$ as a dashed line.
If $x = 0$, then $y = 4$ and if $y = 0$, then $x = 2$.
Because $(0, 0)$ makes the inequality true, shade the half-plane containing $(0, 0)$
Graph $x - y = 4$ as a dashed line.
If $x = 0$, then $y = -4$. and if $y = 0$, then $x = 4$.
Because $(0, 0)$ makes the inequality false, shade the half-plane not containing $(0, 0)$.

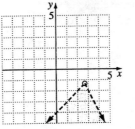

28. $2x - y < 3$

$x + y < 6$

Graph $2x - y = 3$ as a dashed line.

If $x = 0$, then $y = -3$ and if $y = 0$, then $x = \dfrac{3}{2}$.

Because $(0, 0)$ makes the inequality true, shade the half-plane containing $(0, 0)$.
Graph $x + y = 6$ as a dashed line.
If $x = 0$, then $y = 6$ and if $y = 0$, then $x = 6$.
Because $(0, 0)$ makes the inequality true, shade the half-plane containing $(0, 0)$.

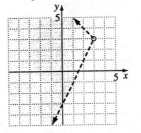

29. $x \geq 2$
$\quad y \leq 3$

Graph $x = 2$ as a solid line.
The points in the half-plane to the right of the line satisfy $x > 2$.
Graph $y = 3$ as a solid line.
The points in the half-plane below the line satisfy $y < 3$.

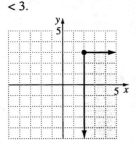

30. $x \geq 4$
$\quad y \leq 2$

Graph $x = 4$ as a solid line.
The points in the half-plane to the right of the line satisfy $x > 4$.
Graph $y = 2$ as a solid line.
The points in the half-plane below the line satisfy $y < 2$.

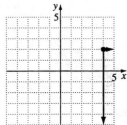

31. $x \leq 5$
$\quad y > -3$

Graph $x = 5$ as a solid line.
The points in the half-plane to the left of the line satisfy $x < 5$.
Graph $y = -3$ as a dashed line.
The points in the half-plane above the line satisfy $y > -3$.

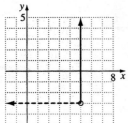

32. $x \leq 3$
$\quad y > -1$

Graph $x = 3$ as a solid line.
the points in the half-plane to the left of the line satisfy $x < 3$.
Graph $y = -1$ as a dashed line.
The points in the half-plane above the line satisfy $y > -1$.

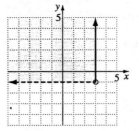

33. $x - y \leq 1$
$\quad x \geq 2$

Graph $x - y = 1$ as a solid line.
If $x = 0$, then $y = -1$ and if $y = 0$, then $x = 1$.
Because $(0, 0)$ satisfies the inequality, shade the half-plane containing $(0, 0)$.
Graph $x = 2$ as a solid line.
The points in the half-plane to the right of $x = 2$ satisfy the inequality $x \geq 2$.

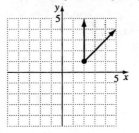

34. $4x - 5y \geq -20$
$\quad x \geq -3$

Graph $4x - 5y = -20$ as a solid line.
If $x = 0$, then $y = 4$ and if $y = 0$, then $x = -5$.
Because $(0, 0)$ satisfies the inequality, shade the half-plane containing $(0, 0)$.
Graph $x = -3$ as a solid line.
The points in the half-plane to the right of $x = -3$ satisfy the inequality $x > -3$.

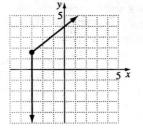

35. To graph $y > 2x - 3$, begin by graphing $y = 2x - 3$ as a dashed line with a y-intercept of -3 and a slope of $\frac{2}{1}$, then shade above the line. To graph $y < -x + 6$, begin by graphing $y = -x + 6$ as a dashed line with a y-intercept of 6 and a slope of $\frac{-1}{1}$, then shade below the line.

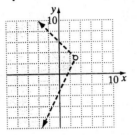

36. To graph $y > -2x + 4$, begin by graphing $y = -2x + 4$ as a dashed line with a y-intercept of 4 and a slope of $\frac{-2}{1}$, then shade below the line. To graph $y < x - 4$, begin by graphing $y = x - 4$ as a dashed line with a y-intercept of -4 and a slope of $\frac{1}{1}$, then shade below this line.

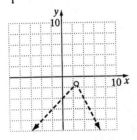

37. To graph $x + 2y \le 4$, begin by graphing $x + 2y = 4$ as a solid line with a y-intercept of 2 and an x-intercept of 4. Because (0, 0) satisfies the inequality, shade the half-plane containing (0, 0). To graph $y \ge x - 3$, begin by graphing $y = x - 3$ as a solid line with a y-intercept of -3 and a slope of $\frac{1}{1}$, then shade above this line.

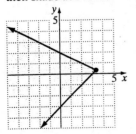

38. To graph $x + y \le 4$, begin by graphing $x + y = 4$ as a solid line with a y-intercept of 4 and an x-intercept of 4. Because (0, 0) satisfies the inequality, shade the half-plane containing (0, 0). To graph $y \ge 2x - 4$, begin by graphing $y = 2x - 4$ as a solid line with a y-intercept of -4 and a slope of $\frac{2}{1}$, then shade above this line.

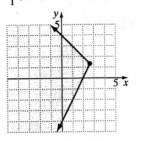

39. Point A is (50, 30). Substitution shows that point A satisfies each inequality for forests.

$T \ge 35$ $5T - 7P < 70$
$50 \ge 35$, true $5(50) - 7(30) < 70$
               $40 < 70$, true

40. Point B is (60, 20). Substitution shows that point B satisfies each inequality for grasslands.

$T \ge 35$ $5T - 7P \ge 70$
$60 \ge 35$, true $5(60) - 7(20) \ge 70$
               $160 \ge 70$, true

$$3T - 35P \le -140$$
$$3(60) - 35(20) \le -140$$
$$-520 \le -140, \text{ true}$$

41. a. $50x + 150y > 2000$

    b.

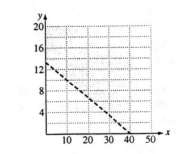

    c. An example of a solution is (30, 8). This represents that 30 children and 8 adults would exceed the 2000 pound weight limit.

42. a. $165x + 110y \le 330$

b.

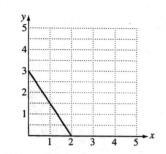

c. An example of a solution is (1, 1). This represents that 1 egg and 1 ounce of meat will satisfy the given dietary restriction.

43. a. $\text{BMI} = \dfrac{703W}{H^2} = \dfrac{703(200)}{(72)^2} \approx 27.1$

b. Locating the point (20, 27.1) on the male chart indicates the man is borderline overweight.

44. a. $\text{BMI} = \dfrac{703W}{H^2} = \dfrac{703(100)}{(50)^2} \approx 28.1$

b. Locating the point (10, 28.1) on the female chart indicates the girl is overweight.

45-49. Answers will vary.

50. c is true.

51. $x + 2y \ge 8$

$\quad x - y \le 2$

$\quad\quad y \le 4$

Graph $x + 2y = 8$ as a solid line.
If $x = 0$, then $y = 4$ and if $y = 0$, then $x = 8$.
Because (0, 0) makes the inequality false, shade the half-plane not containing (0, 0).
Graph $x - y = 2$ as a solid line.
If $x = 0$, then $y = -2$ and if $y = 0$, then $x = 2$.
Because (0, 0) makes the inequality true, shade the half-plane containing (0, 0).

Graph $y = 4$ as a solid line.
The points in the half-plane below the line satisfy $y < 4$.

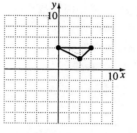

52. Let x represent the number of \$35 tickets sold.
Let y represent the number of \$50 tickets sold.
$x + y \ge 25,000 \quad$ and $\quad 35x + 50y \ge 1,025,000$

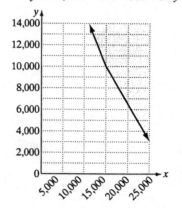

53.

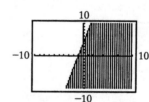

54.

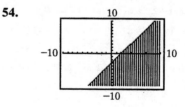

Check Points 7.7

1. The objective function is $z = 25x + 55y$

2. Not more than a total of 80 bookshelves and desks can be manufactured per day. This is represented by the inequality $x + y \leq 80$.

3. Objective function: $z = 25x + 55y$
   Constraints: $x + y \leq 80$
   $$30 \leq x \leq 80$$
   $$10 \leq y \leq 30$$

4. Graph the constraints and find the corners, or vertices, of the region of intersection.

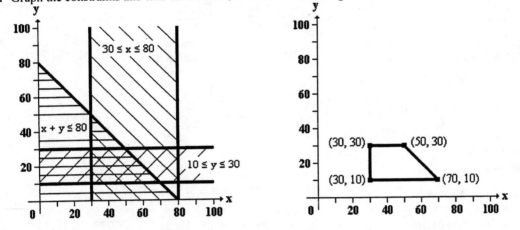

   Find the value of the objective function at each corner of the graphed region.

Corner (x, y)	Objective Function $z = 25x + 55y$ z
(30, 10)	$z = 25(30) + 55(10)$ $= 750 + 550 = 1300$
(30, 30)	$z = 25(30) + 55(30)$ $= 750 + 1650 = 2400$
(50, 30)	$z = 25(50) + 55(30)$ $= 1250 + 1650 = 2900 \leftarrow$ Maximum
(70, 10)	$z = 25(70) + 55(10)$ $= 1750 + 550 = 2300$

The maximum value of z is 2900 and it occurs at the point (50, 30).
In order to maximize profit, 50 bookshelves and 30 desks must be produced each day for a profit of $2900.

Exercise Set 7.7

1. Objective function: $z = 5x + 6y$
   at $(2, 10)$ $z = 5(2) + 6(10) = 70$
   at $(7, 5)$ $z = 5(7) + 6(5) = 65$
   at $(8, 3)$ $z = 5(8) + 6(3) = 58$
   at $(1, 2)$ $z = 5(1) + 6(2) = 17$
   Maximum value = 70
   Minimum value = 17

2. Objective function: $z = 3x + 2y$
   at $(5, 12)$ $z = 3(5) + 2(12) = 39$
   at $(8, 6)$ $z = 3(8) + 2(6) = 36$
   at $(7, 4)$ $z = 3(7) + 2(4) = 29$
   at $(3, 2)$ $z = 3(3) + 2(2) = 13$
   at $(4, 10)$ $z = 3(4) + 2(10) = 32$
   Maximum value = 39
   Minimum value = 13

3. Objective function: $z = 40x + 50y$
   at $(0, 8)$ $z = 40(0) + 50(8) = 400$
   at $(4, 9)$ $z = 40(4) + 50(9) = 610$
   at $(8, 0)$ $z = 40(8) + 50(0) = 320$
   at $(0, 0)$ $z = 40(0) + 50(0) = 0$
   Maximum value = 610
   Minimum value = 0

4. Objective function: $z = 30x + 45y$
   at $(0, 9)$ $z = 30(0) + 45(9) = 405$
   at $(4, 4)$ $z = 30(4) + 45(4) = 300$
   at $(3, 0)$ $z = 30(3) + 45(0) = 90$
   at $(0, 0)$ $z = 30(0) + 45(0) = 0$
   Maximum value = 405
   Minimum value = 0

5. **a.**

   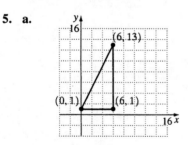

   b.   at $(0, 1)$ $z = 0 + 1 = 1$
   at $(6, 13)$ $z = 6 + 13 = 19$
   at $(6, 1)$ $z = 6 + 1 = 7$

   c.   Maximum = 19
   occurs at $x = 6$ and $y = 13$
   Minimum = 1
   occurs at $x = 0$ and $y = 1$

6. **a.**

   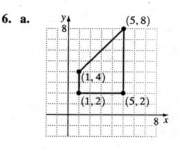

   b.   at $(1, 4)$ $z = 3(1) - 2(4) = -5$
   at $(5, 8)$ $z = 3(5) - 2(8) = -1$
   at $(5, 2)$ $z = 3(5) - 2(2) = 11$
   at $(1, 2)$ $z = 3(1) - 2(2) = -1$

   c.   Maximum = 11
   occurs at $x = 5$ and $y = 2$
   Minimum = -5
   occurs at $x = 1$ and $y = 4$

7. **a.**

   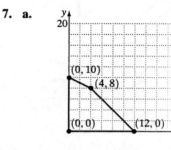

   b.   at $(0, 10)$ $z = 6(0) + 10(10) = 100$
   at $(4, 8)$ $z = 6(4) + 10(8) = 104$
   at $(12, 0)$ $z = 6(12) + 10(0) = 72$
   at $(0, 0)$ $z = 6(0) + 10(0) = 0$

   c.   Maximum = 104
   occurs at $x = 4$ and $y = 8$
   Minimum = 0
   occurs at $x = 0$ and $y = 0$

8. a.

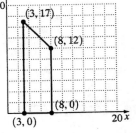

b.

at (0, 2)	$z = 0 + 3(2) = 6$
at (0, 5)	$z = 0 + 3(5) = 15$
at (6, 5)	$z = 6 + 3(5) = 21$
at (6, 0)	$z = 6 + 3(0) = 6$
at (2, 0)	$z = 2 + 3(0) = 2$

c. Maximum = 21
occurs at $x = 6$ and $y = 5$
Minimum = 2
occurs at $x = 2$ and $y = 0$

9. a. $z = 10x + 7y$

b. Constraints
$x + y \le 20$
$x \ge 3$
$x \le 8$

c.

d.

at (3, 0)	$z = 10(3) + 7(0) = 30$
at (8, 0)	$z = 10(8) + 7(0) = 80$
at (3, 17)	$z = 10(3) + 7(17) = 149$
at (8, 12)	$z = 10(8) + 7(12) = 164$

e. The student can earn the maximum amount per week by tutoring for $\underline{8}$ hours per week and working as a teacher's aid for $\underline{12}$ hours per week. The maximum amount that the student can earn each week is $\underline{\$164}$.

10. a. $z = 125x + 200y$

b. $x \le 450$
$y \le 200$
$600x + 900y \le 360,000$

c.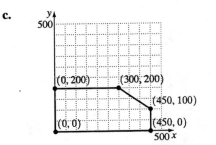

d.

at (0, 0) $z = 125(0) + 200(0) = 0$
at (0, 200) $z = 125(0) + 200(200) = 40,000$
at (300, 200) $z = 125(300) + 200(200)$
     $= 77,500$
at (450, 100) $z = 125(450) + 200(100)$
     $= 76,250$
at (450, 0) $z = 125(450) + 200(0) = 56,250$

e. The television manufacturer will make the greatest profit by manufacturing 300 console televisions each month and 200 wide-screen televisions each month.
The maximum monthly profit is $77,500.

11. Let x represent the number of cartons of food and let y represent the number of cartons of clothing.
Objective function: $z = 12x + 5y$ Constraints: $50x + 20y \le 19{,}000$
$20x + 10y \le 8000$

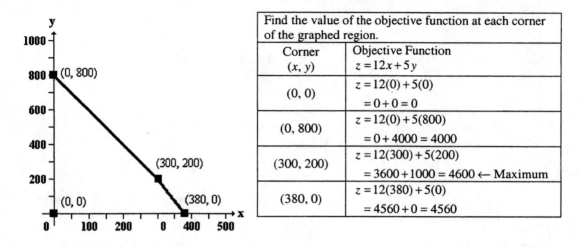

Find the value of the objective function at each corner of the graphed region.	
Corner (x, y)	Objective Function $z = 12x + 5y$
$(0, 0)$	$z = 12(0) + 5(0)$ $= 0 + 0 = 0$
$(0, 800)$	$z = 12(0) + 5(800)$ $= 0 + 4000 = 4000$
$(300, 200)$	$z = 12(300) + 5(200)$ $= 3600 + 1000 = 4600 \leftarrow$ Maximum
$(380, 0)$	$z = 12(380) + 5(0)$ $= 4560 + 0 = 4560$

The maximum the number of people that can be helped is 4600.
This occurs if 300 cartons of food and 200 cartons of clothing are shipped.

12. Let x and y be the number of Model A and Model B, respectively
Objective function: $z = 25x + 15y$ Constraints: $5x + 4y \le 200$
$2x + 3y \le 108$

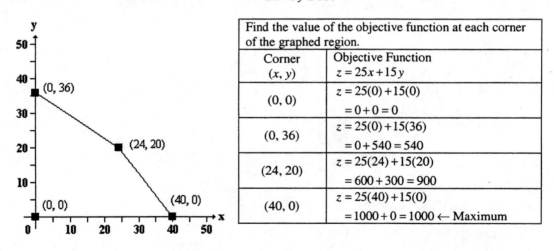

Find the value of the objective function at each corner of the graphed region.	
Corner (x, y)	Objective Function $z = 25x + 15y$
$(0, 0)$	$z = 25(0) + 15(0)$ $= 0 + 0 = 0$
$(0, 36)$	$z = 25(0) + 15(36)$ $= 0 + 540 = 540$
$(24, 20)$	$z = 25(24) + 15(20)$ $= 600 + 300 = 900$
$(40, 0)$	$z = 25(40) + 15(0)$ $= 1000 + 0 = 1000 \leftarrow$ Maximum

To maximize profit, 40 bicycles of Model A and no bicycles of Model B should be produced.

13. Let x and y be the number of parents and students, respectively.
Objective function: $z = 2x + y$ Constraints: $x + y \leq 150$

$$2y \geq x$$

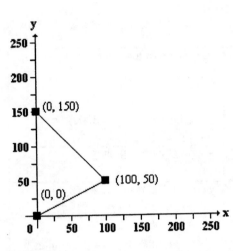

Corner (x, y)	Objective Function $z = 2x + y$
(0, 0)	$z = 2(0) + 0$ $= 0 + 0 = 0$
(0, 150)	$z = 2(0) + 150$ $= 0 + 150 = 150$
(100, 50)	$z = 2(100) + 50$ $= 200 + 50 = 250 \leftarrow$ Maximum

Find the value of the objective function at each corner of the graphed region.

To raise the maximum amount of money, 100 parents and 50 students should attend.

14. Let x and y be the number of American planes and British planes, respectively
Objective function: $z = 30,000x + 20,000y$ Constraints: $x + y \leq 44$

$$16x + 8y \leq 512$$
$$9000x + 5000y \leq 300,000$$

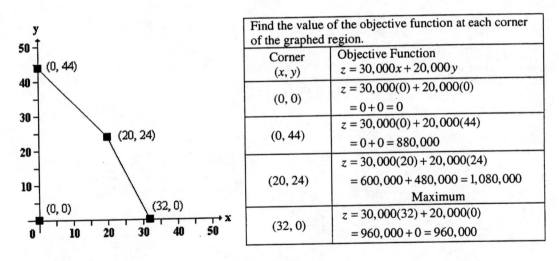

Find the value of the objective function at each corner of the graphed region.

Corner (x, y)	Objective Function $z = 30,000x + 20,000y$
(0, 0)	$z = 30,000(0) + 20,000(0)$ $= 0 + 0 = 0$
(0, 44)	$z = 30,000(0) + 20,000(44)$ $= 0 + 0 = 880,000$
(20, 24)	$z = 30,000(20) + 20,000(24)$ $= 600,000 + 480,000 = 1,080,000$ Maximum
(32, 0)	$z = 30,000(32) + 20,000(0)$ $= 960,000 + 0 = 960,000$

To maximize cargo capacity, 20 American planes and 24 British planes were used.

15-19. Answers will vary.

275

20. Let *x* and *y* be the money invested in stocks and bonds, respectively.

Objective function $z = 0.12x + 0.08y$:   Constraints: $x + y \le 10,000$

$y \ge 3000$

$x \ge 2000$

$y \ge x$

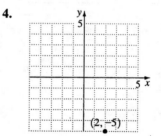

Find the value of the objective function at each corner of the graphed region.	
Corner (x, y)	Objective Function $z = 0.12x + 0.08y$
(2000, 3000)	$z = 0.12(2000) + 0.08(3000)$ $= 240 + 240 = 480$
(3000, 3000)	$z = 0.12(3000) + 0.08(3000)$ $= 360 + 240 = 600$
(2000, 8000)	$z = 0.12(2000) + 0.08(8000)$ $= 240 + 640 = 880$
(5000, 5000)	$z = 0.12(5000) + 0.08(5000)$ $= 600 + 400 = 1000 \leftarrow$ Maximum

To maximize the expected return, invest $5000 in stocks and $5000 bonds.

Chapter 7 Review Exercises

1.

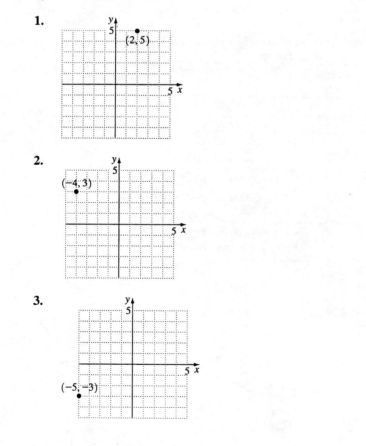

4.

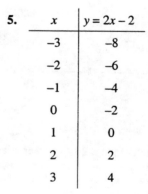

2.

3.

5.

x	$y = 2x - 2$
-3	-8
-2	-6
-1	-4
0	-2
1	0
2	2
3	4

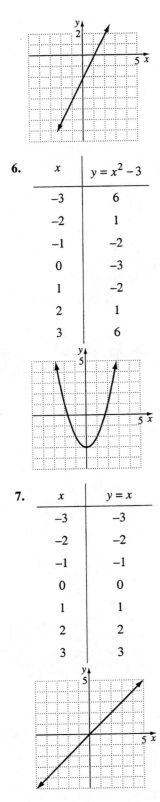

9. $f(x) = -7x + 5$
$f(-3) = -7(-3) + 5 = 21 + 5 = 26$

10. $f(x) = 3x^2 - 5x + 2$
$f(4) = 3(4)^2 - 5(4) + 2 = 48 - 20 + 2 = 30$

11. $f(x) = -3x^2 + 6x + 8$
$f(-4) = -3(-4)^2 + 6(-4) + 8$
$= -48 - 24 + 8 = -64$

6.

x	$y = x^2 - 3$
-3	6
-2	1
-1	-2
0	-3
1	-2
2	1
3	6

12.

x	$f(x) = \dfrac{1}{2}x$
-6	-3
-4	-2
-2	-1
0	0
2	1
4	2
6	3

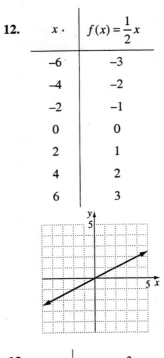

7.

x	$y = x$
-3	-3
-2	-2
-1	-1
0	0
1	1
2	2
3	3

13.

x	$f(x) = x^2 - 2$
-2	2
-1	-1
0	-2
1	-1
2	2

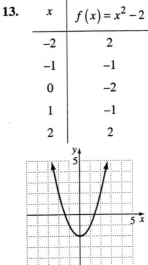

8. $f(x) = 4x + 11$
$f(-2) = 4(-2) + 11 = -8 + 11 = 3$

14. y is not a function of x because it fails the vertical line test.

15. y is a function of x because it passes the vertical line test.

16. y is not a function of x because it fails the vertical line test.

17. a. $f(60) \approx 3.1$; This means about 3.1% of the U.S. population was made up of Jewish Americans in 1960.

    b. The percentage of Jewish Americans in the U.S. population reached a maximum of about 3.7% in 1940.

    c. The percentage of Jewish Americans in the U.S. population reached a minimum of about 1.3% in 1900.

    d. The graph represents a function because it passes the vertical line test.

    e. Generally the percentage rises until 1940 then it decreases.

18. $2x + y = 4$
x-intercept is 2; y-intercept is 4.

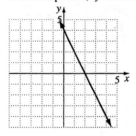

19. $2x - 3y = 6$
x-intercept is 3; y-intercept is –2.

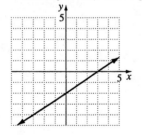

20. $5x - 3y = 15$
x-intercept is 3; y-intercept is –5.

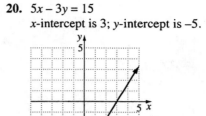

21. Slope $= \dfrac{1-2}{5-3} = -\dfrac{1}{2}$; line falls

22. Slope $= \dfrac{-4-2}{-3-(-1)} = \dfrac{-6}{-2} = 3$; line rises

23. Slope $= \dfrac{4-4}{6-(-3)} = 0$; line horizontal

24. Slope $= \dfrac{-3-3}{5-5} = \dfrac{-6}{0}$ is undefined,
vertical line

25. $y = 2x - 4$; Slope: 2, y-intercept: –4
Plot point (0, –4) and second point using
$m = \dfrac{2}{1} = \dfrac{\text{rise}}{\text{run}}$.

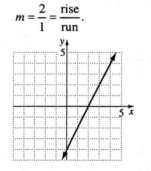

26. $y = -\dfrac{2}{3}x + 5$; Slope: $-\dfrac{2}{3}$, y-intercept: 5
Plot point (0, 5) and second point using
$m = \dfrac{-2}{3} = \dfrac{\text{rise}}{\text{run}}$.

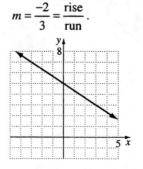

27. $y = \dfrac{3}{4}x - 2$; Slope: $\dfrac{3}{4}$, y-intercept: -2

Plot point $(0, -2)$ and second point using

$m = \dfrac{3}{4} = \dfrac{\text{rise}}{\text{run}}$.

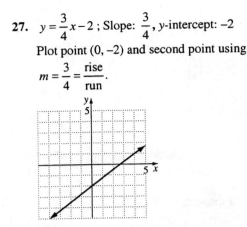

28. $y = \dfrac{1}{2}x + 0$; Slope: $\dfrac{1}{2}$, y-intercept: 0

Plot point $(0, 0)$ and second point using

$m = \dfrac{1}{2} = \dfrac{\text{rise}}{\text{run}}$.

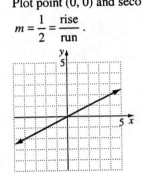

29. a. $2x + y = 0$
$y = -2x$

b. Slope $= -2$
y-intercept $= 0$

c.

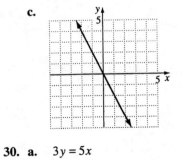

30. a. $3y = 5x$

$y = \dfrac{5}{3}x$

b. Slope $= \dfrac{5}{3}$

y-intercept $= 0$

c.

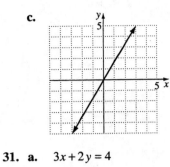

31. a. $3x + 2y = 4$
$2y = -3x + 4$
$y = -\dfrac{3}{2}x + 2$

b. Slope $= -\dfrac{3}{2}$
y-intercept $= 2$

c.

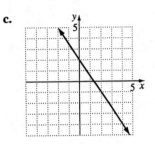

32. $x = 3$

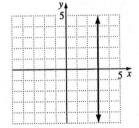

33. $y = -4$

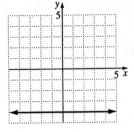

34. $x + 2 = 0$ or $x = -2$

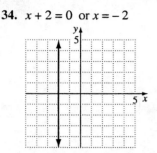

35. a. The y-intercept is (0, 4). The 0 represents 0 years after 1991. Thus, in 1991 there were 4 million SUVs sold in the U.S.

   b. $m = \dfrac{8-4}{11-0} = \dfrac{4}{11}$; The number SUVs sold is increasing at a rate of 4 million every 11 years.

   c. $y = \frac{4}{11}x + 4$

   d. Since 2013 is 22 years after 1991, let $x = 22$.
   $y = \frac{4}{11}(22) + 4 = 12$; It's predicted that there will be 12 million SUVs sold in 2013.

   e. $y = 8$

36. a. The parabola opens upward because $a > 0$ ($a = 1$).

   b. x-intercepts: Set $y = 0$
   $$0 = x^2 - 6x - 7$$
   $$0 = (x-7)(x+1)$$
   $$x - 7 = 0 \quad \text{or} \quad x + 1 = 0$$
   $$x = 7 \qquad\qquad x = -1$$

   c. y-intercept: Set $x = 0$
   $$y = 0^2 - 6(0) - 7 = -7$$

   d. Vertex: $x = \dfrac{-b}{2a} = \dfrac{-(-6)}{2(1)} = 3$
   $$y = (3)^2 - 6(3) - 7 = 9 - 18 - 7 = -16$$
   Vertex is at (3, -16).

e.

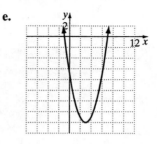

37. a. The parabola opens downward because $a < 0$ ($a = -1$).

   .b. x-intercepts: Set $y = 0$
   $$0 = -x^2 - 2x + 3$$
   $$0 = x^2 + 2x - 3$$
   $$0 = (x+3)(x-1)$$
   $$x + 3 = 0 \quad \text{or} \quad x - 1 = 0$$
   $$x = -3 \qquad\qquad x = 1$$

   c. y-intercept: Set $x = 0$
   $$y = -0^2 - 2(0) + 3 = 3$$

   d. Vertex: $x = \dfrac{-b}{2a} = \dfrac{-(-2)}{2(-1)} = -1$
   $$y = -(-1)^2 - 2(-1) + 3 = -1 + 2 + 3 = 4$$
   Vertex is at (-1, 4).

e.

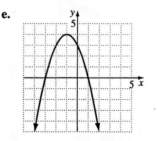

38. a. The parabola opens downward because $a < 0$ ($a = -3$).

   b. x-intercepts: Set $y = 0$
   $$x = \dfrac{-b \pm \sqrt{b^2 - 4ac}}{2a}$$
   $$= \dfrac{-6 \pm \sqrt{6^2 - 4(-3)(1)}}{2(-3)} = \dfrac{-6 \pm \sqrt{48}}{-6}$$
   Thus, $x = \dfrac{-6 + \sqrt{48}}{-6} \approx -0.2$
   or $x = \dfrac{-6 - \sqrt{48}}{-6} \approx 2.2$

c. y-intercept: Set $x = 0$

$y = -3(0)^2 + 6(0) + 1 = 1$

d. Vertex: $x = \dfrac{-b}{2a} = \dfrac{-6}{2(-3)} = 1$

$y = -3(1)^2 + 6(1) + 1 = -3 + 6 + 1 = 4$

Vertex is at $(1, 4)$.

e.

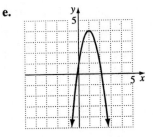

39. Vertex: $x = \dfrac{-b}{2a} = \dfrac{-4.2}{2(-0.05)} = 42$

$y = -0.05(42)^2 + 4.2(42) - 26$

$= -88.2 + 176.4 - 26$

$= 62.2$

The vertex is $(42, 62.2)$ shows 42-year-olds have the maximum percentage of irritable coffee drinkers at 62.2%.

40.

x	$y = 2^x$
-2	$\frac{1}{4}$
-1	$\frac{1}{2}$
0	1
1	2
2	4

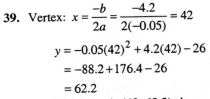

41.

x	$y = 4^{x-1}$
-2	$\frac{1}{64}$
-1	$\frac{1}{16}$
0	$\frac{1}{4}$
1	1
2	4

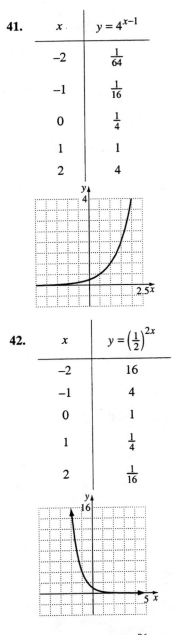

42.

x	$y = \left(\frac{1}{2}\right)^{2x}$
-2	16
-1	4
0	1
1	$\frac{1}{4}$
2	$\frac{1}{16}$

43. $f(86) = 364(1.005)^{86} \approx 559$ ppm

This is nearly double the preindustrial level.

44. $f(20) = 22.4e^{0.045(20)} \approx 55.1$ million

45. The intersection is $(2, 3)$.

Check: $\quad 2 + 3 = 5 \qquad 3(2) - 3 = 3$

$\qquad\qquad 5 = 5$ true $\quad 6 - 3 = 3$

$\qquad\qquad\qquad\qquad\qquad 3 = 3$ true

The solution set is $\{(2, 3)\}$.

46. The intersection is $(-2, -3)$.

Check: $2(-2)-(-3)=-1 \qquad -2-3=-5$

$\qquad\qquad -4+3=-1 \qquad\qquad -5=-5$ true

$\qquad\qquad\qquad -1=-1$ true

The solution set is $\{(-2,-3)\}$.

47. The intersection is $(3, 2)$.

Check: $2=-3+5 \qquad 2(3)-2=4$

$\qquad\quad 2=2$ true $\qquad\quad 6-2=4$

$\qquad\qquad\qquad\qquad\quad 4=4$ true

The solution set is $\{(3,2)\}$.

48. $x=3y+10 \qquad 2x+3y=2$

$2(3y+10)+3y=2$

$\quad 6y+20+3y=2$

$\qquad\qquad\quad 9y=-18$

$\qquad\qquad\quad\ y=-2$

$x=3(-2)+10=-6+10=4$

The solution set is $\{(4,-2)\}$.

49. $y=4x+1 \qquad\qquad 3x+2y=13$

$3x+2(4x+1)=13$

$\quad 3x+8x+2=13$

$\qquad\qquad 11x=11$

$\qquad\qquad\quad x=1$

$y=4(1)+\ 1=5$

The solution set is $\{(1,5)\}$.

50. $x+4y=14$

$x=14-4y \qquad\quad 2x-y=1$

$2(14-4y)-y=1$

$\quad 28-8y-y=1$

$\qquad\qquad -9y=-27$

$\qquad\qquad\quad y=3$

$x=14-4(3)=2$

The solution set is $\{(2,3)\}$.

51. $x+2y=-3$ No change. $\qquad x+2y=-3$

$x-y=-12$ Multiply by -1. $\underline{-x+\ \ y=12}$

$\qquad\qquad\qquad\qquad\qquad\qquad 3y=9$

$\qquad\qquad\qquad\qquad\qquad\qquad\ y=3$

$x-y=-12$

$x-3=-12$

$\quad x=-9$

The solution set is $\{(-9,3)\}$.

52. $2x-y=2$ Mult. by 2. $\quad 4x-2y=4$

$x+2y=11$ No change $\quad \underline{x+2y=11}$

$\qquad\qquad\qquad\qquad\qquad\qquad 5x=15$

$\qquad\qquad\qquad\qquad\qquad\qquad\ x=3$

$x+2y=11$

$3+2y=11$

$\quad 2y=8$

$\quad\ y=4$

The solution set is $\{(3,4)\}$.

53. $5x+3y=1$ Mult. by 3. $\qquad 15x+9y=3$

$3x+4y=-6$ Mult. by -5. $\underline{-15x-20y=30}$

$\qquad\qquad\qquad\qquad\qquad\qquad\qquad -11y=33$

$\qquad\qquad\qquad\qquad\qquad\qquad\qquad\quad\ y=-3$

$5x+3y=1$

$5x+3(-3)=1$

$\qquad 5x=10$

$\qquad\ x=2$

The solution set is $\{(2,-3)\}$.

54. $y=-x+4 \qquad\qquad 3x+3y=-6$

$3x+3(-x+4)=-6$

$\ 3x-3x+12=-6$

$\qquad\qquad 12=-6$, false

There is no solution or $\{\ \}$.

55. $3x+y=8$

$y=8-3x \qquad\qquad 2x-5y=11$

$2x-5(8-3x)=11$

$2x-40+15x=11$

$\qquad\quad 17x=51$

$\qquad\qquad x=3$

$y=8-3(3)=-1$

The solution set is $\{(3,-1)\}$.

56. $3x-2y=6$ Mult. by -2. $\quad -6x+4y=-12$

$6x-4y=12$ No change. $\quad \underline{\ 6x-4y=12}$

$\qquad\qquad\qquad\qquad\qquad\qquad\qquad 0=0$

The system has infinitely many solutions.

The solution set is $\left\{(x,y)\mid 3x-2y=6\right\}$.

57. $3x + 8y = -1$
$x - 2y = -5$
$x = -5 + 2y$　　　$3x + 8y = -1$
　　　　　　　　$3(-5 + 2y) + 8y = -1$
　　　　　　　　$-15 + 6y + 8y = -1$
　　　　　　　　　　　　$14y = 14$
　　　　　　　　　　　　　$y = 1$
$x = -5 + 2y = -5 + 2 = -3$
The numbers are –3 and 1.

58. Let x and y be the cholesterol intake of 1 ounce of shrimp and scallops, respectively.
$3x + 2y = 156$
$5x + 3y = 300 - 45 = 255$
　$15x + 10y = 780$　　Mult. 1st equation by 5.
　$\underline{-15x - 9y = -765}$　Mult. 2nd equation by –3.
　　　　　$y = 15$

　　$3x + 2y = 156$
$3x + 2(15) = 156$
　　　　$3x = 126$
　　　　　$x = 42$
The cholesterol content in an ounce of shrimp is 42 mg. And the cholesterol content in an ounce of scallops is 15 mg.

59. To graph $x - 3y \le 6$, begin by graphing $x - 3y = 6$ with a solid line because $\le$ includes equality.
　test point (0, 0):
　$x - 3y \le 6$
$0 - 3(0) \le 6$
　　$0 \le 6$, true
Since the test point makes the inequality <u>true</u>, shade the half-plane <u>containing</u> test point (0, 0).

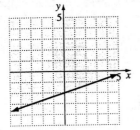

60. To graph $2x + 3y \ge 12$, begin by graphing $2x + 3y = 12$ with a solid line because $\ge$ includes equality.

　test point (0, 0):
　$2x + 3y \ge 12$
$2(0) + 3(0) \ge 12$
　　$0 \ge 12$, false
Since the test point makes the inequality <u>false</u>, shade the half-plane <u>not containing</u> test point (0, 0).

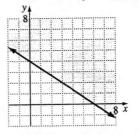

61. To graph $2x - 7y > 14$, begin by graphing $2x - 7y = 14$ with a dashed line because $>$ does not include equality.
　test point (0, 0):
　$2x - 7y > 14$
$2(0) - 7(0) > 14$
　　$0 > 14$, false
Since the test point makes the inequality <u>false</u>, shade the half-plane <u>not containing</u> test point (0, 0).

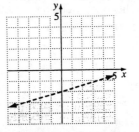

62. To graph $y > \frac{3}{5}x$, begin by graphing $y = \frac{3}{5}x$ as a dashed line passing through the origin with a slope of $\frac{3}{5}$, then shade above the line.

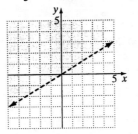

63. To graph $y \leq -\frac{1}{2}x + 2$, begin by graphing

$y = -\frac{1}{2}x + 2$ as a solid line passing through $(0, 2)$

with a slope of $\frac{-1}{2}$, then shade below the line.

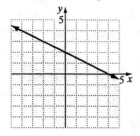

64. To graph $x \leq 2$, begin by graphing $x = 2$ as a solid vertical line passing through $x = 2$, then shade to the left of the line.

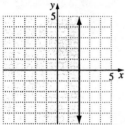

65. To graph $y > -3$, begin by graphing $y = -3$ as a dashed horizontal line passing through $y = -3$, then shade above the line.

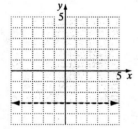

66. $3x - y \leq 6$
    $x + y \geq 2$
Graph $3x - y = 6$ as a solid line.
Because $(0, 0)$ makes the inequality true, shade the half-plane containing $(0,0)$.
Graph $x + y = 2$ as a solid line.
Because $(0, 0)$ makes the inequality false, shade the half-plane not containing $(0, 0)$.

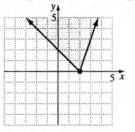

67. $x + y < 4$
    $x - y < 4$
Graph $x + y = 4$ as a dashed line.
Because $(0, 0)$ makes the inequality true, shade the half-plane containing $(0, 0)$.
Graph $x - y = 4$ as a dashed line.
Because $(0, 0)$ makes the inequality true, shade the half-plane containing $(0, 0)$.

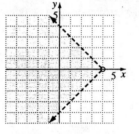

68. $x \leq 3$
    $y > -2$
Graph $x = 3$ as a solid line.
The points in the half-plane to the left of the line satisfy $x < 3$.
Graph $y = -2$ as a dashed line.
The points in the half-plane above the line satisfy $y > -2$.

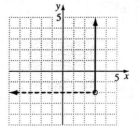

69. $4x + 6y = 24$

$\qquad y > 2$

Graph $4x + 6y = 24$ as a solid line.

Because $(0, 0)$ makes the inequality true, shade the half-plane containing $(0, 0)$.

Graph $y = 2$ as a dashed line.

The points in the half-plane above the line satisfy $y > 2$.

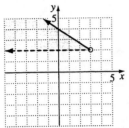

70. $x + y \le 6$

$\qquad y \ge 2x - 3$

Graph $x + y = 6$ as a solid line.

Because $(0, 0)$ makes the inequality true, shade the half-plane containing $(0, 0)$.

Graph $y = 2x - 3$ as a solid line.

Because $(0, 0)$ makes the inequality true, shade the half-plane containing $(0, 0)$.

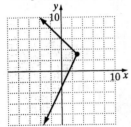

71. $y < -x + 4$

$\qquad y > x - 4$

Graph $y < -x + 4$ as a dashed line.

Because $(0, 0)$ makes the inequality true, shade the half-plane containing $(0, 0)$.

Graph $y = x - 4$ as a dashed line.

Because $(0, 0)$ makes the inequality true, shade the half-plane containing $(0, 0)$.

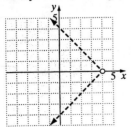

72. $z = 2x + 3y$

at $(1, 0)$ $\qquad z = 2(1) + 3(0) = 2$

at $\left(\dfrac{1}{2}, \dfrac{1}{2}\right)$ $\quad z = 2\left(\dfrac{1}{2}\right) + 3\left(\dfrac{1}{2}\right) = \dfrac{5}{2}$

at $(2, 2)$ $\qquad z = 2(2) + 3(2) = 10$

at $(4, 0)$ $\qquad z = 2(4) + 3(0) = 8$

Maximum value of the objective function is 10.

Minimum value of the objective function is 2.

73. $z = 2x + 3y$

Constraints: $\qquad x \le 6$

$\qquad\qquad\qquad y \le 5$

$\qquad\qquad x + y \ge 2$

$\qquad\qquad\qquad x \ge 0$

$\qquad\qquad\qquad y \ge 0$

a.

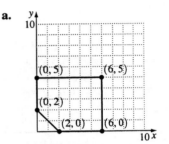

b. at $(0, 2)$ $z = 2(0) + 3(2) = 6$

at $(0, 5)$ $z = 2(0) + 3(5) = 15$

at $(6, 5)$ $z = 2(6) + 3(5) = 27$

at $(6, 0)$ $z = 2(6) + 3(0) = 12$

at $(2, 0)$ $z = 2(2) + 3(0) = 4$

c. The maximum value of the objective function is 27. It occurs at $x = 6$ and $y = 5$.

The minimum value of the objective function is 4. It occurs at $x = 2$ and $y = 0$.

74. a. $z = 500x + 350y$

b. $x + y \le 200$

$\qquad x \ge 10$; $y \ge 80$

d. at $(10, 80)$ $z = 500(10) + 350(80) = 33,000$

at $(10, 190)$ $z = 500(10) + 350(190) = 71,500$

at $(120, 80)$ $z = 500(120) + 350(80) = 88,000$

c. The company will make the greatest profit by producing 120 units of writing paper and 80 units of newsprint each day. The maximum daily profit is $88,000.

Chapter 7 Test

1.

x	$y = (x-1)^2$
-1	4
0	1
1	0
2	1
3	4

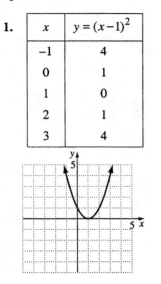

2. $f(-2) = 3(-2)^2 - 7(-2) - 5 = 12 + 14 - 5 = 21$

3. Set $y = 0$ Set $x = 0$
   $4x - 2 \cdot 0 = -8$ $4 \cdot 0 - 2y = -8$
          $4x = -8$ $-2y = -8$
           $x = -2$ $y = 4$
   x-intercept is -2. y-intercept is 4.

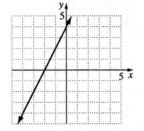

4. Slope $= \dfrac{-2-4}{-5-(-3)} = \dfrac{-6}{-2} = 3$

5. Slope $= \dfrac{530-320}{5-0} = \dfrac{210}{5} = 42$
   This indicates that one-way fares are increasing at $42 per year.

6. $y = \dfrac{2}{3}x - 1$

   Slope: $\dfrac{2}{3}$, y-intercept: -1

   Plot the point $(0, -1)$ and a second point using

   $m = \dfrac{2}{3} = \dfrac{\text{rise}}{\text{run}}$.

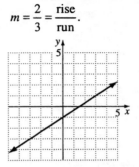

7. $f(x) = -2x + 3$
   Slope: -2, y-intercept: 3
   Plot the point $(0, 3)$ and a second point using

   $m = \dfrac{-2}{1} = \dfrac{\text{rise}}{\text{run}}$.

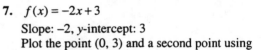

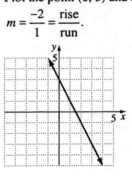

8. a. $a = 1 > 0$; parabola opens upward.

  b. Vertex: $x = \dfrac{-b}{2a} = \dfrac{-(-2)}{2(1)} = 1$

       $f(1) = (1)^2 - 2(1) - 8 = -9$

     Vertex is at $(1, -9)$.

  c. x-intercepts: set $y = 0$

     $0 = x^2 - 2x - 8$

     $0 = (x - 4)(x + 2)$

     $x - 4 = 0$ or $x + 2 = 0$

       $x = 4$ $x = -2$

     x-intercepts are -2 and 4.

  d. y-intercept: set $x = 0$

     $f(0) = (0)^2 - 2(0) - 8 = -8$

     y-intercept is -8.

  e.

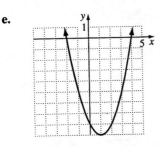

9. Vertex: $x = \dfrac{-b}{2a} = \dfrac{-96}{2(-16)} = 3$

$y = -16(3)^2 + 96(3) + 3 = 147$

The vertex $(3, 147)$ represents that after 3 seconds the baseball will reach its maximum height of 147 feet.

10.

x	$f(x) = 3^x$
-2	$\frac{1}{9}$
-1	$\frac{1}{3}$
0	1
1	3
2	9

11. $f(0.08) = 6e^{12.77(0.08)} \approx 17\%$

12. The intersection is $(2, 4)$

Check: $2 + 4 = 6$ $4(2) - 4 = 4$

         $6 = 6$ true $8 - 4 = 4$

                            $4 = 4$ true

The solution set is $\{(2, 4)\}$.

13. $x = y + 4$ $3x + 7y = -18$

     $3(y + 4) + 7y = -18$

      $3y + 12 + 7y = -18$

            $10y = -30$

              $y = -3$

$x = -3 + 4 = 1$

The solution set is $\{(1, -3)\}$.

14. $5x + 4y = 10$ $\xrightarrow{\text{Mult. by 3}}$ $15x + 12y = 30$

    $3x + 5y = -7$ $\xrightarrow{\text{Mult. by } -5}$ $\underline{-15x - 25y = 35}$

                                           $-13y = 65$

                                              $y = -5$

       $5x + 4y = 10$

    $5x + 4(-5) = 10$

           $5x = 30$

             $x = 6$

The solution set is $\{(6, -5)\}$.

15. Let x represent the daily charge at the hotel.
Let y represent the daily charge for the rental car.

$3x + 2y = 360$ $\xrightarrow{\text{Mult. by 3}}$ $9x + 6y = 1080$

$4x + 3y = 500$ $\xrightarrow{\text{Mult. by } -2}$ $\underline{-8x - 6y = -1000}$

                                              $x = 80$

          $3x + 2y = 360$

       $3(80) + 2y = 360$

               $2y = 120$

                 $y = 60$

The daily charge at the hotel is \$80.
The daily charge for the rental car is \$60.

16. $3x - 2y < 6$

Graph $3x - 2y = 6$ as a dashed line.

x-intercept:

$3x - 2 \cdot 0 = 6$

$3x = 6$

$x = 2$

y-intercept:

$3 \cdot 0 - 2y = 6$

$-2y = 6$

$y = -3$

Test point: $(0, 0)$.

Is $3 \cdot 0 - 2 \cdot 0 < 6$?

$0 < 6$, true

Shade the half-plane containing $(0, 0)$.

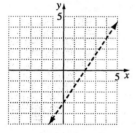

17. Graph $y = \frac{1}{2}x - 1$ as a solid line.

Use y-intercept of -1 and slope of $\frac{1}{2}$

Shade below this line.

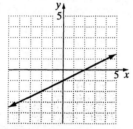

18. $2x - y \le 4$

$2x - y > -1$

Graph $2x - y = 4$ as a solid line.

Because $(0, 0)$ makes the inequality true, shade the half-plane containing $(0, 0)$.

Graph $2x - y = -1$ as a dashed line.

Because $(0, 0)$ makes the inequality true, shade the half-plane containing $(0, 0)$.

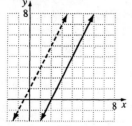

19. $z = 3x + 2y$

at $(2, 0)$ $z = 3(2) + 2(0) = 6$

at $(2, 6)$ $z = 3(2) + 2(6) = 18$

at $(6, 3)$ $z = 3(6) + 2(3) = 24$

at $(8, 0)$ $z = 3(8) + 2(0) = 24$

The maximum value of the objective function is 24.

The minimum value of the objective function is 6.

20.

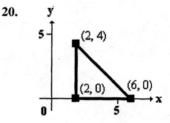

Objective function: $z = 3x + 5y$

at $(2, 0)$ $z = 3(2) + 5(0) = 6$

at $(6, 0)$ $z = 3(6) + 5(0) = 18$

at $(2, 4)$ $z = 3(2) + 5(4) = 26$

The maximum value of the objective function is 26.

21.

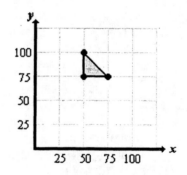

Objective function: $z = 200x + 250y$

Constraints: $x \ge 50$; $y \ge 75$; $x + y \le 150$

Substitute vertices into objective function:

at $(50, 100)$ $z = 200(50) + 250(100) = 35,000$

at $(75, 75)$ $z = 200(75) + 250(75) = 33,750$

at $(50, 75)$ $z = 200(50) + 250(75) = 28,750$

The company will make the greatest profit by producing 50 regular jet skis and 100 deluxe jet skis each week. The maximum weekly profit is $35,000.

Chapter 8
Consumer Mathematics and Financial Management

Check Points 8.1

1. Step 1: $\dfrac{1}{8} = 1 \div 8 = 0.125$

Step 2: $0.125 \cdot 100 = 12.5$

Step 3: 12.5%

2. $0.023 = 2.3\%$

3. a. $67\% = 0.67$

b. $250\% = 2.50 = 2.5$

4. $A = PB$

$A = 0.13 \cdot 8000$

$A = 1040$

Thus, 1040 Americans suffer spinal cord injuries due to sports injuries each year.

5. $A = PB$

$9 = 0.60 \cdot B$

$\dfrac{9}{0.60} = \dfrac{0.60B}{0.60}$

$15 = B$

6. $A = PB$

$1.3 = P \cdot 26$

$\dfrac{1.3}{26} = \dfrac{P \cdot 26}{26}$

$0.05 = P$

Thus, 1.3 is 5% of 26.

7. a. 6% of $\$1260 = 0.06 \times \$1260 = \$75.60$

The tax paid is $\$75.60$

b. $\$1260.00 + \$75.60 = \$1335.60$

The total cost is $\$1335.60$

8. a. 35% of $\$380 = 0.35 \times \$380 = \$133$

The discount is $\$133$

b. $\$380 - \$133 = \$247$

The sale price is $\$247$

9. a. Percent of increase $= \dfrac{\text{amount of increase}}{\text{original amount}}$

$= \dfrac{4}{6} = 0.66\frac{2}{3} = 66\frac{2}{3}\%$

b. Percent of decrease $= \dfrac{\text{amount of decrease}}{\text{original amount}}$

$= \dfrac{4}{10} = 0.4 = 40\%$

10. Amount of decrease: $\$940 - \$611 = \$329$

$\dfrac{\text{amount of decrease}}{\text{original amount}} = \dfrac{\$329}{\$940} = 0.35 = 35\%$

There was a 35% decrease from 1998 to 1999.

11. Amount of increase: $12\% - 10\% = 2\%$

$\dfrac{\text{amount of increase}}{\text{original amount}} = \dfrac{2\%}{10\%} = 0.2 = 20\%$

There was a 20% increase for this episode.

12. a. 20% of $\$1200 = 0.20 \times \$1200 = \$240$

Taxes for year 1 are $\$1200 - \$240 = \$960$

20% of $\$960 = 0.20 \times \$960 = \$192$

Taxes for year 2 are $\$960 + \$192 = \$1152$

b. $\dfrac{\$1200 - \$1152}{\$1200} = \dfrac{\$48}{\$1200} = 0.04 = 4\%$

Taxes for year 2 are 4% less than the original amount.

Exercise Set 8.1

1. $\dfrac{2}{5} = 2 \div 5 = 0.4 = 40\%$

2. $\dfrac{3}{5} = 3 \div 5 = 0.6 = 60\%$

3. $\dfrac{1}{4} = 1 \div 4 = 0.25 = 25\%$

4. $\dfrac{3}{4} = 3 \div 4 = 0.75 = 75\%$

5. $\dfrac{3}{8} = 3 \div 8 = 0.375 = 37.5\%$

6. $\dfrac{7}{8} = 7 \div 8 = 0.875 = 87.5\%$

7. $\dfrac{1}{40} = 1 \div 40 = 0.025 = 2.5\%$

8. $\dfrac{3}{40} = 3 \div 40 = 0.075 = 7.5\%$

9. $\dfrac{9}{80} = 9 \div 80 = 0.1125 = 11.25\%$

10. $\dfrac{13}{80} = 13 \div 80 = 0.1625 = 16.25\%$

11. $0.59 = 59\%$

12. $0.96 = 96\%$

13. $0.3844 = 38.44\%$

14. $0.003 = 0.3\%$

15. $2.87 = 287\%$

16. $9.83 = 983\%$

17. $14.87 = 1487\%$

18. $19.63 = 1963\%$

19. $100 = 10,000\%$

20. $95 = 9500\%$

21. $72\% = 0.72$

22. $38\% = 0.38$

23. $43.6\% = 0.436$

24. $6.25\% = 0.0625$

25. $130\% = 1.3$

26. $260\% = 2.6$

27. $2\% = 0.02$

28. $6\% = 0.06$

29. $\dfrac{1}{2}\% = 0.5\% = 0.005$

30. $\dfrac{3}{4}\% = 0.75\% = 0.0075$

31. $\dfrac{5}{8}\% = 0.625\% = 0.00625$

32. $\dfrac{1}{8}\% = 0.125\% = 0.00125$

33. $62\dfrac{1}{2}\% = 62.5\% = .625$

34. $87\dfrac{1}{2}\% = 87.5\% = .875$

35. $A = PB$
$A = 0.03 \cdot 200$
$A = 6$

36. $A = PB$
$A = 0.08 \cdot 300$
$A = 24$

37. $A = PB$
$A = 0.18 \cdot 40$
$A = 7.2$

38. $A = PB$
$A = 0.16 \cdot 90$
$A = 14.4$

39. $A = PB$
$3 = 0.60 \cdot B$
$\dfrac{3}{0.60} = \dfrac{0.60B}{0.60}$
$5 = B$

40. $A = PB$
$8 = 0.40 \cdot B$
$\dfrac{8}{0.40} = \dfrac{0.40B}{0.40}$
$20 = B$

41. $A = PB$
$40.8 = 0.24 \cdot B$
$\dfrac{40.8}{0.24} = \dfrac{0.24B}{0.24}$
$170 = B$

42. $A = PB$
$51.2 = 0.32 \cdot B$
$\dfrac{51.2}{0.32} = \dfrac{0.32B}{0.32}$
$160 = B$

43. $A = PB$
$3 = P \cdot 15$
$\dfrac{3}{15} = \dfrac{P \cdot 15}{15}$
$0.2 = P$
$P = 20\%$

44.
$$A = PB$$
$$18 = P \cdot 90$$
$$\frac{18}{90} = \frac{P \cdot 90}{90}$$
$$0.2 = P$$
$$P = 20\%$$

45.
$$A = PB$$
$$0.3 = P \cdot 2.5$$
$$\frac{0.3}{2.5} = \frac{P \cdot 2.5}{2.5}$$
$$0.12 = P$$
$$P = 12\%$$

46.
$$A = PB$$
$$0.6 = P \cdot 7.5$$
$$\frac{0.6}{7.5} = \frac{P \cdot 7.5}{7.5}$$
$$0.08 = P$$
$$P = 8\%$$

47. $A = PB$
$$A = 0.34 \cdot 1200$$
$$A = 408 \text{ women}$$

48. $A = PB$
$$A = 0.41 \cdot 1200$$
$$A = 492 \text{ men}$$

49.
$$A = PB$$
$$1,242,000 = 0.04 \cdot B$$
$$\frac{1,242,000}{0.04} = \frac{0.04B}{0.04}$$
$$31,050,000 = B$$
$$B = 31,050,000 \text{ Hispanic Americans}$$

50.
$$A = PB$$
$$612,000 = 0.90 \cdot B$$
$$\frac{612,000}{0.90} = \frac{0.90B}{0.90}$$
$$680,000 = B$$
$$B = 680,000 \text{ inmates}$$

51.
$$A = PB$$
$$7500 = P \cdot 60,000$$
$$\frac{7500}{60,000} = \frac{P \cdot 60,000}{60,000}$$
$$0.125 = P$$
$$P = 12.5\%$$

52.
$$A = PB$$
$$225,000 = P \cdot 500,000$$
$$\frac{225,000}{500,000} = \frac{P \cdot 500,000}{500,000}$$
$$0.45 = P$$
$$P = 45\%$$

53.
$$A = PB$$
$$112 + 12 = P \cdot 400$$
$$\frac{124}{400} = \frac{P \cdot 400}{400}$$
$$0.31 = P$$
$$P = 31\%$$

54.
$$A = PB$$
$$108 + 48 = P \cdot 400$$
$$\frac{156}{400} = \frac{P \cdot 400}{400}$$
$$0.39 = P$$
$$P = 39\%$$

55. $(0.15)(60) = \$9$

56. $3502 + 0.28(35,000 - 23,000) = \$6862$

57. a. $(0.06)(16,800) = \$1,008$

   b. $16,800 + 1008 = \$17,808$

58. a. $(0.07)(96) = \$6.72$

   b. $96 + 6.72 = \$102.72$

59. a. $(0.12)(860) = \$103.20$

   b. $860 - 103.20 = \$756.80$

60. a. $(0.40)(16.50) = \$6.60$

   b. $16.50 - 6.60 = \$9.90$

61. $\dfrac{89,200 - 32,600}{32,600} = 1.736 = 173.6\%$

62. $\dfrac{87,400 - 67,100}{67,100} = 0.303 = 30.3\%$

63. $\dfrac{86,400 - 72,100}{86,400} = 0.166 = 16.6\%$

64. $\dfrac{92,300 - 39,600}{92,300} = 0.571 = 57.1\%$

65. $\dfrac{840-714}{840}=0.15=15\%$

66. $\dfrac{380-266}{380}=0.30=30\%$

67. Amount after first year
$= 10,000-(0.3)(10,000)$
$= \$7000$
Amount after second year
$= 7000+(0.4)(7000)$
$= \$9800$
Your adviser is not using percentages properly.

Actual change:
$\dfrac{10,000-9800}{10,000}=0.02=2\%$ decrease.

68. The salesman is misusing percentages.
$100\%-30\%=70\%$
20% of $70\% = 0.70(0.20)=0.14=14\%$
Percent reduction $= 30\%+14\%=44\%$

69. No, a larger percentage does not necessarily imply a larger expenditure.

70-75. Answers will vary.

76. c is true.
$1-\left(\dfrac{1}{10}+\dfrac{1}{3}+\dfrac{1}{5}\right)=1-\dfrac{19}{30}=\dfrac{11}{30}\approx 0.36\overline{6}=36\tfrac{2}{3}\%$

77. Tax owed $= \dfrac{\$3.40}{\$100}\cdot\dfrac{\$78,500}{1}=\$2669$
Discount $= (0.03)(2669)=\$80.07$
Tax paid $= 2669-80.07=\$2588.93$

78. January sales $= 60\cdot 200=\$12,000$
Number of customers in February
$= 60-(0.10)(60)=60-6=54$
Price of washing machine in February
$= 200+(0.20)(200)=200+40=\$240$
February sales $= 54\cdot\$240=\$12,960$
$12,960-12,000=\$960$ increase.

Check Points 8.2

1. $I=Prt=(\$3000)(0.05)(1)=\$150$

2. $I=Prt=(\$2400)(0.07)(2)=\$336$

3. $A=P(1+rt)=2040\left[1+(0.075)\left(\dfrac{4}{12}\right)\right]=\$2091$

4. $A=P(1+rt)$
$6800=5000\left[1+r(2)\right]$
$6800=5000+10,000r$
$1800=10,000r$
$\dfrac{1800}{10,000}=\dfrac{10,000r}{10,000}$
$0.18=r$
$r=18\%$

5. $A=P(1+rt)$
$4000=P\left[1+(0.08)\left(\tfrac{6}{12}\right)\right]$
$4000=P(1.04)$
$\dfrac{4000}{1.04}=\dfrac{P(1.04)}{1.04}$
$3846.153\approx P$
$P\approx\$3846.16$

6. a. $I=Prt=(5000)(0.12)(2)=1200$
The loan's discount is $1200.

b. Amount received: $\$5000-\$1200=\$3800$

c. $I=Prt$
$1200=(3800)(r)(2)$
$1200=7600r$
$\dfrac{1200}{7600}=\dfrac{7600r}{7600}$
$0.158=r$
$r=15.8\%$

Exercise Set 8.2

1. $I=(\$4000)(0.06)(1)=\$240$

2. $I=(\$7000)(0.05)(1)=\$350$

3. $I=(\$180)(0.03)(2)=\$10.80$

4. $I=(\$260)(0.04)(3)=\$31.20$

5. $I=(\$5000)(0.085)\left(\dfrac{9}{12}\right)=\$318.75$

6. $I=(\$18,000)(0.075)\left(\dfrac{18}{12}\right)=\$2025$

7. $I = (\$15,500)(0.11)\left(\dfrac{90}{360}\right) = \$426.25$

8. $I = (\$12,600)(0.09)\left(\dfrac{60}{360}\right) = \$189$

9. $A = P(1+rt) = 3000\left[1+(0.07)(2)\right] = \$3420$

10. $A = P(1+rt) = 2000\left[1+(0.06)(3)\right] = \$2360$

11. $A = P(1+rt) = 26,000\left[1+(0.095)(5)\right] = \$38,350$

12. $A = P(1+rt) = 24,000\left[1+(0.085)(6)\right] = \$36,240$

13. $A = P(1+rt) = 9000\left[1+(0.065)\left(\tfrac{8}{12}\right)\right] = \$9390$

14. $A = P(1+rt) = 6000\left[1+(0.045)\left(\tfrac{9}{12}\right)\right] = \$6202.50$

15.
$$A = P(1+rt)$$
$$2150 = 2000\left[1+r(1)\right]$$
$$2150 = 2000+2000r$$
$$150 = 2000r$$
$$\frac{150}{2000} = \frac{2000r}{2000}$$
$$0.075 = r$$
$$r = 7.5\%$$

16.
$$A = P(1+rt)$$
$$3180 = 3000\left[1+r(1)\right]$$
$$3180 = 3000+3000r$$
$$180 = 3000r$$
$$\frac{180}{3000} = \frac{3000r}{3000}$$
$$0.06 = r$$
$$r = 6\%$$

17.
$$A = P(1+rt)$$
$$5900 = 5000\left[1+r(2)\right]$$
$$900 = 5000+10,000r$$
$$900 = 10,000r$$
$$\frac{900}{10,000} = \frac{10,000r}{10,000}$$
$$0.09 = r$$
$$r = 9\%$$

18.
$$A = P(1+rt)$$
$$14,060 = 10,000\left[1+r(2)\right]$$
$$14,060 = 10,000+20,000r$$
$$4060 = 20,000r$$
$$\frac{4060}{20,000} = \frac{20,000r}{20,000}$$
$$0.203 = r$$
$$r = 20.3\%$$

19.
$$A = P(1+rt)$$
$$2840 = 2300\left[1+r\left(\tfrac{9}{12}\right)\right]$$
$$2840 = 2300+1725r$$
$$540 = 1725r$$
$$\frac{540}{1725} = \frac{1725r}{1725}$$
$$0.313 = r$$
$$r = 31.3\%$$

20.
$$A = P(1+rt)$$
$$1820 = 1700\left[1+r\left(\tfrac{6}{12}\right)\right]$$
$$1820 = 1700+850r$$
$$120 = 850r$$
$$\frac{120}{850} = \frac{850r}{850}$$
$$0.141 = r$$
$$r = 14.1\%$$

21.
$$A = P(1+rt)$$
$$6000 = P\left[1+(0.08)(2)\right]$$
$$6000 = P(1.16)$$
$$\frac{6000}{1.16} = \frac{P(1.16)}{1.16}$$
$$5172.414 \approx P$$
$$P \approx \$5172.42$$

22.
$$A = P(1+rt)$$
$$8500 = P\left[1+(0.07)(3)\right]$$
$$8500 = P(1.21)$$
$$\frac{8500}{1.21} = \frac{P(1.21)}{1.21}$$
$$7024.793 \approx P$$
$$P \approx \$7024.80$$

23.
$$A = P(1+rt)$$
$$14,000 = P[1+(0.095)(6)]$$
$$14,000 = P(1.57)$$
$$\frac{14,000}{1.57} = \frac{P(1.57)}{1.57}$$
$$8917.197 \approx P$$
$$P \approx \$8917.20$$

24.
$$A = P(1+rt)$$
$$16,000 = P[1+(0.115)(5)]$$
$$16,000 = P(1.575)$$
$$\frac{16,000}{1.575} = \frac{P(1.575)}{1.575}$$
$$10158.7302 \approx P$$
$$P \approx \$10158.74$$

25.
$$A = P(1+rt)$$
$$5000 = P[1+(0.145)\left(\frac{9}{12}\right)]$$
$$5000 = P(1.10875)$$
$$\frac{5000}{1.10875} = \frac{P(1.10875)}{1.10875}$$
$$4509.583 \approx P$$
$$P \approx \$4509.59$$

26.
$$A = P(1+rt)$$
$$2000 = P[1+(0.126)\left(\frac{8}{12}\right)]$$
$$2000 = P(1.084)$$
$$\frac{2000}{1.084} = \frac{P(1.084)}{1.084}$$
$$1845.018 \approx P$$
$$P \approx \$1845.02$$

27. a. $I = Prt = (2000)(0.07)\left(\frac{8}{12}\right) = \$93.33$

    b. Amount received: $\$2000 - \$93.33 = \$1906.67$

    c.
$$I = Prt$$
$$93.33 = (1906.67)(r)\left(\frac{8}{12}\right)$$
$$93.33 = 1271.113r$$
$$\frac{93.33}{1271.113} = \frac{1271.113r}{1271.113}$$
$$0.073 = r$$
$$r = 7.3\%$$

28. a. $I = Prt = (3000)(0.08)\left(\frac{9}{12}\right) = \$180$

    b. Amount received: $\$3000 - \$180 = \$2820$

    c.
$$I = Prt$$
$$180 = (2820)(r)\left(\frac{9}{12}\right)$$
$$180 = 2115r$$
$$\frac{180}{2115} = \frac{2115r}{2115}$$
$$0.085 = r$$
$$r = 8.5\%$$

29. a. $I = Prt = (12,000)(0.065)(2) = \$1560$

    b. Amount received: $\$12,000 - \$1560 = \$10,440$

    c.
$$I = Prt$$
$$1560 = (10,440)(r)(2)$$
$$1560 = 20,880r$$
$$\frac{1560}{20,880} = \frac{20,880r}{20,880}$$
$$0.075 = r$$
$$r = 7.5\%$$

30. a. $I = Prt = (20,000)(0.085)(3) = \$5100$

    b. Amount received: $\$20,000 - \$5100 = \$14,900$

    c.
$$I = Prt$$
$$5100 = (14,900)(r)(2)$$
$$5100 = 44,700r$$
$$\frac{5100}{44,700} = \frac{44,700r}{44,700}$$
$$0.114 = r$$
$$r = 11.4\%$$

31. a. $I = Prt$
$$= (\$4000)(0.0825)\left(\frac{9}{12}\right)$$
$$= \$247.50$$

    b. $\$4000 + \$247.50 = \$4247.50$

32. a. $I = Prt$

$$= (\$20,000)(0.12)\left(\frac{7}{12}\right)$$

$$= \$1400$$

b. $\$20,000 + \$1400 = \$21,400$

33. $A = P(1 + rt)$

$$2000 = 1400\left[1 + r(2)\right]$$

$$2000 = 1400 + 2800r$$

$$600 = 2800r$$

$$\frac{600}{2800} = \frac{2800r}{2800}$$

$$0.214 = r$$

$$r = 21.4\%$$

34. $A = P(1 + rt)$

$$1000 = 981.60\left[1 + r(2)\right]$$

$$1000 = 981.6 + 1963.2r$$

$$18.4 = 1963.2r$$

$$\frac{18.4}{1963.2} = \frac{1963.2r}{1963.2}$$

$$0.075 = r$$

$$r = 7.5\%$$

35. $A = P(1 + rt)$

$$3000 = P\left[1 + (0.065)(2)\right]$$

$$3000 = P(1.13)$$

$$\frac{3000}{1.13} = \frac{P(1.13)}{1.13}$$

$$2654.867 \approx P$$

$$P \approx \$2654.87$$

36. $A = P(1 + rt)$

$$8000 = P\left[1 + (0.055)(2)\right]$$

$$8000 = P(1.11)$$

$$\frac{8000}{1.11} = \frac{P(1.11)}{1.11}$$

$$7207.207 \approx P$$

$$P \approx \$7207.21$$

37-39. Answers will vary.

40. $A = P(1 + rt)$

$$2P = P(1 + rt)$$

$$\frac{2P}{P} = \frac{P(1 + rt)}{P}$$

$$2 = 1 + rt$$

$$1 = rt$$

$$\frac{1}{r} = \frac{rt}{r}$$

$$\frac{1}{r} = t$$

$$t = \frac{1}{r}$$

41. a. $A = P(1 + rt)$

$$A = 5000\left[1 + (0.055)t\right]$$

$$A = 5000 + 275t$$

b. The slope is 275. This means the *rate of change* for the account is $275 per year.

Check Points 8.3

1. a. $A = \$1000(1 + 0.04)^5 \approx \$1216.65$

b. $\$1216.65 - \$1000 = \$216.65$

2. a. $A = \$4200\left(1 + \dfrac{0.04}{4}\right)^{4 \cdot 10} \approx \$6253.23$

b. $\$6253.23 - \$4200 = \$2053.23$

3. $P = \dfrac{A}{\left(1 + \dfrac{r}{n}\right)^{nt}}$

$A = \$10,000, \; r = 0.06, \; n = 52, \; t = 8$

$$P = \frac{10,000}{\left(1 + \dfrac{0.06}{52}\right)^{52 \cdot 8}} \approx \frac{10,000}{1.6156273} \approx \$6189.55$$

4. a. $A = \$6000\left(1 + \dfrac{0.10}{12}\right)^{12 \cdot 1} \approx \$6628.28$

b.
$$A = P(1 + rt)$$
$$6628.28 = 6000\left[1 + (r)(1)\right]$$
$$6628.28 = 6000 + 6000r$$
$$628.28 = 6000r$$
$$\dfrac{628.28}{6000} = \dfrac{6000r}{6000}$$
$$0.105 \approx r$$
$$r \approx 10.5\%$$

5. $Y = \left(1 + \dfrac{r}{n}\right)^{n} - 1$

$Y = \left(1 + \dfrac{0.08}{4}\right)^{4} - 1 \approx 0.0824 = 8.24\%$

Exercise Set 8.3

1. a. $A = \$10,000(1 + 0.04)^{2} = \$10,816$

b. $\$10,816 - \$10,000 = \$816$

2. a. $A = \$8000(1 + 0.06)^{3} = \$9528.13$

b. $\$9528.13 - \$8000 = \$1528.13$

3. a. $A = \$3000\left(1 + \dfrac{0.05}{2}\right)^{2 \cdot 4}$
$= \$3000(1.025)^{8}$
$= \$3655.21$

b. $\$3655.21 - \$3000 = \$655.21$

4. a. $A = \$4000\left(1 + \dfrac{0.04}{2}\right)^{2 \cdot 5}$
$= \$4000(1.02)^{10}$
$= \$4875.98$

b. $\$4875.98 - \$4000 = \$875.98$

5. a. $A = \$9500\left(1 + \dfrac{0.06}{4}\right)^{4 \cdot 5}$
$= \$9500(1.015)^{20}$
$= \$12,795.12$

b. $\$12,795.12 - \$9500 = \$3295.12$

6. a. $A = \$2500\left(1 + \dfrac{0.08}{4}\right)^{4 \cdot 6}$
$= \$2500(1.02)^{24}$
$= \$4021.09$

b. $\$4021.09 - \$2500 = \$1521.09$

7. a. $A = \$4500\left(1 + \dfrac{0.045}{12}\right)^{12 \cdot 3}$
$= \$4500(1.0038)^{36}$
$= \$5149.12$

b. $\$5149.12 - \$4500 = \$649.12$

8. a. $A = \$2500\left(1 + \dfrac{0.065}{12}\right)^{12 \cdot 4}$
$= \$2500(1.0054)^{48}$
$= \$3240.05$

b. $\$3240.05 - \$2500 = \$740.05$

9. a. $A = \$1500\left(1 + \dfrac{0.085}{360}\right)^{360 \cdot 2.5}$
$= \$1500(1.000236)^{900}$
$= \$1855.10$

b. $\$1855.10 - \$1500 = \$355.10$

10. a. $A = \$1200\left(1 + \dfrac{0.085}{360}\right)^{360 \cdot 3.5}$
$= \$1200(1.000236)^{1260}$
$= \$1615.73$

b. $\$1615.73 - \$1200 = \$415.73$

11. a. $A = \$20,000\left(1 + \dfrac{0.045}{360}\right)^{360 \cdot 20}$
$= \$20,000(1.000125)^{7200}$
$= \$49,189.30$

b. $\$49,189.30 - \$20,000 = \$29,189.30$

12. a. $A = \$25,000\left(1 + \dfrac{0.055}{360}\right)^{360 \cdot 20}$
$= \$25,000(1.000153)^{7200}$
$= \$75,097.84$

b. $\$75,097.84 - \$25,000 = \$50,097.84$

13. $A = \$10,000, r = 0.06, n = 2, t = 3$

$$P = \frac{10,000}{\left(1+\frac{0.06}{2}\right)^{2\cdot3}} = \frac{10,000}{(1.03)^6} = \$8374.85$$

14. $A = \$12,000, r = 0.07, n = 2, t = 4$

$$P = \frac{12,000}{\left(1+\frac{0.07}{2}\right)^{2\cdot4}} = \frac{12,000}{(1.035)^8} = \$9112.94$$

15. $A = \$10,000, r = 0.095, n = 12, t = 3$

$$P = \frac{10,000}{\left(1+\frac{0.095}{12}\right)^{12\cdot3}} = \frac{10,000}{(1.00791667)^{36}} = \$7528.59$$

16. $A = \$22,000, r = 0.105, n = 12, t = 4$

$$P = \frac{22,000}{\left(1+\frac{0.105}{12}\right)^{12\cdot4}} = \frac{22,000}{(1.00875)^{48}} = \$14,481.47$$

17. a. $A = \$10,000\left(1+\frac{0.045}{4}\right)^{4\cdot1}$

$$= \$10,000(1.01125)^4$$

$$= \$10,457.65$$

b.
$$A = P(1+rt)$$
$$10,457.65 = 10,000\left[1+r(1)\right]$$
$$10,457.65 = 10,000+10,000r$$
$$457.65 = 10,000r$$
$$\frac{457.65}{10,000} = \frac{10,000r}{10,000}$$
$$0.046 \approx r$$
$$r \approx 4.6\%$$

18. a. $A = \$12,000\left(1+\frac{0.065}{4}\right)^{4\cdot1}$

$$= \$12,000(1.01625)^4$$

$$= \$12,799.22$$

b.
$$A = P(1+rt)$$
$$12,799.22 = 12,000\left[1+r(1)\right]$$
$$12,799.22 = 12,000+12,000r$$
$$799.22 = 12,000r$$
$$\frac{799.22}{12,000} = \frac{12,000r}{12,000}$$
$$0.067 \approx r$$
$$r \approx 6.7\%$$

19. $Y = \left(1+\frac{0.06}{2}\right)^2 - 1 = 0.061 = 6.1\%$

20. $Y = \left(1+\frac{0.06}{4}\right)^4 - 1 \approx 0.061 = 6.1\%$

21. $Y = \left(1+\frac{0.06}{12}\right)^{12} - 1 \approx 0.062 = 6.2\%$

22. $Y = \left(1+\frac{0.06}{360}\right)^{360} - 1 \approx 0.062 = 6.2\%$

23. $Y = \left(1+\frac{0.06}{1000}\right)^{1000} - 1 \approx 0.062 = 6.2\%$

24. $Y = \left(1+\frac{0.06}{100,000}\right)^{1000} - 1 \approx 0.062 = 6.2\%$

25. $Y = \left(1+\frac{0.08}{12}\right)^{12} - 1 \approx 0.0830 = 8.3\%$

$$Y = \left(1+\frac{0.0825}{1}\right)^1 - 1 \approx 0.0825 = 8.3\%$$

The investments are virtually equal.

26. $Y = \left(1+\frac{0.05}{12}\right)^{12} - 1 \approx 0.0512 = 5.1\%$

$$Y = \left(1+\frac{0.0525}{4}\right)^4 - 1 \approx 0.0535 = 5.4\%$$

5.25% compounded quarterly is better.

27. $Y = \left(1+\frac{0.055}{2}\right)^2 - 1 \approx 0.0558 = 5.6\%$

$$Y = \left(1+\frac{0.054}{360}\right)^{360} - 1 \approx 0.05548 = 5.5\%$$

5.5% compounded semiannually is better.

28. $Y = \left(1 + \dfrac{0.07}{1}\right)^1 - 1 = 0.07 = 7\%$

$Y = \left(1 + \dfrac{0.0685}{360}\right)^{360} - 1 \approx 0.07089 = 7.1\%$

6.85% compounded daily is better.

29. $A = P\left(1 + \dfrac{r}{n}\right)^{nt}$

a. $A = \$24\left(1 + \dfrac{0.05}{12}\right)^{12 \cdot 374}$

$= \$24(1.00416667)^{4488}$

$\approx \$3,052,400,000$

b. $A = \$24\left(1 + \dfrac{0.05}{360}\right)^{360 \cdot 374}$

$= \$24(1.00013889)^{134,640}$

$\approx \$3,169,200,000$

30. $A = P\left(1 + \dfrac{r}{n}\right)^{nt}$

$A = \$450,000\left(1 + \dfrac{0.06}{360}\right)^{360 \cdot 212}$

$= \$450,000(1.00016667)^{76,320}$

$\approx \$150,306,600,000$

31. $A = P\left(1 + \dfrac{r}{n}\right)^{nt}$

$A = \$10,000\left(1 + \dfrac{0.09}{12}\right)^{12 \cdot 21}$

$= \$10,000(1.0075)^{252}$

$= \$65,728.51$

32. $P = \dfrac{A}{\left(1 + \dfrac{r}{n}\right)^{nt}}$

$A = \$80,000, r = 0.06, n = 2, t = 13$

$P = \dfrac{80,000}{\left(1 + \dfrac{0.06}{2}\right)^{2 \cdot 13}} = \dfrac{80,000}{(1.03)^{26}} = \$37,095.58$

33. $P = \dfrac{A}{\left(1 + \dfrac{r}{n}\right)^{nt}}$

$A = \$500,000, r = 0.09, n = 12, t = 65 - 30 = 35$

$P = \dfrac{500,000}{\left(1 + \dfrac{0.09}{12}\right)^{12 \cdot 35}} = \dfrac{500,000}{(1.0075)^{420}} = \$21,679.39$

34. $Y = \left(1 + \dfrac{0.045}{12}\right)^{12} - 1 \approx 0.0459 = 4.6\%$

$Y = \left(1 + \dfrac{0.044}{360}\right)^{360} - 1 \approx 0.0450 = 4.5\%$

The First Internet Bank of Indiana account offering 4.5% compounded monthly is better.

35. $A = \$1000 \dfrac{\left(1 + \dfrac{0.07}{1}\right)^{1 \cdot 30} - 1}{\dfrac{0.07}{1}} \approx \$94,460.79$

36. $A = \$100 \dfrac{\left(1 + \dfrac{0.08}{12}\right)^{12 \cdot 16} - 1}{\dfrac{0.08}{12}} \approx \$38,720.91$

37-41. Answers will vary.

42. $A = P\left(1 + \dfrac{r}{n}\right)^{nt}$

Have $6000 in the account for 6 years:

$A = \$6000\left(1 + \dfrac{0.05}{2}\right)^{2 \cdot 6} = \$8069.33$

Have $4000 in the account for 4 years:

$A = \$4000\left(1 + \dfrac{0.05}{2}\right)^{2 \cdot 4} = \$4873.61$

Balance after 6 years $= \$8069.33 + \$4873.61$
$= \$12,942.94$

43. $A = P\left(1 + \dfrac{r}{n}\right)^{nt}$

Start with $5000 in account for 2 years: $A = \$5000\left(1 + \dfrac{0.08}{12}\right)^{12 \cdot 2} = \$5864.44$

Then withdraw $1500, which leaves $5864.44 − $1500 = $4364.44

Leave $4364.44 in the account for 1 year: $A = \$4364.44\left(1 + \dfrac{0.08}{12}\right)^{12 \cdot 1} = \$4726.69$

Then add $2000, so now have $4726.69 + $2000 = $6726.69

Have $6726.69 in account for 3 years: $A = 6726.69\left(1 + \dfrac{0.08}{12}\right)^{12 \cdot 3} = \$8544.49$

44. Substitute Y for r in $A = P(1 + rt)$

Thus, $A = P(1 + Yt)$

Substitute $P(1 + Yt)$ for A in $A = P\left(1 + \dfrac{r}{n}\right)^{nt}$ and substitute 1 for t.

$$P(1 + Yt) = P\left(1 + \dfrac{r}{n}\right)^{nt}$$

$$\frac{P[1 + Y(1)]}{P} = \frac{P\left(1 + \dfrac{r}{n}\right)^{n(1)}}{P}$$

$$1 + Y = \left(1 + \dfrac{r}{n}\right)^{n}$$

$$Y = \left(1 + \dfrac{r}{n}\right)^{n} - 1$$

Check Points 8.4

1. a. Amount financed = $14,000 − $280 = $13,720

b. Total installment price = 60·$315 + $280 = $19,180

c. Finance charge = $19,180 − $14,000 = $5180

2. Find the finance charge per $100 financed: $\dfrac{\$5180}{\$13,720} \cdot \$100 = \$37.76$

For 60 monthly payments, $37.76 is closest to $38.06 in Table 8.3. Therefore the APR is 13.5%.

3. a. $u = \dfrac{kRV}{100 + V}$, where $k = 60 - 24 = 36$, $R = \$315$, $V = \$22.17$

V is found by looking up the APR from Check Point 2 in the "36-payments" row of table 8.3

Interest saved $= u = \dfrac{36(\$315)(\$22.17)}{100 + 22.17} \approx \$2057.85$

b. Payoff amount = (Payment number 24) + (Total of remaining payments after payment 24) − (Interest saved)
= $315 + 36·$315 − $2057.85 = $9597.15

4. a. $u = \dfrac{k(k+1)}{n(n+1)} \cdot F$, where $k = 36$, $n = 60$, $F = \$5180$ (Computed in Check Point 1)

Interest saved $= u = \dfrac{36(36+1)}{60(60+1)} \cdot 5180 \approx \$1885.18$

b.   Payoff amount = (Payment number 24) + (Total of remaining payments after payment 24) – (Interest saved)

$= \$315 + 36 \cdot \$315 - \$1885.18 = \$9769.82$

5. a.   The interest is $I = Prt = (\$4720 - \$1000) \times 0.016 \times 1 = \$3720 \times 0.016 \times 1 = \$59.52$

b.   New balance $= \$3720 + \$59.52 + \$1025 + \$45 = \$4849.52$

c.   Minimum monthly payment $= \dfrac{\text{balance owed}}{36} = \dfrac{\$4849.52}{36} \approx \$135$.

6. a.   Unpaid Balance Method: $I = Prt = (\$6800 - \$500) \times 0.018 \times 1 = \$6300 \times 0.018 \times 1 = \$113.40$

b.   Previous Balance Method: $I = Prt = \$6800 \times 0.018 \times 1 = \$122.40$

c.   Average daily balance $= \dfrac{(\$6800)(7) + (\$6300)(24)}{31} \approx \$6412.90$

Average Daily Balance Method: $I = Prt = \$6412.90 \times 0.018 \times 1 \approx \$115.43$.

Exercise Set 8.4

1. a.   Amount financed $= \$27{,}000 - \$5000 = \$22{,}000$

b.   Total installment price $= 60 \cdot \$410 + \$5000 = \$29{,}600$

c.   Finance charge $= \$29{,}600 - \$27{,}000 = \$2{,}600$

2. a.   Amount financed $= \$2450 - \$550 = \$1900$

b.   Total installment price $= 24 \cdot \$94.50 + \$550 = \$2818$

c.   Financed charge $= \$2818 - \$2450 = \$368$

3. a.   Amount financed $= \$1100 - 100 = \$1000$

b.   Total installment price $= 12 \cdot \$110 + \$100 = \$1420$

c.   Finance charge $= \$1420 - \$1100 = \$320$

4. a.   Amount financed $= \$5675 - \$1223 = \$4452$

b.   Total installment price $= 48 \cdot \$125 + \$1223 = \$7223$

c.   Finance charge $= \$7223 - \$5675 = \$1548$

5. In the row for 12 monthly payments, find the value $6.90. That value is in the column for 12.5%.

6. In the row for 18 monthly payments, find the value $12.72. That value is in the column for 15.5%.

7. In the row for 24 monthly payments, find the value $15.80. That value is in the column for 14.5%.

8. In the row for 12 monthly payments, find the value $8.59. That value is in the column for 15.5%.

9. Finance charge per $100 financed $= \dfrac{\text{Finance charge}}{\text{Amount financed}} \cdot \$100 = \dfrac{\$1279}{\$4450} \cdot \$100 \approx \$28.74$

   Using Table 8.3 with 48 monthly payments the APR is 13.0%.

10. Finance charge per $100 financed $= \dfrac{\text{Finance charge}}{\text{Amount financed}} \cdot \$100 = \dfrac{\$264}{\$1200} \cdot \$100 = \$22.00$

    Using Table 8.3 with 30 monthly payments, the APR is 16.0%.

11. **a.** Amount financed $= \$17{,}500 - \$500 = \$17{,}000$

    b. Total installment price $= 60 \cdot \$360.55 + \$500 = \$22{,}133$

    c. Finance charge $= \$22{,}133 - \$17{,}500 = \$4633$

    d. Finance charge per $100 financed $= \dfrac{\$4633}{\$17{,}000} \cdot \$100 \approx \$27.25$. The APR is 10.0%.

12. **a.** Amount financed $= \$18{,}000 - \$600 = \$17{,}400$

    b. Total installment price $= 60 \cdot \$385 + \$600 = \$23{,}700$

    c. Finance charge $= \$23{,}700 - \$18{,}000 = \$5700$

    d. Finance charge per $100 financed $= \dfrac{\$5700}{\$17{,}400} \cdot \$100 \approx \$32.76$. The APR is 12.0%

13. **a.** $u = \dfrac{kRV}{100 + V}$, where $k = 60 - 24 = 36$, $R = \$360.55$, and $V = \$16.16$

    V is found by looking up the APR from Exercise 11d in the "36-payments" row of table 8.3

    Interest saved $= u = \dfrac{36(\$360.55)(\$16.16)}{100 + 16.16} \approx \$1805.73$

    b. Payoff amount = (Payment number 24) + (Total of remaining payments after payment 24) − (Interest saved)
    $= \$360.55 + 36 \cdot \$360.55 - \$1805.73$
    $= \$11{,}534.62$

    c. $u = \dfrac{k(k + 1)}{n(n + 1)} \cdot F$, where $k = 36$, $n = 60$, and $F = \$4633$ (Computed in exercise 11c)

    Interest saved $= u = \dfrac{36(36 + 1)}{60(60 + 1)} \cdot 4633 \approx \$1686.11$

    d. Payoff amount = (Payment number 24) + (Total of remaining payments after payment 24) − (Interest saved)
    $= \$360.55 + 36 \cdot \$360.55 - \$1686.11$
    $= \$11{,}654.24$

14. **a.** $u = \dfrac{kRV}{100 + V}$, where $k = 60 - 24 = 36$, $R = \$385$, and $V = \$19.57$

    V is found by looking up the APR from Exercise 12d in the "36-payments" row of table 8.3

    Interest saved $= u = \dfrac{(36)(385)(19.57)}{100 + 19.57} \approx \$2268.46$

b. Payoff amount = (Payment number 24) + (Total of remaining payments after payment 24) – (Interest saved)

$$= \$385 + 36 \cdot \$385 - \$2268.46$$

$$= \$11,976.54$$

c. $u = \dfrac{k(k+1)}{n(n+1)} \cdot F$, where $k = 36$, $n = 60$, and $F = \$5700$ (Computed in Exercise 12c)

Interest saved = $u = \dfrac{36(36+1)}{60(60+1)} \cdot 5700 = \$2074.43$

d. Payoff amount = (Payment number 24) + (Total of remaining payments after payment 24) – (Interest saved)

$$= \$385 + 36 \cdot \$385 - \$2074.43$$

$$= \$12,170.57$$

15. a. Unpaid balance = $950 – $100 = $850
$I = Prt = (\$850)(0.013)(1) = \$11.05$

b. Balance due June 9
= $850 + $11.05 + $85 + $67
= $1013.05

c. Minimum monthly payment = $\dfrac{\$1013.05}{36} \approx \$28$

16. a. Unpaid balance = $425 – $75 = $350
$I = Prt = (350)(0.0175)(1) = \$6.13$

b. Balance due October 9 = $350 + $6.13 + $45 + $77 = $478.13

c. Minimum monthly payment = $40 because the new balance is between $450.01 and $500.00

17. a. $I = Prt = (\$330.90)(0.015)(1) = \$4.96$

b. New Balance = $445.59 + $278.06 – $110 + $4.96 = $618.61

c. Minimum monthly payment = $\dfrac{\$618.61}{10} = \$61.86$ because the new balance is over $500.

18. a. $I = Prt = (\$205.60)(0.018)(1) = \$3.70$

b. New balance = $220 + $90 – $60 + $3.70 = $253.70

c. Minimum monthly payment = $20 because the new balance is between $250.01 and $300.

19. a. Unpaid balance = $3000 – $2500 = $500
$I = Prt = (\$500)(0.015)(1) = \$7.50$

b. Previous balance
$I = Prt = (\$3000)(0.015)(1) = \$45$

c. Average daily balance = $\dfrac{(\$3000)(5) + (\$500)(25)}{30} \approx \$916.67$

$I = Prt = (\$916.67)(0.015)(1) = \$13.75$

20. a. Unpaid balance = $2000 – $400 = $1600
$I = Prt = (\$1600)(0.022)(1) = \$35.20$

b. Previous balance

$I = Prt = (\$2000)(0.022)(1) = \$44$

c. Average daily balance $= \dfrac{(\$2000)(5) + (\$1600)(26)}{31} \approx \$1664.52$

$I = Prt = (\$1664.52)(0.022)(1) = \$36.62$

21-29. Answers will vary.

30. d is true because $12 \times 2.2\% = 26.4\%$

31. The payments will be greater than $\dfrac{\$1400 - \$200}{30} = \$40$ because a finance charge must be paid.

Answer b is reasonable.

32. Answer c is reasonable because 1% of \$360 is \$3.60 so 1.3% of \$359.58 must be slightly higher than \$3.60.
Actual value: $I = Prt = (\$359.58)(0.013)(1) = \$4.67$

33. Answers will vary.

34.

Option A:	Interest	Payment	Balance
Month 1	$22.50	$300.00	$1222.50
Month 2	$18.34	$300.00	$940.84
Month 3	$14.11	$300.00	$654.95
Month 4	$9.82	$300.00	$364.77
Month 5	$5.47	$300.00	$70.24
Month 6	$1.05	$71.29	$0.00
	$71.29		

Option B:	Interest	Payment	Balance
Month 1	$22.50	$322.50	$1200
Month 2	$18.00	$318.00	$900
Month 3	$13.50	$313.50	$600
Month 4	$9.00	$309.00	$300
Month 5	$4.50	$304.50	$0
	$67.50		

Interest saved $= \$71.29 - \$67.50 = \$3.79$

35. a. Number of days $= 31$

Average daily balance $= \dfrac{\$11,664.15}{30} = \$376.26$

b. Finance charge $= (0.013)(376.26) = \$4.89$

c. Balance due $= \$466.15 + \$4.89 = \$471.04$

36. a. Number of days $= 31$

Average daily balance $= \dfrac{\$18,150.27}{31} = \$585.49$

b. Finance charge $= (0.0075)(\$585.49) = \$4.39$

c. Balance due $= \$631.77 + \$4.39 = \$636.16$

Check Points 8.5

1. **a.** Down payment $= 0.10(\$240,000) = \$24,000$

    b. Amount of mortgage $= \$240,000 - \$24,000 = \$216,000$

    c. Three points $= 0.03(\$216,000) = \$6480$

    d. Thousands of dollars of mortgage: $\dfrac{\$216,000}{\$1000} = 216$

    Monthly payment $= \$6.32 \cdot 216 = \$1365.12$

    e. Total cost of interest = (Total of all monthly payments) – (Amount of the mortgage)
    $$= 360 \times \$1365.12 - \$216,000$$
    $$= 275,443.20$$

2. Monthly Payment:

    $$PMT = PV \dfrac{\frac{r}{n}}{1 - \left(1 + \frac{r}{n}\right)^{-nt}}$$

    $$= 216,000 \dfrac{\frac{0.065}{12}}{1 - \left(1 + \frac{0.065}{12}\right)^{-12 \cdot 15}}$$

    $$\approx \$1881.59$$

    Total cost of interest = (Total of all monthly payments) – (Amount of the mortgage)
    $$= 180 \times \$1881.59 - \$216,000$$
    $$= 122,686.20$$

    Amount saved with 15 year mortgage:
    $$= \$275,443.20 - \$122,686.20 = \$152,757$$

3. Interest for first month $= Prt = \$200,000 \times 0.07 \times \dfrac{1}{12} \approx \$1166.67$

    Principle payment $= \$1550.00 - \$1166.67 = \$383.33$
    Balance of loan $= \$200,000 - \$383.33 = \$199,616.67$

    Interest for second month $= Prt = \$199,616.67 \times 0.07 \times \dfrac{1}{12} \approx \$1164.43$

    Principle payment $= \$1550.00 - \$1164.43 = \$385.57$
    Balance of loan $= \$199,616.67 - \$385.57 = \$199,231.10$

Payment Number	Interest Payment	Principal Payment	Balance of Loan
1	$1166.67	$383.33	$199,616.67
2	$1164.43	$385.57	$199,231.10

Exercise Set 8.5

1. **a.** Down payment $= 0.20(\$125,000)$
$$= \$25,000$$

 b. Amount of mortgage $= \$125,000 - \$25,000$
$$= \$100,000$$

 c. Three points $= 0.03(\$100,000) = \$3000$

 d. $\dfrac{\$100,000}{\$1000} = 100$ thousands of dollars of mortgage
 Monthly payment $= \$6.65 \cdot 100 = \$665$

 e. Total cost of interest $=$ (Total of all monthly payments) $-$ (Amount of the mortgage)
$$= 360 \cdot \$665 - \$100,000$$
$$= \$139,400$$

2. **a.** Down payment $= 0.05(\$85,000) = \$4250$

 b. Amount of mortgage $= \$85,000 - \$4250 = \$80,750$

 c. One point $= 0.01(\$80,750) = \$807.50$

 d. $\dfrac{\$80,750}{\$1000} = 80.75$ thousands of dollars of mortgage
 Monthly payment $= \$7.34 \cdot 80.75 \approx \$593$

 e. Total cost of interest $=$ (Total of all monthly payments) $-$ (Amount of the mortgage)
$$= 360 \cdot \$593 - \$80,750$$
$$= \$132,730$$

3. Down payment $= 0.05(\$40,000) = \$2000$
 Mortgage amount $= \$40,000 - \$2000 = \$38,000$
 $\dfrac{\$38,000}{\$1000} = 38$ thousands of dollars of mortgage

 20-year option:
 Monthly payment $= \$8.36 \cdot 38 \approx \$318$
 Total cost of interest $= 20 \cdot 12 \cdot \$318 - \$38,000 = \$38,320$

 30-year option:
 Monthly payment $= \$7.34 \cdot 38 \approx \$279$
 Total cost of interest $= 360 \cdot \$279 - \$38,000 = \$62,440$

 Interest savings with 20-year option $= \$62,440 - \$38,320 = \$24,120$

4. Down payment $= 0.15(\$160,000) = \$24,000$
 Mortgage amount $= \$160,000 - \$24,000 = \$136,000$

 $\dfrac{\$136,000}{\$1000} = 136$ thousands of dollars of mortgage

 15-year option:
 Monthly payment $= \$9.56 \cdot 136 \approx \$1300$
 Total cost of interest $= 15 \cdot 12 \cdot \$1300 - \$136,000 = \$98,000$

30-year option:
Monthly payment = $7.34 · 136 ≈ $998
Total cost of interest = 30 · 12 · $998 − $136,000 = $223,280

Interest savings with 15-year option = $223,280 − $98,000 = $125,280

5. $\dfrac{\$100,000}{\$1000}$ = 100 thousands of dollars of mortgage

30-year mortgage:
Monthly payment = $7.34 · 100 = $734
Total cost of interest = 360 · $734 − $100,000 = $164,240

20-year mortgage:
Monthly payment = $8.06 · 100 = $806
Total cost of interest = 20 · 12 · $806 − $100,000 = $93,440

The 20-year mortgage at 7.5% is more economical.

6. $\dfrac{\$90,000}{\$1000}$ = 90 thousands of dollars of mortgage

30-year mortgage:
Monthly payment = $7.34 · 90 ≈ $661
Total cost of interest = 360 · $661 − $90,000 = $147,960

15-year mortgage:
Monthly payment = $9.28 · 90 ≈ $835
Total cost of interest = 15 · 12 · $835 − $90,000 = $60,300

The 15-year mortgage at 7.5% is more economical.

7. Down payment = 0.30($80,000,000)
= $24,000,000

Amount of mortgage
= $80,000,000 − $24,000,000
= $56,000,000

Monthly payment = $6.32 · 56,000 ≈ $353,920

$$PMT = PV\frac{\frac{r}{n}}{1-\left(1+\frac{r}{n}\right)^{-nt}}$$

$$= 56,000,000\frac{\frac{0.063}{12}}{1-\left(1+\frac{0.063}{12}\right)^{-12\cdot30}}$$

$$\approx \$346,624.76$$

Total cost of interest = 360 · $346,624.76 − $56,000,000
$$\approx \$68,784,914$$

8. a. Down Payment: $0.10 \times \$180,000 = \$18,000$
Amount of mortgage: $\$180,000 - \$18,000 = \$162,000$
Monthly Payment:

$$PMT = PV \dfrac{\dfrac{r}{n}}{1-\left(1+\dfrac{r}{n}\right)^{-nt}}$$

$$= 162,000 \dfrac{\dfrac{0.063}{12}}{1-\left(1+\dfrac{0.063}{12}\right)^{-12\cdot30}}$$

$$\approx \$1002.74$$

b. $$PV = PMT \dfrac{1-\left(1+\dfrac{r}{n}\right)^{-nt}}{\dfrac{r}{n}}$$

$$= 1002.74 \dfrac{1-\left(1+\dfrac{0.063}{12}\right)^{-12\cdot20}}{\dfrac{0.063}{12}}$$

$$\approx \$136,641.85$$

c. $$PV = PMT \dfrac{1-\left(1+\dfrac{r}{n}\right)^{-nt}}{\dfrac{r}{n}}$$

$$= 1002.74 \dfrac{1-\left(1+\dfrac{0.063}{12}\right)^{-12\cdot10}}{\dfrac{0.063}{12}}$$

$$\approx \$89,106.30$$

9. a. Down Payment: $0.10 \times \$220,000 = \$22,000$
Amount of mortgage: $\$220,000 - \$22,000 = \$198,000$
Monthly Payment:

$$PMT = PV \dfrac{\dfrac{r}{n}}{1-\left(1+\dfrac{r}{n}\right)^{-nt}}$$

$$= 198,000 \dfrac{\dfrac{0.064}{12}}{1-\left(1+\dfrac{0.064}{12}\right)^{-12\cdot30}}$$

$$\approx \$1238.50$$

b. $$PV = PMT \dfrac{1-\left(1+\dfrac{r}{n}\right)^{-nt}}{\dfrac{r}{n}}$$

$$= 1238.50 \dfrac{1-\left(1+\dfrac{0.064}{12}\right)^{-12\cdot20}}{\dfrac{0.064}{12}}$$

$$\approx \$167,433.30$$

c. $PV = PMT \dfrac{1 - \left(1 + \frac{r}{n}\right)^{-nt}}{\frac{r}{n}}$

$= 1238.50 \dfrac{1 - \left(1 + \frac{0.064}{12}\right)^{-12 \cdot 10}}{\frac{0.064}{12}}$

$\approx \$109{,}563.15$

10. a. Down Payment: $0.05 \times \$100{,}000 = \$5{,}000$

Amount of mortgage: $\$100{,}000 - \$5{,}000 = \$95{,}000$

Monthly Payment:

$PMT = PV \dfrac{\frac{r}{n}}{1 - \left(1 + \frac{r}{n}\right)^{-nt}}$

$= 95{,}000 \dfrac{\frac{0.065}{12}}{1 - \left(1 + \frac{0.065}{12}\right)^{-12 \cdot 30}}$

$\approx \$600.46$

b. $PV = PMT \dfrac{1 - \left(1 + \frac{r}{n}\right)^{-nt}}{\frac{r}{n}}$

$= 600.46 \dfrac{1 - \left(1 + \frac{0.065}{12}\right)^{-12 \cdot 25}}{\frac{0.065}{12}}$

$\approx \$88{,}930.43$

c. Maximum amount available:

$= (0.80)(125{,}000) - 88{,}930.43$

$= 100{,}000 - 88{,}930.43$

$= \$11{,}069.57$

11. a. Down Payment: $0.05 \times \$120{,}000 = \$6{,}000$

Amount of mortgage: $\$120{,}000 - \$6{,}000 = \$114{,}000$

Monthly Payment:

$PMT = PV \dfrac{\frac{r}{n}}{1 - \left(1 + \frac{r}{n}\right)^{-nt}}$

$= 114{,}000 \dfrac{\frac{0.07}{12}}{1 - \left(1 + \frac{0.07}{12}\right)^{-12 \cdot 30}}$

$\approx \$758.44$

b. $PV = PMT\dfrac{1-\left(1+\frac{r}{n}\right)^{-nt}}{\frac{r}{n}}$

$= 758.44\dfrac{1-\left(1+\frac{0.07}{12}\right)^{-12\cdot20}}{\frac{0.07}{12}}$

$\approx \$97,826.12$

c. Maximum amount available:

$= (0.80)(250,000) - 97,826.12$

$= 200,000 - 97,826.12$

$= \$102,173.88$

12-20. Answers will vary.

21. In the formula $PV = PMT\dfrac{1-\left(1+\frac{r}{n}\right)^{-nt}}{\frac{r}{n}}$

note that the exponent, $-nt$, is the negative of the number of remaining payments. In a 30-year mortgage there are 360 payments. After x payments, there are $360 - x$ remaining payments. The negative of $360 - x$ can be written as $x - 360$.

Thus the formula is $PV = 1238.50\dfrac{1-\left(1+\frac{0.064}{12}\right)^{x-360}}{\frac{0.064}{12}}$

22. Begin with $PMT = PV\dfrac{\frac{r}{n}}{1-\left(1+\frac{r}{n}\right)^{-nt}}$

Next multiply both sides by $\dfrac{1-\left(1+\frac{r}{n}\right)^{-nt}}{\frac{r}{n}}$

which gives:

$PMT\dfrac{1-\left(1+\frac{r}{n}\right)^{-nt}}{\frac{r}{n}} = PV\dfrac{\frac{r}{n}}{1-\left(1+\frac{r}{n}\right)^{-nt}}\cdot\dfrac{1-\left(1+\frac{r}{n}\right)^{-nt}}{\frac{r}{n}}$

Canceling produces:

$PMT\dfrac{1-\left(1+\frac{r}{n}\right)^{-nt}}{\frac{r}{n}} = PV$

Finally, interchange the sides: $PV = PMT\dfrac{1-\left(1+\frac{r}{n}\right)^{-nt}}{\frac{r}{n}}$

Check Points 8.6

1. a. High price = $63.38,
Low price = $42.37

b. Dividend = $0.72·3000 = $2160

c. Annual return for dividends alone = 1.5%
1.5% is much lower than the 3.5% bank rate.

d. Shares traded =
72,032·100 = 7,203,200 shares

e. High price = $49.94,
Low price = $48.33

f. Price at close = $49.50

g. The price went up $0.03 per share.

h. Annual earnings per share $= \dfrac{\$49.50}{37} \approx \$1.34$

2. a. Earnings per share
$19.16 − $6.88 = $12.28
Total earnings
$12.28×500 = $6140

b. Total sale price $19.16×500 = $9580
Broker's commission
$9580×0.025 = $239.50

Exercise Set 8.6

1. a. High price = $73.25,
Low price = $45.44

b. Dividend = $1.20·700 = $840

c. Annual return for dividends alone = 2.2%
2.2% is lower than a 3% bank rate.

d. Shares traded = 5915·100 = 591,500 shares

e. High price = $56.38,
Low price = $54.38

f. Price at close = $55.50

g. The price went up $1.25 per share.

h. Annual earnings per share $= \dfrac{\$55.50}{17}$
$\approx \$3.26$

2. a. High price = $78.34, Low price = $35.38

b. Dividend = $2.18·700 = $1526

c. Annual return for dividends alone = 4.7%
4.7% is higher than a 3% bank rate.

d. Shares traded = 7473·100 = 747,300 shares

e. High price = $48.19, Low price = $46.63

f. Price at close = $46.88

g. The price went down $1.31 per share

h. Annual earnings per share
$= \dfrac{\$46.88}{22} \approx \$2.13$

3. a. Earnings per share = $65.00 − $39.06
= $25.94
Total earnings = 250($25.94) = $6485

b. Total sale price = 250($65.00)
= $16,250
Broker's commission = 0.025($16,250)
= $406.25

4. a. Earnings per share
= $72.44 − $36.75 = $35.69
Total earnings
= 350($35.69) = $12,491.50

b. Total sale price = 350($72.44) = $25,354
Broker's commission
= 0.025($25,354) = $633.85

5. a. Cost of stock = 400($37.50) = $15,000

b. Broker's commission = 0.02($15,000)
= $300

6. a. Cost of stock = 600($56.25) = $33,750

b. Broker's commission = 0.02($33,750)
= $675

7. a. Cost of stock = $240($17.75) = $4260

b. Broker's commission
= 0.025($4260) + 0.125(40)
= $111.50

8. a. Cost of stock = 370($22.75) = $8417.50

   b. Broker's commission
     = 0.025($8417.50) + 0.125(70) = $219.19

9-19. Answers will vary.

Chapter 8 Review Exercises

1. $\dfrac{4}{5} = 4 \div 5 = 0.80 = 80\%$

2. $\dfrac{1}{8} = 1 \div 8 = 0.125 = 12.5\%$

3. $\dfrac{3}{4} = 3 \div 4 = 0.75 = 75\%$

4. $0.72 = 72\%$

5. $0.0035 = 0.35\%$

6. $4.756 = 475.6\%$

7. $65\% = 0.65$

8. $99.7\% = 0.997$

9. $150\% = 1.50$

10. $3\% = 0.03$

11. $0.65\% = 0.0065$

12. $\frac{1}{4}\% = 0.25\% = 0.0025$

13. $A = PB$
    $A = 0.08 \cdot 120$
    $A = 9.6$

14. $A = PB$
    $90 = 0.45 \cdot B$
    $\dfrac{90}{0.45} = B$
    $200 = B$
    $B = 200$

15. $A = PB$
    $36 = P \cdot 75$
    $\dfrac{36}{75} = P$
    $0.48 = P$
    $P = 48\%$

16. $A = PB$
    $1440 = 0.72 \cdot B$
    $\dfrac{1440}{0.72} = B$
    $2000 = B$
    2000 people were polled.

17. $A = PB$
    $A = 0.20 \cdot 2000$
    $A = 400$
    400 people

18. $\dfrac{\$35,000}{\$50,000} = 0.70 = 70\%$ in stock

19. a. Tax = 0.06($24) = $1.44

   b. Total cost = $24 + $1.44 = $25.44

20. a. Amount of discount = 0.35($850)
                      = $297.50

   b. Sale price = $850 − $297.50 = $552.50

21. $\dfrac{45 - 40}{40} = 0.125 = 12.5\%$ increase.

22. $\dfrac{\$56.00 - \$36.40}{\$56.00} = 0.35 = 35\%$ decrease.

23. The statement is not true.
The 10% loss is $1000.
$[0.10 \times 10,000 = 1000]$
This leaves $9000.
The 10% rise is $900.
$[0.10 \times 9,000 = 900]$
Thus there is $9900 in the portfolio.
Find the percent of decrease:
$\dfrac{\text{amount of decrease}}{\text{original amount}} = \dfrac{100}{10,000} = 0.01 = 1\%$
The net loss of $100 is a 1% decrease from the original.

24. $I = Prt = (\$6000)(0.03)(1) = \$180$

25. $I = Prt = (\$8400)(0.05)(6) = \$2520$

26. $I = Prt = (\$20,000)(0.08)\left(\dfrac{9}{12}\right) = \$1200$

27. $I = Prt = (\$36,000)(0.15)\left(\dfrac{60}{360}\right) = \$900$

28. a. $I = Prt$

$\quad = (\$3500)(0.105)\left(\dfrac{4}{12}\right)$

$\quad = \$122.50$

b. Maturity value $= \$3500 + \$122.50$

$\quad\quad\quad\quad\quad\quad\quad = \$3622.50$

29. $A = P(1 + rt)$

$A = 12,000(1 + 0.082 \times \frac{9}{12})$

$A = \$12,738$

30. $A = P(1 + rt)$

$5750 = 5000\big(1 + r(2)\big)$

$5750 = 5000 + 10,000r$

$750 = 10,000r$

$0.075 = r$

$r = 7.5\%$

31. $A = P(1 + rt)$

$16,000 = P\big(1 + (0.065)(3)\big)$

$16,000 = 1.195P$

$13,389.12 = P$

$P = \$13,389.12$

32. $A = P(1 + rt)$

$12,000 = P\big(1 + (0.073)(4)\big)$

$12,000 = 1.292P$

$9287.93 = P$

$P = \$9287.93$

33. $A = P(1 + rt)$

$1800 = 1500\big(1 + r(\frac{1}{2})\big)$

$1800 = 1500 + 750r$

$300 = 750r$

$0.4 = r$

$r = 40\%$

34. a. $I = Prt = (1800)(0.07)\left(\frac{9}{12}\right) = \$94.50$

b. Amount received: $\$1800 - \$94.50 = \$1705.50$

c. $I = Prt$

$94.50 = (1705.50)(r)\left(\frac{9}{12}\right)$

$94.50 = 1279.125r$

$0.0739 = r$

$r = 7.4\%$

35. a. $A = \$7000(1 + 0.03)^5$

$\quad = \$7000(1.03)^5$

$\quad \approx \$8114.92$

b. Interest $= \$8114.92 - \$7000$

$\quad\quad\quad\quad = \$1114.92$

36. a. $A = \$30,000\left(1 + \dfrac{0.025}{4}\right)^{4 \cdot 10}$

$\quad = \$30,000(1.00625)^{40}$

$\quad \approx \$38,490.80$

b. Interest $= \$38,490.80 - \$30,000$

$\quad\quad\quad\quad = \$8490.80$

37. a. $A = \$2500\left(1 + \dfrac{0.04}{12}\right)^{12 \cdot 20}$

$\quad = \$2500(1.003333)^{240}$

$\quad \approx \$5556.46$

b. Interest $= \$5556.46 - \$2500$

$\quad\quad\quad\quad = \$3056.46$

38. $P = \dfrac{100,000}{\left(1 + \dfrac{0.10}{12}\right)^{12 \cdot 18}} \approx \$16,653.64$

39. $P = \dfrac{75,000}{\left(1 + \dfrac{0.05}{4}\right)^{4 \cdot 35}} \approx \$13,175.19$

40. a. $A = \$2000\left(1 + \dfrac{0.06}{4}\right)^{4 \cdot 1}$

$\quad = \$2000(1.015)^4$

$\quad = \$2122.73$

b.
$$A = P(1+rt)$$
$$2122.73 = 2000\left[1+r(1)\right]$$
$$2122.73 = 2000 + 2000r$$
$$122.73 = 2000r$$
$$0.061365 \approx r$$
$$r \approx 6.1\%$$

41. $Y = \left(1+\dfrac{0.055}{4}\right)^4 - 1 \approx 0.0561 = 5.6\%$

5.5% compounded quarterly is equivalent to 5.6% compounded annually.

42. 6.25% compounded monthly:

$$Y = \left(1+\dfrac{0.0625}{12}\right)^{12} - 1 \approx 0.0643 = 6.4\%$$

6.3% compounded annually:

$$Y = \left(1+\dfrac{0.063}{1}\right)^{1} - 1 \approx 0.063 = 6.3\%$$

6.25% compounded monthly is better than 6.3% compounded annually.

43. a. Amount financed $= \$16,500 - \$500$
$$= \$16,000$$

b. Total installment price
$$= 60(\$350) + \$500$$
$$= \$21,500$$

c. Finance charge $= \$21,500 - \$16,500$
$$= \$5000$$

d. Finance charge per $100 financed
$$\dfrac{\$5000}{\$16,000} \times \$100 = \$31.25$$
The APR is approximately 11.5%.

44. a. Interest saved
$k = 12$, $R = \$350$, $v = \$6.34$
$$u = \dfrac{(12)(350)(6.34)}{100+6.34} = \$250.40$$

b. Payoff amount
$$= \$350 + (12)(\$350) - \$250.40$$
$$= \$4299.60$$

45. a. Interest saved
$k = 12$, $n = 60$, $F = \$5000$
$$u = \dfrac{12(12+1)}{60(60+1)} \cdot 5000 \approx \$213.11$$

b. Payoff amount
$$= \$350 + 12(\$350) - \$213.11 = \$4336.89$$

46. The actuarial method saves the borrower more money.

47. a. Unpaid balance $= \$1300 - \$200$
$$= \$1100$$
$$I = Prt = (\$1100)(0.015)(1) = \$16.50$$

b. Balance due
$$= \$1100 + \$380 + \$120 + \$140 + \$16.50$$
$$= \$1756.50$$

c. Minimum monthly payment
$$= \left(\dfrac{1}{36}\right)(\$1756.50)$$
$$= \$48.79$$
$$\approx \$49$$

48. a. Unpaid $= \$3600 - \$2000$
$$= \$1600$$
$$I = Prt = (\$1600)(0.018)(1) = \$28.80$$

b. Previous balance $= \$3600$
$$I = Prt = (\$3600)(0.018)(1) = \$64.80$$

c. Average daily balance
$$= \dfrac{(\$3600)(5) + (\$1600)(26)}{31} \approx \$1922.58$$
$$I = Prt = (\$1922.58)(0.018)(1) = \$34.61$$

49. a. Down payment $= 0.20(\$145,000) = \$29,000$

b. Amount of the mortgage
$$= \$145,000 - \$29,000 = \$116,000$$

c. Two points $= 0.02(\$116,000) = \$2320$

d. $\dfrac{\$116,000}{\$1000}$
$= 116$ thousands of dollars of mortgage
Monthly payment $\$6.65 \cdot 116 = \$771.40$

e. Total cost of interest
$$= 360(\$771.40) - \$116,000$$
$$= \$161,704$$

50. 30-year mortgage at 8.5%:
$$\frac{\$70,000}{\$1000} = 70 \text{ thousands of dollars of mortgage}$$

Monthly payment = $\$7.69 \cdot 70 = \$538.30$
Total cost of interest
$= 360(\$538.30) - \$70,000 = \$123,788$

20-year mortgage at 8%:
Monthly payment = $\$8.36 \cdot 70 = \$585.20$
Total cost of interest = $240(\$585.20) - \$70,000 = \$70,448$

A fixed-rate 20-year mortgage at 8% is more economical.

51. Amortization schedule:

Payment Number	Interest Payment	Principal Payment	Balance of Loan
1	$500	$59.20	$79,940.80
2	$499.63	$59.57	$79,881.23

Calculations for table:
Payment number 1:

$$I = Prt = (\$80,000)(0.075)\left(\frac{1}{12}\right) = \$500$$

Principal Payment = $\$559.20 - \$500 = \$59.20$
Balance of Loan = $\$80,000 - \$59.20 = \$79,940.80$

Payment number 2:

$$I = Prt = (\$79,940.80)(0.075)\left(\frac{1}{12}\right) = \$499.63$$

Principal Payment = $\$559.20 - \$499.63 = \$59.57$
Balance of Loan = $\$79,940.80 - \$59.57 = \$79,881.23$

52. $\dfrac{\$100,000}{\$1000} = 100$ thousands of dollars of mortgage
Option A: Monthly payment = $\$7.69 \cdot 100 = \$769$
Option B: Monthly Payment = $\$6.99 \cdot 100 = \$699$

53. High = $64.06, Low = $26.13

54. Dividend = $0.16(900) = $144

55. Annual return for dividends alone = 0.3%

56. Shares traded yesterday = $5458 \cdot 100$
$= 545,800$ shares

57. High = $61.25, Low = $59.25

58. Price at close = $61

59. Change in price = $1.75 increase

60. Annual earnings per share $\dfrac{\$61}{41} \approx \$1.49$

61. a. Earnings per share = $\$43.75 - \$27.50$
$= \$16.25$
Total earnings = $600(\$16.25) = \$9750$

b. Total sale price = $600(\$43.75)$
$= \$26,250$
Brokers Commission = $0.025(\$26,250)$
$= \$656.25$

62-63. Answers will vary.

Chapter 8 Test

1. $A = PB$
$A = 0.074 \cdot 260$
$A = 19.24$

2. $A = PB$
$48 = 0.30 \cdot B$
$\dfrac{48}{0.30} = B$
$160 = B$
$B = 160$

3. $A = PB$
$18 = P \cdot 80$
$\dfrac{18}{80} = P$
$0.225 = P$
$P = 22.5\%$

4. a. Discount = $0.15(\$120) = \$18$

b. Sale price = $\$120 - \$18 = \$102$

5. Percent increase $\dfrac{12 - 10}{10} = 0.2 = 20\%$

6. Future value:
$$A = \$2000\left(1 + \frac{0.06}{12}\right)^{12 \cdot 5}$$
$$\approx \$2697.70$$

Interest = $\$2697.70 - \$2000$
$= \$697.70$

7. $A = P(1 + rt)$

$A = 2400\left(1 + (0.12)\left(\frac{3}{12}\right)\right)$

$A = \$2472$

The future value is $2472.
The interest earned is $72.

8. $P = \dfrac{100{,}000}{\left(1 + \dfrac{0.10}{2}\right)^{2 \cdot 20}} \approx \$14{,}204.57$

9. $A = P(1 + rt)$

$3000 = 2000\left(1 + r(2)\right)$

$3000 = 2000 + 4000r$

$1000 = 4000r$

$0.25 = r$

$r = 25\%$

10. $A = P(1 + rt)$

$7000 = P\left(1 + (0.09)\left(\frac{6}{12}\right)\right)$

$7000 = 1.045P$

$6698.57 = P$

$P = \$6698.57$

11. $Y = \left(1 + \dfrac{0.045}{4}\right)^4 - 1 \approx 0.0458 = 4.58\%$

4.5% compounded quarterly is equivalent to 4.58% compounded annually.

12. Amount financed $= \$16{,}000 - \$3000$
$ = \$13{,}000$

13. Total installment price $= 60(\$300) + \$3{,}000$
$ = \$21{,}000$

14. Finance charge $= \$21{,}000 - \$16{,}000$
$ = \$5000$

15. Finance charge per $100 financed
$= \dfrac{\$5000}{\$13{,}000} \cdot \$100$
$= \$38.46$
The APR is approximately 13.5%.

16. Interest saved
$k = 60 - 36 = 24, n = 60, F = \$5000$
$u = \dfrac{24(24 + 1)}{60(60 + 1)} \cdot \$5000 = \$819.67$

17. Payoff amount
$= \$300 + (24)(\$300) - \$819.67$
$= \$6680.33$

18. Unpaid balance $= \$880 - \$100 = \$780$
$I = Prt = \$780\,(0.02)(1) = \$15.60$

19. Balance due
$= \$780 + \$350 + \$70 + \$120 + \$15.60$
$= \$1335.60$

20. Minimum monthly payment
$= \dfrac{1}{36}(\$1335.60)$
$= \$37$

21. Average daily balance
$= \dfrac{(\$2400)(3) + (\$900)(27)}{30} = \$1050$
$I = Prt = (\$1050)(0.016)(1) = \$16.80$

22. Down payment $= 0.10(\$120{,}000) = \$12{,}000$

23. Amount of mortgage $= \$120{,}000 - \$12{,}000$
$ = \$108{,}000$

24. Two points $= 0.02(\$108{,}000) = \$2160$

25. $\dfrac{\$108{,}000}{\$1000} = 108$ thousands of dollars of mortgage
Monthly payment $= \$7.69 \cdot 108 = \$830.52$

26. Total cost of interest
$= 360(\$830.52) - \$108{,}000$
$= \$190{,}987.20$

27. $\dfrac{\$100{,}000}{\$1000} = 100$ thousands of dollars of mortgage
Option A 30-year mortgage:
Monthly payment $= \$6.99 \cdot 100 = \$699$

Option B 15-year mortgage:
Monthly payment $= \$8.99 \cdot 100 = \$899$

28. High $= \$25.75$, Low $= \$25.50$

29. Dividend $= \$2.03 \cdot 1000 = \$2030$

30. Total price paid $= 600(\$25.75) = \$15{,}450$
Broker's commission $= 0.025(\$15{,}450) = \$386.25$

Chapter 9
Measurement

Check Points 9.1

1. a. $78 \text{ in.} = \dfrac{78 \text{ in.}}{1} \cdot \dfrac{1 \text{ ft}}{12 \text{ in.}} = 6.5 \text{ ft}$

b. $17,160 \text{ ft} = \dfrac{17,160 \text{ ft}}{1} \cdot \dfrac{1 \text{ mi}}{5280 \text{ ft}} = 3.25 \text{ mi}$

c. $3 \text{ in.} = \dfrac{3 \text{ in.}}{1} \cdot \dfrac{1 \text{ yd}}{36 \text{ in.}} = \dfrac{1}{12} \text{ yd}$

2. a. $8000 \text{ m} = 8 \text{ km}$

b. $53 \text{ m} = 53,000 \text{ mm}$

c. $604 \text{ cm} = 0.0604 \text{ hm}$

d. $6.72 \text{ dam} = 6720 \text{ cm}$

3. a. $8 \text{ ft} = \dfrac{8 \text{ ft}}{1} \cdot \dfrac{30.48 \text{ cm}}{1 \text{ ft}} = 243.84 \text{ cm}$

b. $20 \text{ m} = \dfrac{20 \text{ m}}{1} \cdot \dfrac{1 \text{ yd}}{0.9 \text{ m}} \approx 22.22 \text{ yd}$

c. $30 \text{ m} = 3000 \text{ cm}$
$= \dfrac{3000 \text{ cm}}{1} \cdot \dfrac{1 \text{ in.}}{2.54 \text{ cm}}$
$\approx 1181.1 \text{ in.}$

4. $\dfrac{60 \text{ km}}{\text{hr}} = \dfrac{60 \text{ km}}{\text{hr}} \cdot \dfrac{1 \text{ mi}}{1.6 \text{ km}} = 37.5 \text{ mi/hr}$

Exercise Set 9.1

1. $30 \text{ in.} = \dfrac{30 \text{ in.}}{1} \cdot \dfrac{1 \text{ ft}}{12 \text{ in.}} = 2.5 \text{ ft}$

2. $100 \text{ in.} = \dfrac{100 \text{ in.}}{1} \cdot \dfrac{1 \text{ ft}}{12 \text{ in.}} \approx 8.33 \text{ ft}$

3. $30 \text{ ft} = \dfrac{30 \text{ ft}}{1} \cdot \dfrac{12 \text{ in.}}{1 \text{ ft}} = 360 \text{ in.}$

4. $100 \text{ ft} = \dfrac{100 \text{ ft}}{1} \cdot \dfrac{12 \text{ in.}}{1 \text{ ft}} = 1200 \text{ in.}$

5. $6 \text{ in.} = \dfrac{6 \text{ in.}}{1} \cdot \dfrac{1 \text{ yd}}{36 \text{ in.}} \approx 0.17 \text{ yd}$

6. $21 \text{ in.} = \dfrac{21 \text{ in.}}{1} \cdot \dfrac{1 \text{ yd}}{36 \text{ in.}} \approx 0.58 \text{ yd}$

7. $6 \text{ yd} = \dfrac{6 \text{ yd}}{1} \cdot \dfrac{36 \text{ in.}}{1 \text{ yd}} = 216 \text{ in.}$

8. $21 \text{ yd} = \dfrac{21 \text{ yd}}{1} \cdot \dfrac{36 \text{ in.}}{1 \text{ yd}} = 756 \text{ in.}$

9. $6 \text{ yd} = \dfrac{6 \text{ yd}}{1} \cdot \dfrac{3 \text{ ft}}{1 \text{ yd}} = 18 \text{ ft}$

10. $12 \text{ yd} = \dfrac{12 \text{ yd}}{1} \cdot \dfrac{3 \text{ ft}}{1 \text{ yd}} = 36 \text{ ft}$

11. $6 \text{ ft} = \dfrac{6 \text{ ft}}{1} \cdot \dfrac{1 \text{ yd}}{3 \text{ ft}} = 2 \text{ yd}$

12. $12 \text{ ft} = \dfrac{12 \text{ ft}}{1} \cdot \dfrac{1 \text{ yd}}{3 \text{ ft}} = 4 \text{ yd}$

13. $23,760 \text{ ft} = \dfrac{23,760 \text{ ft}}{1} \cdot \dfrac{1 \text{ mi}}{5280 \text{ ft}} = 4.5 \text{ mi}$

14. $19,800 \text{ ft} = \dfrac{19,800 \text{ ft}}{1} \cdot \dfrac{1 \text{ mi}}{5280 \text{ ft}} = 3.75 \text{ mi}$

15. $0.75 \text{ mi} = \dfrac{0.75 \text{ mi}}{1} \cdot \dfrac{5280 \text{ ft}}{1 \text{ mi}} = 3960 \text{ ft}$

16. $0.25 \text{ mi} = \dfrac{0.25 \text{ mi}}{1} \cdot \dfrac{5280 \text{ ft}}{1 \text{ mi}} = 1320 \text{ ft}$

17. $5 \text{ m} = 500 \text{ cm}$

18. $8 \text{ dam} = 80 \text{ m}$

19. $16.3 \text{ hm} = 1630 \text{ m}$

20. $0.37 \text{ hm} = 37 \text{ m}$

21. $317.8 \text{ cm} = 0.03178 \text{ hm}$

22. 8.64 hm = 86,400 cm

23. 0.023 mm = 0.000023 m

24. 0.00037 km = 37 cm

25. 2196 mm = 21.96 dm

26. 71 dm = 0.0071 km

27. $14 \text{ in.} = \dfrac{14 \text{ in.}}{1} \cdot \dfrac{2.54 \text{ cm}}{1 \text{ in.}} \approx 35.56 \text{ cm}$

28. $26 \text{ in.} = \dfrac{26 \text{ in.}}{1} \cdot \dfrac{2.54 \text{ cm}}{1 \text{ in.}} \approx 66.04 \text{ cm}$

29. $14 \text{ cm} = \dfrac{14 \text{ cm}}{1} \cdot \dfrac{1 \text{ in.}}{2.54 \text{ cm}} \approx 5.51 \text{ in.}$

30. $26 \text{ cm} = \dfrac{26 \text{ cm}}{1} \cdot \dfrac{1 \text{ in.}}{2.54 \text{ cm}} \approx 10.24 \text{ in.}$

31. $265 \text{ mi} = \dfrac{265 \text{ mi}}{1} \cdot \dfrac{1.6 \text{ km}}{1 \text{ mi}} \approx 424 \text{ km}$

32. $776 \text{ mi} = \dfrac{776 \text{ mi}}{1} \cdot \dfrac{1.6 \text{ km}}{1 \text{ mi}} \approx 1241.6 \text{ km}$

33. $265 \text{ km} = \dfrac{265 \text{ km}}{1} \cdot \dfrac{1 \text{ mi}}{1.6 \text{ km}} \approx 165.625 \text{ mi}$

34. $776 \text{ km} = \dfrac{776 \text{ km}}{1} \cdot \dfrac{1 \text{ mi}}{1.6 \text{ km}} \approx 485 \text{ mi}$

35. $12 \text{ m} = \dfrac{12 \text{ m}}{1} \cdot \dfrac{1 \text{ yd}}{0.9 \text{ m}} \approx 13.33 \text{ yd}$

36. $20 \text{ m} = \dfrac{20 \text{ m}}{1} \cdot \dfrac{1 \text{ yd}}{0.9 \text{ m}} \approx 22.22 \text{ yd}$

37. $14 \text{ dm} = 140 \text{ cm} = \dfrac{140 \text{ cm}}{1} \cdot \dfrac{1 \text{ in.}}{2.54 \text{ cm}} \approx 55.12 \text{ in.}$

38. 1.2 dam = 1200 cm

$= \dfrac{1200 \text{ cm}}{1} \cdot \dfrac{1 \text{ in.}}{2.54 \text{ cm}}$

$\approx 472.44 \text{ in.}$

39. $160 \text{ in.} = \dfrac{160 \text{ in.}}{1} \cdot \dfrac{2.54 \text{ cm}}{1 \text{ in.}}$

$\approx 406.4 \text{ cm}$

$= 0.4064 \text{ dam}$

40. $180 \text{ in.} = \dfrac{180 \text{ in.}}{1} \cdot \dfrac{2.54 \text{ cm}}{1 \text{ in.}}$

$\approx 457.2 \text{ cm}$

$= 0.04572 \text{ hm}$

41. $5 \text{ ft} = \dfrac{5 \text{ ft}}{1} \cdot \dfrac{30.48 \text{ cm}}{1 \text{ ft}} \approx 152.4 \text{ cm} \approx 1.524 \text{ m}$

42. $8 \text{ ft} = \dfrac{8 \text{ ft}}{1} \cdot \dfrac{30.48 \text{ cm}}{1 \text{ ft}} \approx 243.84 \text{ cm} \approx 2.4384 \text{ m}$

43. $5 \text{ m} = 500 \text{ cm} = \dfrac{500 \text{ cm}}{1} \cdot \dfrac{1 \text{ ft}}{30.48 \text{ cm}} \approx 16.40 \text{ ft}$

44. $8 \text{ m} = 800 \text{ cm} = \dfrac{800 \text{ cm}}{1} \cdot \dfrac{1 \text{ ft}}{30.48 \text{ cm}} \approx 26.25 \text{ ft}$

45. $\dfrac{96 \text{ km}}{\text{hr}} = \dfrac{96 \text{ km}}{\text{hr}} \cdot \dfrac{1 \text{ mi}}{1.6 \text{ km}} \approx 60 \text{ mi/hr}$

46. $\dfrac{104 \text{ km}}{\text{hr}} = \dfrac{104 \text{ km}}{\text{hr}} \cdot \dfrac{1 \text{ mi}}{1.6 \text{ km}} \approx 65 \text{ mi/hr}$

47. $\dfrac{45 \text{ mi}}{\text{hr}} = \dfrac{45 \text{ mi}}{\text{hr}} \cdot \dfrac{1.6 \text{ km}}{1 \text{ mi}} \approx 72 \text{ km/hr}$

48. $\dfrac{50 \text{ mi}}{\text{hr}} = \dfrac{50 \text{ mi}}{\text{hr}} \cdot \dfrac{1.6 \text{ km}}{1 \text{ mi}} \approx 80 \text{ km/hr}$

49. meter

50. meter

51. millimeter

52. kilometer

53. meter

54. meter

55. millimeter

56. kilometer

57. millimeter

58. millimeter

59. b.

60. c.

61. a.

62. b.

63. c.

64. c.

65. a.

66. b.

67. $2 \cdot 4 \cdot 27$ m $= 216$ m $= 0.216$ km

68. $6 \cdot 700$ m $= 4200$ m $= 4.2$ km

69. 93 million miles $= \dfrac{93{,}000{,}000 \text{ mi}}{1} \cdot \dfrac{1.6 \text{ km}}{1 \text{ mi}}$
$= 148.8$ million kilometers

70. 4690 km $= \dfrac{4690 \text{ km}}{1} \cdot \dfrac{1 \text{ mi}}{1.6 \text{ km}} = 2931.25$ mi

71-77. Answers will vary.

78. 6000 cm $= 6$ dam

79. 900 m $= 9$ hm

80. 7000 dm $= 7$ hm

81. 11,000 mm $= 11$ m

82. 0.0002 km $= 2$ dm

83. 5 yd $= \dfrac{5 \text{ yd}}{1} \cdot \dfrac{36 \text{ in.}}{1 \text{ yd}} \cdot \dfrac{2.54 \text{ cm}}{1 \text{ in.}} = 457.2$ cm

84. 30 mi $= \dfrac{30 \text{ mi}}{1} \cdot \dfrac{5280 \text{ ft}}{1 \text{ mi}} \cdot \dfrac{12 \text{ in.}}{1 \text{ ft}} \cdot \dfrac{2.54 \text{ cm}}{1 \text{ in.}}$
$= 4{,}828{,}032$ cm
≈ 48.28 km

Check Points 9.2

1. The area is 8 square units.

2. $\dfrac{103{,}000 \text{ people}}{10.5 \text{ square miles}}$
≈ 9809.5 people per square mile

3. a. 1.8 acres $= \dfrac{1.8 \text{ acres}}{1} \cdot \dfrac{0.4 \text{ ha}}{1 \text{ acre}} = 0.72$ ha

.b. $\dfrac{\$415{,}000}{0.72 \text{ ha}} = \$576{,}389$ per hectare

4. The volume is 9 cubic units.

5. 10,000 ft$^3 = \dfrac{10{,}000 \text{ ft}^3}{1} \cdot \dfrac{7.48 \text{ gal}}{1 \text{ ft}^3} = 74{,}800$ gal

6. 220,000 cm$^3 = \dfrac{220{,}000 \text{ cm}^3}{1} \cdot \dfrac{1 \text{ L}}{1000 \text{ cm}^3} = 220$ L

Exercise Set 9.2

1. $4 \cdot 4 = 16$ square units

2. $5 \cdot 3 = 15$ square units

3. 8 square units

4. 16 square units

5. 14 cm$^2 = \dfrac{14 \text{ cm}^2}{1} \cdot \dfrac{1 \text{ in.}^2}{6.5 \text{ cm}^2} \approx 2.15$ in.^{2}

6. 20 m$^2 = \dfrac{20 \text{ m}^2}{1} \cdot \dfrac{1 \text{ ft}^2}{0.09 \text{ m}^2} \approx 222.22$ ft^2

7. 30 m$^2 = \dfrac{30 \text{ m}^2}{1} \cdot \dfrac{1 \text{ yd}^2}{0.8 \text{ m}^2} = 37.5$ yd^2

8. 14 mi$^2 = \dfrac{14 \text{ mi}^2}{1} \cdot \dfrac{2.6 \text{ km}^2}{1 \text{ mi}^2} = 36.4$ km^2

9. 10.2 ha $= \dfrac{10.2 \text{ ha}}{1} \cdot \dfrac{1 \text{ acre}}{0.4 \text{ ha}} = 25.5$ acres

10. 20.6 ha $= \dfrac{20.6 \text{ ha}}{1} \cdot \dfrac{1 \text{ acre}}{0.4 \text{ ha}} = 51.5$ acres

11. $14 \text{ in.}^2 = \dfrac{14 \text{ in.}^2}{1} \cdot \dfrac{6.5 \text{ cm}^2}{1 \text{ in.}^2} = 91 \text{ cm}^2$

12. $20 \text{ in.}^2 = \dfrac{20 \text{ in.}^2}{1} \cdot \dfrac{6.5 \text{ cm}^2}{1 \text{ in.}^2} = 130 \text{ cm}^2$

13. $2 \cdot 4 \cdot 3 = 24$ cubic units

14. $4 \cdot 3 \cdot 5 = 60$ cubic units

15. $10,000 \text{ ft}^3 = \dfrac{10,000 \text{ ft}^3}{1} \cdot \dfrac{7.48 \text{ gal}}{1 \text{ ft}^3}$
$= 74,800 \text{ gal}$

16. $25,000 \text{ ft}^3 = \dfrac{25,000 \text{ ft}^3}{1} \cdot \dfrac{7.48 \text{ gal}}{1 \text{ ft}^3}$
$= 187,000 \text{ gal}$

17. $8 \text{ yd}^3 = \dfrac{8 \text{ yd}^3}{1} \cdot \dfrac{200 \text{ gal}}{1 \text{ yd}^3} = 1600 \text{ gal}$

18. $35 \text{ yd}^3 = \dfrac{35 \text{ yd}^3}{1} \cdot \dfrac{200 \text{ gal}}{1 \text{ yd}^3} = 7000 \text{ gal}$

19. $2079 \text{ in.}^3 = \dfrac{2079 \text{ in.}^3}{1} \cdot \dfrac{1 \text{ gal}}{231 \text{ in.}^3} = 9 \text{ gal}$

20. $6237 \text{ in.}^3 = \dfrac{6237 \text{ in.}^3}{1} \cdot \dfrac{1 \text{ gal}}{231 \text{ in.}^3} = 27 \text{ gal}$

21. $2700 \text{ gal} = \dfrac{2700 \text{ gal}}{1} \cdot \dfrac{1 \text{ yd}^3}{200 \text{ gal}} = 13.5 \text{ yd}^3$

22. $1496 \text{ gal} = \dfrac{1496 \text{ gal}}{1} \cdot \dfrac{1 \text{ ft}^3}{7.48 \text{ gal}} = 200 \text{ ft}^3$

23. $45,000 \text{ cm}^3 = \dfrac{45,000 \text{ cm}^3}{1} \cdot \dfrac{1 \text{ L}}{1000 \text{ cm}^3} = 45 \text{ L}$

24. $75,000 \text{ cm}^3 = \dfrac{75,000 \text{ cm}^3}{1} \cdot \dfrac{1 \text{ L}}{1000 \text{ cm}^3} = 75 \text{ L}$

25. $17 \text{ cm}^3 = \dfrac{17 \text{ cm}^3}{1} \cdot \dfrac{1 \text{ L}}{1000 \text{ cm}^3} \cdot \dfrac{1 \text{ mL}}{0.001 \text{ L}} = 17 \text{ mL}$

26. $19 \text{ cm}^3 = \dfrac{19 \text{ cm}^3}{1} \cdot \dfrac{1 \text{ L}}{1000 \text{ cm}^3} \cdot \dfrac{1 \text{ mL}}{0.001 \text{ L}} = 19 \text{ mL}$

27. $1.5 \text{ L} = \dfrac{1.5 \text{ L}}{1} \cdot \dfrac{1000 \text{ cm}^3}{1 \text{ L}} = 1500 \text{ cm}^3$

28. $4.5 \text{ L} = \dfrac{4.5 \text{ L}}{1} \cdot \dfrac{1000 \text{ cm}^3}{1 \text{ L}} = 4500 \text{ cm}^3$

29. $150 \text{ mL} = \dfrac{150 \text{ mL}}{1} \cdot \dfrac{0.001 \text{ L}}{\text{mL}} \cdot \dfrac{1000 \text{ cm}^3}{1 \text{ L}}$
$= 150 \text{ cm}^3$

30. $250 \text{ mL} = \dfrac{250 \text{ mL}}{1} \cdot \dfrac{0.001 \text{ L}}{\text{mL}} \cdot \dfrac{1000 \text{ cm}^3}{1 \text{ L}}$
$= 250 \text{ cm}^3$

31. $12 \text{ kL} = \dfrac{12 \text{ kL}}{1} \cdot \dfrac{1000 \text{ L}}{1 \text{ kL}} \cdot \dfrac{1 \text{ dm}^3}{1 \text{ L}}$
$= 12,000 \text{ dm}^3$

32. $16 \text{ kL} = \dfrac{12 \text{ kL}}{1} \cdot \dfrac{1000 \text{ L}}{1 \text{ kL}} \cdot \dfrac{1 \text{ dm}^3}{1 \text{ L}}$
$= 16,000 \text{ dm}^3$

33. $\dfrac{904,433 \text{ people}}{147,046 \text{ square miles}}$
≈ 6.2 people per square mile

34. $\dfrac{2,269,789 \text{ people}}{84,904 \text{ square miles}}$
≈ 26.7 people per square mile

35. a. $8 \text{ ha} = \dfrac{8 \text{ ha}}{1} \cdot \dfrac{1 \text{ acre}}{0.4 \text{ ha}} = 20 \text{ acres}$

b. $\dfrac{\$250,000}{20 \text{ acres}} = \$12,500 \text{ per acre}$

36. a. $100 \text{ ha} = \dfrac{100 \text{ ha}}{1} \cdot \dfrac{1 \text{ acre}}{0.4 \text{ ha}} = 250 \text{ acres}$

b. $\dfrac{\$350,000}{250 \text{ acres}} = \$1400 \text{ per acre}$

37. square centimeters or square meters

38. square centimeters

Chapter 9: Measurement

39. square kilometers

40. square meters

41. b.

42. b.

43. b.

44. b.

45. $45,000 \text{ ft}^3 = \dfrac{45,000 \text{ ft}^3}{1} \cdot \dfrac{7.48 \text{ gal}}{1 \text{ ft}^3}$
$= 336,600 \text{ gal}$

46. $66,000 \text{ ft}^3 = \dfrac{66,000 \text{ ft}^3}{1} \cdot \dfrac{7.48 \text{ gal}}{1 \text{ ft}^3}$
$= 493,680 \text{ gal}$

47. $4000 \text{ cm}^3 = \dfrac{4000 \text{ cm}^3}{1} \cdot \dfrac{1 \text{ L}}{1000 \text{ cm}^3} = 4 \text{ L}$

48. $17,500 \text{ cm}^3 = \dfrac{17,500 \text{ cm}^3}{1} \cdot \dfrac{1 \text{ L}}{1000 \text{ cm}^3} = 17.5 \text{ L}$

49-54. Answers will vary.

55. $\dfrac{46,690 \text{ people}}{1000 \text{ ha}}$
$\approx \dfrac{46,690 \text{ people}}{1000 \text{ ha}} \cdot \dfrac{260 \text{ ha}}{1 \text{ square mile}}$
$\approx 12,139.4$ people per square mile

56. $\dfrac{1,578,417 \text{ people}}{1} \cdot \dfrac{1 \text{ square mile}}{20.5 \text{ people}}$
$\approx 76,996$ square miles

57. Answers will vary.

58. You must consider how the population is distributed throughout the state. "Elbow room" can vary from region to region.

59. Approximately 6.5 liters. 6.5 mL is only a little more than a teaspoon and 6.5 kL is thousands of gallons.

60. Approximately 1 cm^3. 1 mm^3 is about the size of a pencil tip and 1 dm^3 is bigger than a baseball.

Check Points 9.3

1. a. 4.2 dg = 420 mg

b. 620 cg = 6.2 g

2. $0.145 \text{ m}^3 = \dfrac{0.145 \text{ m}^3}{1} \cdot \dfrac{1000 \text{ kg}}{1 \text{ m}^3} = 145 \text{ kg}$
The water weighs 145 kg.

3. a. $186 \text{ lb} = \dfrac{186 \text{ lb}}{1} \cdot \dfrac{0.45 \text{ kg}}{1 \text{ lb}} = 83.7 \text{ kg}$

b. $83.7 \times 1.2 \text{ mg} = 100.44 \text{ mg}$ dose

4. $F = \dfrac{9}{5} \cdot 50 + 32 = 122$
$50°C = 122°F$

5. $C = \dfrac{5}{9}(59 - 32) = 15$
$59°F = 15°C$

Exercise Set 9.3

1. 7.4 dg = 740 mg

2. 6.9 dg = 690 mg

3. 870 mg = 0.87 g

4. 640 mg = 0.64 g

5. 8 g = 800 cg

6. 7 g = 700 cg

7. 18.6 kg = 18,600 g

8. 0.37 kg = 370 g

9. 0.018 mg = 0.000018 g

10. 0.029 mg = 0.000029 g

11. $0.05 \text{ m}^3 = \dfrac{0.05 \text{ m}^3}{1} \cdot \dfrac{1000 \text{ kg}}{1 \text{ m}^3} = 50 \text{ kg}$

12. $0.02 \text{ m}^3 = \dfrac{0.02 \text{ m}^3}{1} \cdot \dfrac{1000 \text{ kg}}{1 \text{ m}^3} = 20 \text{ kg}$

13. $4.2 \text{ kg} = \dfrac{4.2 \text{ kg}}{1} \cdot \dfrac{1000 \text{ cm}^3}{1 \text{ kg}} = 4200 \text{ cm}^3$

14. $5.8 \text{ kg} = \dfrac{5.8 \text{ kg}}{1} \cdot \dfrac{1000 \text{ cm}^3}{1 \text{ kg}} = 5800 \text{ cm}^3$

15. $1100 \text{ m}^3 = 1100 \text{ t}$

16. $1500 \text{ t} = 1500 \text{ m}^3$

17. $0.04 \text{ kL} = \dfrac{0.04 \text{ kL}}{1} \cdot \dfrac{1000 \text{ kg}}{1 \text{ kL}} \cdot \dfrac{1000 \text{ g}}{1 \text{ kg}} = 40,000 \text{ g}$

18. $0.03 \text{ kL} = \dfrac{0.03 \text{ kL}}{1} \cdot \dfrac{1000 \text{ kg}}{1 \text{ kL}} \cdot \dfrac{1000 \text{ g}}{1 \text{ kg}} = 30,000 \text{ g}$

19. $36 \text{ oz} = \dfrac{36 \text{ oz}}{1} \cdot \dfrac{1 \text{ lb}}{16 \text{ oz}} = 2.25 \text{ lb}$

20. $26 \text{ oz} = \dfrac{26 \text{ oz}}{1} \cdot \dfrac{1 \text{ lb}}{16 \text{ oz}} \approx 1.63 \text{ lb}$

21. $36 \text{ oz} = \dfrac{36 \text{ oz}}{1} \cdot \dfrac{28 \text{ g}}{1 \text{ oz}} = 1008 \text{ g}$

22. $26 \text{ oz} = \dfrac{26 \text{ oz}}{1} \cdot \dfrac{28 \text{ g}}{1 \text{ oz}} = 728 \text{ g}$

23. $540 \text{ lb} = \dfrac{540 \text{ lb}}{1} \cdot \dfrac{0.45 \text{ kg}}{1 \text{ lb}} = 243 \text{ kg}$

24. $220 \text{ lb} = \dfrac{220 \text{ lb}}{1} \cdot \dfrac{0.45 \text{ kg}}{1 \text{ lb}} = 99 \text{ kg}$

25. $80 \text{ lb} = \dfrac{80 \text{ lb}}{1} \cdot \dfrac{0.45 \text{ kg}}{1 \text{ lb}} \cdot \dfrac{1000 \text{ g}}{1 \text{ kg}} = 36,000 \text{ g}$

or $80 \text{ lb} = \dfrac{80 \text{ lb}}{1} \cdot \dfrac{16 \text{ oz}}{1 \text{ lb}} \cdot \dfrac{28 \text{ g}}{1 \text{ oz}} = 35,840 \text{ g}$

26. $150 \text{ lb} = \dfrac{150 \text{ lb}}{1} \cdot \dfrac{0.45 \text{ kg}}{1 \text{ lb}} \cdot \dfrac{1000 \text{ g}}{1 \text{ kg}} = 67,500 \text{ g}$

or $150 \text{ lb} = \dfrac{150 \text{ lb}}{1} \cdot \dfrac{16 \text{ oz}}{1 \text{ lb}} \cdot \dfrac{28 \text{ g}}{1 \text{ oz}} = 67,200 \text{ g}$

27. $540 \text{ kg} = \dfrac{540 \text{ kg}}{1} \cdot \dfrac{1 \text{ lb}}{0.45 \text{ kg}} = 1200 \text{ lb}$

28. $220 \text{ kg} = \dfrac{220 \text{ kg}}{1} \cdot \dfrac{1 \text{ lb}}{0.45 \text{ kg}} \approx 488.89 \text{ lb}$

29. $200 \text{ t} = \dfrac{200 \text{ t}}{1} \cdot \dfrac{1 \text{ T}}{0.9 \text{ t}} \approx 222.22 \text{ T}$

30. $100 \text{ t} = \dfrac{100 \text{ t}}{1} \cdot \dfrac{1 \text{ T}}{0.9 \text{ t}} \approx 111.11 \text{ T}$

31. $10° \text{ C}$

$F = \dfrac{9}{5} \cdot 10 + 32$

$10° \text{ C} = 50° \text{ F}$

32. $20°\text{C}$

$F = \dfrac{9}{5} \cdot 20 + 32$

$20° \text{ C} = 68° \text{F}$

33. $35° \text{ C}$

$F = \dfrac{9}{5} \cdot 35 + 32$

$35°\text{C} = 95°\text{F}$

34. $45°\text{C}$

$F = \dfrac{9}{5} \cdot 45 + 32$

$45° \text{ C} = 113°\text{F}$

35. $57° \text{ C}$

$F = \dfrac{9}{5} \cdot 57 + 32$

$57° \text{ C} = 134.6°\text{F}$

36. $98°\text{C}$

$F = \dfrac{9}{5} \cdot 98 + 32$

$98° \text{ C} = 208.4°\text{F}$

37. $-5° \text{ C}$

$F = \dfrac{9}{5}(-5) + 32$

$-5°\text{C} = 23°\text{F}$

38. $-10°\text{C}$

$F = \dfrac{9}{5}(-10) + 32$

$-10° \text{ C} = 14°\text{F}$

39. 68° F

$$C = \frac{5}{9}(68 - 32)$$

68°F = 20°C

40. 86°F

$$C = \frac{5}{9}(86 - 32)$$

86° F = 30°C

41. 41° F

$$C = \frac{5}{9}(41 - 32)$$

41°F = 5°C

42. 50° F

$$C = \frac{5}{9}(50 - 32)$$

50° F = 10°C

43. 72° F

$$C = \frac{5}{9}(72 - 32)$$

72°F ≈ 22.2°C

44. 90° F

$$C = \frac{5}{9}(90 - 32)$$

90° F ≈ 32.2°C

45. 23° F

$$C = \frac{5}{9}(23 - 32)$$

23°F = −5°C

46. 14° F

$$C = \frac{5}{9}(14 - 32)$$

14° F = −10°C

47. 350° F

$$C = \frac{5}{9}(350 - 32)$$

350°F ≈ 176.7°C

48. 475° F

$$C = \frac{5}{9}(475 - 32)$$

475° F ≈ 246.1°C

49. −22° F

$$C = \frac{5}{9}(-22 - 32)$$

−22°F = −30°C

50. −31° F

$$C = \frac{5}{9}(-31 - 32)$$

−31° F = −35°C

51. milligram

52. kilogram

53. gram

54. tonne

55. kilogram

56. gram

57. kilogram

58. d.

59. b.

60. a.

61. a.

62. b.

63. c.

64. b.

65. 720 g = 0.720 kg
14 − 0.720 = 13.28 kg

66. 5 g = 0.005 kg

$$\frac{4 \text{ kg}}{0.005 \text{ kg per nickel}} = 800 \text{ nickels}$$

67. $85 \text{ g} = \frac{85 \cancel{g}}{1} \cdot \frac{1 \text{ oz}}{28 \cancel{g}} \approx 3.04 \text{ oz}$

Cost = 37 + 3 · 23 = 106 cents or $1.06

68. Answers will vary.

69. $\dfrac{\$3.15}{3\ \text{kg}} = \$1.05$ per kg for economy size

720 g = 0.72 kg

$\dfrac{\$.60}{0.72\ \text{kg}} = \$.83$ per kg for regular size

It is more economical to purchase the regular size.

70. $200\ \text{lb} = \dfrac{200\ \cancel{\text{lb}}}{1} \cdot \dfrac{0.45\ \text{kg}}{1\ \cancel{\text{lb}}} = 90\ \text{kg}$

$90 \times 20\ \text{mg} = 1800\ \text{mg}$ dose

71. $80\ \text{lb} = \dfrac{80\ \cancel{\text{lb}}}{1} \cdot \dfrac{0.45\ \text{kg}}{1\ \cancel{\text{lb}}} = 36\ \text{kg}$

$36 \times 2.5\ \text{mg} = 90\ \text{mg}$ dose

72. a. $\dfrac{1.87\ \text{g}}{\text{tsp}} = \dfrac{1.87\ \text{g}}{\cancel{\text{tsp}}} \cdot \dfrac{2\ \cancel{\text{tsp}}}{1\ \text{dose}} = 3.74\ \text{g/dose}$

b. $\dfrac{1.87\ \text{g}}{\text{tsp}}$

$= \dfrac{1.87\ \text{g}}{\cancel{\text{tsp}}} \cdot \dfrac{\cancel{\text{tsp}}}{5\ \cancel{\text{ml}}} \cdot \dfrac{30\ \cancel{\text{ml}}}{1\ \cancel{\text{oz}}} \cdot \dfrac{4\ \cancel{\text{oz}}}{1\ \text{bottle}}$

$= 44.88\ \text{g/bottle}$

73. a. $\dfrac{21.5\ \text{mg}}{\text{tsp}} = \dfrac{21.5\ \text{mg}}{\cancel{\text{tsp}}} \cdot \dfrac{2\ \cancel{\text{tsp}}}{1\ \text{dose}} = 43\ \text{mg/dose}$

b. $\dfrac{21.5\ \text{mg}}{\text{tsp}}$

$= \dfrac{21.5\ \text{mg}}{\cancel{\text{tsp}}} \cdot \dfrac{\cancel{\text{tsp}}}{5\ \cancel{\text{ml}}} \cdot \dfrac{30\ \cancel{\text{ml}}}{1\ \cancel{\text{oz}}} \cdot \dfrac{4\ \cancel{\text{oz}}}{1\ \text{bottle}}$

$= 516\ \text{mg/bottle}$

74. c.

75. a.

76. a.

77. c.

78. 25.7° C

$F = \dfrac{9}{5}(25.7) + 32$

25.7° C ≈ 78.3° F

79. −7° C

$F = \dfrac{9}{5}(-7) + 32$

−7°C = 19.4° F

80-85. Answers will vary.

86. a. $2000\ \text{g} = 2\ \text{kg} = \dfrac{2\ \cancel{\text{kg}}}{1} \cdot \dfrac{1\ \text{lb}}{0.45\ \cancel{\text{kg}}} \approx 4.4\ \text{lb}$

False

b. $100\ \text{mg} = 0.1\ \text{g} = \dfrac{0.1\ \cancel{\text{g}}}{1} \cdot \dfrac{1\ \text{oz}}{28\ \cancel{\text{g}}} \approx 0.0036\ \text{oz}$

False

c. $50\ \text{g} = \dfrac{50\ \cancel{\text{g}}}{1} \cdot \dfrac{1\ \text{oz}}{28\ \cancel{\text{g}}} \approx 1.8\ \text{oz}$ False

d. $4\ \text{kg} = \dfrac{4\ \cancel{\text{kg}}}{1} \cdot \dfrac{1\ \text{lb}}{0.45\ \cancel{\text{kg}}} \approx 8.9\ \text{lb}$ True

87. a. $\dfrac{3¢}{1\ \cancel{\text{g}}} \cdot \dfrac{1000\ \cancel{\text{g}}}{1\ \cancel{\text{kg}}} \cdot \dfrac{0.45\ \cancel{\text{kg}}}{1\ \text{lb}} = 1350¢$ per pound

False

b. True

c. False

d. False

88. $C = \dfrac{5}{9}(F - 32)$

$\dfrac{9}{5}C = \dfrac{9}{5} \cdot \dfrac{5}{9}(F - 32)$

$\dfrac{9}{5}C = F - 32$

$\dfrac{9}{5}C + 32 = F$

$F = \dfrac{9}{5}C + 32$

Chapter 9: Measurement

Chapter 9 Review Exercises

1. $69 \text{ in.} = \frac{69 \text{ in.}}{1} \cdot \frac{1 \text{ ft}}{12 \text{ in.}} = 5.75 \text{ ft}$

2. $9 \text{ in.} = \frac{9 \text{ in.}}{1} \cdot \frac{1 \text{ yd}}{36 \text{ in.}} = 0.25 \text{ yd}$

3. $21 \text{ ft} = \frac{21 \text{ ft}}{1} \cdot \frac{1 \text{ yd}}{3 \text{ ft}} = 7 \text{ yd}$

4. $13,200 \text{ ft} = \frac{13,200 \text{ ft}}{1} \cdot \frac{1 \text{ mi}}{5280 \text{ ft}} = 2.5 \text{ mi}$

5. $22.8 \text{ m} = 2280 \text{ cm}$

6. $7 \text{ dam} = 70 \text{ m}$

7. $19.2 \text{ hm} = 1920 \text{ m}$

8. $144 \text{ cm} = 0.0144 \text{ hm}$

9. $0.5 \text{ mm} = 0.0005 \text{ m}$

10. $18 \text{ cm} = 180 \text{ mm}$

11. $23 \text{ in.} = \frac{23 \text{ in.}}{1} \cdot \frac{2.54 \text{ cm}}{1 \text{ in.}} = 58.42 \text{ cm}$

12. $19 \text{ cm} = \frac{19 \text{ cm}}{1} \cdot \frac{1 \text{ in.}}{2.54 \text{ cm}} \approx 7.48 \text{ in.}$

13. $330 \text{ mi} = \frac{330 \text{ mi}}{1} \cdot \frac{1.6 \text{ km}}{1 \text{ mi}} = 528 \text{ km}$

14. $600 \text{ km} = \frac{600 \text{ km}}{1} \cdot \frac{1 \text{ mi}}{1.6 \text{ km}} = 375 \text{ mi}$

15. $14 \text{ m} = \frac{14 \text{ m}}{1} \cdot \frac{1 \text{ yd}}{0.9 \text{ m}} \approx 15.56 \text{ yd}$

16. $12 \text{ m} = \frac{12 \text{ m}}{1} \cdot \frac{100 \text{ cm}}{1 \text{ m}} \cdot \frac{1 \text{ in.}}{2.54 \text{ cm}} \cdot \frac{1 \text{ ft}}{12 \text{ in.}} = 39.37 \text{ ft}$

17. $45 \text{ km per hour} = \frac{45 \text{ km}}{1 \text{ hr}} \cdot \frac{1 \text{ mi}}{1.6 \text{ km}}$
$\approx 28.13 \text{ miles/hour}$

18. $60 \text{ mi per hour} = \frac{60 \text{ mi}}{1 \text{ hr}} \cdot \frac{1.6 \text{ km}}{1 \text{ mi}}$
$= 96 \text{ km/hr}$

19. $0.024 \text{ km}; 24,000 \text{ cm}; 2400 \text{ m}$

20. $6 \cdot 800 \text{ m} = 4800 \text{ m} = 4.8 \text{ km}$

21. $3 \cdot 8 = 24 \text{ square units}$

22. $\frac{33,870,000 \text{ people}}{163,707 \text{ square miles}}$
$\approx 206.9 \text{ people per square mile;}$
In California, there is an average of 206.9 people per square mile.

23. $7.2 \text{ ha} = \frac{7.2 \text{ ha}}{1} \cdot \frac{1 \text{ acre}}{0.4 \text{ ha}} = 18 \text{ acres}$

24. $30 \text{ m}^2 = \frac{30 \text{ m}^2}{1} \cdot \frac{1 \text{ ft}^2}{0.09 \text{ m}^2} \approx 333.33 \text{ ft}^2$

25. $12 \text{ mi}^2 = \frac{12 \text{ mi}^2}{1} \cdot \frac{2.6 \text{ km}^2}{1 \text{ mi}^2} = 31.2 \text{ km}^2$

26. a

27. $2 \cdot 4 \cdot 3 = 24 \text{ cubic units}$

28. $33,600 \text{ cubic feet} = \frac{33,600 \text{ ft}^3}{1} \cdot \frac{7.48 \text{ gal}}{1 \text{ ft}^3}$
$= 251,328 \text{ gal}$

29. $76,000 \text{ cm}^3 = \frac{76,000 \text{ cm}^3}{1} \cdot \frac{1 \text{ L}}{1000 \text{ cm}^3} = 76 \text{ L}$

30. c

31-32. Answers will vary.

33. $12.4 \text{ dg} = 1240 \text{ mg}$

34. $12 \text{ g} = 1200 \text{ cg}$

35. $0.012 \text{ mg} = 0.000012 \text{ g}$

36. $450 \text{ mg} = 0.00045 \text{ kg}$

37. $50 \text{ kg} = \frac{50 \text{ kg}}{1} \cdot \frac{1000 \text{ cm}^3}{1 \text{ kg}} = 50,000 \text{ cm}^3$

38. $4 \text{ kL} = \dfrac{4 \text{ kL}}{1} \cdot \dfrac{1000 \text{ kg}}{1 \text{ kL}} \cdot \dfrac{1 \text{ dm}^3}{1 \text{ kg}} = 4000 \text{ dm}^3$

$4000 \text{ dm}^3 = \dfrac{4000 \text{ dm}^3}{1} \cdot \dfrac{1000 \text{ g}}{1 \text{ dm}^3} = 4{,}000{,}000 \text{ g}$

39. $210 \text{ lb} = \dfrac{210 \text{ lb}}{1} \cdot \dfrac{0.45 \text{ kg}}{1 \text{ lb}} = 94.5 \text{ kg}$

40. $392 \text{ g} = \dfrac{392 \text{ g}}{1} \cdot \dfrac{1 \text{ oz}}{28 \text{ g}} = 14 \text{ oz}$

41. Kilograms; Answers will vary.

42. $36 \text{ oz} = \dfrac{36 \text{ oz}}{1} \cdot \dfrac{1 \text{ lb}}{16 \text{ oz}} = 2.25 \text{ lb}$

43. a

44. c

45. $\text{F} = \dfrac{9}{5} \cdot 15 + 32 = 59^\circ \text{ F}$

46. $F = \dfrac{9}{5} \cdot 100 + 32 = 212^\circ \text{ F}$

47. $F = \dfrac{9}{5} \cdot 5 + 32 = 41^\circ \text{F}$

48. $F = \dfrac{9}{5} \cdot 0 + 32 = 32^\circ \text{ F}$

49. $-F = \dfrac{9}{5}(-25) + 32 = -13^\circ \text{ F}$

50. $C = \dfrac{5}{9}(59 - 32) = 15^\circ \text{ C}$

51. $C = \dfrac{5}{9}(41 - 32) = 5^\circ \text{C}$

52. $C = \dfrac{5}{9}(212 - 32) = 100^\circ \text{ C}$

53. $C = \dfrac{5}{9}(98.6 - 32) = 37^\circ \text{ C}$

54. $C = \dfrac{5}{9}(0 - 32) \approx -17.8^\circ \text{C}$

55. $C = \dfrac{5}{9}(14 - 32) = -10^\circ \text{ C}$

56. A decrease of $15^\circ C$ is more than a decrease of $15^\circ F$; Explanations will vary.

Chapter 9 Test

1. $807 \text{ mm} = 0.00807 \text{ hm}$

2. $635 \text{ cm} = \dfrac{635 \text{ cm}}{1} \cdot \dfrac{1 \text{ in.}}{2.54 \text{ cm}} = 250 \text{ in.}$

3. $8 \cdot 600 \text{ m} = 4800 \text{ m} = 4.8 \text{ km}$

4. mm

5. cm

6. km

7. $80 \text{ miles per hour} = \dfrac{80 \text{ mi}}{1 \text{ hr}} \cdot \dfrac{1.6 \text{ km}}{1 \text{ mi}}$

$= 128 \text{ km/hr}$

8. $1 \text{ yd}^2 = (3 \text{ ft})(3 \text{ ft}) = 9 \text{ ft}^2$

A square yard is 9 times greater than a square foot.

9. $\dfrac{39{,}133{,}966 \text{ people}}{195{,}365 \text{ square miles}}$

$\approx 200.3 \text{ people per square mile}$

On average there are 200.3 people living in each square mile of Spain.

10. $18 \text{ ha} = \dfrac{18 \text{ ha}}{1} \cdot \dfrac{1 \text{ acre}}{0.4 \text{ ha}} = 45 \text{ acres}$

11. b

12. Answers will vary.

$1 \text{ m}^3 = (10 \text{ dm})(10 \text{ dm})(10 \text{ dm}) = 1000 \text{ dm}^3$

A cubic meter is 1000 times greater than a cubic decimeter.

13. $10{,}000 \text{ ft}^3 = \dfrac{10{,}000 \text{ ft}^3}{1} \cdot \dfrac{7.48 \text{ gal}}{1 \text{ ft}^3}$

$= 74{,}800 \text{ gal}$

14. b

15. $137 \text{ g} = 0.137 \text{ kg}$

16. $90 \text{ lb} = \dfrac{90 \cancel{\text{ lb}}}{1} \cdot \dfrac{0.45 \text{ kg}}{1 \cancel{\text{ lb}}} = 40.5 \text{ kg}$

17. kg

18. mg

19. $F = \dfrac{9}{5} \cdot 30 + 32 = 86° \text{ F}$

20. $C = \dfrac{5}{9}(176 - 32) = 80°\text{C}$

21. d

Chapter 10
Geometry

Check Points 10.1

1. Hand moves $\dfrac{1}{12}$ of a rotation

   $\dfrac{1}{12} \cdot 360° = 30°$

2. $90° - 19° = 71°$

3. $m\angle DBC + m\angle ABD = 180°$
   $x + (x + 88°) = 180°$
   $2x + 88° = 180°$
   $2x = 92°$
   $x = 46°$
   Thus, $m\angle DBC = 46°$ and $m\angle ABD = 134°$

4. $m\angle 1 = 57°$
   $m\angle 2 = 180° - 57° = 123°$
   $m\angle 3 = m\angle 2 = 123°$

5. $m\angle 1 = m\angle 8 = 29°$
   $m\angle 5 = m\angle 8 = 29°$
   $m\angle 2 = m\angle 8 = 29°$
   $m\angle 6 = 180° - m\angle 8 = 180° - 29° = 151°$
   $m\angle 7 = m\angle 6 = 151°$
   $m\angle 3 = m\angle 7 = 151°$
   $m\angle 4 = m\angle 3 = 151°$

Exercise Set 10.1

1. Hand moves $\dfrac{5}{12}$ of a rotation

   $\dfrac{5}{12} \cdot 360° = 150°$

2. Hand moves $\dfrac{4}{12} = \dfrac{1}{3}$ of a rotation

   $\dfrac{1}{3} \cdot 360° = 120°$

3. Hand moves $\dfrac{4-1}{12} = \dfrac{3}{12} = \dfrac{1}{4}$
   of a rotation

   $\dfrac{1}{4} \cdot 360° = 90°$

4. Hand moves $\dfrac{7-1}{12} = \dfrac{6}{12} = \dfrac{1}{2}$ of a rotation

   $\dfrac{1}{2} \cdot 360° = 180°$

5. $20°$ is acute.

6. $130°$ is obtuse.

7. $160°$ is obtuse.

8. $50°$ is acute.

9. $180°$ is straight.

10. $90°$ is right.

11. $90° - 25° = 65°$

12. $90° - 32° = 58°$

13. $180° - 34° = 146°$

14. $180° - 13° = 167°$

15. Complement:
    $90° - 48° = 42°$
    Supplement:
    $180° - 48° = 132°$

16. Complement:
    $90° - 52° = 38°$
    Supplement:
    $180° - 52° = 128°$

17. Complement:
    $90° - 89° = 1°$
    Supplement:
    $180° - 89° = 91°$

18. Complement:
    $90° - 1° = 89°$
    Supplement:
    $180° - 1° = 179°$

19. Complement:
    $90° - 37.4° = 52.6°$
    Supplement:
    $180° - 37.4° = 142.6°$

20. Complement:
    $90° - 15\dfrac{1}{3}° = 74\dfrac{2}{3}°$
    Supplement:
    $180° - 15\dfrac{1}{3}° = 164\dfrac{2}{3}°$

21. Let x = the measure of the angle's complement.
Then $x + 12°$ represents the angle.
$$x + (x + 12°) = 90°$$
$$2x + 12° = 90°$$
$$2x = 78°$$
$$x = 39°$$
$$x + 12° = 51°$$
The complements are $39°$ and $51°$

22. Let x = the measure of the angle's complement.
Then $x + 56°$ represents the angle.
$$x + (x + 56°) = 90°$$
$$2x + 56° = 90°$$
$$2x = 34°$$
$$x = 17°$$
$$x + 56° = 73°$$
The complements are $17°$ and $73°$

23. Let x = the measure of the angle's supplement.
Then $3x$ represents the angle.
$$x + 3x = 180°$$
$$4x = 180°$$
$$x = 45°$$
$$3x = 135°$$
The supplements are $45°$ and $135°$

24. Let x = the measure of the angle's supplement.
Then $2x + 81°$ represents the angle.
$$x + (2x + 81°) = 180°$$
$$3x + 81° = 180°$$
$$3x = 99°$$
$$x = 33°$$
$$2x + 81° = 147°$$
The supplements are $33°$ and $147°$

25. $m\angle 1 = 180° - 72° = 108°$
$m\angle 2 = 72°$
$m\angle 3 = m\angle 1 = 108°$

26. $m\angle 1 = 180° - 133° = 47°$
$m\angle 2 = 133°$
$m\angle 3 = m\angle 1 = 47°$

27. $m\angle 1 = 90° - 40° = 50°$
$m\angle 2 = 90°$
$m\angle 3 = m\angle 1 = 50°$

28. $m\angle 1 = 90° - 30° = 60°$
$m\angle 2 = 90°$
$m\angle 3 = m\angle 1 = 60°$

29. $m\angle 1 = 180° - 112° = 68°$
$m\angle 2 = m\angle 1 = 68°$
$m\angle 3 = 112°$
$m\angle 4 = 112°$
$m\angle 5 = m\angle 1 = 68°$
$m\angle 6 = m\angle 2 = 68°$
$m\angle 7 = m\angle 3 = 112°$

30. $m\angle 1 = 180° - 54° = 126°$
$m\angle 2 = 54°$
$m\angle 3 = m\angle 1 = 126°$
$m\angle 4 = m\angle 1 = 126°$
$m\angle 5 = 54°$
$m\angle 6 = m\angle 2 = 54°$
$m\angle 7 = m\angle 3 = 126°$

31. $m\angle 1 = 38°$
$m\angle 2 = 90° - 38° = 52°$
$m\angle 3 = 180° - 38° = 142°$

32. $m\angle 2 = 90° - 40° = 50°$
$m\angle 1 = 180° - 40° - 50° = 90°$
$m\angle 3 = m\angle 1 + 40° = 90° + 40° = 130°$

33-42. Answers will vary.

43. Yes; Explanations will vary.

44. d, since $m\angle 1 = m\angle 4$ and $m\angle 4 + m\angle 5 = 90°$

45. $m\angle BGD = m\angle BGC + m\angle CGD$
We know
$m\angle AGB + m\angle BGC + m\angle CGD + m\angle DGE = 180°$.
Since $m\angle AGB = m\angle BGC$ and
$m\angle CGD = m\angle DGE,$ this becomes
$m\angle BGC + m\angle BGC + m\angle CGD + m\angle CGD = 180°$
or $2(m\angle BGC) + 2(m\angle CGD) = 180°$
or $m\angle BGC + m\angle CGD = 90°$
Therefore, $m\angle BGD = 90°$.

Check Points 10.2

1. $m\angle A + 116° + 15° = 180°$
$m\angle A + 131° = 180°$
$m\angle A = 180° - 131°$
$m\angle A = 49°$

2. $m\angle 1 = 180° - 90° = 90°$
$m\angle 2 = 180° - 36° - m\angle 1$
$= 180° - 36° - 90°$
$= 54°$
$m\angle 3 = m\angle 2 = 54°$
$m\angle 4 = 180° - 58° - m\angle 3$
$= 180° - 58° - 54°$
$= 68°$
$m\angle 5 = 180° - m\angle 4$
$= 180° - 68°$
$= 112°$

3. $\dfrac{3}{8} = \dfrac{12}{x}$
$3 \cdot x = 8 \cdot 12$
$3x = 96$
$\dfrac{3x}{3} = \dfrac{96}{3}$
$x = 32$ in.

4. $\dfrac{h}{2} = \dfrac{56}{3.5}$
$3.5 \cdot h = 2 \cdot 56$
$3.5h = 112$
$\dfrac{3.5h}{3.5} = \dfrac{112}{3.5}$
$h = 32$ yd

5. $c^2 = a^2 + b^2$
$c^2 = 7^2 + 24^2$
$c^2 = 49 + 576$
$c^2 = 625$
$c = \sqrt{625}$
$c = 25$ ft

6. $w^2 + 9^2 = 15^2$
$w^2 + 81 = 225$
$w^2 = 144$
$w = \sqrt{144}$
$w = 12$ in.

Exercise Set 10.2

1. $m\angle A = 180° - 46° - 67° = 67°$

2. $m\angle A = 180° - 48° - 59° = 73°$

3. $m\angle A = 180° - 58° - 90° = 32°$

4. $m\angle A = 180° - 55° - 90° = 35°$

5. $m\angle 1 = 180° - 40° - 90° = 50°$
$m\angle 2 = 180° - m\angle 1 = 180° - 50° = 130°$
$m\angle 3 = m\angle 1 = 50°$
$m\angle 4 = m\angle 2 = 130°$
$m\angle 5 = 180° - 80° - m\angle 3$
$= 180° - 80° - 50°$
$= 50°$

6. $m\angle 1 = 180° - 50° - 90° = 40°$
$m\angle 2 = 180° - m\angle 1 = 180° - 40° = 140°$
$m\angle 3 = m\angle 1 = 40°$
$m\angle 4 = m\angle 2 = 140°$
$m\angle 5 = 180° - 105° - m\angle 3$
$= 180° - 105° - 40°$
$= 35°$

7. $m\angle 1 = 180° - 130° = 50°$
$m\angle 2 = m\angle 1 = 50°$
$m\angle 3 = 180° - m\angle 1 - m\angle 2$
$= 180° - 50° - 50°$
$= 80°$
$m\angle 4 = 180° - m\angle 2 = 180° - 50° = 130°$
$m\angle 5 = m\angle 4 = 130°$

8. $m\angle 1 = 180° - 115° = 65°$
$m\angle 2 = m\angle 1 = 65°$
$m\angle 3 = 180° - m\angle 1 - m\angle 2$
$= 180° - 65° - 65°$
$= 50°$
$m\angle 4 = 180° - m\angle 2 = 180° - 65° = 115°$
$m\angle 5 = m\angle 2 = 65°$

9. $m\angle 1 = 55°$
$m\angle 1 + m\angle 2 = 120°$
$55° + m\angle 2 = 120°$
$m\angle 2 = 65°$
$m\angle 1 + m\angle 2 + m\angle 3 = 180°$
$55° + 65° + m\angle 3 = 180°$
$m\angle 3 = 60°$
$m\angle 4 = m\angle 2 = 65°$
$m\angle 5 = m\angle 3 = 60°$
$m\angle 6 = 120°$
$m\angle 7 = m\angle 3 = 60°$
$m\angle 8 = m\angle 7 = 60°$
$m\angle 9 = m\angle 1 = 55°$
$m\angle 10 = m\angle 9 = 55°$

10. $m\angle 1 = 65°$
$m\angle 1 + m\angle 2 = 135°$
$65° + m\angle 2 = 135°$
$m\angle 2 = 70°$
$m\angle 1 + m\angle 2 + m\angle 3 = 180°$
$65° + 70° + m\angle 3 = 180°$
$m\angle 3 = 45°$
$m\angle 4 = m\angle 3 = 45°$
$m\angle 5 = m\angle 2 = 70°$
$m\angle 6 = m\angle 3 = 45°$
$m\angle 7 = m\angle 6 = 45°$
$m\angle 8 = 135°$
$m\angle 9 = m\angle 1 = 65°$
$m\angle 10 = m\angle 9 = 65°$

11. $\dfrac{18}{9} = \dfrac{10}{x}$
$18 \cdot x = 9 \cdot 10$
$18x = 90$
$\dfrac{18x}{18} = \dfrac{90}{18}$
$x = 5$ in.

12. $\dfrac{15}{10} = \dfrac{12}{x}$
$15 \cdot x = 10 \cdot 12$
$15x = 120$
$\dfrac{15x}{15} = \dfrac{120}{15}$
$x = 8$ in.

13. $\dfrac{30}{10} = \dfrac{18}{x}$
$30 \cdot x = 10 \cdot 18$
$30x = 180$
$\dfrac{30x}{30} = \dfrac{180}{30}$
$x = 6$ m

14. $\dfrac{5}{4} = \dfrac{x+5}{5}$
$4(x+5) = 5 \cdot 5$
$4x + 20 = 25$
$4x = 5$
$\dfrac{4x}{4} = \dfrac{5}{4}$
$x = \dfrac{5}{4}$ in.
$x = 1.25$ in.

15. $\dfrac{20}{15} = \dfrac{x}{12}$
$15x = 20 \cdot 12$
$15x = 240$
$\dfrac{15x}{15} = \dfrac{240}{15}$
$x = 16$ in.

16. $\dfrac{5}{7.5} = \dfrac{4}{x}$
$5 \cdot x = 4 \cdot 7.5$
$5x = 30$
$\dfrac{5x}{5} = \dfrac{30}{5}$
$x = 6$ ft

17. Let $x = \overline{CA}$
$\dfrac{CA}{EA} = \dfrac{BC}{DE}$
$\dfrac{x}{15} = \dfrac{3}{9}$
$9x = 3 \cdot 15$
$9x = 45$
$x = 5$
$\overline{CA} = 5$

18. Let $x = \overline{DB}$

Then $x + 3 = \overline{DA}$

$\dfrac{DA}{BA} = \dfrac{DE}{BC}$

$\dfrac{x+3}{3} = \dfrac{9}{3}$

$x + 3 = 9$

$x = 6$

$\overline{DB} = 6$

19. Let $x = \overline{DA}$

$\dfrac{DA}{BA} = \dfrac{DE}{BC}$

$\dfrac{x}{3} = \dfrac{9}{3}$

$x = 9$

$\overline{DA} = 9$

20. Since the lines are parallel, $m\angle EDA = m\angle CBA$ and $m\angle DEA = m\angle BCA$. Clearly $m\angle A = m\angle A$, thus all corresponding angles have equal measure.

21. $c^2 = 8^2 + 15^2$

$c^2 = 64 + 225$

$c^2 = 289$

$c = 17$ m

22. $c^2 = 7^2 + 24^2$

$c^2 = 49 + 576$

$c^2 = 625$

$c = 25$ m

23. $c^2 = 15^2 + 36^2$

$c^2 = 225 + 1296$

$c^2 = 1521$

$c = 39$ m

24. $c^2 = 5^2 + 11^2$

$c^2 = 25 + 121$

$c^2 = 146$

$c \approx 12.1$ in.

25. $a^2 + 16^2 = 20^2$

$a^2 + 256 = 400$

$a^2 = 144$

$a = 12$ cm

26. $a^2 + 5^2 = 13^2$

$a^2 + 25 = 169$

$a^2 = 144$

$a = 12$ ft

27. No; $46.1° + 58.3° + 75.9° = 180.3°$

There is an error of $180.3° - 180° = 0.3°$

28. Let x = height of tree.

$\dfrac{x}{8} = \dfrac{12}{6}$

$6 \cdot x = 12 \cdot 8$

$6x = 96$

$x = 16$ ft

29. Let x = height of tree.

$\dfrac{x}{5} = \dfrac{86}{6}$

$6 \cdot x = 5 \cdot 86$

$6x = 430$

$x \approx 71.7$ ft

30. Let c = the length of the ladder.

$c^2 = 8^2 + 10^2$

$c^2 = 64 + 100$

$c^2 = 164$

$c \approx 12.8$ ft

31. Let x = height of the plane.

$x^2 + 8^2 = 10^2$

$x^2 + 64 = 100$

$x^2 = 36$

$x = 6$ km

32. Let x = distance from home to second base.

$x^2 = 90^2 + 90^2$

$x^2 = 8100 + 8100$

$x^2 = 16,200$

$x \approx 127.3$ ft

33. Let x = the length of the ladder.

$x^2 + 15^2 = 20^2$

$x^2 + 225 = 400$

$x^2 = 175$

$x \approx 13.2$ ft

34. Let c = the length of one support wire.
$$c^2 = 8^2 + 15^2$$
$$c^2 = 64 + 225$$
$$c^2 = 289$$
$$c = 17 \text{ ft}$$
$$2c = 34 \text{ ft}$$

35. Let c = the length of the new road.
$$c^2 = 3000^2 + 4000^2$$
$$c^2 = 9,000,000 + 16,000,000$$
$$c^2 = 25,000,000$$
$$c = 5000 \text{ m}$$
$$c = 5 \text{ km}$$
Thus, the cost is $5 \times \$150,000 = \$750000$

36-43. Answers will vary.

44. No; Answers will vary.

45. $m\angle PQT = 180° - 70° - 60° = 50°$
$$\begin{aligned} m\angle SQR &= 180° - m\angle PQT - 50° \\ &= 180° - 50° - 50° \\ &= 80° \end{aligned}$$
$$\begin{aligned} m\angle R &= 180° - m\angle SQR - 30° \\ &= 180° - 80° - 30° \\ &= 70° \end{aligned}$$

46. Let x = the left portion of $\overline{AB}$
Let y = the right portion of $\overline{AB}$
$$x^2 + 12^2 = 13^2$$
$$x^2 + 144 = 169$$
$$x^2 = 25$$
$$x = 5 \text{ ft}$$

$$y^2 + 12^2 = 20^2$$
$$y^2 + 144 = 400$$
$$y^2 = 256$$
$$y = 16 \text{ ft}$$
$$\overline{AB} = x + y = 5 + 16 = 21 \text{ ft}$$

47. The lengths should satisfy the Pythagorean theorem.
$$c^2 = 16^2 + 20^2$$
$$c^2 = 256 + 400$$
$$c^2 = 656$$
$$c \approx 25.6 \text{ ft, not } 24\tfrac{1}{4} \text{ ft}$$
No, the floor is not squared off properly.

Check Points 10.3

1. Note: 50 yds equals 150 ft and 30 yds equals 90 ft
$$P = 2l + 2w$$
$$P = 2 \cdot 150 \text{ ft} + 2 \cdot 90 \text{ ft} = 480 \text{ ft}$$
$$\text{Cost} = \frac{480 \cancel{\text{ feet}}}{1} \cdot \frac{\$6.50}{\cancel{\text{foot}}} = \$3120$$

2. a. $\begin{aligned} \text{Sum} &= (n-2)180° \\ &= (12-2)\,180° \\ &= 10 \cdot 180° \\ &= 1800° \end{aligned}$

b. $m\angle A = \dfrac{1800°}{12} = 150°$

Exercise Set 10.3

1. Quadrilateral (4 sides)

2. Octagon (8 sides)

3. Pentagon (5 sides)

4. Heptagon (7 sides)

5. a (square), b (rhombus), d (rectangle), and e (parallelogram) all have two pairs of parallel sides.

6. a (square), b (rhombus)

7. a (square), d (rectangle)

8. c (trapezoid), d (rectangle), e (parallelogram)

9. c (trapezoid)

10. a (square)

11. $\begin{aligned} P &= 2 \cdot 3 \text{ cm} + 2 \cdot 12 \text{ cm} \\ &= 6 \text{ cm} + 24 \text{ cm} \\ &= 30 \text{ cm} \end{aligned}$

12. $\begin{aligned} P &= 2 \cdot 9 \text{ cm} + 2 \cdot 14 \text{ cm} \\ &= 18 \text{ cm} + 28 \text{ cm} \\ &= 46 \text{ cm} \end{aligned}$

13. $\begin{aligned} P &= 2 \cdot 6 \text{ yd} + 2 \cdot 8 \text{ yd} \\ &= 12 \text{ yd} + 16 \text{ yd} \\ &= 28 \text{ yd} \end{aligned}$

14. $P = 2 \cdot 7 \text{ in.} + 2 \cdot 18 \text{ in.} = 14 \text{ in.} + 36 \text{ in.} = 50 \text{ in.}$

15. $P = 4 \cdot 250 \text{ in.} = 1000 \text{ in.}$

16. $P = 4 \cdot 3.5 \text{ m} = 14 \text{ m}$

17. $P = 9$ ft $+ 7$ ft $+ 11$ ft $= 27$ ft

18. $P = 10$ yd $+ 16$ yd $+ 8.5$ yd $= 34.5$ yd

19. $P = 3 \cdot 6$ yd $= 18$ yd

20. $P = 6 \cdot 4$ mm $= 24$ mm

21. $P = 12$ yd $+ 12$ yd $+ 9$ yd $+ 9$ yd $+ 21$ yd $+ 21$ yd
$= 84$ yd

22. $P = 4$ in. $+ 9$ in. $+ 13$ in $+ 5$ in. $+ 17$ in. $+ 14$ in.
$= 62$ in.

23. First determine lengths of unknown sides.

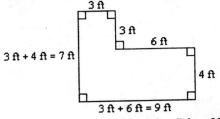

$P = 3$ ft $+ 3$ ft $+ 6$ ft $+ 4$ ft $+ 9$ ft $+ 7$ ft $= 32$ ft

24. First determine lengths of unknown sides.

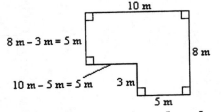

$P = 10$ m $+ 8$ m $+ 5$ m $+ 3$ m $+ 5$ m $+ 5$ m $= 36$ m

25. Sum $= (n - 2)180°$
$= (5 - 2)\ 180°$
$= 3 \cdot 180°$
$= 540°$

26. Sum $= (n - 2)\ 180°$
$= (6 - 2)\ 180°$
$= 4 \cdot 180°$
$= 720°$

27. Sum $= (n - 2)180°$
$= (4 - 2)180°$
$= 2 \cdot 180°$
$= 360°$

28. Sum $= (n - 2)\ 180°$
$= (7 - 2)\ 180°$
$= 5 \cdot 180°$
$= 900°$

29. From Exercise 25, we know the sum of the measures of the angles of a pentagon is 540°. Since

all 5 angles have the same degree measure, $m\angle A = \dfrac{540°}{5} = 108°$.
$m\angle B = 180° - 108° = 72°$

30. From Exercise 26. we know the sum of the measures of the angles of a hexagon is 720°. Since all 6 angles have the same degree measure,
$m\angle A = \dfrac{720°}{6} = 120°$. $m\angle B = 180° - 120° = 60°$

31. a. From Exercise 25, we know the sum of the measures of the angles of a pentagon is 540°.

b. $m\angle A = 540° - 70° - 150° - 90° - 90° = 140°$ and
$m\angle B = 180° - 140° = 40°$

32. a. From Exercise 27, we know the sum of the measures of the angles of a quadrilateral is 360°.

b. $m\angle A = 360° - 90° - 90° - 42° = 138°$ and
$m\angle B = 180° - 138° = 42°$

33. No entry

34. Regular octagon

35. Stop, yield, deer crossing

36. One-way traffic

37. Equilateral triangle

38. Square

39. Yield

40. Stop

41. $P = 2 \cdot 400$ ft $+ 2 \cdot 200$ ft
$= 800$ ft $+ 400$ ft
$= 1200$ ft
$\text{Cost} = \dfrac{1200 \text{ ft}}{1} \cdot \dfrac{1 \text{ yd}}{3 \text{ ft}} \cdot \dfrac{\$14}{1 \text{ yd}} = \$5600$

42. $P = 2l + 2w$
$P = 2 \cdot 70$ ft $+ 2 \cdot 30$ ft $= 200$ ft
$\text{Cost} = \dfrac{200 \text{ feet}}{1} \cdot \dfrac{1 \text{ yd}}{3 \text{ feet}} \cdot \dfrac{\$8}{1 \text{ yd}} \approx \$533.33$

43. Since the side of the square is 8 ft, its perimeter is 32 ft.
32 ft. is equivalent to 384 inches.
Thus, the total number of

$$\text{flowers} = \frac{384}{8} = 48 \text{ flowers}.$$

44. First determine lengths of unknown sides.

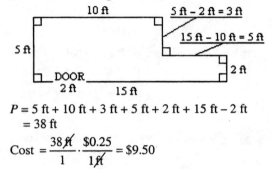

$P = 5 \text{ ft} + 10 \text{ ft} + 3 \text{ ft} + 5 \text{ ft} + 2 \text{ ft} + 15 \text{ ft} - 2 \text{ ft}$
$\quad = 38 \text{ ft}$

$$\text{Cost} = \frac{38 \cancel{\text{ft}}}{1} \cdot \frac{\$0.25}{1 \cancel{\text{ft}}} = \$9.50$$

45-51. Answers will vary.

52. First determine lengths of unknown sides.

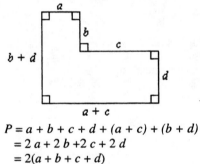

$P = a + b + c + d + (a + c) + (b + d)$
$\quad = 2a + 2b + 2c + 2d$
$\quad = 2(a + b + c + d)$

53. All sides have length a, therefore $P = 6a$.

54. First, find the measures of the two unknown angles:
$180° - 63° = 117°$ and
$180° - 97° = 83°$
Sum of measures of angles $= (n - 2)180°$
$\qquad\qquad\qquad\qquad\quad = (5 - 2)180°$
$\qquad\qquad\qquad\qquad\quad = 540°$
$m\angle 1 = 540° - 117° - 140° - 83° - 135°$
$\qquad\; = 65°$

Check Points 10.4

1. Area of large rectangle:
$A_{\text{large}} = lw$
$\qquad\quad = (13 \text{ ft} + 3 \text{ ft}) \times (3 \text{ ft} + 6 \text{ ft})$
$\qquad\quad = 16 \text{ ft} \cdot 9 \text{ ft}$
$\qquad\quad = 144 \text{ ft}^2$
Area of small rectangle:
$A_{\text{small}} = lw$
$\qquad\quad = 13 \text{ ft} \cdot 6 \text{ ft}$
$\qquad\quad = 78 \text{ ft}^2$
Area of path $= 144 \text{ ft}^2 - 78 \text{ ft}^2 = 66 \text{ ft}^2$

2. First convert the linear measures in feet to linear yards.

$$18 \text{ ft} = \frac{18 \cancel{\text{ft}}}{1} \cdot \frac{1 \text{ yd}}{3 \cancel{\text{ft}}} = 6 \text{ yd}$$

$$21 \text{ ft} = \frac{21 \cancel{\text{ft}}}{1} \cdot \frac{1 \text{ yd}}{3 \cancel{\text{ft}}} = 7 \text{ yd}$$

Area of floor $= 6 \text{ yd} \cdot 7 \text{ yd} = 42 \text{ yd}^2$

$$\text{Cost of carpet} = \frac{42 \cancel{\text{yd}^2}}{1} \cdot \frac{\$16}{1 \cancel{\text{yd}^2}} = \$672$$

3. $A = bh$
$A = 10 \text{ in.} \cdot 6 \text{ in.} = 60 \text{ in.}^2$

4. $A = \dfrac{1}{2} bh$

$A = \dfrac{1}{2} \cdot 12 \text{ ft} \cdot 5 \text{ ft} = 30 \text{ ft}^2$

5. $A = \dfrac{1}{2} h(a + b)$

$\quad = \dfrac{1}{2} \cdot 7 \text{ ft} \cdot (20 \text{ ft} + 10 \text{ ft})$

$\quad = \dfrac{1}{2} \cdot 7 \text{ ft} \cdot 30 \text{ ft}$

$\quad = 105 \text{ ft}^2$

6. $C = \pi d$
$\quad = \pi (10 \text{ in.})$
$\quad = 10\pi \text{ in.}$
$\quad \approx 31.4 \text{ in.}$

7. Find the circumference of the semicircle:

$$C_{\text{semicircle}} = \frac{1}{2}\pi d$$

$$\approx \frac{1}{2}\pi(10 \text{ ft})$$

$$\approx 15.7 \text{ ft}$$

Length of trim $= 10 \text{ ft} + 12 \text{ ft} + 12 \text{ ft} + 15.7 \text{ ft}$

$$= 49.7 \text{ ft}$$

8. First, find the area of pizzas.

Large:	Medium:
$A = \pi r^2$	$A = \pi r^2$
$= \pi(9 \text{ in.})^2$	$= \pi(7 \text{ in.})^2$
$= 81\pi \text{ in.}^2$	$= 49\pi \text{ in.}^2$
$\approx 254 \text{ in.}^2$	$\approx 154 \text{ in.}^2$

Next, find the price per square inch.

Large:	Medium:
$\dfrac{\$20.00}{81\pi \text{ in.}^2}$	$\dfrac{\$14.00}{49\pi \text{ in.}^2}$
$\approx \dfrac{\$20.00}{254 \text{ in.}^2}$	$\approx \dfrac{\$14.00}{154 \text{ in.}^2}$
$\approx \dfrac{\$0.08}{\text{in.}^2}$	$\approx \dfrac{\$0.09}{\text{in.}^2}$

The large pizza is a better buy.

Exercise Set 10.4

1. $A = 6 \text{ m} \cdot 3 \text{ m} = 18 \text{ m}^2$

2. $A = 3 \text{ ft} \cdot 4 \text{ ft} = 12 \text{ ft}^2$

3. $A = (4 \text{ in.})^2 = 16 \text{ in.}^2$

4. $A = (3 \text{ cm})^2 = 9 \text{ cm}^2$

5. $A = 50 \text{ cm} \cdot 42 \text{ cm} = 2100 \text{ cm}^2$

6. $A = 58 \text{ ft} \cdot 43 \text{ ft} = 2494 \text{ ft}^2$

7. $A = \frac{1}{2} \cdot 14 \text{ in.} \cdot 8 \text{ in.} = 56 \text{ in.}^2$

8. $A = \frac{1}{2} \cdot 30 \text{ m} \cdot 33 \text{ m} = 495 \text{ m}^2$

9. $A = \frac{1}{2} \cdot 9.8 \text{ yd} \cdot 4.2 \text{ yd} = 20.58 \text{ yd}^2$

10. $A = \frac{1}{2} \cdot 8 \text{ yd} \cdot 3.5 \text{ yd} = 14 \text{ yd}^2$

11. $a^2 + b^2 = c^2$

$$h^2 + 12^2 = 13^2$$

$$h^2 + 144 = 169$$

$$h^2 = 25$$

$$h = 5$$

$$A = \frac{1}{2} \cdot 12 \text{ in.} \cdot 5 \text{ in.} = 30 \text{ in.}^2$$

12. $a^2 + b^2 = c^2$

$$h^2 + 8^2 = 10^2$$

$$h^2 + 64 = 100$$

$$h^2 = 36$$

$$h = 6$$

$$A = \frac{1}{2} \cdot 8 \text{ m} \cdot 6 \text{ m} = 24 \text{ m}^2$$

13. $A = \frac{1}{2} \cdot 7 \text{ m} \cdot (16 \text{ m} + 10 \text{ m})$

$$= \frac{7}{2} \text{ m} \cdot (26 \text{ m})$$

$$= 91 \text{ m}^2$$

14. $A = \frac{1}{2} \cdot 18 \text{ m} \cdot (37 \text{ m} + 26 \text{ m})$

$$= 9 \text{ m}(63 \text{ m})$$

$$= 567 \text{ m}^2$$

15. $C = 2\pi \cdot 4 \text{ cm} = 8\pi \text{ cm} \approx 25.1 \text{ cm}$

$$A = \pi(4 \text{ cm})^2 = 16\pi \text{ cm}^2 \approx 50.3 \text{ cm}^2$$

16. $C = 2\pi \cdot 9 \text{ m} = 18\pi \text{ m} \approx 56.5 \text{ m}$

$$A = \pi(9 \text{ m})^2 = 81\pi \text{ m}^2 \approx 254.5 \text{ m}^2$$

17. $C = \pi \cdot 12 \text{ yd} = 12\pi \text{ yd} \approx 37.7 \text{ yd}$

$$r = \frac{d}{2} = \frac{12 \text{ yd}}{2} = 6 \text{ yd}$$

$$A = \pi(6 \text{ yd})^2 = 36\pi \text{ yd}^2 \approx 113.1 \text{ yd}^2$$

18. $C = \pi \cdot 40 \text{ ft} = 40\pi \text{ ft} \approx 125.7 \text{ ft}$

$$r = \frac{d}{2} = \frac{40 \text{ ft}}{2} = 20 \text{ ft}$$

$$A = \pi(20 \text{ ft})^2 = 400\pi \text{ ft}^2 \approx 1256.6 \text{ ft}^2$$

19. The figure breaks into a lower rectangle and an upper rectangle.

    Area of lower rectangle: Area of upper rectangle:

    $A = lw$ $A = lw$

    $A = (12 \text{ m})(3 \text{ m})$ $A = (9 \text{ m})(4 \text{ m})$

    $A = 36 \text{ m}^2$ $A = 36 \text{ m}^2$

    Total area $= 36 \text{ m}^2 + 36 \text{ m}^2 = 72 \text{ m}^2$

20. The figure breaks into a lower rectangle and an upper rectangle.

    Area of lower rectangle: Area of upper rectangle:

    $A = lw$ $A = lw$

    $A = (9 \text{ ft})(2 \text{ ft})$ $A = (7 \text{ ft})(3 \text{ ft})$

    $A = 18 \text{ ft}^2$ $A = 21 \text{ ft}^2$

    Total area $= 18 \text{ ft}^2 + 21 \text{ ft}^2 = 39 \text{ ft}^2$

21. The figure breaks into a lower rectangle and an upper triangle.

    Area of rectangle: Area of triangle:

                              $A = \frac{1}{2}bh$

    $A = lw$

    $A = (24 \text{ m})(10 \text{ m})$ $A = \frac{1}{2}(24 \text{ m})(5 \text{ m})$

    $A = 240 \text{ m}^2$ $A = 60 \text{ m}^2$

    Total area $= 240 \text{ m}^2 + 60 \text{ m}^2 = 300 \text{ m}^2$

22. The figure breaks into a left rectangle and a triangle on the right.

    Area of rectangle: Area of triangle:

                              $A = \frac{1}{2}bh$

    $A = lw$

    $A = (6 \text{ cm})(10 \text{ cm})$ $A = \frac{1}{2}(3 \text{ cm})(7 \text{ cm})$

    $A = 60 \text{ cm}^2$ $A = 10.5 \text{ cm}^2$

    Total area $= 60 \text{ cm}^2 + 10.5 \text{ cm}^2 = 70.5 \text{ cm}^2$

23. The figure's area can be obtained by adding the area of a square of side 10 cm, to twice the area of a circle of radius 5 cm.

    Area of square: Area of circles:

    $A = s^2$ $A = \pi r^2$

    $A = (10 \text{ cm})^2$ $A = \pi(5 \text{ cm})^2$

    $A = 100 \text{ cm}^2$ $A = 25\pi \text{ cm}^2$

    Total area $= 100 \text{ cm}^2 + 25\pi \text{ cm}^2 + 25\pi \text{ cm}^2$

                  $= (100 + 50\pi) \text{ cm}^2$

                  $\approx 257.1 \text{ cm}^2$

24. $a^2 + b^2 = c^2$

$h^2 + 9^2 = 15^2$

$h^2 + 81 = 225$

$h^2 = 144$

$h = 12$

The figure's area can be obtained by adding the area of the triangle to half the area of a circle of radius 6 in.

Area of triangle:

$A = \frac{1}{2}bh$

$A = \frac{1}{2} \cdot 9 \text{ in.} \cdot 12 \text{ in.}$

$A = 54 \text{ in.}^2$

Area of circle:

$A = \pi r^2$

$A = \pi (6 \text{ in.})^2$

$A = 36\pi \text{ in.}^2$

Total area $= 54 \text{ in.}^2 + \frac{1}{2} \cdot 36\pi \text{ in.}^2$

$= (54 + 18\pi) \text{ in.}^2$

$\approx 110.5 \text{ in.}^2$

25. First convert the linear measures in feet to linear yards.

$9 \text{ ft} = \frac{9 \text{ ft}}{1} \cdot \frac{1 \text{ yd}}{3 \text{ ft}} = 3 \text{ yd}$

$21 \text{ ft} = \frac{21 \text{ ft}}{1} \cdot \frac{1 \text{ yd}}{3 \text{ ft}} = 7 \text{ yd}$

Area of floor $= 3 \text{ yd} \cdot 7 \text{ yd} = 21 \text{ yd}^2$

Cost of carpet $= \frac{21 \text{ yd}^2}{1} \cdot \frac{\$26.50}{1 \text{ yd}^2} = \$556.50$

26. First convert the linear measures in feet to linear yards.

$60 \text{ ft} = \frac{60 \text{ ft}}{1} \cdot \frac{1 \text{ yd}}{3 \text{ ft}} = 20 \text{ yd}$

$9 \text{ ft} = \frac{9 \text{ ft}}{1} \cdot \frac{1 \text{ yd}}{3 \text{ ft}} = 3 \text{ yd}$

Area of wall $= 20 \text{ yd} \cdot 3 \text{ yd} = 60 \text{ yd}^2$

Cost of plastering $= \frac{60 \text{ yd}^2}{1} \cdot \frac{\$18}{1 \text{ yd}^2} = \$1080$

27. Area of tile $=$ (Area of floor) $-$ (Area of store) $-$ (Area of refrigerator)

$= (12 \text{ ft} \cdot 15 \text{ ft}) - (3 \text{ ft} \cdot 4 \text{ ft}) - (4 \text{ ft} \cdot 5 \text{ ft})$

$= 180 \text{ ft}^2 - 12 \text{ ft}^2 - 20 \text{ ft}^2 = 148 \text{ ft}^2$

28. Area of room $= 12 \text{ ft} \cdot 15 \text{ ft} = 180 \text{ ft}^2$

Convert linear measures of tiles in inches to linear feet.

$3 \text{ in.} = \dfrac{3 \text{ in.}}{1} \cdot \dfrac{1 \text{ ft}}{12 \text{ in.}} = \dfrac{1}{4}$ ft, and $2 \text{ in.} = \dfrac{2 \text{ in.}}{1} \cdot \dfrac{1 \text{ ft}}{12 \text{ in.}} = \dfrac{1}{6}$ ft. Therefore, the area of one tile $= \dfrac{1}{4} \text{ft} \cdot \dfrac{1}{6} \text{ft} = \dfrac{1}{24} \text{ft}^2$

Number of tiles needed $= \dfrac{\text{Area of room}}{\text{Area of one tile}} = \dfrac{180 \text{ ft}^2}{\frac{1}{24} \text{ ft}^2} = 4320 \text{ tiles}$

Cost of tiles $= \dfrac{4320 \text{ tiles}}{1} \cdot \dfrac{\$0.30}{10 \text{ tiles}} = \$129.60$

29. a. Area of lawn = (Area of lot) – (Area of house) – (Area of shed) – (Area of driveway)

$= 200 \text{ft} \cdot 500 \text{ ft} - 60 \text{ ft} \cdot 100 \text{ ft} - (20 \text{ ft})^2 - 100 \text{ ft} \cdot 20 \text{ ft}$

$= 100,000 \text{ ft}^2 - 6000 \text{ ft}^2 - 400 \text{ ft}^2 - 2000 \text{ ft}^2$

$= 91,600 \text{ ft}^2$

Maximum number of bags of fertilizer $= \dfrac{1 \text{ bag}}{4000 \text{ ft}^2} \cdot \dfrac{91,600 \text{ ft}^2}{1} = 22.9 \text{ bags} \rightarrow 23 \text{ bags}$

b. Total cost of fertilizer $= \dfrac{\$25.00}{1 \text{ bag}} \cdot \dfrac{23 \text{ bags}}{2} = \$575$

30. Area of office $= 20 \text{ ft} \cdot 16 \text{ ft} = 320 \text{ ft}^2$

Amount of electrical bills that are deductible $= \dfrac{320 \text{ ft}^2}{2200 \text{ ft}^2} \cdot \$4800 \approx \$698.18$

31. a. Area of a front wall $= \left[20 \text{ ft} \cdot 40 \text{ ft} \right] + \left[\frac{1}{2} \cdot 40 \text{ ft} \cdot 10 \text{ ft} \right] = 1000 \text{ ft}^2$

Area of a side wall $= 50 \text{ ft} \cdot 20 \text{ ft} = 1000 \text{ ft}^2$

Area of windows $= 4 \left[8 \text{ ft} \cdot 5 \text{ ft} \right] + 2 \left[30 \text{ ft} \cdot 2 \text{ ft} \right] = 280 \text{ ft}^2$

Area of doors $= 2 \left[80 \text{ in.} \cdot 36 \text{ in.} \right] = 2 \left[6\frac{2}{3} \text{ ft} \cdot 3 \text{ ft} \right] = 40 \text{ ft}^2$

Area of paint = 2(Area of front wall) + 2(Area of side wall) – (Area of windows and doors)

$= 2 \left(1000 \text{ ft}^2 \right) + 2 \left(1000 \text{ ft}^2 \right) - \left(280 \text{ ft}^2 + 40 \text{ ft}^2 \right)$

$= 2000 \text{ ft}^2 + 2000 \text{ ft}^2 - 320 \text{ ft}^2$

$= 3680 \text{ ft}^2$

b. Two coats will require enough paint for $2 \cdot 3680 \text{ ft}^2 = 7360 \text{ ft}^2$.

$7360 \text{ ft}^2 = \dfrac{7360 \text{ ft}^2}{1} \cdot \dfrac{1 \text{ gallon}}{500 \text{ ft}^2} = 14.72 \text{ gallons} \approx 15 \text{ gallons}$.

c. $\$26.95 \times 15 = \$404.25$ is the cost to buy the paint.

32. Square footage (area) of home $= 54 \text{ ft} \cdot 30 \text{ ft} = 1620 \text{ ft}^2$

Cost of building home $\$95 \cdot 1620 = \$153,900$

33. Area of Master Bedroom $= 14 \text{ ft} \cdot 14 \text{ ft} = 196 \text{ ft}^2$

    Area of Bedroom #2 $= 11 \text{ ft} \cdot 12 \text{ ft} = 132 \text{ ft}^2$

    Area of Bedroom #3 $= 12 \text{ ft} \cdot 11 \text{ ft} = 132 \text{ ft}^2$

    Total area $= 196 \text{ ft}^2 + 132 \text{ ft}^2 + 132 \text{ ft}^2 = 460 \text{ ft}^2$

    Since there are 9 square feet in a square yard, $460 \text{ ft}^2 \approx 51.1 \text{ yd}^2$.

    52 yd^2 at $17.95 per square yard costs $933.40.

34. Area of kitchen $= 12 \text{ ft} \cdot 14 \text{ ft} = 168 \text{ ft}^2$

    Area of dining room $= 10 \text{ ft} \cdot 14 \text{ ft} = 140 \text{ ft}^2$

    Total area $= 168 \text{ ft}^2 + 140 \text{ ft}^2 = 308 \text{ ft}^2$

    Since there are 9 square feet in a square yard, $308 \text{ ft}^2 \approx 34.2 \text{ yd}^2$.

    35 yd^2 at $26.95 per square yard costs $943.25.

35. Amount of fencing $= C = 2\pi \cdot 20 \text{ m} = 40\pi \text{ m} \approx 125.7 \text{ m}$

36. Feet of fringe $= C = \pi d = \pi \cdot 6 \text{ ft} = 6\pi \text{ ft} \approx 18.8 \text{ ft}$

37. $C = 2\pi \cdot 30 \text{ ft} \approx 188.5 \text{ ft}$

    $188.5 \text{ ft} = \dfrac{188.5 \text{ ft}}{1} \cdot \dfrac{12 \text{ in.}}{1 \text{ ft}} = 2262 \text{ in.}$

    Number of plants $= \dfrac{1 \text{ plant}}{6 \text{ in.}} \cdot \dfrac{2262 \text{ in.}}{1} = 377 \text{ plants}$

38. Perimeter of rectangle $= 3 \text{ ft} + 6 \text{ ft} + 6 \text{ ft} = 15 \text{ ft}$

    Perimeter of semicircle $= \dfrac{1}{2}C = \dfrac{1}{2}\pi \cdot 3 \text{ ft} \approx 4.7 \text{ ft}$

    Approximately $15 \text{ ft} + 4.7 \text{ ft} = 19.7 \text{ ft}$ of stripping will be needed.

39. First, find the area of pizzas.

    Large: $\quad$ Medium:

    $A = \pi r^2 \qquad A = \pi r^2$

    $= \pi(7 \text{ in.})^2 \qquad = \pi(3.5 \text{ in.})^2$

    $= 49\pi \text{ in.}^2 \qquad = 12.25\pi \text{ in.}^2$

    $\approx 153.9 \text{ in.}^2 \qquad \approx 38.5 \text{ in.}^2$

    Next, find the price per square inch.

    Large: $\quad$ Medium:

    $\dfrac{\$12.00}{49\pi \text{ in.}^2} \qquad \dfrac{\$5.00}{12.25\pi \text{ in.}^2}$

    $\approx \dfrac{\$12.00}{153.9 \text{ in.}^2} \qquad \approx \dfrac{\$5.00}{38.5 \text{ in.}^2}$

    $\approx \dfrac{\$0.08}{\text{in.}^2} \qquad \approx \dfrac{\$0.13}{\text{in.}^2}$

    The large pizza is a better buy.

40. First, find the area of pizzas.

Large: Small:

$$A = \pi r^2 \qquad\qquad A = \pi r^2$$

$$= \pi(8 \text{ in.})^2 \qquad = \pi(5 \text{ in.})^2$$

$$= 64\pi \text{ in.}^2 \qquad = 25\pi \text{ in.}^2$$

$$\approx 201.1 \text{ in.}^2 \qquad \approx 78.5 \text{ in.}^2$$

2 small pizzas:

$$\approx 2 \cdot 78.5 \text{ in.}^2$$

$$\approx 157 \text{ in.}^2$$

The large pizza is a better buy because it has a larger area for the same price.

41-45. Answers will vary.

46. A square of side 50 ft will enclose the most area.

47. Original Area $= 8\,\text{ft} \cdot 10\,\text{ft} = 80\,\text{ft}^2$

New area $= 12\,\text{ft} \cdot 15\,\text{ft} = 180\,\text{ft}^2$

$$\text{Ratio} = \frac{180\,\text{ft}^2}{80\,\text{ft}^2} = \frac{9}{4}$$

The cost will increase by a factor of $\frac{9}{4}$, or 2.25.

48. First, find the area of the large rectangle that includes the path and the pool.
The length of the large rectangle is 30 ft + 3 ft + 3 ft = 36 ft.
The width of the large rectangle is 14 ft + 3 ft + 3 ft = 20 ft.

Area of large rectangular $= 36\,\text{ft} \cdot 20\,\text{ft} = 720\,\text{ft}^2$
Next, find the area of the pool.

Area of pool $= 30\,\text{ft} \cdot 14\,\text{ft} = 420\,\text{ft}^2$
Area of path = (Area of large Rectangle) – (Area of Pool)

$= 720\,\text{ft}^2 - 420\,\text{ft}^2 = 300\,\text{ft}^2$

$$\text{Cost of resurfacing} = \frac{300\,\text{ft}^2}{1} \cdot \frac{\$2}{\text{ft}^2} = \$600$$

49. $\text{Length of pipeline} = \dfrac{16.8\,\text{mi}}{1} \cdot \dfrac{5280\,\text{ft}}{1\,\text{mi}} = 88{,}704\,\text{ft}$

Area of land $= 88{,}704\,\text{ft} \cdot 200\,\text{ft} = 17{,}740{,}800\,\text{ft}^2$

$$\text{Area of land in acres} = \frac{17{,}740{,}800\,\text{ft}^2}{1} \cdot \frac{1\,\text{acre}}{43{,}560\,\text{ft}^2} \approx 407.2727\,\text{acres}$$

$$\text{Total cost} = \frac{\$32}{1\,\text{acre}} \cdot \frac{407.2727\,\text{acres}}{1} = \$13{,}032.73$$

50. $A =$ (area of large circle) $- 2$(area of small circle)

$$A = \pi(4 \text{ cm})^2 - 2\left[\pi(2 \text{ cm})^2\right]$$

$$A = 16\pi \text{ cm}^2 - 8\pi \text{ cm}^2$$

$$A = 8\pi \text{ cm}^2$$

Check Points 10.5

1. $V = 5\ \text{ft} \cdot 3\ \text{ft} \cdot 7\ \text{ft} = 105\ \text{ft}^3$

2. $= \dfrac{6\ \cancel{\text{ft}}}{1} \cdot \dfrac{1\ \text{yd}}{3\ \cancel{\text{ft}}} = 2\ \text{yd}$

    $V = (2\ \text{yd})^3 = 8\ \text{yd}^3$

3. $B = (6\ \text{ft})^2 = 36\ \text{ft}^2$

    $V = \dfrac{1}{3} \cdot 36\ \text{ft}^2 \cdot 4\ \text{ft}$

    $= 48\ \text{ft}^3$

4. $r = \dfrac{1}{2}(8\ \text{cm}) = 4\ \text{cm}$

    $V = \pi(4\ \text{in.})^2 \cdot 6\ \text{in.} \approx 302\ \text{in.}^3$

5. $V = \dfrac{1}{3}\pi(4\ \text{in.})^2 \cdot 6\ \text{in.} \approx 101\ \text{in.}^3$

6. No, it is not enough air.

    $V = \dfrac{4}{3}\pi(4.5\ \text{in.})^3 \approx 382\ \text{in.}^3$

7. New dimensions: $l = 16\ \text{yd}$, $w = 10\ \text{yd}$, $h = 6\ \text{yd}$

    $SA = 2lw + 2lh + 2wh$

    $= 2 \cdot 16\ \text{yd} \cdot 10\ \text{yd} + 2 \cdot 16\ \text{yd} \cdot 6\ \text{yd} + 2 \cdot 10\ \text{yd} \cdot 6\ \text{yd}$

    $= 320\ \text{yd}^2 + 192\ \text{yd}^2 + 120\ \text{yd}^2$

    $= 632\ \text{yd}^2$

Exercise Set 10.5

1. $V = 3\ \text{in.} \cdot 3\ \text{in.} \cdot 4\ \text{in.} = 36\ \text{in.}^3$

2. $V = 3\ \text{cm} \cdot 5\ \text{cm} \cdot 3\ \text{cm} = 45\ \text{cm}^3$

3. $V = (4\ \text{cm})^3 = 64\ \text{cm}^3$

4. $V = (5\ \text{in.})^3 = 125\ \text{in.}^3$

5. $B = 7\ \text{yd} \cdot 5\ \text{yd} = 35\ \text{yd}^2$

    $V = \dfrac{1}{3} \cdot 35\ \text{yd}^2 \cdot 15\ \text{yd}$

    $= 175\ \text{yd}^3$

6. $B = 8\ \text{yd} \cdot 15\ \text{yd} = 120\ \text{yd}^2$

    $V = \dfrac{1}{3} \cdot 120\ \text{yd}^2 \cdot 20\ \text{yd}$

    $= 800\ \text{yd}^3$

7. $B = 4\ \text{in.} \cdot 7\ \text{in.} = 28\ \text{in.}^2$

    $V = \dfrac{1}{3} \cdot 28\ \text{in.}^2 \cdot 6\ \text{in.}$

    $= 56\ \text{in.}^3$

8. $B = (10\ \text{m})^2 = 100\ \text{m}^2$

    $V = \dfrac{1}{3} \cdot 100\ \text{m}^2 \cdot 12\ \text{m}$

    $= 400\ \text{m}^3$

9. $V = \pi(5\ \text{cm})^2 \cdot 6\ \text{cm} = 150\pi\ \text{cm}^3 \approx 471\ \text{cm}^3$

10. $V = \pi(6\ \text{cm})^2 \cdot 8\ \text{cm} = 288\pi\ \text{cm}^3 \approx 905\ \text{cm}^3$

11. $r = \dfrac{1}{2}(24\ \text{in.}) = 12\ \text{in.}$

    $V = \pi(12\ \text{in.})^2 \cdot 21\ \text{in.} = 3024\pi\ \text{in.}^3 \approx 9500\ \text{in.}^3$

12. $r = \dfrac{1}{2}(14\ \text{cm}) = 7\ \text{cm}$

    $V = \pi(7\ \text{cm})^2 \cdot 12\ \text{cm} = 588\pi\ \text{cm}^3 \approx 1847\ \text{cm}^3$

13. $V = \dfrac{1}{3}\pi(4\ \text{m})^2 \cdot 9\ \text{m} = 48\pi\ \text{m}^3 \approx 151\ \text{m}^3$

14. $V = \dfrac{1}{3}\pi(5\ \text{m})^2 \cdot 16\ \text{m} = 133\dfrac{1}{3}\pi\ \text{m}^3 \approx 419\ \text{m}^3$

15. $r = \dfrac{1}{2} \cdot 6\ \text{yd} = 3\ \text{yd}$

    $V = \dfrac{1}{3}\pi(3\ \text{yd})^2 \cdot 5\ \text{yd} = 15\pi\ \text{yd}^3 \approx 47\ \text{yd}^3$

16. $r = \dfrac{1}{2} \cdot 6\ \text{yd} = 3\ \text{yd}$

    $V = \dfrac{1}{3}\pi(3\ \text{yd})^2 \cdot 7\ \text{yd} = 21\pi\ \text{yd}^3 \approx 66\ \text{yd}^3$

17. $V = \dfrac{4}{3}\pi(6\ \text{m})^3 = 288\pi\ \text{m}^3 \approx 905\ \text{m}^3$

18. $V = \dfrac{4}{3}\pi(15\ \text{m})^3 = 4500\pi\ \text{m}^3 \approx 14{,}137\ \text{m}^3$

19. $r = \dfrac{1}{2} \cdot 18 \text{ cm} = 9 \text{ cm}$

$V = \dfrac{4}{3}\pi(9 \text{ cm})^3 = 972\pi \text{ cm}^3 \approx 3054 \text{ cm}^3$

20. $r = \dfrac{1}{2} \cdot 24 \text{ in.} = 12 \text{ in.}$

$V = \dfrac{4}{3}\pi(12 \text{ in.})^3 = 2304\pi \text{ in.}^3 \approx 7238 \text{ in.}^3$

21. Surface Area $= 2(5 \text{ m} \cdot 3 \text{ m}) + 2(2 \text{ m} \cdot 3 \text{ m}) + 2(5 \text{ m} \cdot 2 \text{ m})$
$= 2 \cdot 15 \text{ m}^2 + 2 \cdot 6 \text{ m}^2 + 2 \cdot 10 \text{ m}^2$
$= 30 \text{ m}^2 + 12 \text{ m}^2 + 20 \text{ m}^2$
$= 62 \text{ m}^2$

22. Surface area $= 2(6 \text{ m} \cdot 3 \text{ m}) + 2(4 \text{ m} \cdot 3 \text{ m}) + 2(6 \text{ m} \cdot 4 \text{ m})$
$= 2(18 \text{ m}^2) + 2(12 \text{ m}^2) + 2(24 \text{ m}^2)$
$= 36 \text{ m}^2 + 24 \text{ m}^2 + 48 \text{ m}^2$
$= 108 \text{ m}^2$

23. Surface Area $= 6(4 \text{ ft})^2 = 96 \text{ ft}^2$

24. Surface Area $= 6(6 \text{ ft})^2 = 216 \text{ ft}^2$

25. Volume = (volume of cone) + (volume of hemisphere)
$V = \dfrac{1}{3}\pi(6 \text{ cm})^2 \cdot 15 \text{ cm} + \dfrac{1}{2}\left[\dfrac{4}{3}\pi(6 \text{ cm})^3\right] = 324\pi \text{ cm}^3 \approx 1018 \text{ cm}^3$

26. Volume = (Volume of right circular cylinder) + (Volume of cone)
$V = \pi(6 \text{ in.})^2 \cdot 11 \text{ in.} + \dfrac{1}{3}\pi(6 \text{ in.})^2(14 \text{ in.} - 11 \text{ in.}) = 432\pi \text{ in.}^3 \approx 1357 \text{ in.}^3$

27. First convert all linear measures in feet to linear yards.

$12 \text{ ft} = \dfrac{12 \text{ ft}}{1} \cdot \dfrac{1 \text{ yd}}{3 \text{ ft}} = 4 \text{ yd}$

$9 \text{ ft} = \dfrac{9 \text{ ft}}{1} \cdot \dfrac{1 \text{ yd}}{3 \text{ ft}} = 3 \text{ yd}$

$6 \text{ ft} = \dfrac{6 \text{ ft}}{1} \cdot \dfrac{1 \text{ yd}}{3 \text{ ft}} = 2 \text{ yd}$

Total dirt $= 4 \text{ yd} \cdot 3 \text{ yd} \cdot 2 \text{ yd} = 24 \text{ yd}^3$

Total cost $= \dfrac{24 \text{ yd}^3}{1} \cdot \dfrac{1 \text{ truck}}{6 \text{ yd}^3} \cdot \dfrac{\$10}{1 \text{ truck}} = \$40$

28. First convert all linear measures in feet to linear yards.

$$15 \text{ ft} = \frac{15 \text{ ft}}{1} \cdot \frac{1 \text{ yd}}{3 \text{ ft}} = 5 \text{ yd}$$

$$8 \text{ ft} = \frac{8 \text{ ft}}{1} = \frac{1 \text{ yd}}{3 \text{ ft}} = \frac{8}{3} \text{ yd}$$

$$9 \text{ in.} = \frac{9 \text{ in.}}{1} \cdot \frac{1 \text{ ft}}{12 \text{ in.}} \cdot \frac{1 \text{ yd}}{3 \text{ ft}} = \frac{1}{4} \text{ yd}$$

Volume of walkway $= 5 \text{ yd} \cdot \frac{8}{3} \text{ yd} \cdot \frac{1}{4} \text{ yd} = \frac{10}{3} \text{ yd}^3$

$$\text{Cost} = \frac{\$30}{1 \text{ yd}^3} \cdot \frac{\frac{10}{3} \text{ yd}^3}{1} = \$100$$

29. Volume of house $= 1400 \text{ ft}^2 \cdot 9 \text{ ft} = 12{,}600 \text{ ft}^3$
No. This furnace will not be adequate.

30. Change in height $= 20 \text{ yd} - 6 \text{ yd} = 14 \text{ yd}$
Water used $= 50 \text{ yd} \cdot 30 \text{ yd} \cdot 14 \text{ yd} = 21{,}000 \text{ yd}^3$

31. a. First convert linear measures in feet to linear yards.

$$756 \text{ ft} = \frac{756 \text{ ft}}{1} \cdot \frac{1 \text{ yd}}{3 \text{ ft}} = 252 \text{ yd}$$

$$480 \text{ ft} = \frac{480 \text{ ft}}{1} \cdot \frac{1 \text{ yd}}{3 \text{ ft}} = 160 \text{ yd}$$

$$B = (252 \text{ yd})^2 = 63{,}504 \text{ yd}^2$$

$$V = \frac{1}{3} \cdot 63{,}504 \text{ yd}^2 \cdot 160 \text{ yd}$$
$$= 3{,}386{,}880 \text{ yd}^3$$

b. $\dfrac{1 \text{ block}}{1.5 \text{ yd}^3} \cdot \dfrac{3{,}386{,}880 \text{ yd}^3}{1} = 2{,}257{,}920 \text{ blocks}$

32. First convert all linear measures in feet to linear yards.

$$120 \text{ ft} = \frac{120 \text{ ft}}{1} \cdot \frac{1 \text{ yd}}{3 \text{ ft}} = 40 \text{ yd}$$

$$980 \text{ ft} = \frac{980 \text{ ft}}{1} = \frac{1 \text{ yd}}{3 \text{ ft}} \approx 326.667 \text{ yd}$$

$$B = (40 \text{ yd})^2 = 1600 \text{ yd}^2$$

$$V \approx \frac{1}{3} \cdot 1600 \text{ yd}^2 \cdot 327 \text{ yd} \approx 174{,}222 \text{ yd}^3$$

33. Volume of tank $= \pi(3 \text{ ft})^2 \cdot \frac{7}{3} \text{ ft} \approx 66 \text{ ft}^3$
Yes. The volume of the tank is less than 67 cubic feet.

34. Volume of can 1 $= \pi(3 \text{ in.})^2 \cdot 5 \text{ in.} \approx 141 \text{ in.}^3$

Volume of can 2 $= \pi\left(\dfrac{5}{2} \text{ in.}\right)^2 \cdot 6 \text{ in.} \approx 118 \text{ in.}^3$

The can with a diameter of 6 inches and a height of 5 inches contains more soup.

35. Volume of pool (in cubic feet) $= \pi(12 \text{ ft})^2 \cdot 4 \text{ ft} = 576\pi \text{ ft}^3 \approx 1809.6 \text{ ft}^3$

Volume of pool (in gallons) $= 1809.6 \text{ ft}^3 = \dfrac{1809.6 \text{ ft}^3}{1} \cdot \dfrac{7.48 \text{ gallons}}{1 \text{ ft}^3} \approx 13{,}536 \text{ gallons}$

Cost to fill the pool $= \$2 \cdot 13.535 \approx \$27$

36. $V = 3 \cdot \dfrac{1}{2} \cdot \pi(4 \text{ m})^2 \cdot 50{,}000 \text{ m} = 1{,}200{,}000\pi \text{ m}^3 \approx 3{,}769{,}911 \text{ m}^3$

37-38. Answers will vary.

39. New volume $= \dfrac{4}{3}\pi(2r)^3 = \dfrac{4}{3}\pi \cdot 8r^3 = 8\left(\dfrac{4}{3}\pi r^3\right)$

The volume is multiplied by 8.

40. $10 \cdot 10 \cdot 10 = 1000$ times

41. Volume of darkly shaded region $=$ (Volume of rectangular solid) $-$ (Volume of pyramid)

$$= 6 \text{ cm} \cdot 6 \text{ cm} \cdot 7 \text{ cm} - \dfrac{1}{3}(6 \text{ cm})^2 \cdot 7 \text{ cm}$$

$$= 168 \text{ cm}^3$$

42. Volume of darkly shaded region $=$ (volume of outer cylinder) $-$ (volume of inner cylinder)

$$= \pi(3 \text{ in.})^2 \cdot 10 \text{ in.} - \pi(1 \text{ in.})^2 \cdot 10 \text{ in.}$$

$$\approx 251 \text{ in.}^3$$

43. Surface area $=$ (Areas of 3 rectangles) $+$ (Area of 2 triangles)

$$= (5 \text{ cm} \cdot 6 \text{ cm} + 4 \text{ cm} \cdot 6 \text{ cm} + 3 \text{ cm} \cdot 6 \text{ cm}) + 2\left(\dfrac{1}{2} \cdot 3 \text{ cm} \cdot 4 \text{ cm}\right)$$

$$= 72 \text{ cm}^2 + 12 \text{ cm}^2$$

$$= 84 \text{ cm}^2$$

Check Points 10.6

1. $c^2 = a^2 + b^2 = 3^2 + 4^2 = 25$

$c = \sqrt{25} = 5$

$\sin A = \dfrac{3}{5}$

$\cos A = \dfrac{4}{5}$

$\tan A = \dfrac{3}{4}$

2. $\tan A = \dfrac{a}{b}$

$\tan 62° = \dfrac{a}{140}$

$a = 140 \tan 62° \approx 263 \text{ cm}$

3.
$$\cos A = \frac{b}{c}$$
$$\cos 62° = \frac{140}{c}$$
$$c \cos 62° = 140$$
$$c = \frac{140}{\cos 62°}$$
$$c \approx 298 \text{ cm}$$

4. Let a = the height of the tower.
$$\tan 85.4° = \frac{a}{80}$$
$$a = 80 \tan 85.4° \approx 994 \text{ ft}$$

5. $\tan A = \dfrac{14}{10}$
$$A = \tan^{-1}\left(\frac{14}{10}\right) \approx 54°$$

Exercise Set 10.6

1. $\sin A = \dfrac{3}{5}$
$$\cos A = \frac{4}{5}$$
$$\tan A = \frac{3}{4}$$

2. $\sin A = \dfrac{6}{10} = \dfrac{3}{5}$
$$\cos A = \frac{8}{10} = \frac{4}{5}$$
$$\tan A = \frac{6}{8} = \frac{3}{4}$$

3. First find the length of missing side.
$$a^2 = 29^2 - 21^2 = 400$$
$$a = 20$$
$$\sin A = \frac{20}{29}$$
$$\cos A = \frac{21}{29}$$
$$\tan A = \frac{20}{21}$$

4. First find the length of missing side.
$$a^2 = 17^2 - 15^2 = 64$$
$$a = 8$$
$$\sin A = \frac{8}{17}$$
$$\cos A = \frac{15}{17}$$
$$\tan A = \frac{8}{15}$$

5. First find the length of missing side.
$$b^2 = 26^2 - 10^2 = 576$$
$$b = 24$$
$$\sin A = \frac{10}{26} = \frac{5}{13}$$
$$\cos A = \frac{24}{26} = \frac{12}{13}$$
$$\tan A = \frac{10}{24} = \frac{5}{12}$$

6. First find the length of missing side.
$$a^2 = 41^2 - 40^2 = 81$$
$$a = 9$$
$$\sin A = \frac{9}{41}$$
$$\cos A = \frac{40}{41}$$
$$\tan A = \frac{9}{40}$$

7. First find the length of missing side.
$$a^2 = 35^2 - 21^2 = 784$$
$$a = 28$$
$$\sin A = \frac{28}{35} = \frac{4}{5}$$
$$\cos A = \frac{21}{35} = \frac{3}{5}$$
$$\tan A = \frac{28}{21} = \frac{4}{3}$$

8. First find the length of missing side.
$$b^2 = 25^2 - 24^2 = 49$$
$$b = 7$$
$$\sin A = \frac{24}{25}$$
$$\cos A = \frac{7}{25}$$
$$\tan A = \frac{24}{7}$$

9. $\tan A = \dfrac{a}{b}$

$\tan 37° = \dfrac{a}{250}$

$a = 250 \tan 37° \approx 188$ cm

10. $\tan A = \dfrac{a}{b}$

$\tan 61° = \dfrac{a}{10}$

$a = 10 \tan 61° \approx 18$ cm

11. $\cos 34° = \dfrac{b}{220}$

$b = 220 \cos 34° \approx 182$ in.

12. $\cos 72° = \dfrac{b}{15}$

$b = 15 \cos 72° \approx 5$ cm

13. $\sin 34° = \dfrac{a}{13}$

$a = 13 \sin 34° \approx 7$ m

14. $\sin 49° = \dfrac{a}{18}$

$a = 18 \sin 49° \approx 14$ m

15. $\tan 33° = \dfrac{14}{b}$

$b = \dfrac{14}{\tan 33°} \approx 22$ yd

16. $\tan 44° = \dfrac{23}{b}$

$b = \dfrac{23}{\tan 44°} \approx 24$ yd

17. $\sin 30° = \dfrac{20}{c}$

$c = \dfrac{20}{\sin 30°} = 40$ m

18. $\sin 23° = \dfrac{16}{c}$

$c = \dfrac{16}{\sin 23°} \approx 41$ m

19. $m\angle B = 90° - 40° = 50°$

Side a: $\tan 40° = \dfrac{a}{22}$

$a = 22 \tan 40° \approx 18$ yd

Side c: $\cos 40° = \dfrac{22}{c}$

$c = \dfrac{22}{\cos 40°} \approx 29$ yd

$m\angle B = 50°$, $a \approx 18$ yd, $c \approx 28$ yd

20. $m\angle B = 90° - 57° = 33°$

Side a: $\tan 57° = \dfrac{a}{48}$

$a = 48 \tan 57° \approx 74$ yd

Side c: $\cos 57° = \dfrac{48}{c}$

$c = \dfrac{48}{\cos 57°} \approx 88$ yd

$m\angle B = 33°$, $a \approx 74$ yd, $b \approx 88$ yd

21. $m\angle B = 90° - 52° = 38°$

Side a: $\sin 52° = \dfrac{a}{54}$

$a = 54 \sin 52° \approx 43$ cm

Side b: $\cos 52° = \dfrac{b}{54}$

$b = 54 \cos 52° \approx 33$ cm

$m\angle B = 38°$, $a \approx 43$ cm, $b \approx 33$ cm

22. $m\angle B = 90° - 39° = 51°$

Side a: $\sin 39° = \dfrac{a}{86}$

$a = 86 \sin 39° \approx 54$ cm

Side b: $\cos 39° = \dfrac{b}{86}$

$b = 86 \cos 39° \approx 67$ cm

$m\angle B = 51°$, $a \approx 54$ cm, $b \approx 67$ cm

23. $\sin A = \dfrac{30}{50}$

$A = \sin^{-1}\left(\dfrac{30}{50}\right) \approx 37°$

24. $\tan A = \dfrac{10}{24}$

$A = \tan^{-1}\left(\dfrac{10}{24}\right) \approx 23°$

25. $\cos A = \dfrac{15}{17}$

$A = \cos^{-1}\left(\dfrac{15}{17}\right) \approx 28°$

26. $\sin A = \dfrac{11}{65}$

$A = \sin^{-1}\left(\dfrac{11}{65}\right) \approx 10°$

27. $\tan 40° = \dfrac{a}{630}$

$a = 630 \tan 40° \approx 529$ yd

28. $\tan 40° = \dfrac{h}{35}$

$h = 35 \tan 40° \approx 29$ ft

29. $\sin 10° = \dfrac{500}{c}$

$c = \dfrac{500}{\sin 10°} \approx 2879$ ft

30. $\sin 5° = \dfrac{a}{5000}$

$a = 5000 \sin 5° \approx 436$ ft

31. Let h = the height of the tower.

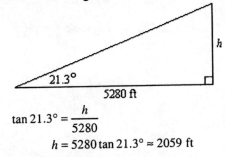

$\tan 21.3° = \dfrac{h}{5280}$

$h = 5280 \tan 21.3° \approx 2059$ ft

32. Let h = the height of the building.

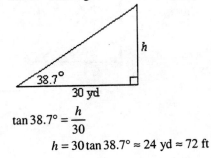

$\tan 38.7° = \dfrac{h}{30}$

$h = 30 \tan 38.7° \approx 24$ yd ≈ 72 ft

33. Let x = the distance.

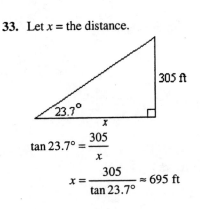

$\tan 23.7° = \dfrac{305}{x}$

$x = \dfrac{305}{\tan 23.7°} \approx 695$ ft

34. Let x = the distance.

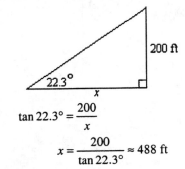

$\tan 22.3° = \dfrac{200}{x}$

$x = \dfrac{200}{\tan 22.3°} \approx 488$ ft

35. $\tan x = \dfrac{125}{172}$

$x = \tan^{-1}\left(\dfrac{125}{172}\right) \approx 36°$

36. $\tan x = \dfrac{555}{1320}$

$x = \tan^{-1}\left(\dfrac{555}{1320}\right) \approx 23°$

37. $m\angle P = 36°$

$\tan 36° = \dfrac{1000}{d}$

$d = \dfrac{1000}{\tan 36°} \approx 1376$ ft

38. The angle of elevation from the car to the helicopter is also 72°.

$\tan 72° = \dfrac{800}{d}$

$d = \dfrac{800}{\tan 72°} \approx 260$ ft

39. Let A = the angle of elevation.

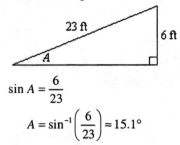

$$\sin A = \frac{6}{23}$$

$$A = \sin^{-1}\left(\frac{6}{23}\right) \approx 15.1°$$

40. Let A = the angle of elevation.

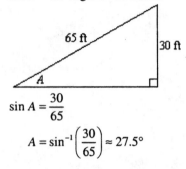

$$\sin A = \frac{30}{65}$$

$$A = \sin^{-1}\left(\frac{30}{65}\right) \approx 27.5°$$

41-48. Answers will vary.

49. The sine and cosine of an acute angle cannot be greater than or equal to 1 because they are each the ratio of a leg of a right triangle to the hypotenuse. The hypotenuse of a right triangle is always the longest side; this results in a value less than 1.

50. As the angle gets close to 90°, the tangent gets very large. The tangent at 90° is undefined.

51.

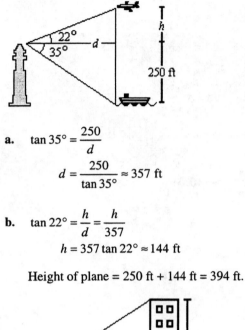

a. $\tan 35° = \dfrac{250}{d}$

$$d = \frac{250}{\tan 35°} \approx 357 \text{ ft}$$

b. $\tan 22° = \dfrac{h}{d} = \dfrac{h}{357}$

$$h = 357 \tan 22° \approx 144 \text{ ft}$$

Height of plane = 250 ft + 144 ft = 394 ft.

52.

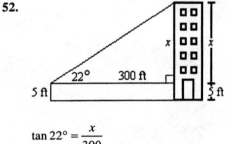

$$\tan 22° = \frac{x}{300}$$

$$x = 300 \tan 22° \approx 121 \text{ ft}$$

Height of building = 121 ft + 5 ft = 126 ft

Check Points 10.7

1. Answers will vary. Possible answer:

The upper left and lower right vertices are odd.
The lower left and upper right vertices are even.
One possible tracing:
Start at the upper left, trace around the square, then trace down the diagonal.

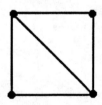

Exercise Set 10.7

1. **a.** *A* and *C* are even vertices.
    B and *D* are odd vertices.
    Because this graph has two odd vertices, by Euler's second rule, it is traversable.

    b. Sample path: *D, A, B, D, C, B*

2. **a.** *A, B, C* are even vertices. *D* and *E* are odd vertices. Because this graph has two odd vertices, by Euler's second rule, it is traversable.

    b. Sample path: *D, A, B, E, C, D, E*

3. **a.** *C, D, E* are even vertices.
    A and *B* are odd vertices.
    Because this graph has two odd vertices, by Euler's second rule, it is traversable.

    b. Sample path: *A, D, C, B, D, E, A, B*

4. **a.** *A, B, C* are even vertices. *D* and *E* are odd vertices. Because this graph has two odd vertices, by Euler's second rule, it is traversable.

    b. Sample path: *D, A, C, D, E, B, A, B, C, E*

5. *A, B, D, E* are odd vertices.
    Because this graph has more than two odd vertices, by Euler's third rule, it is not traversable.

6. **a.** *A, D, E, F* are even vertices. *B* and *C* are odd vertices. Because this graph has two odd vertices, by Euler's second rule, it is traversable.

    b. Sample path: *B, E, D, B, E, F, D, C, F, C, A, B, C*

7. 3

8. 2

9. 2

10. 4

11. Pitcher and wrench

12. Answers will vary.

13. The sum of the angles in such a triangle is greater than 180°.

14. The sum of the angles of such a quadrilateral is greater than 360°.

15. Yes

16. Yes

17. No

18.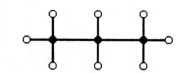

19. Each vertex for a carbon atom is even, with degree 4.
Each vertex for a hydrogen atom is odd with degree 1.

20. No, the graph is not traversable because there are more than 2 odd vertices.

21. 2 doors connect room A to the outside. This is shown in the graph by connecting 2 edges from A to E.

22. 2 doors connect room C to the outside. This is shown in the graph by connecting 2 edges from C to E.

23. Yes. B and D are the only two odd vertices. It is traversable by Euler's second rule.

24. Sample path: $B, E, A, B, D, C, A, E, C, E, D$

25-41. Answers will vary.

Chapter 10 Review Exercises

1. $\angle 3$

2. $\angle 5$

3. $\angle 4$ and $\angle 6$

4. $\angle 1$ and $\angle 6$

5. $\angle 1$ and $\angle 4$

6. $\angle 2$

7. $\angle 5$

8. $180° - 115° = 65°$

9. $90° - 41° = 49°$

10. Measure of complement $= 90° - 73° = 17°$

11. Measure of supplement $= 180° - 46° = 134°$

12. $m\angle 1 = 180° - 70° = 110°$
$m\angle 2 = 70°$
$m\angle 3 = m\angle 1 = 110°$

13. $m\angle 1 = 180° - 42° = 138°$
$m\angle 2 = 42°$
$m\angle 3 = m\angle 1 = 138°$
$m\angle 4 = m\angle 1 = 138°$
$m\angle 5 = m\angle 2 = 42°$
$m\angle 6 = 42°$
$m\angle 7 = m\angle 3 = 138°$

14. $m\angle A = 180° - 60° - 48° = 72°$

15. $m\angle A = 90° - 39° = 51°$

16. $m\angle 1 = 180° - 50° - 40° = 90°$
$m\angle 2 = 180° - 90° = 90°$
$m\angle 3 = 180° - 40° = 140°$
$m\angle 4 = 40°$
$m\angle 5 = m\angle 3 = 140°$

17. $m\angle 2 = 180° - 115° = 65°$
$\angle 1$ is in a triangle with angles of $65°$ and $35°$.
Thus, $m\angle 1 = 180° - 65° - 35° = 80°$
$m\angle 3 = 115°$
$m\angle 4 = m\angle 1 = 80°$
$m\angle 5 = 180° - 80° = 100°$
$m\angle 6 = m\angle 1 = 80°$

18. $\dfrac{8}{4} = \dfrac{10}{x}$
$8x = 40$
$x = 5$ ft

19. $\dfrac{9}{x} = \dfrac{7+5}{5}$
$\dfrac{9}{x} = \dfrac{12}{5}$
$12x = 45$
$x = \dfrac{45}{12} = 3.75$ ft

20. $c^2 = 8^2 + 6^2$
$c^2 = 64 + 36$
$c^2 = 100$
$c = 10$ ft

21. $c^2 = 6^2 + 4^2$
$c^2 = 36 + 16$
$c^2 = 52$
$c \approx 7.2$ in.

22. $b^2 = 15^2 - 11^2$
$b^2 = 225 - 121$
$b^2 = 104$
$b \approx 10.2$ cm

23. $\dfrac{x}{5} = \dfrac{9+6}{6}$
$\dfrac{x}{5} = \dfrac{15}{6}$
$6x = 75$
$x = 12.5$ ft

24. $a^2 = 25^2 - 20^2$
$a^2 = 625 - 400$
$a^2 = 225$
$a = 15$ ft

25. $b^2 = 13^2 + 5^2$
$b^2 = 169 - 25$
$b^2 = 144$
$b = 12$ yd

26. Rectangle, square

27. Rhombus, square

28. Parallelogram, rhombus, trapezoid

29. $P = 2\,(6\text{ cm}) + 2(9\text{ cm})$
$= 12$ cm $+ 18$ cm
$= 30$ cm

30. $P = 2 \cdot 1000$ yd $+ 2 \cdot 1240$ yd
$= 2000$ yd $+ 2480$ yd
$= 4480$ yd

31. First find the lengths of missing sides.

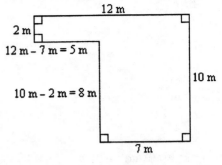

12 m

2 m

12 m − 7 m = 5 m

10 m

10 m − 2 m = 8 m

7 m

$P = 12$ m $+ 10$ m $+ 7$ m $+ 8$ m $+ 5$ m $+ 2$ m
$= 44$ m

32. Sum $= (n-2)\,180°$
$= (12-2)\,180°$
$= 10 \cdot 180°$
$= 1800°$

33. Sum $= (n-2)\,180°$
$= (8-2)\,180°$
$= 6 \cdot 180°$
$= 1080°$

34. Sum of measures of angles $= (n-2)180°$
$= (8-2)180°$
$= 6 \cdot 180°$
$= 1080°$

$m\angle 1 = \dfrac{1080°}{8} = 135°$
$m\angle 2 = 180° - 135° = 45°$

35. Amount of baseboard
$=$ Perimeter of room $-$ Lengths of doorways
$= 2 \cdot 35$ ft $+ 2 \cdot 15$ ft $- 4 \cdot 3$ ft
$= 70$ ft $+ 30$ ft $- 12$ ft
$= 88$ ft
Cost $= \dfrac{\$1.50}{1\,\text{ft}} \cdot \dfrac{88\,\text{ft}}{1} = \$132$

36. $A = 5$ ft $\cdot 6.5$ ft $= 32.5\,\text{ft}^2$

37. $A = 5$ m $\cdot 4$ m $= 20\ \text{m}^2$

38. $A = \dfrac{1}{2} \cdot 20$ cm $\cdot 5$ cm $= 50\,\text{cm}^2$

39. $A = \frac{1}{2} \cdot 10 \text{ yd} \cdot (22 \text{ yd} + 5 \text{ yd})$

$= \frac{1}{2} \cdot 10 \text{ yd} \cdot (27 \text{ yd})$

$= 135 \text{ yd}^2$

40. $C = \pi \cdot 20 \text{ m} = 20\pi \text{ m} \approx 62.8 \text{ m}$

$r = \frac{1}{2} d = \frac{1}{2} \cdot 20 \text{ m} = 10 \text{ m}$

$A = \pi r^2 = \pi (10 \text{ m})^2 = 100\pi \text{ m}^2 \approx 314.2 \text{ m}^2$

41. Area = (Area of square) + (Area of triangle)

$= (12 \text{ in.})^2 + \frac{1}{2} \cdot 12 \text{ in.} \cdot 8 \text{ in.}$

$= 144 \text{ in.}^2 + 48 \text{ in.}^2$

$= 192 \text{ in.}^2$

42. Area = (Area of top rectangle)

  + (Area of bottom rectangle)

$= 8 \text{ m} \cdot 2 \text{ m} + 6 \text{ m} \cdot 2 \text{ m}$

$= 16 \text{ m}^2 + 12 \text{ m}^2$

$= 28 \text{ m}^2$

43. First convert linear measurements in feet to linear yards.

$15 \text{ ft} = \frac{15 \cancel{\text{ft}}}{1} \cdot \frac{1 \text{ yd}}{3 \cancel{\text{ft}}} = 5 \text{ yd}$

$21 \text{ ft} = \frac{21 \cancel{\text{ft}}}{1} \cdot \frac{1 \text{ yd}}{3 \cancel{\text{ft}}} = 7 \text{ yd}$

Area $= 5 \text{ yd} \cdot 7 \text{ yd} = 35 \text{ yd}^2$

Cost $= \frac{\$22.50}{1 \cancel{\text{yd}^2}} \cdot \frac{35 \cancel{\text{yd}^2}}{1} = \$787.50$

44. Area of floor $= 40 \text{ ft} \cdot 50 \text{ ft} = 2000 \text{ ft}^2$

Area of each tile $= (2 \text{ ft})^2 = 4 \text{ ft}^2$

Number of tiles $= \frac{2000 \text{ ft}^2}{4 \text{ ft}^2} = 500$ tiles

Cost $= \frac{\$13}{10 \cancel{\text{tiles}}} \cdot \frac{500 \cancel{\text{tiles}}}{1} = \$650$

45. $C = \pi d = \pi \cdot 10 \text{ yd} = 10\pi \text{ yd} \approx 31 \text{ yd}$

46. $V = 5 \text{ cm} \cdot 3 \text{ cm} \cdot 4 \text{ cm} = 60 \text{ cm}^3$

47. $V = $ (Volume of rectangular solid)

  + (Volume of Pyramid)

$= 8 \text{ m} \cdot 9 \text{ m} \cdot 10 \text{ m} + \frac{1}{3} (8 \text{ m} \cdot 9 \text{ m}) \, 10 \text{ m}$

$\approx 720 \text{ m}^3 + 240 \text{ m}^3 = 960 \text{ m}^3$

48. $V = \pi (4 \text{ yd})^2 \cdot 8 \text{ yd} = 128\pi \text{ yd}^3 \approx 402 \text{ yd}^3$

49.

$V = \frac{1}{3} \pi (40 \text{ in.})^2 \cdot 28 \text{ in.} = \frac{44{,}800}{3} \pi \text{ in.}^3 \approx 46{,}914 \text{ in.}^3$

50. $V = \frac{4}{3} \pi (6 \text{ m})^3 = 288\pi \text{ m}^3 \approx 905 \text{ m}^3$

51. Surface area

$= 2(5 \text{ m})(3 \text{ m}) + 2(3 \text{ m})(6 \text{ m}) + 2(5 \text{ m})(6 \text{ m})$

$= 30 \text{ m}^2 + 36 \text{ m}^2 + 60 \text{ m}^2$

$= 126 \text{ m}^2$

52. Volume of one box $= 8 \text{ m} \cdot 4 \text{ m} \cdot 3 \text{ m} = 96 \text{ m}^3$

Volume of 50 boxes $= 50 \cdot 96 \text{ m}^3 = 4800 \text{ m}^3$

53. $V = \frac{1}{3} (145 \text{ m})^2 \cdot 93 \text{ m} = 651{,}775 \text{ m}^3$

54. First convert linear measures in feet to linear yards.

$27 \text{ ft} = \frac{27 \cancel{\text{ft}}}{1} \cdot \frac{1 \text{ yd}}{3 \cancel{\text{ft}}} = 9 \text{ yd}$

$4 \text{ ft} = \frac{4 \cancel{\text{ft}}}{1} \cdot \frac{1 \text{ yd}}{3 \cancel{\text{ft}}} = \frac{4}{3} \text{ yd}$

$6 \text{ in.} = \frac{6 \cancel{\text{in.}}}{1} \cdot \frac{1 \text{ yd}}{36 \cancel{\text{in.}}} = \frac{1}{6} \text{ yd}$

Volume $= 9 \text{ yd} \cdot \frac{4}{3} \text{ yd} \cdot \frac{1}{6} \text{ yd} = 2 \text{ yd}^3$

Cost $= \frac{\$40}{1 \cancel{\text{yd}^3}} \cdot \frac{2 \cancel{\text{yd}^3}}{1} = \$80$

55. First compute length of hypotenuse

$c^2 = 12^2 + 9^2 = 144 + 81 = 225$

$c = 15$

$\sin A = \frac{9}{15} = \frac{3}{5}$

$\cos A = \frac{12}{15} = \frac{4}{5}$

$\tan A = \frac{9}{12} = \frac{3}{4}$

56. $\tan 23° = \dfrac{a}{100}$

$a = 100 \tan 23° \approx 42$ mm

57. $\sin 61° = \dfrac{20}{c}$

$c = \dfrac{20}{\sin 61°} \approx 23$ cm

58. $\sin 48° = \dfrac{a}{50}$

$a = 50 \sin 48° \approx 37$ in.

59. $\sin A = \dfrac{17}{20}$

$A = \sin^{-1}\left(\dfrac{17}{20}\right) \approx 58°$

60. $\dfrac{1}{2}$ mi $= \dfrac{0.5 \text{ mi}}{1} \cdot \dfrac{5280 \text{ ft}}{1 \text{ mi}} = 2640$ ft

$\sin 17° = \dfrac{h}{2640}$

$h = 2640 \sin 17° \approx 772$ ft

61. $\tan 32° = \dfrac{d}{50}$

$d = 50 \tan 32° \approx 31$ m

62.

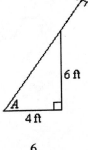

$\tan A = \dfrac{6}{4}$

$A = \tan^{-1}\left(\dfrac{6}{4}\right) \approx 56°$

63. The graph is not traversable because there are more than two odd vertices.

64. All vertices have even degrees, so the graph is traversable. Possible path: *A, B, C, D, A, B, C, D, A*

65. 0

66. 2

67. 1

68. 2

Chapter 10 Test

1. Measure of complement $= 90° - 54° = 36°$
   Measure of supplement $= 180° - 54° = 126°$

2. $m\angle 1 = 133°$ because alternate exterior angles are equal.

3. $m\angle 1 = 180° - 40° - 70° = 70°$

4. First find measures of other angles of triangle.

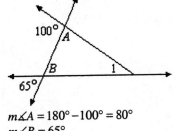

$m\angle A = 180° - 100° = 80°$
$m\angle B = 65°$
$m\angle 1 = 180° - 80° - 65° = 35°$

5. $\dfrac{x}{8} = \dfrac{4}{10}$

$10x = 4 \cdot 8$

$10x = 32$

$x = \dfrac{32}{10} = 3.2$ in.

6. $b^2 = 26^2 - 24^2$
   $b^2 = 676 - 576$
   $b^2 = 100$
   $b = 10$ ft

7. Sum $= (n - 2)\, 180°$
   $= (10 - 2)\, 180°$
   $= 8 \cdot 180°$
   $= 1440°$

8. First find lengths of missing sides.

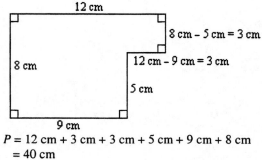

$P = 12 \text{ cm} + 3 \text{ cm} + 3 \text{ cm} + 5 \text{ cm} + 9 \text{ cm} + 8 \text{ cm}$
$= 40 \text{ cm}$

9. d

10. $A = \frac{1}{2}bh$

$A = \frac{1}{2} \cdot 47 \text{ m} \cdot 22 \text{ m} = 517 \text{ m}^2$

11. $A = \frac{1}{2} \cdot 15 \text{ in.}(40 \text{ in.} + 30 \text{ in.})$

$= \frac{1}{2} \cdot 15 \text{ in.}(70 \text{ in.})$

$= 525 \text{ in.}^2$

12. a. $a^2 + b^2 = c^2$

$a^2 + 5^2 = 13^2$

$a^2 + 25 = 169$

$a^2 = 144$

$a = 12 \text{ cm}$

b. $P = 5 \text{ cm} + 12 \text{ cm} + 13 \text{ cm} = 30 \text{ cm}$

c. $A = \frac{1}{2}bh = \frac{1}{2} \cdot 12 \text{ cm} \cdot 5 \text{ cm} = 30 \text{ cm}^2$

13. $C = \pi d = \pi \cdot 40 \text{ m} = 40\pi \text{ m} \approx 125.7 \text{ m}$

$A = \pi r^2 = \pi(20 \text{ m})^2 = 400\pi \text{ m}^2 \approx 1256.6 \text{ m}^2$

14. Area of floor $8 \text{ ft} \cdot 6 \text{ ft} = 48 \text{ ft}^2$
Convert inches to feet:

$8 \text{ in.} = \frac{8 \text{ in.}}{1} \cdot \frac{1 \text{ ft}}{12 \text{ in.}} = \frac{2}{3} \text{ ft}$

Area of one tile

$= \left(\frac{2}{3} \text{ ft}\right)^2 = \frac{4}{9} \text{ ft}^2$

Number of tiles

$= \frac{48 \text{ ft}^2}{\frac{4}{9} \text{ ft}^2} = 108 \text{ tiles}$

15. $V = 3 \text{ ft} \cdot 2 \text{ ft} \cdot 3 \text{ ft} = 18 \text{ ft}^3$

16. $V = \frac{1}{3}(4 \text{ m} \cdot 3 \text{ m}) 4 \text{ m} = 16 \text{ m}^3$

17. $V = \pi(5 \text{ cm})^2 \cdot 7 \text{ cm} = 175\pi \text{ cm}^3 \approx 550 \text{ cm}^3$

18. $\sin 28° = \frac{40}{c}$

$c = \frac{40}{\sin 28°} \approx 85 \text{ cm}$

19.

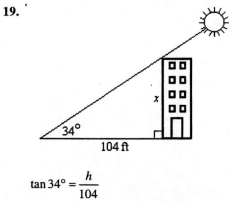

$\tan 34° = \frac{h}{104}$

$h = 104 \tan 34° \approx 70 \text{ ft}$

20. The graph is traversable because there are two odd vertices (*B* and *E*). Sample path: *BCAECDE*

21. Answers will vary.

Chapter 11
Counting Methods and Probability Theory

Check Points 11.1

1. Multiply the number of choices for each of the two courses of the meal:

    <u>Appetizers</u> : <u>Main Courses:</u>

       10   ×   15   = 150

2. Multiply the number of choices for each of the two courses:

    <u>Psychology</u> : <u>Social Science:</u>

       10   ×   4   = 40

3. Multiply the number of choices for each of the three decisions:

    <u>Size</u> : <u>Crust</u> : <u>Topping:</u>

     2 × 3 × 5 = 30

4. Multiply the number of choices for each of the five options:

    <u>Color:</u> <u>A/C:</u> <u>Electric/Gas:</u> <u>Onboard Computer:</u> <u>Global Positioning System:</u>

      10 × 2 ×   2   ×   2   ×   2   = 160

5. Multiply the number of choices for each of the six questions:

    <u>Question #1:</u> <u>Question #2:</u> <u>Question #3:</u> <u>Question #4:</u> <u>Question #5:</u> <u>Question #6:</u>

       3   ×   3   ×   3   ×   3   ×   3   ×   3   = 3^6 = 729

6. Multiply the number of choices for each of the five digits:

    $\overbrace{1-9}$ $\overbrace{0-9}$ $\overbrace{0-9}$ $\overbrace{0-9}$ $\overbrace{0-9}$

    <u>Digit 1:</u> <u>Digit 2:</u> <u>Digit 3:</u> <u>Digit 4:</u> <u>Digit 5:</u>

       9   ×   10   ×   10   ×   10   ×   10   = 90,000

Exercise Set 11.1

1. $8 \cdot 10 = 80$

2. $9 \cdot 3 = 27$

3. $3 \cdot 4 = 12$

4. $5 \cdot 6 = 30$

5. $3 \cdot 2 = 6$

6. $26 \cdot 9 = 234$

7. Multiply the number of choices for each of the three decisions:

    <u>Drink:</u> <u>Size:</u> <u>Flavor:</u>

      2   ×   4   ×   5   = 40

8. Multiply the number of choices for each of the three decisions:

    <u>Size</u> : <u>Crust</u> : <u>Topping</u> :

      3 ×   4   ×   6   = 72

9. Multiply the number of choices for each of the four menu categories:

Main Course:		Vegetables:		Beverages:		Desserts:		
4	×	3	×	4	×	3	=	144

This includes, for example, an order of ham and peas with tea and cake.
This also includes an order of beef and peas with milk and pie.

10. Multiply the number of choices for each of the four apartment options:

Option A:		Option B:		Option C:		Option D:		
3	×	2	×	2	×	3	=	36

This includes, for example, a first floor, golf course view apartment with one bedroom and one bathroom.
This also includes a first floor, lake view apartment with two bedrooms and one bathroom.

11. Multiply the number of choices for each of the three categories:

Gender:		Age:		Payment method:		
2	×	2	×	2	=	8

12. Multiply the number of choices for each of the three groups of highways.

A to B:		B to C:		C to D:		
3	×	2	×	4	=	24

13. Multiply the number of choices for each of the five options:

Color:		A/C:		Transmission:		Windows:		CD Player:		
6	×	2	×	2	×	2	×	2	=	96

14. Multiply the number of choices for each of the five options:

Color:		A/C:		Sun Roof:		Transmission:		Brakes:		
9	×	2	×	2	×	2	×	2	=	144

15. Multiply the number of choices for each of the five questions:

Question 1:		Question 2:		Question 3:		Question 4:		Question 5:		
3	×	3	×	3	×	3	×	3	=	243

16. This situation involves making choices with eight groups of items. Each question is considered a group and each group has 3 choices. Multiply choices: $3 \times 3 \times 3 \times 3 \times 3 \times 3 \times 3 \times 3 = 3^8 = 6561$

17. Multiply the number of choices for each of the three digits:

Digit 1:		Digit 2:		Digit 3:		
8	×	2	×	9	=	144

18. Multiply the number of choices for each of the four digits:

Digit 4:		Digit 5:		Digit 6:		Digit 7:		
10	×	10	×	10	×	10	=	10,000

19. Multiply the number of choices for each of the letters and digits:

Letter 1:		Letter 2:		Digit 1:		Digit 2:		Digit 3:		
26	×	26	×	10	×	10	×	10	=	676,000

20. Multiply the number of choices for each of the four letters:

Letter 1:		Letter 2:		Letter 3:		Letter 4:		
2	×	26	×	26	×	26	=	35,152

21. This situation involves making choices with seven groups of items. Each stock is a group, and each group has three choices. Multiply choices: $3 \times 3 \times 3 \times 3 \times 3 \times 3 \times 3 = 3^7 = 2187$

22. This situation involves making choices with nine groups of items. Each digit is a group, and each group has ten choices. Multiply choices: $10 \times 10 \times 10 \times 10 \times 10 \times 10 \times 10 \times 10 \times 10 = 10^9 = 1,000,000,000$

23-25. Answers will vary.

26. Multiply the number of choices for each of the four digits:

1–9	0–9	0–9	1, 3, 5, 7, 9
Digit 1:	Digit 2:	Digit 3:	Digit 4:
9 $\times$	10 $\times$	10 $\times$	5 = 4500

27. Multiply the number of choices for each of the four groups of items:

Bun:	Sauce:	Lettuce:	Tomatoes:
12 $\times$	30 $\times$	4 $\times$	3 = 4320

Total time $= 10 \times 4320 = 43,200$ minutes, which is $43,200 \div 60 = 720$ hours.

Check Points 11.2

1. There is only one choice each for the first and last performers. This leaves two choices for the second performer and then one for the third.

U2	'N Sync, Aerosmith		Rolling Stones
1st Performer:	2nd Performer:	3rd Performer:	4th Performer:
1 $\times$	2 $\times$	1 $\times$	1 = 2

2. The number of choices decreases by 1 each time a book is selected.

1st Book:	2nd Book:	3rd Book:	4th Book:	5th Book:
5 $\times$	4 $\times$	3 $\times$	2 $\times$	1 = 120

3. a. $\dfrac{9!}{6!} = \dfrac{9 \cdot 8 \cdot 7 \cdot 6!}{6!} = \dfrac{9 \cdot 8 \cdot 7 \cdot \cancel{6!}}{\cancel{6!}} = 9 \cdot 8 \cdot 7 = 504$

   b. $\dfrac{16!}{11!} = \dfrac{16 \cdot 15 \cdot 14 \cdot 13 \cdot 12 \cdot 11!}{11!} = \dfrac{16 \cdot 15 \cdot 14 \cdot 13 \cdot 12 \cdot \cancel{11!}}{\cancel{11!}} = 16 \cdot 15 \cdot 14 \cdot 13 \cdot 12 = 524,160$

   c. $\dfrac{100!}{99!} = \dfrac{100 \cdot 99!}{99!} = \dfrac{100 \cdot \cancel{99!}}{\cancel{99!}} = 100$

4. $_7P_4 = \dfrac{7!}{(7-4)!} = \dfrac{7!}{3!} = \dfrac{7 \cdot 6 \cdot 5 \cdot 4 \cdot 3!}{3!} = \dfrac{7 \cdot 6 \cdot 5 \cdot 4 \cdot \cancel{3!}}{\cancel{3!}} = 7 \cdot 6 \cdot 5 \cdot 4 = 840$

5. $_9P_5 = \dfrac{9!}{(9-5)!} = \dfrac{9!}{4!} = \dfrac{9 \cdot 8 \cdot 7 \cdot 6 \cdot 5 \cdot 4!}{4!} = \dfrac{9 \cdot 8 \cdot 7 \cdot 6 \cdot 5 \cdot \cancel{4!}}{\cancel{4!}} = 9 \cdot 8 \cdot 7 \cdot 6 \cdot 5 = 15,120$

6. There a 7 letters with 2 O's and 3 S's. Thus, $\dfrac{n!}{p!q!} = \dfrac{7!}{2!3!} = \dfrac{7 \cdot 6 \cdot 5 \cdot 4 \cdot \cancel{3!}}{2 \cdot 1 \cdot \cancel{3!}} = 420$

Exercise Set 11.2

1. The number of choices decreases by 1 each time a performer is selected.

1st Performer:	2nd Performer:	3rd Performer:	4th Performer:	5th Performer:	6th Performer:	
6	× 5	× 4	× 3	× 2	× 1	= 720

2. The number of choices decreases by 1 each time a singer is selected.

1st Singer:	2nd Singer:	3rd Singer:	4th Singer:	5th Singer:	
5	× 4	× 3	× 2	× 1	= 120

3. The number of choices decreases by 1 each time a sentence is selected.

1st Sentence:	2nd Sentence:	3rd Sentence:	4th Sentence:	5th Sentence:	
5	× 4	× 3	× 2	× 1	= 120

4. The number of choices decreases by 1 each time a suspect is selected.

1st Person:	2nd:	3rd Person:	4th:	5th Person:	6th:	7th Person:	8th:	
8	× 7	× 6	× 5	× 4	× 3	× 2	× 1	= 40,320

5. There is only one choice for the 6th performer. The number of choices decreases by 1 each time a performer is selected.

1st Performer:	2nd Performer:	3rd Performer:	4th Performer:	5th Performer:	6th Performer:	
5	× 4	× 3	× 2	× 1	× 1	= 120

6. There is only one choice for the 5th singer. The number of choices decreases by 1 each time a singer is selected.

1st Singer:	2nd Singer:	3rd Singer:	4th Singer:	5th Singer:	
4	× 3	× 2	× 1	× 1	= 24

7. The number of choices decreases by 1 each time a book is selected.

1st Book:	2nd:	3rd Book:	4th:	5th Book:	6th:	7th Book:	8th:	9th Book:	
9	× 8	× 7	× 6	× 5	× 4	× 3	× 2	× 1	= 362,880

8. The number of choices decreases by 1 each time a book is selected.

1st Photo:	2nd:	3rd Photo:	4th:	5th Photo:	6th:	7th Photo:	8th:	9th Photo:	10th:	
10	× 9	× 8	× 7	× 6	× 5	× 4	× 3	× 2	× 1	= 3,628,800

9. There is only one choice each for the first and last sentences. For the other values, the number of choices decreases by 1 each time a sentence is selected.

1st Sentence:	2nd Sentence:	3rd Sentence:	4th Sentence:	5th Sentence:	
1	× 3	× 2	× 1	× 1	= 6

10. There is only one choice each for the first and second sentences. For the other values, the number of choices decreases by 1 each time a sentence is selected.

1st Sentence:	2nd Sentence:	3rd Sentence:	4th Sentence:	5th Sentence:	
1	× 1	× 3	× 2	× 1	= 6

11. There are two choices for the first movie and one for the second. There is only one choice for the last movie. This leaves two choices for the third movie and one for the fourth.

G rated		Other two movies		NC-17 Rated	
1st Movie:	2nd Movie:	3rd Movie:	4th Movie:	5th Movie:	
2	× 1	× 2	× 1	× 1	= 4

12. There is only one choice each for the fourth and fifth seats. For the other values, the number of choices decreases by 1 each time a seat is selected.

$$
\overset{\text{counselor}}{\underset{\text{4th Seat:}}{}} \quad \overset{\text{food fighter}}{\underset{\text{5th Seat:}}{}}
$$

1st Seat:	2nd Seat:	3rd Seat:	4th Seat:	5th Seat:	6th Seat:	7th Seat:
5	× 4	× 3	× 1	× 1	× 2	× 1 = 120

13. $\dfrac{9!}{6!} = \dfrac{9 \cdot 8 \cdot 7 \cdot 6!}{6!} = 9 \cdot 8 \cdot 7 = 504$

14. $\dfrac{12!}{10!} = \dfrac{12 \cdot 11 \cdot 10!}{10!} = 12 \cdot 11 = 132$

15. $\dfrac{29!}{25!} = \dfrac{29 \cdot 28 \cdot 27 \cdot 26 \cdot 25!}{25!}$
$= 29 \cdot 28 \cdot 27 \cdot 26$
$= 570,024$

16. $\dfrac{31!}{28!} = \dfrac{31 \cdot 30 \cdot 29 \cdot 28!}{28!} = 31 \cdot 30 \cdot 29 = 26,970$

17. $\dfrac{19!}{11!} = \dfrac{19 \cdot 18 \cdot 17 \cdot 16 \cdot 15 \cdot 14 \cdot 13 \cdot 12 \cdot 11!}{11!}$
$= 19 \cdot 18 \cdot 17 \cdot 16 \cdot 15 \cdot 14 \cdot 13 \cdot 12$
$= 3,047,466,240$

18. $\dfrac{17!}{9!} = \dfrac{17 \cdot 16 \cdot 15 \cdot 14 \cdot 13 \cdot 12 \cdot 11 \cdot 10 \cdot 9!}{9!}$
$= 17 \cdot 16 \cdot 15 \cdot 14 \cdot 13 \cdot 12 \cdot 11 \cdot 10$
$= 980,179,200$

19. $\dfrac{600!}{599!} = \dfrac{600 \cdot 599!}{599!} = 600$

20. $\dfrac{700!}{699!} = \dfrac{700 \cdot 699!}{699!} = 700$

21. $\dfrac{104!}{102!} = \dfrac{104 \cdot 103 \cdot 102!}{102!} = 104 \cdot 103 = 10,712$

22. $\dfrac{106!}{104!} = \dfrac{106 \cdot 105 \cdot 104!}{104!} = 106 \cdot 105 = 11,130$

23. $7! - 3! = 5040 - 6 = 5034$

24. $6! - 3! = 720 - 6 = 714$

25. $(7-3)! = 4! = 4 \cdot 3 \cdot 2 \cdot 1 = 24$

26. $(6-3)! = 3! = 3 \cdot 2 \cdot 1 = 6$

27. $\left(\dfrac{12}{4}\right)! = 3! = 3 \cdot 2 \cdot 1 = 6$

28. $\left(\dfrac{45}{9}\right)! = 5! = 5 \cdot 4 \cdot 3 \cdot 2 \cdot 1 = 120$

29. $\dfrac{7!}{(7-2)!} = \dfrac{7!}{5!} = \dfrac{7 \cdot 6 \cdot 5!}{5!} = 7 \cdot 6 = 42$

30. $\dfrac{8!}{(8-5)!} = \dfrac{8!}{3!}$
$= \dfrac{8 \cdot 7 \cdot 6 \cdot 5 \cdot 4 \cdot 3!}{3!}$
$= 8 \cdot 7 \cdot 6 \cdot 5 \cdot 4$
$= 6720$

31. $\dfrac{13!}{(13-3)!} = \dfrac{13!}{10!}$
$= \dfrac{13 \cdot 12 \cdot 11 \cdot 10!}{10!}$
$= 13 \cdot 12 \cdot 11$
$= 1716$

32. $\dfrac{17!}{(17-3)!} = \dfrac{17!}{14!}$
$= \dfrac{17 \cdot 16 \cdot 15 \cdot 14!}{14!}$
$= 17 \cdot 16 \cdot 15$
$= 4080$

33. $_9P_4 = \dfrac{9!}{(9-4)!}$
$= \dfrac{9!}{5!}$
$= \dfrac{9 \cdot 8 \cdot 7 \cdot 6 \cdot 5!}{5!}$
$= 9 \cdot 8 \cdot 7 \cdot 6$
$= 3024$

34. $_7P_3 = \dfrac{7!}{(7-3)!}$

$= \dfrac{7!}{4!}$

$= \dfrac{7 \cdot 6 \cdot 5 \cdot 4!}{4!}$

$= 7 \cdot 6 \cdot 5$

$= 210$

35. $_8P_5 = \dfrac{8!}{(8-5)!}$

$= \dfrac{8!}{3!}$

$= \dfrac{8 \cdot 7 \cdot 6 \cdot 5 \cdot 4 \cdot 3!}{3!}$

$= 8 \cdot 7 \cdot 6 \cdot 5 \cdot 4$

$= 6720$

36. $_{10}P_4 = \dfrac{10!}{(10-4)!}$

$= \dfrac{10!}{6!}$

$= \dfrac{10 \cdot 9 \cdot 8 \cdot 7 \cdot 6!}{6!}$

$= 10 \cdot 9 \cdot 8 \cdot 7$

$= 5040$

37. $_6P_6 = \dfrac{6!}{(6-6)!} = \dfrac{6!}{0!} = \dfrac{6 \cdot 5 \cdot 4 \cdot 3 \cdot 2 \cdot 1}{1} = 720$

38. $_9P_9 = \dfrac{9!}{(9-9)!}$

$= \dfrac{9!}{0!}$

$= \dfrac{9 \cdot 8 \cdot 7 \cdot 6 \cdot 5 \cdot 4 \cdot 3 \cdot 2 \cdot 1}{1}$

$= 362,880$

39. $_8P_0 = \dfrac{8!}{(8-0)!} = \dfrac{8!}{8!} = 1$

40. $_6P_0 = \dfrac{6!}{(6-0)!} = \dfrac{6!}{6!} = 1$

41. $_{10}P_3 = \dfrac{10!}{(10-3)!}$

$= \dfrac{10!}{7!}$

$= \dfrac{10 \cdot 9 \cdot 8 \cdot 7!}{7!}$

$= 10 \cdot 9 \cdot 8$

$= 720$

42. $_7P_4 = \dfrac{7!}{(7-4)!}$

$= \dfrac{7!}{3!}$

$= \dfrac{7 \cdot 6 \cdot 5 \cdot 4 \cdot 3!}{3!}$

$= 7 \cdot 6 \cdot 5 \cdot 4$

$= 840$

43. $_{13}P_7 = \dfrac{13!}{(13-7)!}$

$= \dfrac{13!}{6!}$

$= \dfrac{13 \cdot 12 \cdot 11 \cdot 10 \cdot 9 \cdot 8 \cdot 7 \cdot 6!}{6!}$

$= 13 \cdot 12 \cdot 11 \cdot 10 \cdot 9 \cdot 8 \cdot 7$

$= 8,648,640$

44. $_{20}P_3 = \dfrac{20!}{(20-3)!}$

$= \dfrac{20!}{17!}$

$= \dfrac{20 \cdot 19 \cdot 18 \cdot 17!}{17!}$

$= 20 \cdot 19 \cdot 18$

$= 6840$

45. $_6P_3 = \dfrac{6!}{(6-3)!}$

$= \dfrac{6!}{3!}$

$= \dfrac{6 \cdot 5 \cdot 4 \cdot 3!}{3!}$

$= 6 \cdot 5 \cdot 4$

$= 120$

46. $_8P_3 = \dfrac{8!}{(8-3)!}$

$= \dfrac{8!}{5!}$

$= \dfrac{8 \cdot 7 \cdot 6 \cdot 5!}{5!}$

$= 8 \cdot 7 \cdot 6$

$= 336$

47. $_9P_5 = \dfrac{9!}{(9-5)!}$

$= \dfrac{9!}{4!}$

$= \dfrac{9 \cdot 8 \cdot 7 \cdot 6 \cdot 5 \cdot 4!}{4!}$

$= 9 \cdot 8 \cdot 7 \cdot 6 \cdot 5$

$= 15,120$

48. $_7P_4 = \dfrac{7!}{(7-4)!}$

$= \dfrac{7!}{3!}$

$= \dfrac{7 \cdot 6 \cdot 5 \cdot 4 \cdot 3!}{3!}$

$= 7 \cdot 6 \cdot 5 \cdot 4$

$= 840$

49. $\dfrac{n!}{p!q!} = \dfrac{6!}{2!2!} = \dfrac{6 \cdot 5 \cdot 4 \cdot 3 \cdot 2 \cdot 1}{2 \cdot 1 \cdot 2 \cdot 1} = 180$

50. $\dfrac{n!}{p!q!} = \dfrac{7!}{2!2!} = \dfrac{7 \cdot 6 \cdot 5 \cdot 4 \cdot 3 \cdot 2 \cdot 1}{2 \cdot 1 \cdot 2 \cdot 1} = 1260$

51. $\dfrac{n!}{p!q!r!s!} = \dfrac{11!}{3!2!2!2!}$

$= \dfrac{11 \cdot 10 \cdot 9 \cdot 8 \cdot 7 \cdot 6 \cdot 5 \cdot 4 \cdot 3!}{3! \cdot 2 \cdot 1 \cdot 2 \cdot 1 \cdot 2 \cdot 1}$

$= 831,600$

52. $\dfrac{n!}{p!q!r!} = \dfrac{9!}{4!2!2!} = \dfrac{9 \cdot 8 \cdot 7 \cdot 6 \cdot 5 \cdot 4!}{4! \cdot 2 \cdot 1 \cdot 2 \cdot 1} = 3780$

53. $\dfrac{n!}{p!q!} = \dfrac{7!}{4!2!} = \dfrac{7 \cdot 6 \cdot 5 \cdot 4!}{4! \cdot 2 \cdot 1} = 105$

54. $\dfrac{n!}{p!q!r!} = \dfrac{7!}{2!2!2!} = \dfrac{7 \cdot 6 \cdot 5 \cdot 4 \cdot 3 \cdot 2 \cdot 1}{2 \cdot 1 \cdot 2 \cdot 1 \cdot 2 \cdot 1} = 630$

55. $\dfrac{n!}{p!q!} = \dfrac{8!}{4!3!} = \dfrac{8 \cdot 7 \cdot 6 \cdot 5 \cdot 4!}{4! \cdot 3 \cdot 2 \cdot 1} = 280$

56. $\dfrac{n!}{p!q!} = \dfrac{9!}{5!3!} = \dfrac{9 \cdot 8 \cdot 7 \cdot 6 \cdot 5!}{5! \cdot 3 \cdot 2 \cdot 1} = 504$

57-62. Answers will vary.

63. Because the letter B is repeated in the word BABE, the number of permutations is given by

$\dfrac{n!}{p!} = \dfrac{4!}{2!} = \dfrac{4 \cdot 3 \cdot 2 \cdot 1}{2 \cdot 1} = 12$

64. $_{12}P_{10} = \dfrac{12!}{(12-10)!}$

$= \dfrac{12!}{2!}$

$= \dfrac{12 \cdot 11 \cdot 10 \cdot 9 \cdot 8 \cdot 7 \cdot 6 \cdot 5 \cdot 4 \cdot 3 \cdot 2!}{2!}$

$= 12 \cdot 11 \cdot 10 \cdot 9 \cdot 8 \cdot 7 \cdot 6 \cdot 5 \cdot 4 \cdot 3$

$= 239,500,800$

65. Multiply the number of ways to select the two first place horses by the number of orders in which the remaining four horses can finish.

$_6C_2 \times _4P_4 = 15 \times 24 = 360$

66. First select 3 out of the 8 jazz groups.

There are $_8P_3 = \dfrac{8!}{(8-3)!} = \dfrac{8!}{5!} = 336$ ways to arrange the 1st, 3rd, and 8th performers.

This leaves 13 groups (5 remaining jazz groups and 8 rock groups) to be arranged.

There are $_{13}P_{13} = \dfrac{13!}{(13-13)!} = \dfrac{13!}{0!} = 13! = 6,227,020,800$ ways to arrange the remaining performers.

The total number of arrangements is found by multiplying these values: $336 \times 6,227,020,800 = 2.09 \times 10^{12}$

67. There are 5! ways to arrange the women, and 5! ways to arrange the men. The total number of arrangements is found by multiplying these values: $(5!)(5!) = 120 \cdot 120 = 14,400$

68. Multiply the number of choices for each of the four digits:

Digit 1:		Digit 2:		Digit 3:		Digit 4:		
2, 4		2, 4, 6, 7, 8, 9		2, 4, 6, 7, 8, 9		7, 9		
2	×	6	×	6	×	2	=	144

69. $_nP_{n-2} = \dfrac{n!}{(n-(n-2))!} = \dfrac{n!}{(n-n+2)!} = \dfrac{n!}{2!} = \dfrac{n(n-1)(n-2)\times\cdots\times3\times2\times1}{2} = n(n-1)(n-2)\times\cdots\times3$

Check Points 11.3

1. a. Order does not matter. This problem involves combinations.

   b. Order matters. This problem involves permutations.

2. $_7C_3 = \dfrac{7!}{(7-3)!3!} = \dfrac{7!}{4!3!} = \dfrac{7\cdot6\cdot5\cdot4!}{4!\cdot3\cdot2\cdot1} = \dfrac{7\cdot6\cdot5\cdot\cancel{4!}}{\cancel{4!}\cdot3\cdot2\cdot1} = \dfrac{7\cdot6\cdot5}{3\cdot2\cdot1} = 35$

3. $_{16}C_4 = \dfrac{16!}{(16-4)!4!} = \dfrac{16!}{12!4!} = \dfrac{16\cdot15\cdot14\cdot13\cdot12!}{12!\cdot4\cdot3\cdot2\cdot1} = \dfrac{16\cdot15\cdot14\cdot13\cdot\cancel{12!}}{\cancel{12!}\cdot4\cdot3\cdot2\cdot1} = \dfrac{16\cdot15\cdot14\cdot13}{4\cdot3\cdot2\cdot1} = 1820$

4. Choose the Democrats: $_{50}C_3 = \dfrac{50!}{(50-3)!3!} = \dfrac{50!}{47!3!} = \dfrac{50\cdot49\cdot48\cdot47!}{47!\cdot3\cdot2\cdot1} = \dfrac{50\cdot49\cdot48\cdot\cancel{47!}}{\cancel{47!}\cdot3\cdot2\cdot1} = \dfrac{50\cdot49\cdot48}{3\cdot2\cdot1} = 19,600$

    Choose the Republicans: $_{49}C_2 = \dfrac{49!}{(49-2)!2!} = \dfrac{49!}{47!2!} = \dfrac{49\cdot48\cdot47!}{47!\cdot2\cdot1} = \dfrac{49\cdot48\cdot\cancel{47!}}{\cancel{47!}\cdot2\cdot1} = \dfrac{49\cdot48}{2\cdot1} = 1176$

    Multiply the choices: $19,600 \times 1176 = 23,049,600$

Exercise Set 11.3

1. Order matters. This problem involves permutations.

2. Order does not matter. This problem involves combinations.

3. Order does not matter. This problem involves combinations.

4. Order matters. This problem involves permutations.

5. Order does not matter. This problem involves combinations.

6. Order does not matter. This problem involves combinations.

7. Order matters. This problem involves permutations.

8. Order matters. This problem involves permutations.

9. Order matters. This problem involves permutations.

10. Order does not matter. This problem involves combinations.

11. $_6C_5 = \dfrac{6!}{(6-5)!5!} = \dfrac{6!}{1!5!} = \dfrac{6 \cdot 5!}{1 \cdot 5!} = 6$

12. $_8C_7 = \dfrac{8!}{(8-7)!7!} = \dfrac{8!}{1!7!} = \dfrac{8 \cdot 7!}{1 \cdot 7!} = 8$

13. $_9C_5 = \dfrac{9!}{(9-5)!5!} = \dfrac{9!}{4!5!} = \dfrac{9 \cdot 8 \cdot 7 \cdot 6 \cdot 5!}{4 \cdot 3 \cdot 2 \cdot 1 \cdot 5!} = 126$

14. $_{10}C_6 = \dfrac{10!}{(10-6)!6!} = \dfrac{10!}{4!6!} = \dfrac{10 \cdot 9 \cdot 8 \cdot 7 \cdot 6!}{4 \cdot 3 \cdot 2 \cdot 1 \cdot 6!} = 210$

15. $_{11}C_4 = \dfrac{11!}{(11-4)!4!} = \dfrac{11!}{7!4!} = \dfrac{11 \cdot 10 \cdot 9 \cdot 8 \cdot 7!}{7! \cdot 4 \cdot 3 \cdot 2 \cdot 1} = 330$

16. $_{12}C_5 = \dfrac{12!}{(12-5)!5!} = \dfrac{12!}{7!5!} = \dfrac{12 \cdot 11 \cdot 10 \cdot 9 \cdot 8 \cdot 7!}{7! \cdot 5 \cdot 4 \cdot 3 \cdot 2 \cdot 1} = 792$

17. $_8C_1 = \dfrac{8!}{(8-1)!1!} = \dfrac{8!}{7!1!} = \dfrac{8 \cdot 7!}{7!1} = 8$

18. $_7C_1 = \dfrac{7!}{(7-1)!1!} = \dfrac{7!}{6!1!} = \dfrac{7 \cdot 6!}{6!1} = 7$

19. $_7C_7 = \dfrac{7!}{(7-7)!7!} = \dfrac{7!}{0!7!} = 1$

20. $_4C_4 = \dfrac{4!}{(4-4)!4!} = \dfrac{4!}{0!4!} = 1$

21. $_{30}C_3 = \dfrac{30!}{(30-3)!3!} = \dfrac{30!}{27!3!} = \dfrac{30 \cdot 29 \cdot 28 \cdot 27!}{27! \cdot 3 \cdot 2 \cdot 1} = 4060$

22. $_{25}C_4 = \dfrac{25!}{(25-4)!4!} = \dfrac{25!}{21!4!} = \dfrac{25 \cdot 24 \cdot 23 \cdot 22 \cdot 21!}{21! \cdot 4 \cdot 3 \cdot 2 \cdot 1} = 12,650$

23. $_5C_0 = \dfrac{5!}{(5-0)!0!} = \dfrac{5!}{5!0!} = 1$

24. $_6C_0 = \dfrac{6!}{(6-0)!0!} = \dfrac{6!}{6!0!} = 1$

25. $\dfrac{_7C_3}{_5C_4} = \dfrac{\frac{7!}{(7-3)!3!}}{\frac{5!}{(5-4)!4!}} = \dfrac{\frac{7!}{4!3!}}{\frac{5!}{1!4!}} = \dfrac{\frac{7\cdot6\cdot5\cdot4!}{4!\cdot3\cdot2\cdot1}}{\frac{5\cdot4!}{1\cdot4!}} = \dfrac{35}{5} = 7$

26. $\dfrac{_{10}C_3}{_6C_4} = \dfrac{\frac{10!}{(10-3)!3!}}{\frac{6!}{(6-4)!4!}} = \dfrac{\frac{10!}{7!3!}}{\frac{6!}{2!4!}} = \dfrac{\frac{10\cdot9\cdot8\cdot7!}{7!\cdot3\cdot2\cdot1}}{\frac{6\cdot5\cdot4!}{2\cdot1\cdot4!}} = \dfrac{120}{15} = 8$

27. $_6C_3 = \dfrac{6!}{(6-3)!3!} = \dfrac{6!}{3!3!} = \dfrac{6\cdot5\cdot4\cdot3!}{3!3\cdot2\cdot1} = 20$

28. $_{11}C_4 = \dfrac{11!}{(11-4)!4!} = \dfrac{11!}{7!4!} = \dfrac{11\cdot10\cdot9\cdot8\cdot7!}{7!4\cdot3\cdot2\cdot1} = 330$

29. $_{12}C_4 = \dfrac{12!}{(12-4)!4!} = \dfrac{12!}{8!4!} = \dfrac{12\cdot11\cdot10\cdot9\cdot8!}{8!4\cdot3\cdot2\cdot1} = 495$

30. $_{14}C_6 = \dfrac{14!}{(14-6)!6!} = \dfrac{14!}{8!6!} = \dfrac{14\cdot13\cdot12\cdot11\cdot10\cdot9\cdot8!}{8!6\cdot5\cdot4\cdot3\cdot2\cdot1} = 3003$

31. $_{17}C_8 = \dfrac{17!}{(17-8)!8!} = \dfrac{17!}{9!8!} = \dfrac{17\cdot16\cdot15\cdot14\cdot13\cdot12\cdot11\cdot10\cdot9!}{9!8\cdot7\cdot6\cdot5\cdot4\cdot3\cdot2\cdot1} = 24,310$

32. $_{16}C_4 = \dfrac{16!}{(16-4)!4!} = \dfrac{16!}{12!4!} = \dfrac{16\cdot15\cdot14\cdot13\cdot12!}{12!4\cdot3\cdot2\cdot1} = 1820$

33. $_{31}C_3 = \dfrac{31!}{(31-3)!3!} = \dfrac{31!}{28!3!} = \dfrac{31\cdot30\cdot29\cdot28!}{28!3\cdot2\cdot1} = 4495$

34. $_{100}C_{18} = \dfrac{100!}{(100-18)!18!} = \dfrac{100!}{82!18!}$

$= \dfrac{100\cdot99\cdot98\cdot97\cdot96\cdot95\cdot94\cdot93\cdot92\cdot91\cdot90\cdot89\cdot88\cdot87\cdot86\cdot85\cdot84\cdot83\cdot82!}{82!18\cdot17\cdot16\cdot15\cdot14\cdot13\cdot12\cdot11\cdot10\cdot9\cdot8\cdot7\cdot6\cdot5\cdot4\cdot3\cdot2\cdot1} \approx 3.07\times10^{19}$

35. $_{53}C_6 = \dfrac{53!}{(53-6)!6!} = \dfrac{53!}{47!6!} = \dfrac{53\cdot52\cdot51\cdot50\cdot49\cdot48\cdot47!}{47!6\cdot5\cdot4\cdot3\cdot2\cdot1} = 22,957,480$

36. $_{59}C_6 = \dfrac{59!}{(59-6)!6!} = \dfrac{59!}{53!6!} = \dfrac{59\cdot58\cdot57\cdot56\cdot55\cdot54\cdot53!}{53!6\cdot5\cdot4\cdot3\cdot2\cdot1} = 45,057,474$

37. Choose the men: $_7C_4 = \dfrac{7!}{(7-4)!4!} = \dfrac{7!}{3!4!} = \dfrac{7\cdot6\cdot5\cdot4!}{3\cdot2\cdot1\cdot4!} = 35$

Choose the women: $_7C_5 = \dfrac{7!}{(7-5)!5!} = \dfrac{7!}{2!5!} = \dfrac{7\cdot6\cdot5!}{2\cdot1\cdot5!} = 21$

Multiply the choices: $35 \cdot 21 = 735$

38. Choose the professors: $_5C_2 = \dfrac{5!}{(5-2)!2!} = \dfrac{5!}{3!2!} = \dfrac{5 \cdot 4 \cdot 3!}{3!2 \cdot 1} = 10$

Choose the students: $_{15}C_{10} = \dfrac{15!}{(15-10)!10!} = \dfrac{15!}{5!10!} = \dfrac{15 \cdot 14 \cdot 13 \cdot 12 \cdot 11 \cdot 10!}{5 \cdot 4 \cdot 3 \cdot 2 \cdot 1 \cdot 10!} = 3003$

Multiply the choices: $10 \times 3003 = 30,030$

39. Choose the Republicans: $_{55}C_4 = \dfrac{55!}{(55-4)!4!} = \dfrac{55!}{51!4!} = \dfrac{55 \cdot 54 \cdot 53 \cdot 52 \cdot 51!}{51!4 \cdot 3 \cdot 2 \cdot 1} = 341,055$

Choose the Democrats: $_{45}C_3 = \dfrac{45!}{(45-3)!3!} = \dfrac{45!}{42!3!} = \dfrac{45 \cdot 44 \cdot 43 \cdot 42!}{42!3 \cdot 2 \cdot 1} = 14,190$

Multiply the choices: $341,055 \times 14,190 = 4,839,570,450$

40. Choose the multiple-choice questions: $_{10}C_8 = \dfrac{10!}{(10-8)!8!} = \dfrac{10!}{2!8!} = \dfrac{10 \cdot 9 \cdot 8!}{2 \cdot 1 \cdot 8!} = 45$

Choose the open-ended problems: $_5C_3 = \dfrac{5!}{(5-3)!3!} = \dfrac{5!}{2!3!} = \dfrac{5 \cdot 4 \cdot 3!}{2 \cdot 1 \cdot 3!} = 10$

Multiply the choices: $45 \cdot 10 = 450$

41-44. Answers will vary.

45. Selections for 6/53 lottery: $_{53}C_6 = \dfrac{53!}{(53-6)!6!} = \dfrac{53!}{47!6!} = \dfrac{53 \cdot 52 \cdot 51 \cdot 50 \cdot 49 \cdot 48 \cdot 47!}{47!6 \cdot 5 \cdot 4 \cdot 3 \cdot 2 \cdot 1} = 22,957,480$

Selections for 5/36 lottery: $_{36}C_5 = \dfrac{36!}{(36-5)!5!} = \dfrac{36!}{31!5!} = \dfrac{36 \cdot 35 \cdot 34 \cdot 33 \cdot 32 \cdot 31!}{31!5 \cdot 4 \cdot 3 \cdot 2 \cdot 1} = 376,992$

The 5/36 lottery is easier to win because there are fewer possible selections.

46.

$_nP_r = 6 \cdot {_nC_r}$

$\dfrac{n!}{(n-r)!} = 6 \cdot \dfrac{n!}{(n-r)!r!}$ [apply the cross products principle]

$n!(n-r)!r! = 6 \cdot n!(n-r)!$ [divide both sides by $n!(n-r)!$]

$\dfrac{\cancel{n!}\cancel{(n-r)!}r!}{\cancel{n!}\cancel{(n-r)!}} = \dfrac{6 \cdot \cancel{n!}\cancel{(n-r)!}}{\cancel{n!}\cancel{(n-r)!}}$

$r! = 6$

$r! = 3 \cdot 2 \cdot 1$

$r = 3$

No, there is not enough information to determine the value of n. The number of permutations will be six times the number of combinations for all values of n when $r = 3$.

47. For a group of 20 people:

$_{20}C_2 = \dfrac{20!}{(20-2)!2!} = \dfrac{20!}{18!2!} = \dfrac{20 \cdot 19 \cdot 18!}{18!2 \cdot 1} = 190$ handshakes

Time $= 3 \times 190 = 570$ seconds, which gives $570 \div 60 = 9.5$ minutes.

For a group of 40 people:

$_{40}C_2 = \dfrac{40!}{(40-2)!2!} = \dfrac{40!}{38!2!} = \dfrac{40 \cdot 39 \cdot 38!}{38!2 \cdot 1} = 780$ handshakes

Time $= 3 \times 780 = 2340$ seconds, which gives $2340 \div 60 = 39$ minutes.

48. Since there are 5 defective phones, we must select 4 out of the 15 good phones.

$$_{15}C_4 = \frac{15!}{(15-4)!4!} = \frac{15!}{11!4!} = \frac{15 \cdot 14 \cdot 13 \cdot 12 \cdot 11!}{11!4 \cdot 3 \cdot 2 \cdot 1} = 1365$$

Check Points 11.4

1. a. The event of getting a 2 can occur in one way.

$$P(2) = \frac{\text{number of ways a 2 can occur}}{\text{total number of possible outcomes}} = \frac{1}{6}$$

b. The event of getting a number less than 4 can occur in three ways: 1, 2, 3.

$$P(\text{less than 4}) = \frac{\text{number of ways a number less than 4 can occur}}{\text{total number of possible outcomes}} = \frac{3}{6} = \frac{1}{2}$$

c. The event of getting a number greater than 7 cannot occur.

$$P(\text{greater than 7}) = \frac{\text{number of ways a number greater than 7 can occur}}{\text{total number of possible outcomes}} = \frac{0}{6} = 0$$

The probability of an event that cannot occur is 0.

d. The event of getting a number less than 7 can occur in six ways: 1, 2, 3, 4, 5, 6.

$$P(\text{less than 7}) = \frac{\text{number of ways a number less than 7 can occur}}{\text{total number of possible outcomes}} = \frac{6}{6} = 1$$

The probability of any certain event is 1.

2. a. $P(\text{ace}) = \dfrac{\text{number of ways a ace can occur}}{\text{total number of possibilities}} = \dfrac{4}{52} = \dfrac{1}{13}$

b. $P(\text{red card}) = \dfrac{\text{number of ways a red card can occur}}{\text{total number of possible outcomes}} = \dfrac{26}{52} = \dfrac{1}{2}$

c. $P(\text{red king}) = \dfrac{\text{number of ways a red king can occur}}{\text{total number of possible outcomes}} = \dfrac{2}{52} = \dfrac{1}{26}$

3. The table shows the four equally likely outcomes. The Cc and cC children will be carriers who are not actually sick.

$$P(\text{carrier, not sick}) = P(Cc) = \frac{\text{number of ways } Cc \text{ or } cC \text{ can occur}}{\text{total number of possible outcomes}} = \frac{2}{4} = \frac{1}{2}$$

4. $P(\text{selecting a Muslim from the Arab American population})$

$$= \frac{\text{number of Arab Americans who are Muslims}}{\text{total number of Arab Americans}} = \frac{0.69}{3.00} = \frac{69}{300} = \frac{23}{100} = 0.23$$

Exercise Set 11.4

1. $P(4) = \dfrac{\text{number of ways a 4 can occur}}{\text{total number of possible outcomes}} = \dfrac{1}{6}$

2. $P(5) = \dfrac{\text{number of ways a five can occur}}{\text{total number of possible outcomes}} = \dfrac{1}{6}$

3. $P(\text{odd number}) = \dfrac{\text{number of ways an odd number can occur}}{\text{total number of possible outcomes}} = \dfrac{3}{6} = \dfrac{1}{2}$

4. $P(\text{greater than 3}) = \dfrac{\text{number of ways a number of greater than 3 can occur}}{\text{total number of possible outcomes}} = \dfrac{3}{6} = \dfrac{1}{2}$

5. $P(\text{less than 3}) = \dfrac{\text{number of ways a number less than 3 can occur}}{\text{total number of possible outcomes}} = \dfrac{2}{6} = \dfrac{1}{3}$

6. $P(\text{greater than 4}) = \dfrac{\text{number of ways a number greater than 4 can occur}}{\text{total number of possible outcomes}} = \dfrac{2}{6} = \dfrac{1}{3}$

7. $P(\text{less than 7}) = \dfrac{\text{number of ways a number less than 7 can occur}}{\text{total number of possible outcomes}} = \dfrac{6}{6} = 1$

8. $P(\text{less than 8}) = \dfrac{\text{number of ways a number less than 8 can occur}}{\text{total number of possible outcomes}} = \dfrac{6}{6} = 1$

9. $P(\text{greater than 7}) = \dfrac{\text{number of ways a number greater than 7 can occur}}{\text{total number of possible outcomes}} = \dfrac{0}{6} = 0$

10. $P(\text{greater than 8}) = \dfrac{\text{number of ways a number greater than 8 can occur}}{\text{total number of possible outcomes}} = \dfrac{0}{6} = 0$

11. $P(\text{queen}) = \dfrac{\text{number of ways a queen can occur}}{\text{total number of possibilities}} = \dfrac{4}{52} = \dfrac{1}{13}$

12. $P(\text{jack}) = \dfrac{\text{number of ways a jack can occur}}{\text{total number of possibilities}} = \dfrac{4}{52} = \dfrac{1}{13}$

13. $P(\text{club}) = \dfrac{\text{number of ways a club can occur}}{\text{total number of possibilities}} = \dfrac{13}{52} = \dfrac{1}{4}$

14. $P(\text{diamond}) = \dfrac{\text{number of ways a diamond can occur}}{\text{total number of possibilities}} = \dfrac{13}{52} = \dfrac{1}{4}$

15. $P(\text{picture card}) = \dfrac{\text{number of ways a picture card can occur}}{\text{total number of possibilities}} = \dfrac{12}{52} = \dfrac{3}{13}$

16. $P(\text{greater than 3 and less than 7}) = \dfrac{\text{number of ways a card greater than 3 and less than 7 can occur}}{\text{total number of possibilities}} = \dfrac{12}{52} = \dfrac{3}{13}$

17. $P(\text{queen of spades}) = \dfrac{\text{number of ways a queen of spades can occur}}{\text{total number of possibilities}} = \dfrac{1}{52}$

18. $P(\text{ace of clubs}) = \dfrac{\text{number of ways an ace of clubs can occur}}{\text{total number of possibilities}} = \dfrac{1}{52}$

19. $P(\text{diamond and spade}) = \dfrac{\text{number of ways a diamond and a spade can occur}}{\text{total number of possibilities}} = \dfrac{0}{52} = 0$

20. $P(\text{green heart}) = \dfrac{\text{number of ways a card with a green heart can occur}}{\text{total number of possibilities}} = \dfrac{0}{52} = 0$

21. $P(\text{two heads}) = \dfrac{\text{number of ways two heads can occur}}{\text{total number of possibilities}} = \dfrac{1}{4}$

22. $P(\text{two tails}) = \dfrac{\text{number of ways two tails can occur}}{\text{total number of possibilities}} = \dfrac{1}{4}$

23. $P(\text{same on each toss}) = \dfrac{\text{number of ways the same outcome on each toss can occur}}{\text{total number of possibilities}} = \dfrac{2}{4} = \dfrac{1}{2}$

24. $P(\text{different on each toss}) = \dfrac{\text{number of ways different outcomes on each toss can occur}}{\text{total number of possibilities}} = \dfrac{2}{4} = \dfrac{1}{2}$

25. $P(\text{head on second toss}) = \dfrac{\text{number of ways a head on the second toss can occur}}{\text{total number of possibilities}} = \dfrac{2}{4} = \dfrac{1}{2}$

26. $P(\text{at least one head}) = \dfrac{\text{number of ways at least one head can occur (HH, HT, TH)}}{\text{total number of possibilities}} = \dfrac{3}{4}$

27. $P(\text{exactly one female child}) = \dfrac{\text{number of ways exactly one female child can occur}}{\text{total number of possibilities}} = \dfrac{3}{8}$

28. $P(\text{exactly one male child}) = \dfrac{\text{number of ways exactly one male child can occur}}{\text{total number of possibilities}} = \dfrac{3}{8}$

29. $P(\text{exactly two male children}) = \dfrac{\text{number of ways exactly two male children can occur}}{\text{total number of possibilities}} = \dfrac{3}{8}$

30. $P(\text{exactly two female children}) = \dfrac{\text{number of ways exactly two female children can occur}}{\text{total number of possibilities}} = \dfrac{3}{8}$

31. $P(\text{at least one male child}) = \dfrac{\text{number of ways at least one male child can occur}}{\text{total number of possiblities}} = \dfrac{7}{8}$

32. $P(\text{at least two female children}) = \dfrac{\text{number of ways at least two female children can occur}}{\text{total number of possibilities}} = \dfrac{4}{8} = \dfrac{1}{2}$

33. $P(\text{four male children}) = \dfrac{\text{number of ways four male children can occur}}{\text{total number of possibilities}} = \dfrac{0}{8} = 0$

34. $P(\text{fewer than four female children}) = \dfrac{\text{number of ways fewer than four female children can occur}}{\text{total number of possibilities}} = \dfrac{8}{8} = 1$

35. $P(\text{two even numbers}) = \dfrac{\text{number of ways two even numbers can occur}}{\text{total number of possibilities}} = \dfrac{9}{36} = \dfrac{1}{4}$

36. $P(\text{two odd numbers}) = \dfrac{\text{number of ways two odd numbers can occur}}{\text{total number of possibilities}} = \dfrac{9}{36} = \dfrac{1}{4}$

37. $P(\text{two numbers whose sum is 5}) = \dfrac{\text{number of ways two numbers whose sum is 5 can occur}}{\text{total number of possibilities}} = \dfrac{4}{36} = \dfrac{1}{9}$

38. $P(\text{two numbers of whose sum is 6}) = \dfrac{\text{number of ways two numbers whose sum is 6 can occur}}{\text{total number of possibilities}} = \dfrac{5}{36}$

39. $P(\text{two numbers whose sum exceeds 12})$

$= \dfrac{\text{number of ways two numbers whose sum exceeds 12 can occur}}{\text{total number of possibilities}} = \dfrac{0}{36} = 0$

40. $P(\text{two numbers whose sum is less than 13})$

$= \dfrac{\text{number of ways two numbers whose sum is less than 13 can occur}}{\text{total number of possibilities}} = \dfrac{36}{36} = 1$

41. $P(\text{red region}) = \dfrac{\text{number of ways a red region can occur}}{\text{total number of possibilities}} = \dfrac{3}{10}$

42. $P(\text{yellow region}) = \dfrac{\text{number of ways a yellow region can occur}}{\text{total number of possibilities}} = \dfrac{2}{10} = \dfrac{1}{5}$

43. $P(\text{blue region}) = \dfrac{\text{number of ways a blue region can occur}}{\text{total number of possibilities}} = \dfrac{2}{10} = \dfrac{1}{5}$

44. $P(\text{brown region}) = \dfrac{\text{number of ways a brown region can occur}}{\text{total number of possibilities}} = \dfrac{3}{10}$

45. $P(\text{region that is red or blue}) = \dfrac{\text{number of ways a region that is red or blue can occur}}{\text{total number of possibilities}} = \dfrac{5}{10} = \dfrac{1}{2}$

46. $P(\text{region that is yellow or brown}) = \dfrac{\text{number of ways a region that is yellow or brown can occur}}{\text{total number of possibilities}} = \dfrac{5}{10} = \dfrac{1}{2}$

47. $P(\text{region that is red and blue}) = \dfrac{\text{number of ways a region that is red and blue can occur}}{\text{total number of possibilities}} = \dfrac{0}{10} = 0$

48. $P(\text{region that is yellow and brown}) = \dfrac{\text{number of ways a region that is yellow and brown can occur}}{\text{total number of possibilities}} = \dfrac{0}{10} = 0$

49. $P(\text{sickle cell anemia}) = \dfrac{\text{number of ways sickle cell anemia can occur}}{\text{total number of possibilities}} = \dfrac{1}{4}$

50. $P(\text{sickle cell trait}) = \dfrac{\text{number of ways sickle cell trait can occur}}{\text{total number of possibilities}} = \dfrac{2}{4} = \dfrac{1}{2}$

51. $P(\text{healthy}) = \dfrac{\text{number of ways a healthy child can occur}}{\text{total number of possibilities}} = \dfrac{1}{4}$

52. $P(\text{sickle cell anemia}) = \dfrac{\text{number of ways sickle cell anemia can occur}}{\text{total number of possibilities}} = \dfrac{0}{4} = 0$

53. $P(\text{sickle cell trait}) = \dfrac{\text{number of ways sickle cell trait can occur}}{\text{total number of possibilities}} = \dfrac{2}{4} = \dfrac{1}{2}$

54. $P(\text{healthy}) = \dfrac{\text{number of ways a healthy child can occur}}{\text{total number of possibilities}} = \dfrac{2}{4} = \dfrac{1}{2}$

55. $P(\text{weight training}) = \dfrac{\text{number surveyed who weight train}}{\text{total number surveyed}} = \dfrac{320}{2000} = \dfrac{4}{25} = 0.16$

56. $P(\text{running / jogging}) = \dfrac{\text{number surveyed who run/jog}}{\text{total number surveyed}} = \dfrac{280}{2000} = \dfrac{7}{50} = 0.14$

57. $P(\text{biking}) = \dfrac{\text{number surveyed who bike}}{\text{total number surveyed}} = \dfrac{240}{2000} = \dfrac{3}{25} = 0.12$

58. $P(\text{walking/hiking}) = \dfrac{\text{number surveyed who walk/hike}}{\text{total number surveyed}} = \dfrac{1140}{2000} = \dfrac{57}{100} = 0.57$

59. $P(\text{female}) = \dfrac{\text{number of single parent females in U.S. military}}{\text{total number of single parents in U.S. military}} = \dfrac{23}{89} \approx 0.258$

60. $P(\text{male}) = \dfrac{\text{number of single parent males in U.S. military}}{\text{total number of single parents in U.S. military}} = \dfrac{66}{89} \approx 0.742$

61. $P(\text{in Army}) = \dfrac{\text{number of single parents in the Army}}{\text{total number of single parents in U.S. military}} = \dfrac{36}{89} \approx 0.404$

62. $P(\text{in Navy}) = \dfrac{\text{number of single parents in the Navy}}{\text{total number of single parents in U.S. military}} = \dfrac{29}{89} \approx 0.326$

63. $P(\text{woman in Air Force}) = \dfrac{\text{number of single parent women in U.S. Air Force}}{\text{total number of single parents in U.S. military}} = \dfrac{6}{89} \approx 0.067$

64. $P(\text{man in Marine Corps}) = \dfrac{\text{number of single parent men in U.S. Marine Corps}}{\text{total number of single parents in U.S. military}} = \dfrac{5}{89} \approx 0.056$

65-71. Answers will vary.

72. According to the data, 1% of the 10,000 employees use cocaine.
This means there are $(0.01)(10,000) = 100$ cocaine users and $(0.99)(10,000) = 9900$ nonusers.

90% of the 100 users will correctly test positive, which is $(0.90)(100) = 90$ correct positives.

10% of the 9900 nonusers will incorrectly test positive, which is $(0.10)(9900) = 990$ incorrect positives.

Therefore, the total number testing positive will be $90 + 990 = 1080$
Of these 1080 positive tests, only 90 are correct. This gives the following probability fraction:

$$P(\text{someone who tests positive is a user}) = \frac{\text{correct positives}}{\text{correct positives} + \text{incorrect positives}} = \frac{90}{1080} = \frac{1}{12}$$

Answers will vary on the written portion of this exercise.

73. The area of the target is $(12 \text{ in.})^2 = 144 \text{ in.}^2$

The area of the yellow region is $(9 \text{ in.})^2 - (6 \text{ in.})^2 + (3 \text{ in.})^2 = 54 \text{ in.}^2$

The probability that the dart hits a yellow region is $\dfrac{54 \text{ in.}^2}{144 \text{ in.}^2} = 0.375$

74. First count the number of three-digit numbers that read the same forward and backward:

$$\overbrace{\underset{9}{\underline{\text{Digit 1:}}}}^{1-9} \times \overbrace{\underset{10}{\underline{\text{Digit 2:}}}}^{0-9} \times \overset{\text{Same as 1st digit}}{\underset{1}{\underline{\text{Digit 3:}}}} = 90$$

$P(\text{three-digit number reads the same forward and backward})$

$$= \frac{\text{number of three-digit numbers that read the same forward and backward}}{\text{total number of three-digit numbers}} = \frac{90}{900} = \frac{1}{10}$$

Check Points 11.5

1. total number of permutations $= 5! = 5 \cdot 4 \cdot 3 \cdot 2 \cdot 1 = 120$
number of arrangements with U2 first, the Rolling Stones fourth, and the Beatles last.

$$\overset{\text{U2}}{\underset{1 \times}{\underline{\text{1st:}}}} \quad \overset{\text{'N Sync, Aerosmith}}{\underset{2 \times \quad 1}{\underline{\text{2nd:} \quad \text{3rd:}}}} \times \overset{\text{Rolling Stones}}{\underset{1}{\underline{\text{4th:}}}} \times \overset{\text{Beatles}}{\underset{1}{\underline{\text{5th:}}}} = 2$$

$$P(\text{U2 first, Rolling Stones fourth, and the Beatles last}) = \frac{2}{120} = \frac{1}{60}$$

2. Number of LOTTO selections: $_{49}C_6 = \dfrac{49!}{(49-6)!6!} = \dfrac{49!}{43!6!} = \dfrac{49 \cdot 48 \cdot 47 \cdot 46 \cdot 45 \cdot 44 \cdot 43!}{43! 6 \cdot 5 \cdot 4 \cdot 3 \cdot 2 \cdot 1} = 13,983,816$

$$P(\text{winning}) = \frac{\text{one LOTTO ticket}}{\text{total number of LOTTO combinations}} = \frac{1}{13,983,816} \approx 0.0000000715$$

3. total number of combinations: $_{10}C_3 = \dfrac{10!}{(10-3)!3!} = \dfrac{10!}{7!3!} = \dfrac{10 \cdot 9 \cdot 8 \cdot 7!}{7! 3 \cdot 2 \cdot 1} = 120$

a. total number of combinations of 3 men: $_6C_3 = \dfrac{6!}{(6-3)!3!} = \dfrac{6!}{3!3!} = \dfrac{6 \cdot 5 \cdot 4 \cdot 3!}{3 \cdot 2 \cdot 1 \cdot 3!} = 20$

$$P(3 \text{ men}) = \frac{\text{number of combinations with 3 men}}{\text{total number of combinations}} = \frac{20}{120} = \frac{1}{6}$$

b. Select 2 out of 6 men: $_6C_2 = \dfrac{6!}{(6-2)!2!} = \dfrac{6!}{4!2!} = \dfrac{6 \cdot 5 \cdot 4!}{4!2 \cdot 1} = 15$

Select 1 out of 4 women: $_4C_1 = \dfrac{4!}{(4-1)!1!} = \dfrac{4!}{3!1!} = \dfrac{4 \cdot 3!}{3!} = \dfrac{4 \cdot 3!}{3!} = 4$

total number of combinations of 2 men and 1 woman: $15 \times 4 = 60$

$P(\text{2 men, 1 woman}) = \dfrac{\text{number of combinations with 2 men, 1 woman}}{\text{total number of combinations}} = \dfrac{60}{120} = \dfrac{1}{2}$

Exercise Set 11.5

1. a. $5! = 5 \cdot 4 \cdot 3 \cdot 2 \cdot 1 = 120$

b.

$$\overbrace{\text{Martha}}\ \overbrace{\text{Lee, Nancy, Paul}}\ \overbrace{\text{Armando}}$$

$$\underline{\text{1st:}}\ \ \underline{\text{2nd:}}\ \underline{\text{3rd:}}\ \underline{\text{4th:}}\ \ \ \underline{\text{5th:}}$$

$$1\ \times\ 3\ \times\ 2\ \times\ 1\ \times\ \ 1\ \ = 6$$

c. $P(\text{Martha first and Armando last}) = \dfrac{6}{120} = \dfrac{1}{20}$

2. a. $6! = 6 \cdot 5 \cdot 4 \cdot 3 \cdot 2 \cdot 1 = 720$

b.

$$\underline{\text{1st woman:}}\ \ \underline{\text{1st man:}}\ \ \underline{\text{2nd woman:}}\ \ \underline{\text{2nd man:}}\ \ \underline{\text{3rd woman:}}\ \ \underline{\text{3rd man:}}$$

$$3\ \ \ \times\ \ \ 3\ \ \ \times\ \ \ 2\ \ \ \ \times\ \ \ 2\ \ \times\ \ \ 1\ \ \ \times\ \ \ 1\ \ \ = 36$$

c. $P(\text{first person is a woman and line alternates by gender}) = \dfrac{36}{720} = \dfrac{1}{20}$

3. a. total number of permutations $= 6! = 6 \cdot 5 \cdot 4 \cdot 3 \cdot 2 \cdot 1 = 720$

number of permutations with E first $= 1 \cdot 5 \cdot 4 \cdot 3 \cdot 2 \cdot 1 = 120$

$P(\text{E first}) = \dfrac{\text{number of permutations with E first}}{\text{total number of permutations}} = \dfrac{120}{720} = \dfrac{1}{6}$

b. number of permutations with C fifth and B last $= 4 \cdot 3 \cdot 2 \cdot 1 \cdot 1 \cdot 1 = 24$

$P(\text{C fifth and B last}) = \dfrac{\text{number of permutations with C fifth and B last}}{\text{total number of permutations}} = \dfrac{24}{720} = \dfrac{1}{30}$

c. $P(\text{D, E, C, A, B, F}) = \dfrac{\text{number of permutations with order D, E, C, A, B, F}}{\text{total number of permutations}} = \dfrac{1}{720}$

d. number of permutations with A or B first $= 2 \cdot 5 \cdot 4 \cdot 3 \cdot 2 \cdot 1 = 240$

$P(\text{A or B first}) = \dfrac{\text{number of permutations with A or B first}}{\text{total number of permutations}} = \dfrac{240}{720} = \dfrac{1}{3}$

4. a. total number of permutations $= 7 \cdot 6 \cdot 5 \cdot 4 \cdot 3 \cdot 2 \cdot 1 = 5040$
number of permutations with D first $= 1 \cdot 6 \cdot 5 \cdot 4 \cdot 3 \cdot 2 \cdot 1 = 720$

$$P(\text{D first}) = \frac{\text{number of permutations with D first}}{\text{total number of permutations}} = \frac{720}{5040} = \frac{1}{7}$$

b. number of permutations with E sixth and B last $= 5 \cdot 4 \cdot 3 \cdot 2 \cdot 1 \cdot 1 \cdot 1 = 120$

$$P(\text{E sixth and B last}) = \frac{\text{number of permutations with E sixth and B last}}{\text{total number of permutations}} = \frac{120}{5040} = \frac{1}{42}$$

c. $P(\text{C, D, B, A, G, F, E}) = \dfrac{\text{number of permutations with order C, D, B, A, G, F, E}}{\text{total number of permutations}} = \dfrac{1}{5040}$

d. number of permutations with F or G first $= 2 \cdot 6 \cdot 5 \cdot 4 \cdot 3 \cdot 2 \cdot 1 = 1440$

$$P(\text{F or G first}) = \frac{\text{number of permutations with F or G first}}{\text{total number of permutations}} = \frac{1440}{5040} = \frac{2}{7}$$

5. a. $_9C_3 = \dfrac{9!}{(9-3)!\,3!} = \dfrac{9!}{6!\,3!} = \dfrac{9 \cdot 8 \cdot 7 \cdot 6!}{6!\,3 \cdot 2 \cdot 1} = 84$

b. $_5C_3 = \dfrac{5!}{(5-3)!\,3!} = \dfrac{5!}{2!\,3!} = \dfrac{5 \cdot 4 \cdot 3!}{2 \cdot 1 \cdot 3!} = 10$

c. $P(\text{all women}) = \dfrac{\text{number of ways to select 3 women}}{\text{total number of possible combinations}} = \dfrac{10}{84} = \dfrac{5}{42}$

6. a. $_{11}C_4 = \dfrac{11!}{(11-4)!\,4!} = \dfrac{11!}{7!\,4!} = \dfrac{11 \cdot 10 \cdot 9 \cdot 8 \cdot 7!}{7!\,4 \cdot 3 \cdot 2 \cdot 1} = 330$

b. $_6C_4 = \dfrac{6!}{(6-4)!\,4!} = \dfrac{6!}{2!\,4!} = \dfrac{6 \cdot 5 \cdot 4!}{2 \cdot 1 \cdot 4!} = 15$

c. $P(\text{all Republicans}) = \dfrac{\text{number of ways to select 4 Republicans}}{\text{total number of possible combinations}} = \dfrac{15}{330} = \dfrac{1}{22}$

7. $_{51}C_6 = \dfrac{51!}{(51-6)!\,6!} = \dfrac{51!}{45!\,6!} = \dfrac{51 \cdot 50 \cdot 49 \cdot 48 \cdot 47 \cdot 46 \cdot 45!}{45!\,6 \cdot 5 \cdot 4 \cdot 3 \cdot 2 \cdot 1} = 18,009,460$

$$P(\text{winning}) = \frac{\text{number of ways of winning}}{\text{total number of possible combinations}} = \frac{1}{18,009,460} \approx 0.0000000555$$

If 100 different tickets are purchased, $P(\text{winning}) = \dfrac{100}{18,009,460} \approx 0.00000555$

8. $_{30}C_5 = \dfrac{30!}{(30-5)!\,5!} = \dfrac{30!}{25!\,5!} = \dfrac{30 \cdot 29 \cdot 28 \cdot 27 \cdot 26 \cdot 25!}{25!\,5 \cdot 4 \cdot 3 \cdot 2 \cdot 1} = 142,506$

$$P(\text{winning}) = \frac{\text{number of ways of winning}}{\text{total number of possible combinations}} = \frac{1}{142,506} \approx 0.00000702$$

If 100 different tickets are purchased, $P(\text{winning}) = \dfrac{100}{142,506} \approx 0.000702$.

9. a. $_{25}C_6 = \dfrac{25!}{(25-6)!6!} = \dfrac{25!}{19!6!} = \dfrac{25 \cdot 24 \cdot 23 \cdot 22 \cdot 21 \cdot 20 \cdot 19!}{19!6 \cdot 5 \cdot 4 \cdot 3 \cdot 2 \cdot 1} = 177,100$

$P(\text{all are defective}) = \dfrac{\text{number of ways to choose 6 defective transistors}}{\text{total number of possible combinations}} = \dfrac{1}{177,100} \approx 0.00000565$

b. $_{19}C_6 = \dfrac{19!}{(19-6)!6!} = \dfrac{19!}{13!6!} = \dfrac{19 \cdot 18 \cdot 17 \cdot 16 \cdot 15 \cdot 14 \cdot 13!}{13!6 \cdot 5 \cdot 4 \cdot 3 \cdot 2 \cdot 1} = 27,132$

$P(\text{none are defective}) = \dfrac{\text{number of ways to choose 6 good transistors}}{\text{total number of possible permutations}} = \dfrac{27,132}{177,100} = \dfrac{969}{6325} \approx 0.153$

10. a. $_{13}C_5 = \dfrac{13!}{(13-5)!5!} = \dfrac{13!}{8!5!} = \dfrac{13 \cdot 12 \cdot 11 \cdot 10 \cdot 9 \cdot 8!}{8!5 \cdot 4 \cdot 3 \cdot 2 \cdot 1} = 1287$

$_{6}C_5 = \dfrac{6!}{(6-5)!5!} = \dfrac{6!}{1!5!} = \dfrac{6 \cdot 5!}{1 \cdot 5!} = 6$

$P(\text{all lawyers}) = \dfrac{\text{number of ways to select 5 lawyers}}{\text{total number of possible combinations}} = \dfrac{6}{1287} = \dfrac{2}{429} \approx 0.00466$

b. $_{7}C_5 = \dfrac{7!}{(7-5)!5!} = \dfrac{7!}{2!5!} = \dfrac{7 \cdot 6 \cdot 5!}{2 \cdot 1 \cdot 5!} = 21$

$P(\text{none are lawyers}) = \dfrac{\text{number of ways to select 5 teachers}}{\text{total number of possible combinations}} = \dfrac{21}{1287} = \dfrac{7}{429} \approx 0.0163$

11. total number of possible combinations: $_{10}C_3 = \dfrac{10!}{(10-3)!3!} = \dfrac{10!}{7!3!} = \dfrac{10 \cdot 9 \cdot 8 \cdot 7!}{7!3 \cdot 2 \cdot 1} = 120$

number of ways to select one Democrat: $_{6}C_1 = \dfrac{6!}{(6-1)!1!} = \dfrac{6!}{5!1!} = \dfrac{6 \cdot 5!}{5!1} = 6$

number of ways to select two Republicans: $_{4}C_2 = \dfrac{4!}{(4-2)!2!} = \dfrac{4!}{2!2!} = \dfrac{4 \cdot 3 \cdot 2!}{2!2 \cdot 1} = 6$

number of ways to select one Democrat and two Republicans: $_{6}C_1 \cdot {}_{4}C_2 = 6 \cdot 6 = 36$

$P(\text{one Democrat and two Republicans}) = \dfrac{36}{120} = \dfrac{3}{10} = 0.3$

12. total number of possible combinations: $_{20}C_4 = \dfrac{20!}{(20-4)!4!} = \dfrac{20!}{16!4!} = \dfrac{20 \cdot 19 \cdot 18 \cdot 17 \cdot 16!}{16!4 \cdot 3 \cdot 2 \cdot 1} = 4845$

number of ways to select two parents: $_{15}C_2 = \dfrac{15!}{(15-2)!2!} = \dfrac{15!}{13!2!} = \dfrac{15 \cdot 14 \cdot 13!}{13!2 \cdot 1} = 105$

number of ways to select two teachers: $_{5}C_2 = \dfrac{5!}{(5-2)!2!} = \dfrac{5!}{3!2!} = \dfrac{5 \cdot 4 \cdot 3!}{3!2 \cdot 1} = 10$

number of ways to select two parents and two teachers: $_{15}C_2 \cdot {}_{5}C_2 = 105 \cdot 10 = 1050$

$P(\text{two parents and two teachers}) = \dfrac{1050}{4845} = \dfrac{70}{323} \approx 0.217$

13. a. $_{52}C_5 = \dfrac{52!}{(52-5)!5!} = \dfrac{52!}{47!5!} = \dfrac{52 \cdot 51 \cdot 50 \cdot 49 \cdot 48 \cdot 47!}{47!5 \cdot 4 \cdot 3 \cdot 2 \cdot 1} = 2,598,960$

b. $_{13}C_5 = \dfrac{13!}{(13-5)!5!} = \dfrac{13!}{8!5!} = \dfrac{13 \cdot 12 \cdot 11 \cdot 10 \cdot 9 \cdot 8!}{8!5 \cdot 4 \cdot 3 \cdot 2 \cdot 1} = 1287$

c. $P(\text{diamond flush}) = \dfrac{\text{number of possible 5-card diamond flushes}}{\text{total number of possible combinations}} = \dfrac{1287}{2,598,960} \approx 0.000495$

14. a. $_{52}C_5 = \dfrac{52!}{(52-5)!5!} = \dfrac{52!}{47!5!} = \dfrac{52 \cdot 51 \cdot 50 \cdot 49 \cdot 48 \cdot 47!}{47!5 \cdot 4 \cdot 3 \cdot 2 \cdot 1} = 2,598,960$

b. $_4C_4 = \dfrac{4!}{(4-4)!4!} = \dfrac{4!}{0!4!} = 1$

c. $_4C_1 = \dfrac{4!}{(4-1)!1!} = \dfrac{4!}{3!1!} = \dfrac{4 \cdot 3!}{3!1} = 4$

d. $_4C_4 \cdot {_4C_1} = 1 \cdot 4 = 4$

e. $P(\text{4 aces and 1 king}) = \dfrac{\text{number of hands with 4 aces and 1 king}}{\text{total number of possible combinations}} = \dfrac{4}{2,598,960} \approx 0.00000154$

15. total number of possible combinations: $_{52}C_3 = \dfrac{52!}{(52-3)!3!} = \dfrac{52!}{49!3!} = \dfrac{52 \cdot 51 \cdot 50 \cdot 49!}{49!3 \cdot 2 \cdot 1} = 22,100$

number of ways to select 3 picture cards: $_{12}C_3 = \dfrac{12!}{(12-3)!3!} = \dfrac{12!}{9!3!} = \dfrac{12 \cdot 11 \cdot 10 \cdot 9!}{9!3 \cdot 2 \cdot 1} = 220$

$P(\text{3 picture cards}) = \dfrac{220}{22,100} = \dfrac{11}{1105} \approx 0.00995$

16. total number of possible combinations: $_{52}C_4 = \dfrac{52!}{(52-4)!4!} = \dfrac{52!}{48!4!} = \dfrac{52 \cdot 51 \cdot 50 \cdot 49 \cdot 48!}{48!4 \cdot 3 \cdot 2 \cdot 1} = 270,725$

number of ways to select 4 hearts: $_{13}C_4 = \dfrac{13!}{(13-4)!4!} = \dfrac{13!}{9!4!} = \dfrac{13 \cdot 12 \cdot 11 \cdot 10 \cdot 9!}{9!4 \cdot 3 \cdot 2 \cdot 1} = 715$

$P(\text{all 4 are hearts}) = \dfrac{715}{270,725} = \dfrac{11}{4165} \approx 0.00264$

17. total number of possible combinations: $_{52}C_4 = \dfrac{52!}{(52-4)!4!} = \dfrac{52!}{48!4!} = \dfrac{52 \cdot 51 \cdot 50 \cdot 49 \cdot 48!}{48!4 \cdot 3 \cdot 2 \cdot 1} = 270,725$

number of ways to select 2 queens: $_4C_2 = \dfrac{4!}{(4-2)!2!} = \dfrac{4!}{2!2!} = \dfrac{4 \cdot 3 \cdot 2!}{2!2 \cdot 1} = 6$

number of ways to select 2 kings: $_4C_2 = 6$

number of ways to select 2 queens and 2 kings: $_4C_2 \cdot {_4C_2} = 6 \cdot 6 = 36$

$P(\text{2 queens and 2 kings}) = \dfrac{36}{270,725} \approx 0.000133$

18. total number of possible combinations: $_{52}C_4 = \dfrac{52!}{(52-4)!\,4!} = \dfrac{52!}{48!\,4!} = \dfrac{52 \cdot 51 \cdot 50 \cdot 49 \cdot 48!}{48!\,4 \cdot 3 \cdot 2 \cdot 1} = 270,725$

number of ways to select 3 jacks: $_4C_3 = \dfrac{4!}{(4-3)!\,3!} = \dfrac{4!}{1!\,3!} = \dfrac{4 \cdot 3!}{1 \cdot 3!} = 4$

number of ways to select 1 queen: $_4C_1 = \dfrac{4!}{(4-1)!\,1!} = \dfrac{4!}{3!\,1!} = \dfrac{4 \cdot 3!}{3!\,1} = 4$

number of ways to select 3 jacks and 1 queen: $_4C_3 \cdot {_4C_1} = 4 \cdot 4 = 16$

$P(3 \text{ jacks and 1 queen}) = \dfrac{16}{270,725} \approx 0.0000591$

19-21. Answers will vary.

22. total number of possible combinations: $3 \cdot 2 \cdot 2 \cdot 3 = 36$
number of combinations the person wants: $1 \cdot 1 \cdot 1 \cdot 2 = 2$

$P(\text{what the person wants is available}) = \dfrac{\text{number of combinations the person wants}}{\text{total number of possible combinations}} = \dfrac{2}{36} = \dfrac{1}{18}$

23. Refer to solution 7: $_{51}C_6 = 18,009,460$

$P(\text{winning}) = \dfrac{\text{number of ways of winning }(x)}{\text{total number of possible combinations}} = \dfrac{x}{18,009,460} = \dfrac{1}{2}$, therefore $x = 9,004,730$.

At \$1 per ticket, a person must spend \$9,004,730 to have a probability of winning of $\dfrac{1}{2}$.

24. Other players could also purchase the winning combination and share the prize money, possibly making this person's share of the prize less than what this person paid for the tickets.

25. total number of possible combinations:

	Digit 1:		Digit 2:		Digit 3:	
	5	×	4	×	3	= 60

number of even numbers greater than 500:

	Digit 1: 5		Digit 2: 1, 3, and 2 or 4		Digit 3: 2 or 4	
	1	×	3	×	2	= 6

$P(\text{even and greater than 500}) = \dfrac{\text{number of even numbers greater than 500}}{\text{total number of possible combinations}} = \dfrac{6}{60} = \dfrac{1}{10}$

26. total number of possible combinations: $_{52}C_5 = \dfrac{52!}{(52-5)!\,5!} = \dfrac{52!}{47!\,5!} = \dfrac{52 \cdot 51 \cdot 50 \cdot 49 \cdot 48 \cdot 47!}{47!\,5 \cdot 4 \cdot 3 \cdot 2 \cdot 1} = 2,598,960$

number of ways to select one ace: $_4C_1 = \dfrac{4!}{(4-1)!\,1!} = \dfrac{4!}{3!\,1!} = \dfrac{4 \cdot 3!}{3!\,1} = 4$

Note: one card is an ace, so the other four must not be aces.
number of ways to select 4 cards with no face cards and no aces:

$_{36}C_4 = \dfrac{36!}{(36-4)!\,4!} = \dfrac{36!}{32!\,4!} = \dfrac{36 \cdot 35 \cdot 34 \cdot 33 \cdot 32!}{32!\,4 \cdot 3 \cdot 2 \cdot 1} = 58,905$

number of hands with one ace and no face cards: $_4C_1 \cdot {_{36}C_4} = 4 \cdot 58,905 = 235,620$

$P(\text{one ace and no face cards}) = \dfrac{\text{number of hands with one ace and no face cards}}{\text{total number of possible combinations}} = \dfrac{235,620}{2,598,960} \approx 0.0907$

Check Points 11.6

1. $P(\text{not a diamond}) = 1 - P(\text{diamond}) = 1 - \dfrac{13}{52} = \dfrac{39}{52} = \dfrac{3}{4}$

2. First, find the probability that the person selected <u>is</u> in the Marines.

   $P(\text{Marines}) = \dfrac{160 + 10}{1370} = \dfrac{170}{1370} = \dfrac{17}{137}$

   Thus, $P(\text{not in Marines}) = 1 - P(\text{Marines}) = 1 - \dfrac{17}{137} = \dfrac{137}{137} - \dfrac{17}{137} = \dfrac{120}{137}$

3. $P(4 \text{ or } 5) = P(4) + P(5) = \dfrac{1}{6} + \dfrac{1}{6} = \dfrac{2}{6} = \dfrac{1}{3}$

4. $P(\text{math or psychology}) = P(\text{math}) + P(\text{psychology}) - P(\text{math and psychology}) = \dfrac{23}{50} + \dfrac{11}{50} - \dfrac{7}{50} = \dfrac{27}{50}$

5. $P(\text{odd or less than 5}) = P(\text{odd}) + P(\text{less than 5}) - P(\text{odd and less than 5}) = \dfrac{4}{8} + \dfrac{4}{8} - \dfrac{2}{8} = \dfrac{6}{8} = \dfrac{3}{4}$

6. $P(\text{Navy or is a man}) = P(\text{Navy}) + P(\text{man}) - P(\text{Navy and man}) = \dfrac{370}{1370} + \dfrac{1170}{1370} - \dfrac{320}{1370} = \dfrac{1220}{1370} = \dfrac{122}{137}$

7. There are 2 red queens. Number of favorable outcomes = 2, Number of unfavorable outcomes = 50

   a. Odds in favor of getting a red queen are 2 to 50 or 2:50 which reduces to 1:25.

   b. Odds against getting a red queen are 50 to 2 or 50:2 which reduces to 25:1.

8. number of unfavorable outcomes = 995, number of favorable outcomes = 5
   Odds against winning the scholarship are 995 to 5 or 995:5 which reduces to 199:1.

9. number of unfavorable outcomes = 15, number of favorable outcomes = 1
   Odds in favor of the horse winning the race are 1 to 15

   $P(\text{the horse wins race}) = \dfrac{1}{1 + 15} = \dfrac{1}{16} = 0.0625$ or 6.3%.

Exercise Set 11.6

1. $P(\text{not an ace}) = 1 - P(\text{ace}) = 1 - \dfrac{4}{52} = \dfrac{48}{52} = \dfrac{12}{13}$

2. $P(\text{not a 3}) = 1 - P(3) = 1 - \dfrac{4}{52} = 1 - \dfrac{1}{13} = \dfrac{12}{13}$

3. $P(\text{not a heart}) = 1 - P(\text{heart}) = 1 - \dfrac{13}{52} = \dfrac{39}{52} = \dfrac{3}{4}$

4. $P(\text{not a club}) = 1 - P(\text{club}) = 1 - \dfrac{13}{52} = \dfrac{39}{52} = \dfrac{3}{4}$

5. $P(\text{not a picture card}) = 1 - P(\text{picture card}) = 1 - \dfrac{12}{52} = \dfrac{40}{52} = \dfrac{10}{13}$

6. $P(\text{not a red picture card}) = 1 - P(\text{red picture card}) = 1 - \dfrac{6}{52} = \dfrac{46}{52} = \dfrac{23}{26}$

7. $P(\text{not a straight flush}) = 1 - P(\text{straight flush}) = 1 - \dfrac{36}{2,598,960} = \dfrac{2,598,924}{2,598,960} \approx 0.999986$

8. $P(\text{not four of a kind}) = 1 - P(\text{four of a kind}) = 1 - \dfrac{624}{2,598,960} = \dfrac{2,598,336}{2,598,960} \approx 0.999760$

9. $P(\text{not a full house}) = 1 - P(\text{full house}) = 1 - \dfrac{3744}{2,598,960} = \dfrac{2,595,216}{2,598,960} \approx 0.998559$

10. $P(\text{not a flush}) = 1 - P(\text{flush}) = 1 - \dfrac{5108}{2,598,960} = \dfrac{2,593,852}{2,598,960} \approx 0.998035$

11. **a.** 0.10 (read from graph)

   b. $1.00 - 0.10 = 0.90$

12. **a.** 0.78 (read from graph)

   b. $1.00 - 0.78 = 0.22$

13. $30.3\% + 23.0\% = 53.3\% = 0.533$

14. $30.3\% + 7.0\% = 37.3\% = 0.373$

15. $P(2 \text{ or } 3) = P(2) + P(3) = \dfrac{4}{52} + \dfrac{4}{52} = \dfrac{8}{52} = \dfrac{2}{13}$

16. $P(7 \text{ or } 8) = P(7) + P(8) = \dfrac{4}{52} + \dfrac{4}{52} = \dfrac{8}{52} = \dfrac{2}{13}$

17. $P(\text{red 2 or black 3}) = P(\text{red 2}) + P(\text{black 3}) = \dfrac{2}{52} + \dfrac{2}{52} = \dfrac{4}{52} = \dfrac{1}{13}$

18. $P(\text{red 7 or black 8}) = P(\text{red 7}) + P(\text{black 8}) = \dfrac{2}{52} + \dfrac{2}{52} = \dfrac{4}{52} = \dfrac{1}{13}$

19. $P(\text{2 of hearts or 3 of spades}) = P(\text{2 of hearts}) + P(\text{3 of spades}) = \dfrac{1}{52} + \dfrac{1}{52} = \dfrac{2}{52} = \dfrac{1}{26}$

20. $P(\text{7 or hearts or 8 of spades}) = P(\text{7 of hearts}) + P(\text{8 of spades}) = \dfrac{1}{52} + \dfrac{1}{52} = \dfrac{2}{52} = \dfrac{1}{26}$

21. $P(\text{professor or instructor}) = P(\text{professor}) + P(\text{instructor}) = \dfrac{8}{44} + \dfrac{10}{44} = \dfrac{18}{44} = \dfrac{9}{22}$

22. $P(\text{Independent or Green}) = P(\text{Independent}) + P(\text{Green}) = \dfrac{8}{67} + \dfrac{4}{67} = \dfrac{12}{67}$

23. $P(\text{even or less than 5}) = P(\text{even}) + P(\text{less than 5}) - P(\text{even and less than 5}) = \dfrac{3}{6} + \dfrac{4}{6} - \dfrac{2}{6} = \dfrac{5}{6}$

24. $P(\text{odd or less than 4}) = P(\text{odd}) + P(\text{less than 4}) - P(\text{odd and less than 4}) = \dfrac{3}{6} + \dfrac{3}{6} - \dfrac{2}{6} = \dfrac{4}{6} = \dfrac{2}{3}$

25. $P(7 \text{ or red}) = P(7) + P(\text{red}) - P(\text{red } 7) = \dfrac{4}{52} + \dfrac{26}{52} - \dfrac{2}{52} = \dfrac{28}{52} = \dfrac{7}{13}$

26. $P(5 \text{ or black}) = P(5) + P(\text{black}) - P(\text{black } 5) = \dfrac{4}{52} + \dfrac{26}{52} - \dfrac{2}{52} = \dfrac{28}{52} = \dfrac{7}{13}$

27. $P(\text{heart or picture card}) = P(\text{heart}) + P(\text{picture card}) - P(\text{heart and picture card}) = \dfrac{13}{52} + \dfrac{12}{52} - \dfrac{3}{52} = \dfrac{22}{52} = \dfrac{11}{26}$

28. $P(\text{greater than 2 and less than 7, or diamond})$
$= P(\text{greater than 2 and less than 7}) + P(\text{diamond}) - P(\text{diamond greater than 2 and less than 7})$
$= \dfrac{16}{52} + \dfrac{13}{52} - \dfrac{4}{52} = \dfrac{25}{52}$

29. $P(\text{odd or less than 6}) = P(\text{odd}) + P(\text{less than 6}) - P(\text{odd and less than 6}) = \dfrac{4}{8} + \dfrac{5}{8} - \dfrac{3}{8} = \dfrac{6}{8} = \dfrac{3}{4}$

30. $P(\text{odd or greater than 3}) = P(\text{odd}) + P(\text{greater than 3}) - P(\text{odd and greater than 3}) = \dfrac{4}{8} + \dfrac{5}{8} - \dfrac{2}{8} = \dfrac{7}{8}$

31. $P(\text{even or greater than 5}) = P(\text{even}) + P(\text{greater than 5}) - P(\text{even and greater than 5}) = \dfrac{4}{8} + \dfrac{3}{8} - \dfrac{2}{8} = \dfrac{5}{8}$

32. $P(\text{even or less than 4}) = P(\text{even}) + P(\text{less than 4}) - P(\text{even and less than 4}) = \dfrac{4}{8} + \dfrac{3}{8} - \dfrac{1}{8} = \dfrac{6}{8} = \dfrac{3}{4}$

33. $P(\text{professor or male}) = P(\text{professor}) + P(\text{male}) - P(\text{male professor}) = \dfrac{19}{40} + \dfrac{22}{40} - \dfrac{8}{40} = \dfrac{33}{40}$

34. $P(\text{professor or female}) = P(\text{professor}) + P(\text{female}) - P(\text{female professor}) = \dfrac{19}{40} + \dfrac{18}{40} - \dfrac{11}{40} = \dfrac{26}{40} = \dfrac{13}{20}$

35. $P(\text{teach. assist. or female}) = P(\text{teach. assist.}) + P(\text{female}) - P(\text{female teach. assist.}) = \dfrac{21}{40} + \dfrac{18}{40} - \dfrac{7}{40} = \dfrac{32}{40} = \dfrac{4}{5}$

36. $P(\text{teaching assistant or male}) = P(\text{teach. assist.}) + P(\text{male}) - P(\text{male teach. assist.}) = \dfrac{21}{40} + \dfrac{22}{40} - \dfrac{14}{40} = \dfrac{29}{40}$

37. $P(\text{Democrat or business major}) = P(\text{Democrat}) + P(\text{business major}) - P(\text{Democrat and business major})$
$= \dfrac{29}{50} + \dfrac{11}{50} - \dfrac{5}{50} = \dfrac{35}{50} = \dfrac{7}{10}$

38. $P(\text{math or english}) = P(\text{math}) + P(\text{english}) - P(\text{math and english}) = \dfrac{135}{200} + \dfrac{85}{200} - \dfrac{65}{200} = \dfrac{155}{200} = \dfrac{31}{40}$

39. $P(\text{not completed 4 years or more of college}) = 1 - P(\text{completed 4 years or more of college}) = 1 - \dfrac{45}{174} = \dfrac{174}{174} - \dfrac{45}{174} = \dfrac{43}{58}$

40. $P(\text{not completed 4 years of high school}) = \dfrac{29}{174} = \dfrac{1}{6}$

41. $P(\text{completed 4 years of high school only or less than 4 years of college}) = \dfrac{56 + 44}{174} = \dfrac{100}{174} = \dfrac{50}{87}$

42. $P(\text{completed less than 4 years of high school or 4 years of high school only}) = \dfrac{29 + 56}{174} = \dfrac{85}{174}$

43. $P(\text{completed 4 years of high school only or is a man})$
    $= P(\text{completed 4 years of high school only}) + P(\text{man}) - P(\text{completed 4 years of high school only and is a man})$
    $= \dfrac{56}{174} + \dfrac{82}{174} - \dfrac{25}{174} = \dfrac{113}{174}$

44. $P(\text{completed 4 years of high school only or is a woman})$
    $= P(\text{completed 4 years of high school only}) + P(\text{woman}) - P(\text{completed 4 years of high school only and is a woman})$
    $= \dfrac{56}{174} + \dfrac{92}{174} - \dfrac{31}{174} = \dfrac{117}{174} = \dfrac{39}{58}$

45. number of favorable outcomes $= 45$, number of unfavorable outcomes $= 174 - 45 = 129$
    Odds in favor of an American over the age of 25 having four years (or more) of college are 45:129, or 15:43.
    Odds against an American over the age of 25 having four years (or more) of college are 129:45, or 43:15.

46. number of favorable outcomes $= 29$, number of unfavorable outcomes $= 174 - 29 = 145$
    Odds in favor of an American over the age of 25 having less than four years of high school are 29:145, or 1:5.
    Odds against an American over the age of 25 having less than four years of high school are 145:29, or 5:1.

47. number of favorable outcomes $= 4$, number of unfavorable outcomes $= 2$
    Odds in favor of getting a number greater than 2 are 4:2, or 2:1.

48. number of favorable outcomes $= 4$, number of unfavorable outcomes $= 2$
    Odds in favor of getting a number less than 5 are 4:2, or 2:1.

49. number of unfavorable outcomes $= 2$, number of favorable outcomes $= 4$
    Odds against getting a number greater than 2 or 2:4, or 1:2.

50. number of unfavorable outcomes $= 2$, number of favorable outcomes $= 4$
    Odds against getting a number less than 5 are 2:4, or 1:2.

51. number of favorable outcomes $= 9$, number of unfavorable outcomes $= 100 - 9 = 91$

    a. Odds in favor of a child in a one-parent household having a parent who is a college graduate are 9:91.

    b. Odds against a child in a one-parent household having a parent who is a college graduate are 91:9.

52. number of favorable outcomes $= 29$, number of unfavorable outcomes $= 100 - 29 = 71$

    a. Odds in favor of a child in a two-parent household having parents who are college graduates are 29:71.

    b. Odds against a child in a two-parent household having parents who are college graduates are 71:29.

53. number of favorable outcomes = 13, number of unfavorable outcomes = 39
Odds in favor of a heart are 13:39, or 1:3.

54. number of favorable outcomes = 12, number of unfavorable outcomes = 40
Odds in favor of a picture card are 12:40, or 3:10.

55. number of favorable outcomes = 26, number of unfavorable outcomes = 26
Odds in favor of a red card are 26:26, or 1:1.

56. number of favorable outcomes = 26, number of unfavorable outcomes = 26
Odds in favor of a black card are 26:26, or 1:1.

57. number of unfavorable outcomes = 48, number of favorable outcomes = 4
Odds against a 9 are 48:4, or 12:1.

58. number of unfavorable outcomes = 48, number of favorable outcomes = 4
Odds against a 5 are 48:4, or 12:1.

59. number of unfavorable outcomes = 50, number of favorable outcomes = 2
Odds against a black king are 50:2, or 25:1.

60. number of unfavorable outcomes = 50, number of favorable outcomes = 2
Odds against a red jack are 50:2, or 25:1.

61. number of unfavorable outcomes = 47, number of favorable outcomes = 5
Odds against a spade greater than 3 and less than 9 are 47:5.

62. number of unfavorable outcomes = 47, number of favorable outcomes = 5
Odds against a club greater than 4 and less than 9 are 47:5.

63. number of unfavorable outcomes = 980, number of favorable outcomes = 20
Odds against winning are 980:20, or 49:1.

64. number of unfavorable outcomes = 4970, number of favorable outcomes = 30
Odds against winning are 4970:30, or 497:3.

65. number of favorable outcomes = 1, number of unfavorable outcomes = 19
Odds in favor of being a victim are 1:19.

66. number of favorable outcomes = 1, number of unfavorable outcomes = 3
Odds in favor of high cholesterol level are 1:3.

67. $P(\text{winning}) = \dfrac{3}{3+4} = \dfrac{3}{7}$

68. $P(\text{winning}) = \dfrac{3}{3+7} = \dfrac{3}{10}$

69. $P(\text{miss free throw}) = \dfrac{4}{21+4} = \dfrac{4}{25} = 0.16 = 16\%$
In 100 free throws, on average he missed 16, so he made $100 - 16 = 84$.

70. $P(\text{still alive at age 70}) = \dfrac{193}{193+270} = \dfrac{193}{463} \approx 41.7\%$

71-77. Answers will vary.

78. a. P(Democrat who is not a business major)

$= 1 - P$(not a Democrat or Democrat and business major)

$= 1 - [P$(not a Democrat) $+ P$(Democrat and business major)]

$= 1 - \left(\dfrac{21}{50} + \dfrac{5}{50} \right)$

$= 1 - \dfrac{26}{50}$

$= \dfrac{24}{50}$

$= \dfrac{12}{25}$

b. P(neither Democrat nor business major)

$= 1 - P$(Democrat or business major)

$= 1 - [P$(Democrat)$+P$(business major)$-P$(Democrat and business major)]

$= 1 - \left(\dfrac{29}{50} + \dfrac{11}{50} - \dfrac{5}{50} \right)$

$= 1 - \dfrac{35}{50}$

$= \dfrac{15}{50}$

$= \dfrac{3}{10}$

79. P(driving intoxicated or driving accident)

$= P$(driving intoxicated) $+ P$(driving accident) $- P$(driving accident while intoxicated)

Substitute the three given probabilities and solve for the unknown probability:

$$0.35 = 0.32 + 0.09 - P(\text{driving accident while intoxicated})$$

P(driving accident while intoxicated) $= 0.32 + 0.09 - 0.35$

P(driving accident while intoxicated) $= 0.06$

Check Points 11.7

1. P(green and green) $= P$(green) $\cdot P$(green) $= \dfrac{2}{38} \cdot \dfrac{2}{38} = \dfrac{1}{19} \cdot \dfrac{1}{19} = \dfrac{1}{361} \approx 0.00277$

2. P(4 boys in a row) $= P$(boy and boy and boy and boy)$=P$(boy) $\cdot P$(boy) $\cdot P$(boy) $\cdot P$(boy) $= \dfrac{1}{2} \cdot \dfrac{1}{2} \cdot \dfrac{1}{2} \cdot \dfrac{1}{2} = \dfrac{1}{16}$

3. a. P(hit four years in a row) $= P$(hit) $\cdot P$(hit) $\cdot P$(hit) $\cdot P$(hit) $= \dfrac{5}{19} \cdot \dfrac{5}{19} \cdot \dfrac{5}{19} \cdot \dfrac{5}{19} = \dfrac{625}{130,321} \approx 0.005$

b. Note: P(not hit in any single year) $= 1 - P$(hit in any single year) $= 1 - \dfrac{5}{19} = \dfrac{14}{19}$, . Therefore,

P(not hit in next four years)

$= P$(not hit) $\cdot P$(not hit) $\cdot P$(not hit) $\cdot P$(not hit) $= \dfrac{14}{19} \cdot \dfrac{14}{19} \cdot \dfrac{14}{19} \cdot \dfrac{14}{19} = \dfrac{38,416}{130,321} \approx 0.295$

c. $P(\text{hit at least once in next four years}) = 1 - P(\text{not hit in next four years}) = 1 - \dfrac{38,416}{130,321} = \dfrac{91,905}{130,321} \approx 0.705$

4. $P(2 \text{ kings}) = P(\text{king}) \cdot P(\text{king given the first card was a king}) = \dfrac{4}{52} \cdot \dfrac{3}{51} = \dfrac{1}{13} \cdot \dfrac{1}{17} = \dfrac{1}{221} \approx 0.00452$

5. $P(3 \text{ hearts}) = P(\text{heart}) \cdot P(\text{heart given the first card was a heart}) \cdot P(\text{heart given the first two cards were hearts})$

$$= \dfrac{13}{52} \cdot \dfrac{12}{51} \cdot \dfrac{11}{50} = \dfrac{1}{4} \cdot \dfrac{4}{17} \cdot \dfrac{11}{50} = \dfrac{1}{1} \cdot \dfrac{1}{17} \cdot \dfrac{11}{50} = \dfrac{11}{850} \approx 0.0129$$

6. $P\big(\text{heart}\,\big|\,\text{red}\big) = \dfrac{13}{26} = \dfrac{1}{2}$

7. a. $P\big(\text{conservative}\,\big|\,\text{male}\big) = \dfrac{\text{number of conservative males}}{\text{number of males}} = \dfrac{39}{16 + 45 + 39} = \dfrac{39}{100}$

b. $P\big(\text{female}\,\big|\,\text{liberal}\big) = \dfrac{\text{number of liberal females}}{\text{number of liberals}} = \dfrac{20}{16 + 20} = \dfrac{20}{36} = \dfrac{5}{9}$

Exercise Set 11.7

1. $P(\text{green and red}) = P(\text{green}) \cdot P(\text{red}) = \dfrac{2}{6} \cdot \dfrac{3}{6} = \dfrac{1}{3} \cdot \dfrac{1}{2} = \dfrac{1}{6}$

2. $P(\text{yellow and green}) = P(\text{yellow}) \cdot P(\text{green}) = \dfrac{1}{6} \cdot \dfrac{2}{6} = \dfrac{1}{6} \cdot \dfrac{1}{3} = \dfrac{1}{18}$

3. $P(\text{yellow and yellow}) = P(\text{yellow}) \cdot P(\text{yellow}) = \dfrac{1}{6} \cdot \dfrac{1}{6} = \dfrac{1}{36}$

4. $P(\text{red and red}) = P(\text{red}) \cdot P(\text{red}) = \dfrac{3}{6} \cdot \dfrac{3}{6} = \dfrac{1}{2} \cdot \dfrac{1}{2} = \dfrac{1}{4}$

5. $P(\text{color other than red each time}) = P(\text{not red}) \cdot P(\text{not red}) = \dfrac{3}{6} \cdot \dfrac{3}{6} = \dfrac{1}{2} \cdot \dfrac{1}{2} = \dfrac{1}{4}$

6. $P(\text{color other than green each time}) = P(\text{not green}) \cdot P(\text{not green}) = \dfrac{4}{6} \cdot \dfrac{4}{6} = \dfrac{2}{3} \cdot \dfrac{2}{3} = \dfrac{4}{9}$

7. $P(\text{green and red and yellow}) = P(\text{green}) \cdot P(\text{red}) \cdot P(\text{yellow}) = \dfrac{2}{6} \cdot \dfrac{3}{6} \cdot \dfrac{1}{6} = \dfrac{1}{3} \cdot \dfrac{1}{2} \cdot \dfrac{1}{6} = \dfrac{1}{36}$

8. $P(\text{red and red and green}) = P(\text{red}) \cdot P(\text{red}) \cdot P(\text{green}) = \dfrac{3}{6} \cdot \dfrac{3}{6} \cdot \dfrac{2}{6} = \dfrac{1}{2} \cdot \dfrac{1}{2} \cdot \dfrac{1}{3} = \dfrac{1}{12}$

9. $P(\text{red every time}) = P(\text{red}) \cdot P(\text{red}) \cdot P(\text{red}) = \dfrac{3}{6} \cdot \dfrac{3}{6} \cdot \dfrac{3}{6} = \dfrac{1}{2} \cdot \dfrac{1}{2} \cdot \dfrac{1}{2} = \dfrac{1}{8}$

10. $P(\text{green every time}) = P(\text{green}) \cdot P(\text{green}) \cdot P(\text{green}) = \dfrac{2}{6} \cdot \dfrac{2}{6} \cdot \dfrac{2}{6} = \dfrac{1}{3} \cdot \dfrac{1}{3} \cdot \dfrac{1}{3} = \dfrac{1}{27}$

11. $P(2 \text{ and } 3) = P(2) \cdot P(3) = \dfrac{1}{6} \cdot \dfrac{1}{6} = \dfrac{1}{36}$

12. $P(5 \text{ and } 1) = P(5) \cdot P(1) = \dfrac{1}{6} \cdot \dfrac{1}{6} = \dfrac{1}{36}$

13. $P(\text{even and greater than 2}) = P(\text{even}) \cdot P(\text{greater than 2}) = \dfrac{3}{6} \cdot \dfrac{4}{6} = \dfrac{1}{2} \cdot \dfrac{2}{3} = \dfrac{1}{3}$

14. $P(\text{odd and less than 3}) = P(\text{odd}) \cdot P(\text{less than 3}) = \dfrac{3}{6} \cdot \dfrac{2}{6} = \dfrac{1}{2} \cdot \dfrac{1}{3} = \dfrac{1}{6}$

15. $P(\text{picture card and heart}) = P(\text{picture card}) \cdot P(\text{heart}) = \dfrac{12}{52} \cdot \dfrac{13}{52} = \dfrac{3}{13} \cdot \dfrac{1}{4} = \dfrac{3}{52}$

16. $P(\text{jack and club}) = P(\text{jack}) \cdot P(\text{club}) = \dfrac{4}{52} \cdot \dfrac{13}{52} = \dfrac{1}{13} \cdot \dfrac{1}{4} = \dfrac{1}{52}$

17. $P(2 \text{ kings}) = P(\text{king}) \cdot P(\text{king}) = \dfrac{4}{52} \cdot \dfrac{4}{52} = \dfrac{1}{13} \cdot \dfrac{1}{13} = \dfrac{1}{169}$

18. $P(3 \text{ each time}) = P(3) \cdot P(3) = \dfrac{4}{52} \cdot \dfrac{4}{52} = \dfrac{1}{13} \cdot \dfrac{1}{13} = \dfrac{1}{169}$

19. $P(\text{red each time}) = P(\text{red}) \cdot P(\text{red}) = \dfrac{26}{52} \cdot \dfrac{26}{52} = \dfrac{1}{2} \cdot \dfrac{1}{2} = \dfrac{1}{4}$

20. $P(\text{black each time}) = P(\text{black}) \cdot P(\text{black}) = \dfrac{26}{52} \cdot \dfrac{26}{52} = \dfrac{1}{2} \cdot \dfrac{1}{2} = \dfrac{1}{4}$

21. $P(\text{all heads}) = P(\text{heads}) \cdot P(\text{heads}) \cdot P(\text{heads}) \cdot P(\text{heads}) \cdot P(\text{heads}) \cdot P(\text{heads}) = \dfrac{1}{2} \cdot \dfrac{1}{2} \cdot \dfrac{1}{2} \cdot \dfrac{1}{2} \cdot \dfrac{1}{2} \cdot \dfrac{1}{2} = \dfrac{1}{64}$

22. $P(\text{all tails}) = P(\text{tails}) \cdot P(\text{tails}) \cdot P(\text{tails}) \cdot P(\text{tails}) \cdot P(\text{tails}) \cdot P(\text{tails}) \cdot P(\text{tails}) = \dfrac{1}{2} \cdot \dfrac{1}{2} \cdot \dfrac{1}{2} \cdot \dfrac{1}{2} \cdot \dfrac{1}{2} \cdot \dfrac{1}{2} \cdot \dfrac{1}{2} = \dfrac{1}{128}$

23. $P(\text{head and number greater than 4}) = P(\text{head}) \cdot P(\text{number greater than 4}) = \dfrac{1}{2} \cdot \dfrac{2}{6} = \dfrac{1}{6}$

24. $P(\text{tail and number less than 5}) = P(\text{tail}) \cdot P(\text{number less than 5}) = \dfrac{1}{2} \cdot \dfrac{4}{6} = \dfrac{1}{2} \cdot \dfrac{2}{3} = \dfrac{1}{3}$

25. a. $P(\text{hit two years in a row}) = P(\text{hit}) \cdot P(\text{hit}) = \dfrac{1}{16} \cdot \dfrac{1}{16} = \dfrac{1}{256}$

b. $P(\text{Hit three consecutive years}) = P(\text{hit}) \cdot P(\text{hit}) \cdot P(\text{hit}) = \dfrac{1}{16} \cdot \dfrac{1}{16} \cdot \dfrac{1}{16} = \dfrac{1}{4096}$

c. $P(\text{not hit in next ten years}) = [P(\text{not hit})]^{10} = \left(1 - \dfrac{1}{16}\right)^{10} = \left(\dfrac{15}{16}\right)^{10} \approx 0.524$

d. P(hit at least once in next ten years) $= 1 - P$(not hit in next ten years) $\approx 1 - 0.524 \approx 0.476$

26. a. P(flood two years in a row) $= P$(flood) $\cdot P$(flood) $= \dfrac{1}{10} \cdot \dfrac{1}{10} = \dfrac{1}{100}$

b. P(flood three consecutive years) $= P$(flood) $\cdot P$(flood) $\cdot P$(flood) $= \dfrac{1}{10} \cdot \dfrac{1}{10} \cdot \dfrac{1}{10} = \dfrac{1}{1000}$

c. P(no flooding in ten years) $= [P(\text{no flood})]^{10} = [1 - P(\text{flood})]^{10} = \left(1 - \dfrac{1}{10}\right)^{10} = \left(\dfrac{9}{10}\right)^{10} \approx 0.349$

d. P(flooding at least once in ten years) $= 1 - P$(no flooding in ten years) $\approx 1 - 0.349 \approx 0.651$

27. P(all four rate their health as excellent) $= (0.22)(0.22)(0.22)(0.22) = (0.22)^4 \approx 0.00234 \approx 0.234\%$

28. P(all four rate their health as poor) $= (0.06)(0.06)(0.06)(0.06) = (0.06)^4 \approx 0.000013 \approx 0.0013\%$

29. P(solid and solid) $= P$(solid) $\cdot P$(solid given first was solid) $= \dfrac{15}{30} \cdot \dfrac{14}{29} = \dfrac{1}{2} \cdot \dfrac{14}{29} = \dfrac{7}{29}$

30. P(two caramel) $= P$(caramel) $\cdot P$(caramel given first was caramel) $= \dfrac{10}{30} \cdot \dfrac{9}{29} = \dfrac{1}{3} \cdot \dfrac{9}{29} = \dfrac{3}{29}$

31. P(coconut then caramel) $= P$(coconut) $\cdot P$(caramel given first was coconut) $= \dfrac{5}{30} \cdot \dfrac{10}{29} = \dfrac{1}{6} \cdot \dfrac{10}{29} = \dfrac{5}{87}$

32. P(coconut then solid)$=P$(coconut) $\cdot P$(solid given first was coconut) $= \dfrac{5}{30} \cdot \dfrac{15}{29} = \dfrac{1}{6} \cdot \dfrac{15}{29} = \dfrac{5}{58}$

33. P(two Democrats) $= P$(Democrat) $\cdot P$(Democrat given first was Democrat) $= \dfrac{5}{15} \cdot \dfrac{4}{14} = \dfrac{1}{3} \cdot \dfrac{2}{7} = \dfrac{2}{21}$

34. P(two Republicans) $= P$(Republican) $\cdot P$(Republican given first was Republican)
$$= \dfrac{6}{15} \cdot \dfrac{5}{14} = \dfrac{2}{5} \cdot \dfrac{5}{14} = \dfrac{1}{7}$$

35. P(Independent then Republican) $= P$(Independent) $\cdot P$(Republican given first was Independent)
$$= \dfrac{4}{15} \cdot \dfrac{6}{14} = \dfrac{4}{15} \cdot \dfrac{3}{7} = \dfrac{4}{35}$$

36. P(Independent then Democrat)$=P$(Independent) $\cdot P$(Democrat given first was Independent)
$$= \dfrac{4}{15} \cdot \dfrac{5}{14} = \dfrac{2}{21}$$

37. P(no Independents) $= P$(not Independent) $\cdot P$(not Independent given first was not Independent)
$$= \dfrac{11}{15} \cdot \dfrac{10}{14} = \dfrac{11}{15} \cdot \dfrac{5}{7} = \dfrac{11}{21}$$

38. $P(\text{no Democrats}) = P(\text{not Democrat}) \cdot P(\text{not Democrat given first was not Democrat}) = \dfrac{10}{15} \cdot \dfrac{9}{14} = \dfrac{2}{3} \cdot \dfrac{9}{14} = \dfrac{3}{7}$

39. $P(\text{three cans of apple juice})$

$= P(\text{apple juice}) \cdot P\left(\begin{array}{c}\text{apple juice given} \\ \text{first was apple juice}\end{array}\right) \cdot P\left(\begin{array}{c}\text{apple juice given first} \\ \text{two were apple juice}\end{array}\right) = \dfrac{6}{20} \cdot \dfrac{5}{19} \cdot \dfrac{4}{18} = \dfrac{1}{57}$

40. $P(\text{three cans of grape juice})$

$= P(\text{grape juice}) \cdot P\left(\begin{array}{c}\text{grape juice given} \\ \text{first was grape juice}\end{array}\right) \cdot P\left(\begin{array}{c}\text{grape juice given first} \\ \text{two were grape juice}\end{array}\right) = \dfrac{8}{20} \cdot \dfrac{7}{19} \cdot \dfrac{6}{18} = \dfrac{14}{285}$

41. $P(\text{grape juice then orange juice then mango juice})$

$= P(\text{grape juice}) \cdot P\left(\begin{array}{c}\text{orange juice given} \\ \text{first was grape juice}\end{array}\right) \cdot P\left(\begin{array}{c}\text{mango juice given first was grape juice} \\ \text{and second was orange juice}\end{array}\right) = \dfrac{8}{20} \cdot \dfrac{4}{19} \cdot \dfrac{2}{18} = \dfrac{8}{855}$

42. $P(\text{apple juice then grape juice then orange juice})$

$= P(\text{apple juice}) \cdot P\left(\begin{array}{c}\text{grape juice given} \\ \text{first was apple juice}\end{array}\right) \cdot P\left(\begin{array}{c}\text{orange juice given first was apple juice} \\ \text{and second was grape juice}\end{array}\right) = \dfrac{6}{20} \cdot \dfrac{8}{19} \cdot \dfrac{4}{18} = \dfrac{8}{285}$

43. $P(\text{no grape juice})$

$= P(\text{not grape juice}) \cdot P\left(\begin{array}{c}\text{not grape juice given} \\ \text{first was not grape juice}\end{array}\right) \cdot P\left(\begin{array}{c}\text{not grape juice given first} \\ \text{two were not grape juice}\end{array}\right) = \dfrac{12}{20} \cdot \dfrac{11}{19} \cdot \dfrac{10}{18} = \dfrac{11}{57}$

44. $P(\text{no apple juice})$

$= P(\text{not apple juice}) \cdot P\left(\begin{array}{c}\text{not apple juice given} \\ \text{first was not apple juice}\end{array}\right) \cdot P\left(\begin{array}{c}\text{not apple juice given first} \\ \text{two were not apple juice}\end{array}\right) = \dfrac{14}{20} \cdot \dfrac{13}{19} \cdot \dfrac{12}{18} = \dfrac{91}{285}$

45. $P(3|\text{red}) = \dfrac{1}{5}$

46. $P(7|\text{yellow}) = \dfrac{1}{3}$

47. $P(\text{even}|\text{yellow}) = \dfrac{2}{3}$

48. $P(\text{odd}|\text{red}) = \dfrac{3}{5}$

49. $P(\text{red}|\text{odd}) = \dfrac{3}{4}$

50. $P(\text{yellow}|\text{odd}) = \dfrac{1}{4}$

51. $P(\text{red}|\text{at least } 5) = \dfrac{3}{4}$

52. $P(\text{yellow}|\text{at most 3}) = \dfrac{1}{3}$

53. $P(\text{breast cancer}) = \dfrac{720+80}{720+80+6944+92,256} = \dfrac{800}{100,000} = \dfrac{1}{125} \approx 0.008$

54. $P(\text{does not have breast cancer}) = \dfrac{6944+92,256}{720+80+6944+92,256} = \dfrac{99,200}{100,000} = \dfrac{124}{125} \approx 0.992$

55. $P(\text{positive mammogram}|\text{breast cancer}) = \dfrac{720}{720+80} = \dfrac{720}{800} = \dfrac{9}{10} \approx 0.9$

56. $P(\text{positive mammogram}|\text{does not have breast cancer}) = \dfrac{6944}{6944+92,256} = \dfrac{6944}{99,200} = \dfrac{7}{100} \approx 0.07$

57. $P(\text{breast cancer}|\text{positive mammogram}) = \dfrac{720}{720+6944} = \dfrac{720}{7664} = \dfrac{45}{479} \approx 0.094$

58. $P(\text{does not have breast cancer}|\text{positive mammogram}) = \dfrac{6944}{720+6944} = \dfrac{6944}{7664} = \dfrac{434}{479} \approx 0.906$

59. $P(\text{not liberal}) = \dfrac{35+13+15+20}{7+35+13+10+15+20} = \dfrac{83}{100}$

60. $P(\text{not conservative}) = \dfrac{7+35+10+15}{7+35+13+10+15+20} = \dfrac{67}{100}$

61. $P(\text{liberal or moderate}) = \dfrac{(7+10)+(35+15)}{7+35+13+10+15+20} = \dfrac{67}{100}$

62. $P(\text{moderate or conservative}) = \dfrac{(35+15)+(13+20)}{7+35+13+10+15+20} = \dfrac{83}{100}$

63.
$$= P(\text{conservative or attended college})$$
$$= P(\text{conservative}) + P(\text{attended college}) - P(\text{conservative and attended college})$$
$$= \dfrac{13+20}{100} + \dfrac{10+15+20}{100} - \dfrac{20}{100}$$
$$= \dfrac{33}{100} + \dfrac{45}{100} - \dfrac{20}{100}$$
$$= \dfrac{58}{100}$$
$$= \dfrac{29}{50}$$

64. $P(\text{liberal or only high school education})$

$= P(\text{liberal}) + P(\text{only high school education}) - P(\text{liberal and only high school education})$

$= \dfrac{7+10}{100} + \dfrac{7+35+13}{100} - \dfrac{7}{100}$

$= \dfrac{17}{100} + \dfrac{55}{100} - \dfrac{7}{100}$

$= \dfrac{65}{100}$

$= \dfrac{13}{20}$

65. $P(\text{conservative}|\text{only high school education}) = \dfrac{13}{7+35+13} = \dfrac{13}{55}$

66. $P(\text{moderate}|\text{college attendance}) = \dfrac{15}{10+15+20} = \dfrac{15}{45} = \dfrac{1}{3}$

67. $P(\text{only high school education}|\text{conservative}) = \dfrac{13}{13+20} = \dfrac{13}{33}$

68. $P(\text{attended college}|\text{moderate}) = \dfrac{15}{35+15} = \dfrac{15}{50} = \dfrac{3}{10}$

69. $P(\text{two liberals}) = P(\text{liberal}) \cdot P(\text{liberal}|\text{first person selected is liberal}) = \dfrac{17}{100} \cdot \dfrac{16}{99} = \dfrac{68}{2475}$

70. $P(\text{two conservatives}) = P(\text{conservative}) \cdot P(\text{conservative}|\text{first person selected is conservative}) = \dfrac{33}{100} \cdot \dfrac{32}{99} = \dfrac{8}{75}$

71. $P(\text{moderate, then conservative}) = P(\text{moderate}) \cdot P(\text{conservative}|\text{first person selected is moderate}) = \dfrac{50}{100} \cdot \dfrac{33}{99} = \dfrac{1}{6}$

72. $P(\text{moderate, then liberal}) = P(\text{moderate}) \cdot P(\text{liberal}|\text{first person selected is moderate}) = \dfrac{50}{100} \cdot \dfrac{17}{99} = \dfrac{17}{198}$

73-80. Answers will vary.

81. $P(\text{no one hospitalized}) = [P(\text{not hospitalized})]^5 = (0.9)(0.9)(0.9)(0.9)(0.9) = (0.9)^5 \approx 0.59049 \approx 59.0\%$

82. $P(\text{2 on 1st, 3rd, and 4th rolls only}) = P(2) \cdot P(\text{not 2}) \cdot P(2) \cdot P(2) \cdot P(\text{not 2}) = \dfrac{1}{6} \cdot \dfrac{5}{6} \cdot \dfrac{1}{6} \cdot \dfrac{1}{6} \cdot \dfrac{5}{6} = \dfrac{25}{7776}$

83. a. Answers will vary.

   b. $P(\text{three different birthdays}) = \dfrac{365}{365} \cdot \dfrac{364}{365} \cdot \dfrac{363}{365} \approx 0.992$

   c. $P(\text{at least two have same birthday}) = 1 - P(\text{three different birthdays}) = 1 - 0.992 = 0.008$

d. $P(20$ different birthdays$)$

$$= \frac{365 \cdot 364 \cdot 363 \cdot 362 \cdot 361 \cdot 360 \cdot 359 \cdot 358 \cdot 357 \cdot 356 \cdot 355 \cdot 354 \cdot 353 \cdot 352 \cdot 351 \cdot 350 \cdot 349 \cdot 348 \cdot 347 \cdot 346}{365 \cdot 365 \cdot 365 \cdot 365 \cdot 365 \cdot 365 \cdot 365 \cdot 365 \cdot 365 \cdot 365 \cdot 365 \cdot 365 \cdot 365 \cdot 365 \cdot 365 \cdot 365 \cdot 365 \cdot 365 \cdot 365 \cdot 365} \approx 0.589$$

$P($at least two have same birthday$) = 1 - P(20$ different birthdays$) = 1 - 0.589 = 0.411$

e. 23 people (determine by trial-and-error using method shown in part d)

84. There are 5 odd numbered cards and therefore there are $_5C_2 = 10$ ways to get two odd cards.

There are 4 even numbered cards and therefore there are $_4C_2 = 6$ ways to get two even cards.

Note that the sum of two odds is an even number and that the sum of two evens is also an even number.
Since selecting one even card and one odd card would result in an odd sum, we only need to consider the 16 possible outcomes calculated above.

$$P(\text{both odd} | \text{sum even}) = \frac{\text{number of outcomes with both odd and even sum}}{\text{number of outcomes where the sum is even}} = \frac{10}{16} = \frac{5}{8}$$

Check Points 11.8

1. $E = 1 \cdot \frac{1}{4} + 2 \cdot \frac{1}{4} + 3 \cdot \frac{1}{4} + 4 \cdot \frac{1}{4} = \frac{1+2+3+4}{4} = \frac{10}{4} = 2.5$

2. $E = 0 \cdot \frac{1}{16} + 1 \cdot \frac{4}{16} + 2 \cdot \frac{6}{16} + 3 \cdot \frac{4}{16} + 4 \cdot \frac{1}{16} = \frac{0+4+12+12+4}{16} = \frac{32}{16} = 2$

3. a. $E = \$0(0.01) + \$2000(0.15) + \$4000(0.08) + \$6000(0.05) + \$8000(0.01) + \$10{,}000(0.70) = \$8000$

This means that in the long run, the average cost of a claim is expected to be $8000

b. An average premium charge of $8000 would cause the company to neither lose nor gain money.

4. $E = (1)\left(\frac{1}{5}\right) + \left(-\frac{1}{4}\right)\left(\frac{4}{5}\right) = \frac{1}{5} + \left(-\frac{1}{5}\right) = 0$

Since the expected value is 0, there is nothing to gain or lose on average by guessing.

5. Values of gain or loss:
Grand Prize: $\$1000 - \$2 = \$998$, Consolation Prize: $\$50 - \$2 = \$48$, Nothing: $\$0 - \$2 = -\$2$

$$E = (-\$2)\left(\frac{997}{1000}\right) + (\$48)\left(\frac{2}{1000}\right) + (\$998)\left(\frac{1}{1000}\right) = \frac{-\$1994 + \$96 + \$998}{1000} = -\frac{\$900}{1000} = -\$0.90$$

The expected value for one ticket is $-\$0.90$. This means that in the long run a player can expect to lose $0.90 for each ticket bought. Buying five tickets will make your likelihood of winning five times greater, however there is no advantage to this strategy because the *cost* of five tickets is also five times greater than one ticket.

6. $E = (\$2.20)\left(\frac{20}{80}\right) + (-\$1.00)\left(\frac{60}{80}\right) = \frac{\$44 - \$60}{80} = \frac{-\$16}{80} = -\$0.20$

This means that in the long run a player can expect to lose an average of $0.20 for each $1 bet.

Exercise Set 11.8

1. $E = 1 \cdot \frac{1}{2} + 2 \cdot \frac{1}{4} + 3 \cdot \frac{1}{4} = 1.75$

2. $E = 1 \cdot \frac{1}{8} + 2 \cdot \frac{1}{8} + 3 \cdot \frac{1}{2} + 4 \cdot \frac{1}{4} = 2.875$

3. **a.** $E = \$0(0.65)+\$50,000(0.20) + \$100,000(0.10) + \$150,000(0.03) + \$200,000(0.01) + \$250,000(0.01) = \$29,000$

   b. $\$29,000$

   c. $\$29,050$

4. **a.** $E = \$0(0.70) + \$20,000(0.20) + \$40,000(0.06) + \$60,000(0.02) + \$80,000(0.01) + \$100,000(0.01) = \$9400$

   b. $\$9400$

   c. $\$9450$

5. $E = -\$10,000(0.9) + \$90,000(0.1) = \$0$. This means on the average there will be no gain or loss.

6. $E = -\$1500\left(\dfrac{4}{5}\right) + \$38,500\left(\dfrac{1}{5}\right) = \$6500$. This means an expected gain on the average.

7. $E = -\$99,999\left(\dfrac{27}{10,000,000}\right) + \$1\left(\dfrac{9,999,973}{10,000,000}\right) = \$0.73$

8. $E = -\$9,900(0.002) + \$100(0.998) = \$80$

9. Probabilities after eliminating one possible answer: Guess Correctly: $\dfrac{1}{4}$, Guess Incorrectly: $\dfrac{3}{4}$

   $E = (1)\left(\dfrac{1}{4}\right) + \left(-\dfrac{1}{4}\right)\left(\dfrac{3}{4}\right) = \dfrac{1}{4} + \left(-\dfrac{3}{16}\right) = \dfrac{1}{16}$ expected points on a guess if one answer is eliminated.
   Yes, it is advantageous to guess after eliminating one possible answer.

10. Probabilities after eliminating two possible answers: Guess Correctly: $\dfrac{1}{3}$, Guess Incorrectly: $\dfrac{2}{3}$

    $E = (1)\left(\dfrac{1}{3}\right) + \left(-\dfrac{1}{4}\right)\left(\dfrac{2}{3}\right) = \dfrac{1}{3} + \left(-\dfrac{1}{6}\right) = \dfrac{1}{6}$ expected points on a guess if two answers are eliminated.
    Yes, it is advantageous to guess after eliminating two possible answers.

11. First mall: $E = \$300,000\left(\dfrac{1}{2}\right) - \$100,000\left(\dfrac{1}{2}\right) = \$100,000$

    Second mall: $E = \$200,000\left(\dfrac{3}{4}\right) - \$60,000\left(\dfrac{1}{4}\right) = \$135,000$

    Choose the second mall.

12. Site A: $E = \$80(0.2) - \$10(0.8) = \$8$ million
    Site B: $E = \$120(0.1) - \$18(0.9) = -\$4.2$ million
    Site A has the larger expected profit.
    $\$8$ million $- (-\$4.2$ million$) = \$12.2$ million
    Site A's profit exceeds Site B's by $\$12.2$ million.

13. **a.** $E = \$700,000(0.2) + \$0(0.8) = \$140,000$

    b. No

14. $E = \$80\left(\dfrac{99}{100}\right) - \$270\left(\dfrac{1}{100}\right) = \$76.50$

15. $E = \$4\left(\dfrac{1}{6}\right) - \$1\left(\dfrac{5}{6}\right) = -\$\dfrac{1}{6} \approx -\$0.17$. This means an expected loss of approximately $0.17 per game.

16. $E = -\$.25\left(\dfrac{1}{6}\right) + \$.75\left(\dfrac{1}{6}\right) + \$1.75\left(\dfrac{1}{6}\right) - \$1.25\left(\dfrac{3}{6}\right) = -\$0.25$. This means an expected loss of $0.25 per game.

17. $E = \$1\left(\dfrac{18}{38}\right) - \$1\left(\dfrac{20}{38}\right) \approx -\$0.053$. This means an expected loss of approximately $0.053 per $1.00 bet.

18. $E = \$4\left(\dfrac{3}{10}\right) + \$2\left(\dfrac{1}{10}\right) - \$2\left(\dfrac{4}{10}\right) - \$3\left(\dfrac{2}{10}\right) = \$0$. A player should expect to break even.

19. $E = \$499\left(\dfrac{1}{1000}\right) - \$1\left(\dfrac{999}{1000}\right) = -\$0.50$. This means an expected loss of $0.50 per $1.00 bet.

20-25. Answers will vary.

26. First determine the probabilities.

Total number of possible combinations $= {}_{35}C_5 = \dfrac{35!}{30!5!} = 324,632$

Number of ways to select all 5 $= {}_5C_5 = 1$

Number of ways to select 4 of the 5 winning numbers and 1 of the 30 losing numbers $= {}_5C_4 \times {}_{30}C_1 = 5 \times 30 = 150$

Number of ways to select 3 of the 5 winning numbers and 2 of the 30 losing numbers $= {}_5C_3 \times {}_{30}C_2 = 10 \times 435 = 4350$

$P(\text{all } 5) = \dfrac{1}{324,632}$; $P(4 \text{ of } 5) = \dfrac{150}{324,632}$; $P(3 \text{ of } 5) = \dfrac{4350}{324,632}$; $P(\text{losing}) = \dfrac{324,632 - 1 - 150 - 4350}{324,632} = \dfrac{320,131}{324,632}$

$E = \$49,999\left(\dfrac{1}{324,632}\right) + \$499\left(\dfrac{150}{324,632}\right) + \$4\left(\dfrac{4350}{324,632}\right) - \$1\left(\dfrac{320,131}{324,632}\right) \approx -\$0.55$

This means an expected loss of $0.55 per $1.00 ticket.

27. Let $x =$ the charge for the policy. Note, the expected value, $E = \$60$.

$\$60 = (x - \$200,000)(0.0005) + (x)(0.9995)$

$\$60 = 0.0005x - \$100 + 0.9995x$

$\$160 = x$

The insurance company should charge $160 for the policy.

Chapter 11 Review Exercises

1. Use the Fundamental Counting Principle with two groups of items. $20 \cdot 40 = 800$

2. Use the Fundamental Counting Principle with two groups of items. $4 \cdot 5 = 20$

3. Use the Fundamental Counting Principle with two groups of items. $100 \cdot 99 = 9900$

4. Use the Fundamental Counting Principle with three groups of items. $5 \cdot 5 \cdot 5 = 125$

5. Use the Fundamental Counting Principle with five groups of items. $3 \cdot 3 \cdot 3 \cdot 3 \cdot 3 = 243$

6. Use the Fundamental Counting Principle with four groups of items. $5 \cdot 2 \cdot 2 \cdot 3 = 60$

7. Use the Fundamental Counting Principle with six groups of items. $6 \cdot 5 \cdot 4 \cdot 3 \cdot 2 \cdot 1 = 720$

8. Use the Fundamental Counting Principle with five groups of items. $5 \cdot 4 \cdot 3 \cdot 2 \cdot 1 = 120$

9. Use the Fundamental Counting Principle with seven groups of items. $1 \cdot 5 \cdot 4 \cdot 3 \cdot 2 \cdot 1 \cdot 1 = 120$

10. $\dfrac{16!}{14!} = \dfrac{16 \cdot 15 \cdot 14!}{14!} = 240$

11. $\dfrac{800!}{799!} = \dfrac{800 \cdot 799!}{799!} = 800$

12. $5! - 3! = 5 \cdot 4 \cdot 3 \cdot 2 \cdot 1 - 3 \cdot 2 \cdot 1 = 120 - 6 = 114$

13. $\dfrac{11!}{(11-3)!} = \dfrac{11!}{8!} = \dfrac{11 \cdot 10 \cdot 9 \cdot 8!}{8!} = 990$

14. $_{10}P_6 = \dfrac{10!}{(10-6)!} = \dfrac{10!}{4!} = \dfrac{10 \cdot 9 \cdot 8 \cdot 7 \cdot 6 \cdot 5 \cdot 4!}{4!} = 151,200$

15. $_{100}P_2 = \dfrac{100!}{(100-2)!} = \dfrac{100!}{98!} = \dfrac{100 \cdot 99 \cdot 98!}{98!} = 9900$

16. $_{15}P_4 = \dfrac{15!}{(15-4)!} = \dfrac{15!}{11!} = \dfrac{15 \cdot 14 \cdot 13 \cdot 12 \cdot 11!}{11!} = 32,760$

17. $_{20}P_5 = \dfrac{20!}{(20-5)!} = \dfrac{20!}{15!} = \dfrac{20 \cdot 19 \cdot 18 \cdot 17 \cdot 16 \cdot 15!}{15!} = 1,860,480$

18. $\dfrac{n!}{p!q!} = \dfrac{7!}{3!2!} = \dfrac{7 \cdot 6 \cdot 5 \cdot 4 \cdot 3!}{3! \cdot 2 \cdot 1} = 420$

19. $\dfrac{n!}{p!q!} = \dfrac{6!}{3!2!} = \dfrac{6 \cdot 5 \cdot 4 \cdot 3!}{3! \cdot 2 \cdot 1} = 60$

20. Order does not matter. This problem involves combinations.

21. Order matters. This problem involves permutations.

22. Order does not matter. This problem involves combinations.

23. $_{11}C_7 = \dfrac{11!}{(11-7)!7!} = \dfrac{11!}{4!7!} = \dfrac{11 \cdot 10 \cdot 9 \cdot 8 \cdot 7!}{4 \cdot 3 \cdot 2 \cdot 1 \cdot 7!} = 330$

24. $_{14}C_5 = \dfrac{14!}{(14-5)!5!} = \dfrac{14!}{9!5!} = \dfrac{14 \cdot 13 \cdot 12 \cdot 11 \cdot 10 \cdot 9!}{9! \cdot 5 \cdot 4 \cdot 3 \cdot 2 \cdot 1} = 2002$

25. $_{10}C_4 = \dfrac{10!}{(10-4)!4!} = \dfrac{10!}{6!4!} = \dfrac{10 \cdot 9 \cdot 8 \cdot 7 \cdot 6!}{6! \cdot 4 \cdot 3 \cdot 2 \cdot 1} = 210$

26. $_{13}C_5 = \dfrac{13!}{(13-5)!5!} = \dfrac{13!}{8!5!} = \dfrac{13 \cdot 12 \cdot 11 \cdot 10 \cdot 9 \cdot 8!}{8! \cdot 5 \cdot 4 \cdot 3 \cdot 2 \cdot 1} = 1287$

27. $20 C_3 = \dfrac{20!}{(20-3)!3!} = \dfrac{20!}{17!3!} = \dfrac{20 \cdot 19 \cdot 18 \cdot 17!}{17!3 \cdot 2 \cdot 1} = 1140$

28. Choose the Republicans: $12 C_5 = \dfrac{12!}{(12-5)!5!} = \dfrac{12!}{7!5!} = \dfrac{12 \cdot 11 \cdot 10 \cdot 9 \cdot 8 \cdot 7!}{7!5 \cdot 4 \cdot 3 \cdot 2 \cdot 1} = 792$

   Choose the Democrats: $8 C_4 = \dfrac{8!}{(8-4)!4!} = \dfrac{8!}{4!4!} = \dfrac{8 \cdot 7 \cdot 6 \cdot 5 \cdot 4!}{4!4 \cdot 3 \cdot 2 \cdot 1} = 70$

   Multiply the choices: $792 \cdot 70 = 55,440$

29. $P(6) = \dfrac{\text{number of ways a 6 can occur}}{\text{total number of possible outcomes}} = \dfrac{1}{6}$

30. $P(\text{less than 5}) = \dfrac{\text{number of ways a number less than 5 can occur}}{\text{total number of possible outcomes}} = \dfrac{4}{6} = \dfrac{2}{3}$

31. $P(\text{less than 7}) = \dfrac{\text{number of ways a number less than 7 can occur}}{\text{total number of possible outcomes}} = \dfrac{6}{6} = 1$

32. $P(\text{greater than 6}) = \dfrac{\text{number of ways a number greater than 6 can occur}}{\text{total number of possible outcomes}} = \dfrac{0}{6} = 0$

33. $P(5) = \dfrac{\text{number of ways a 5 can occur}}{\text{total number of possible outcomes}} = \dfrac{4}{52} = \dfrac{1}{13}$

34. $P(\text{picture card}) = \dfrac{\text{number of ways a picture card can occur}}{\text{total number of possible outcomes}} = \dfrac{12}{52} = \dfrac{3}{13}$

35. $P(\text{greater than 4 and less than 8}) = \dfrac{\text{number of ways a card greater than 4 and less than 8 can occur}}{\text{total number of possible outcomes}} = \dfrac{12}{52} = \dfrac{3}{13}$

36. $P(\text{4 of diamonds}) = \dfrac{\text{number of ways a 4 of diamonds can occur}}{\text{total number of possible outcomes}} = \dfrac{1}{52}$

37. $P(\text{red ace}) = \dfrac{\text{number of ways a red ace can occur}}{\text{total number of possible outcomes}} = \dfrac{2}{52} = \dfrac{1}{26}$

38. $P(\text{chocolate}) = \dfrac{\text{number of ways a chocolate can occur}}{\text{total number of possible outcomes}} = \dfrac{15}{30} = \dfrac{1}{2}$

39. $P(\text{caramel}) = \dfrac{\text{number of ways a caramel can occur}}{\text{total number of possible outcomes}} = \dfrac{10}{30} = \dfrac{1}{3}$

40. $P(\text{peppermint}) = \dfrac{\text{number of ways a peppermint can occur}}{\text{total number of possible outcomes}} = \dfrac{5}{30} = \dfrac{1}{6}$

41. a. $P(\text{carrier without the disease}) = \dfrac{\text{number of ways to be a carrier without the disease}}{\text{total number of possible outcomes}} = \dfrac{2}{4} = \dfrac{1}{2}$

b. $P(\text{disease}) = \dfrac{\text{number of ways to have the disease}}{\text{total number of possible outcomes}} = \dfrac{0}{4} = 0$

42. $P(\text{Cuban American}) = \dfrac{1.2}{20.6 + 1.2 + 3.4 + 3.0 + 6.8} = \dfrac{1.2}{35} = \dfrac{12}{350} = \dfrac{6}{175} \approx 0.03$

43. $P(\text{Mexican American}) = \dfrac{20.6}{20.6 + 1.2 + 3.4 + 3.0 + 6.8} = \dfrac{20.6}{35} = \dfrac{206}{350} = \dfrac{103}{175} \approx 0.59$

44. number of ways to visit in order D, B, A, C = 1
total number of possible permutations = $4 \cdot 3 \cdot 2 \cdot 1 = 24$

$P(\text{D, B, A, C}) = \dfrac{1}{24}$

45. number of permutations with C last = $5 \cdot 4 \cdot 3 \cdot 2 \cdot 1 \cdot 1 = 120$
total number of possible permutations = $6 \cdot 5 \cdot 4 \cdot 3 \cdot 2 \cdot 1 = 720$

$P(\text{C last}) = \dfrac{120}{720} = \dfrac{1}{6}$

46. number of permutations with B first and A last = $1 \cdot 4 \cdot 3 \cdot 2 \cdot 1 \cdot 1 = 24$
total number of possible permutations = $6 \cdot 5 \cdot 4 \cdot 3 \cdot 2 \cdot 1 = 720$

$P(\text{B first and A last}) = \dfrac{24}{720} = \dfrac{1}{30}$

47. number of permutations in order F, E, A, D, C, B = 1
total number of possible permutations = $6 \cdot 5 \cdot 4 \cdot 3 \cdot 2 \cdot 1 = 720$

$P(\text{F, E, A, D, C, B}) = \dfrac{1}{720}$

48. number of permutations with A or C first = $2 \cdot 5 \cdot 4 \cdot 3 \cdot 2 \cdot 1 = 240$
total number of possible permutations = $6 \cdot 5 \cdot 4 \cdot 3 \cdot 2 \cdot 1 = 720$

$P(\text{A or C first}) = \dfrac{240}{720} = \dfrac{1}{3}$

49. **a.** number of ways to win = 1
total number of possible combinations:

$_{20}C_5 = \dfrac{20!}{(20-5)!5!} = \dfrac{20!}{15!5!} = \dfrac{20 \cdot 19 \cdot 18 \cdot 17 \cdot 16 \cdot 15!}{15! \cdot 5 \cdot 4 \cdot 3 \cdot 2 \cdot 1} = 15{,}504$

$P(\text{winning with one ticket}) = \dfrac{1}{15{,}504} \approx 0.0000645$

b. number of ways to win = 100

$P(\text{winning with 100 different tickets}) = \dfrac{100}{15{,}504} \approx 0.00645$

50. a. number of ways to select 4 Democrats: $_6C_4 = \dfrac{6!}{(6-4)!4!} = \dfrac{6!}{2!4!} = \dfrac{6\cdot 5\cdot 4!}{2\cdot 1\cdot 4!} = 15$

total number of possible combinations: $_{10}C_4 = \dfrac{10!}{(10-4)!4!} = \dfrac{10!}{6!4!} = \dfrac{10\cdot 9\cdot 8\cdot 7\cdot 6!}{6!4\cdot 3\cdot 2\cdot 1} = 210$

$P(\text{all Democrats}) = \dfrac{15}{210} = \dfrac{1}{14}$

b. number of ways to select 2 Democrats: $_6C_2 = \dfrac{6!}{(6-2)!2!} = \dfrac{6!}{4!2!} = \dfrac{6\cdot 5\cdot 4!}{4!2\cdot 1} = 15$

number of ways to select 2 Republicans: $_4C_2 = \dfrac{4!}{(4-2)!2!} = \dfrac{4!}{2!2!} = \dfrac{4\cdot 3\cdot 2!}{2!2\cdot 1} = 6$

number of ways to select 2 Democrats and 2 Republicans $= 15\cdot 6 = 90$

$P(\text{2 Democrats and 2 Republicans}) = \dfrac{90}{210} = \dfrac{3}{7}$

51. number of ways to get 2 picture cards: $_6C_2 = \dfrac{6!}{(6-2)!2!} = \dfrac{6!}{4!2!} = \dfrac{6\cdot 5\cdot 4!}{4!2\cdot 1} = 15$

number of ways to get one non-picture card $= 20$
number of ways to get 2 picture cards and one non-picture card $= 15\cdot 20 = 300$

total number of possible combinations: $_{26}C_3 = \dfrac{26!}{(26-3)!3!} = \dfrac{26!}{23!3!} = \dfrac{26\cdot 25\cdot 24\cdot 23!}{23!3\cdot 2\cdot 1} = 2600$

$P(\text{2 picture cards}) = \dfrac{300}{2600} = \dfrac{3}{26}$

52. $P(\text{not a 5}) = 1 - P(5) = 1 - \dfrac{1}{6} = \dfrac{5}{6}$

53. $P(\text{not less than 4}) = 1 - P(\text{less than 4}) = 1 - \dfrac{3}{6} = 1 - \dfrac{1}{2} = \dfrac{1}{2}$

54. $P(\text{3 or 5}) = P(3) + P(5) = \dfrac{1}{6} + \dfrac{1}{6} = \dfrac{2}{6} = \dfrac{1}{3}$

55. $P(\text{less than 3 or greater than 4}) = P(\text{less than 3}) + P(\text{greater than 4}) = \dfrac{2}{6} + \dfrac{2}{6} = \dfrac{1}{3} + \dfrac{1}{3} = \dfrac{2}{3}$

56. $P(\text{less than 5 or greater than 2}) = P(\text{less than 5}) + P(\text{greater than 2}) - P(\text{less than 5 and greater than 2})$

$$= \dfrac{4}{6} + \dfrac{4}{6} - \dfrac{2}{6} = 1$$

57. $P(\text{not a picture card}) = 1 - P(\text{picture card}) = 1 - \dfrac{12}{52} = 1 - \dfrac{3}{13} = \dfrac{10}{13}$

58. $P(\text{not a diamond}) = 1 - P(\text{diamond}) = 1 - \dfrac{13}{52} = 1 - \dfrac{1}{4} = \dfrac{3}{4}$

59. $P(\text{ace or king}) = P(\text{ace}) + P(\text{king}) = \dfrac{4}{52} + \dfrac{4}{52} = \dfrac{1}{13} + \dfrac{1}{13} = \dfrac{2}{13}$

60. $P(\text{black 6 or red 7}) = P(\text{black 6}) + P(\text{red 7}) = \dfrac{2}{52} + \dfrac{2}{52} = \dfrac{1}{26} + \dfrac{1}{26} = \dfrac{2}{26} = \dfrac{1}{13}$

61. $P(\text{queen or red card}) = P(\text{queen}) + P(\text{red card}) - P(\text{red queen}) = \dfrac{4}{52} + \dfrac{26}{52} - \dfrac{2}{52} = \dfrac{28}{52} = \dfrac{7}{13}$

62. $P(\text{club or picture card}) = P(\text{club}) + P(\text{picture card}) - P(\text{club and picture card}) = \dfrac{13}{52} + \dfrac{12}{52} - \dfrac{3}{52} = \dfrac{22}{52} = \dfrac{11}{26}$

63. $P(\text{not 4}) = 1 - P(4) = 1 - \dfrac{1}{6} = \dfrac{5}{6}$

64. $P(\text{not yellow}) = 1 - P(\text{yellow}) = 1 - \dfrac{1}{6} = \dfrac{5}{6}$

65. $P(\text{not red}) = 1 - P(\text{red}) = 1 - \dfrac{3}{6} = 1 - \dfrac{1}{2} = \dfrac{1}{2}$

66. $P(\text{red or yellow}) = P(\text{red}) + P(\text{yellow}) = \dfrac{3}{6} + \dfrac{1}{6} = \dfrac{4}{6} = \dfrac{2}{3}$

67. $P(\text{red or even}) = P(\text{red}) + P(\text{even}) - P(\text{red and even}) = \dfrac{3}{6} + \dfrac{3}{6} - \dfrac{0}{6} = 1$

68. $P(\text{red or greater than 3}) = P(\text{red}) + P(\text{greater than 3}) - P(\text{red and greater than 3}) = \dfrac{3}{6} + \dfrac{3}{6} - \dfrac{1}{6} = \dfrac{5}{6}$

69. $P(\text{African American or male}) = P(\text{African American}) + P(\text{male}) - P(\text{African American male})$
$$= \dfrac{50 + 20}{200} + \dfrac{50 + 90}{200} - \dfrac{50}{200} = \dfrac{160}{200} = \dfrac{4}{5}$$

70. $P(\text{female or white}) = P(\text{female}) + P(\text{white}) - P(\text{white female}) = \dfrac{20 + 40}{200} + \dfrac{90 + 40}{200} - \dfrac{40}{200} = \dfrac{150}{200} = \dfrac{3}{4}$

71. $P(\text{public college}) = \dfrac{252}{350} = \dfrac{18}{25}$

72. $P(\text{not from high-income family}) = 1 - P(\text{from high-income family}) = 1 - \dfrac{50}{350} = \dfrac{350}{350} - \dfrac{50}{350} = \dfrac{300}{350} = \dfrac{6}{7}$

73. $P(\text{from middle-income family or high-income family}) = \dfrac{160 + 50}{350} = \dfrac{210}{350} = \dfrac{3}{5}$

74. $P(\text{attended private college or is from a high income family})$
$= P(\text{private college}) + P(\text{high income family}) - P(\text{attended private college and is from a high income family})$
$= \dfrac{98}{350} + \dfrac{50}{350} - \dfrac{28}{350} = \dfrac{120}{350} = \dfrac{12}{35}$

75. number of favorable outcomes = 4, number of unfavorable outcomes = 48
Odds in favor of getting a queen are 4:48, or 1:12. Odds against getting a queen are 12:1.

76. number of favorable outcomes = 20, number of unfavorable outcomes = 1980
Odds against winning are 1980: 20, or 99:1.

77. $P(\text{win}) = \dfrac{3}{3+1} = \dfrac{3}{4}$

78. $P(\text{yellow then red}) = P(\text{yellow}) \cdot P(\text{red}) = \dfrac{2}{6} \cdot \dfrac{4}{6} = \dfrac{1}{3} \cdot \dfrac{2}{3} = \dfrac{2}{9}$

79. $P(1 \text{ then } 3) = P(1) \cdot P(3) = \dfrac{1}{6} \cdot \dfrac{1}{6} = \dfrac{1}{36}$

80. $P(\text{yellow both times}) = P(\text{yellow}) \cdot P(\text{yellow}) = \dfrac{2}{6} \cdot \dfrac{2}{6} = \dfrac{1}{3} \cdot \dfrac{1}{3} = \dfrac{1}{9}$

81. $P(\text{yellow then 4 then odd}) = P(\text{yellow}) \cdot P(4) \cdot P(\text{odd}) = \dfrac{2}{6} \cdot \dfrac{1}{6} \cdot \dfrac{3}{6} = \dfrac{1}{3} \cdot \dfrac{1}{6} \cdot \dfrac{1}{2} = \dfrac{1}{36}$

82. $P(\text{red every time}) = P(\text{red}) \cdot P(\text{red}) \cdot P(\text{red}) = \dfrac{4}{6} \cdot \dfrac{4}{6} \cdot \dfrac{4}{6} = \dfrac{2}{3} \cdot \dfrac{2}{3} \cdot \dfrac{2}{3} = \dfrac{8}{27}$

83. $P(\text{five boys in a row}) = P(\text{boy}) \cdot P(\text{boy}) \cdot P(\text{boy}) \cdot P(\text{boy}) \cdot P(\text{boy}) = \dfrac{1}{2} \cdot \dfrac{1}{2} \cdot \dfrac{1}{2} \cdot \dfrac{1}{2} \cdot \dfrac{1}{2} = \dfrac{1}{2^5} = \dfrac{1}{32}$

84. a. $P(\text{flood two years in a row}) = P(\text{flood}) \cdot P(\text{flood}) = (0.2)(0.2) = 0.04$

b. $P(\text{flood for three consecutive years}) = P(\text{flood}) \cdot P(\text{flood}) \cdot P(\text{flood}) = (0.2)(0.2)(0.2) = 0.008$

c. $P(\text{no flooding for four consecutive years}) = [1 - P(\text{flood})]^4 = (1 - 0.2)^4 = (0.8)^4 = 0.4096$

d. $P(\text{flood at least once in next four years}) = 1 - P(\text{no flooding for four consecutive years})$
$= 1 - 0.4096 = 0.5904$

85. $P(\text{music major then psychology major}) = P(\text{music major}) \cdot P\left(\begin{array}{c}\text{psychology major given} \\ \text{first was music major}\end{array}\right) = \dfrac{2}{9} \cdot \dfrac{4}{8} = \dfrac{2}{9} \cdot \dfrac{1}{2} = \dfrac{1}{9}$

86. $P(\text{two business majors}) = P(\text{bus. major}) \cdot P(\text{bus. major given first was bus. major}) = \dfrac{3}{9} \cdot \dfrac{2}{8} = \dfrac{1}{3} \cdot \dfrac{1}{4} = \dfrac{1}{12}$

87. $P(\text{solid then two cherry})$
$= P(\text{solid}) \cdot P\left(\begin{array}{c}\text{cherry given} \\ \text{first was solid}\end{array}\right) \cdot P\left(\begin{array}{c}\text{cherry given first was solid} \\ \text{and second was cherry}\end{array}\right) = \dfrac{30}{50} \cdot \dfrac{5}{49} \cdot \dfrac{4}{48} = \dfrac{3}{5} \cdot \dfrac{5}{49} \cdot \dfrac{1}{12} = \dfrac{1}{196}$

88. $P(5 | \text{odd}) = \dfrac{1}{3}$

89. $P(\text{vowel} | \text{precedes the letter k}) = \dfrac{3}{10}$

90. a. $P(\text{odd}|\text{red}) = \dfrac{2}{4} = \dfrac{1}{2}$

    b. $P(\text{yellow}|\text{at least 3}) = \dfrac{2}{7}$

91. $P(\text{does not have TB}) = \dfrac{11+124}{9+1+11+124} = \dfrac{135}{145} = \dfrac{27}{29}$

92. $P(\text{tests positive}) = \dfrac{9+11}{9+1+11+124} = \dfrac{20}{145} = \dfrac{4}{29}$

93. $P(\text{does not have TB or tests positive})$

    $= P(\text{does not have TB}) + P(\text{tests positive}) - P(\text{does not have TB and tests positive})$

    $= \dfrac{11+124}{145} + \dfrac{9+11}{145} - \dfrac{11}{145}$

    $= \dfrac{144}{145}$

94. $P(\text{does not have TB}|\text{positive test}) = \dfrac{11}{9+11} = \dfrac{11}{20}$

95. $P(\text{tests positive}|\text{does not have TB}) = \dfrac{11}{11+124} = \dfrac{11}{135}$

96. $P(\text{has TB}|\text{negative Test}) = \dfrac{1}{1+124} = \dfrac{1}{125}$

97. $P(\text{two people with TB}) = P(\text{TB}) \cdot P(\text{TB}|\text{first person selected has TB}) = \dfrac{10}{145} \cdot \dfrac{9}{144} = \dfrac{1}{232}$

98. $P(\text{two people with positive tests}) = P(\text{positive test}) \cdot P(\text{positive test}|\text{first person has positive test}) = \dfrac{20}{145} \cdot \dfrac{19}{144} = \dfrac{19}{1044}$

99. $E = 1 \cdot \dfrac{1}{4} + 2 \cdot \dfrac{1}{8} + 3 \cdot \dfrac{1}{8} + 4 \cdot \dfrac{1}{4} + 5 \cdot \dfrac{1}{4} = 3.125$

100. a. $E = \$0(0.9999995) + (-\$1,000,000)(0.0000005) = -\$.50$
    The insurance company spends an average of $0.50 per person insured.

    b. charge $9.50 – (–$0.50) = $10.00

101. $E = \$27,000\left(\dfrac{1}{4}\right) + (-\$3000)\left(\dfrac{3}{4}\right) = \$4500.$ The expected gain is $4500 per bid.

102. $E = \$1\left(\dfrac{2}{4}\right) + \$1\left(\dfrac{1}{4}\right) + (-\$4)\left(\dfrac{1}{4}\right) = -\$0.25.$ The expected loss is $0.25 per game.

Chapter 11 Test

1. Use the Fundamental Counting Principle with five groups of items. $10 \cdot 2 \cdot 2 \cdot 2 \cdot 3 = 240$

2. Use the Fundamental Counting Principle with four groups of items. $4 \cdot 3 \cdot 2 \cdot 1 = 24$

3. Use the Fundamental Counting Principle with seven groups of items. $1 \cdot 6 \cdot 5 \cdot 4 \cdot 3 \cdot 2 \cdot 1 = 720$

4. $_{11}P_3 = \dfrac{11!}{(11-3)!} = \dfrac{11!}{8!} = \dfrac{11 \cdot 10 \cdot 9 \cdot 8!}{8!} = 990$

5. $_{10}C_4 = \dfrac{10!}{(10-4)!4!} = \dfrac{10!}{6!4!} = \dfrac{10 \cdot 9 \cdot 8 \cdot 7 \cdot 6!}{6!4 \cdot 3 \cdot 2 \cdot 1} = 210$

6. $\dfrac{n!}{p!q!} = \dfrac{7!}{3!2!} = \dfrac{7 \cdot 6 \cdot 5 \cdot 4 \cdot 3!}{3! \cdot 2 \cdot 1} = 420$

7. $P(\text{freshman}) = \dfrac{12}{50} = \dfrac{6}{25}$

8. $P(\text{not a sophomore}) = 1 - P(\text{sophomore}) = 1 - \dfrac{16}{50} = 1 - \dfrac{8}{25} = \dfrac{17}{25}$

9. $P(\text{junior or senior}) = P(\text{junior}) + P(\text{senior}) = \dfrac{20}{50} + \dfrac{2}{50} = \dfrac{22}{50} = \dfrac{11}{25}$

10. $P(\text{greater than 4 and less than 10}) = \dfrac{20}{52} = \dfrac{5}{13}$

11. $P(C \text{ first, } A \text{ next-to-last, } E \text{ last})$

    $= P(C) \cdot P(A \text{ given } C \text{ was first}) \cdot P(E \text{ given } C \text{ was first and } A \text{ was next-to-last}) = \dfrac{1}{7} \cdot \dfrac{1}{6} \cdot \dfrac{1}{5} = \dfrac{1}{210}$

12. total number of possible combinations: $_{15}C_6 = \dfrac{15!}{(15-6)!6!} = \dfrac{15!}{9!6!} = \dfrac{15 \cdot 14 \cdot 13 \cdot 12 \cdot 11 \cdot 10 \cdot 9!}{9!6 \cdot 5 \cdot 4 \cdot 3 \cdot 2 \cdot 1} = 5005$

    $P(\text{winning with 50 tickets}) = \dfrac{50}{5005} = \dfrac{10}{1001} \approx 0.00999$

13. $P(\text{red or blue}) = P(\text{red}) + P(\text{blue}) = \dfrac{2}{8} + \dfrac{2}{8} = \dfrac{4}{8} = \dfrac{1}{2}$

14. $P(\text{red then blue}) = P(\text{red}) \cdot P(\text{blue}) = \dfrac{2}{8} \cdot \dfrac{2}{8} = \dfrac{1}{4} \cdot \dfrac{1}{4} = \dfrac{1}{16}$

15. $P(\text{flooding for three consecutive years}) = P(\text{flood}) \cdot P(\text{flood}) \cdot P(\text{flood}) = \dfrac{1}{20} \cdot \dfrac{1}{20} \cdot \dfrac{1}{20} = \dfrac{1}{8000}$

16. $P(\text{black or picture card}) = P(\text{black}) + P(\text{picture card}) - P(\text{black picture card}) = \dfrac{26}{52} + \dfrac{12}{52} - \dfrac{6}{52} = \dfrac{32}{52} = \dfrac{8}{13}$

17. $P(\text{freshman or female}) = P(\text{freshman}) + P(\text{female}) - P(\text{female freshman}) = \dfrac{10+15}{50} + \dfrac{15+5}{50} - \dfrac{15}{50} = \dfrac{30}{50} = \dfrac{3}{5}$

18. $P(\text{both red}) = P(\text{red}) \cdot P(\text{red given first ball was red}) = \dfrac{5}{20} \cdot \dfrac{4}{19} = \dfrac{1}{4} \cdot \dfrac{4}{19} = \dfrac{1}{19}$

19. $P(\text{all correct}) = P(\text{correct}) \cdot P(\text{correct}) \cdot P(\text{correct}) \cdot P(\text{correct}) = \dfrac{1}{4} \cdot \dfrac{1}{4} \cdot \dfrac{1}{4} \cdot \dfrac{1}{4} = \left(\dfrac{1}{4}\right)^4 = \dfrac{1}{256}$

20. number of favorable outcomes = 20, number of unfavorable outcomes = 15
    Odds against being a man are 15:20, or 3:4.

21. **a.** Odds in favor are 4:1.   **b.** $P(\text{win}) = \dfrac{4}{1+4} = \dfrac{4}{5}$

22. $P(\text{not brown eyes}) = \dfrac{18+10+20+12}{22+18+10+18+20+12} = \dfrac{60}{100} = \dfrac{3}{5}$

23. $P(\text{brown eyes or blue eyes}) = \dfrac{22+18+18+20}{22+18+10+18+20+12} = \dfrac{78}{100} = \dfrac{39}{50}$

24. $P(\text{female or green eyes}) = P(\text{female}) + P(\text{green eyes}) - P(\text{female and green eyes})$
$$= \dfrac{18+20+12}{100} + \dfrac{10+12}{100} - \dfrac{12}{100}$$
$$= \dfrac{50}{100} + \dfrac{33}{100} - \dfrac{12}{100}$$
$$= \dfrac{71}{100}$$

25. $P(\text{male} | \text{blue eyes}) = \dfrac{18}{18+20} = \dfrac{18}{38} = \dfrac{9}{19}$

26. $P(\text{two people with green eyes}) = P(\text{green eyes}) \cdot P(\text{green eyes} | \text{first person has green eyes}) = \dfrac{22}{100} \cdot \dfrac{21}{99} = \dfrac{7}{150}$

27. $E = \$65{,}000(0.2) + (-\$15{,}000)(0.8) = \$1000$. This means the expected gain is $1000 for this bid.

28. $E = (-\$19) \cdot \dfrac{10}{20} + (-\$18) \cdot \dfrac{5}{20} + (-\$15) \cdot \dfrac{3}{20} + (-\$10) \cdot \dfrac{1}{20} + (\$80) \cdot \dfrac{1}{20}$
$$= \dfrac{-\$190 - \$90 - \$45 - \$10 + \$80}{20} = \dfrac{-\$255}{20} = -\$12.75$$
This expected value of $-\$12.75$ means that a player will lose an average of $12.75 per play in the long run.

Chapter 12
Statistics

Check Points 12.1

1. **a.** The population is the set containing all the of the city's homeless people.

   b. This is not a good idea. This sample of people currently in a shelter is more likely to hold opinions that favor required residence in city shelters than the population of all the city's homeless.

2. The sampling technique described in Check Point 1b does not produce a random sample because homeless people who do not go to shelters have no chance of being selected for the survey. In this instance, an appropriate method would be to randomly select neighborhoods of the city and then randomly survey homeless people within the selected neighborhood.

3.

Grade	Number of students
A	3
B	5
C	9
D	2
F	1
	20

4.

Exam Scores (class)	Tally	Number of students (frequency)
40 – 49	|	1
50 – 59	⊓⊔⊔	5
60 – 69	||||	4
70 – 79	⊓⊔⊔ ⊓⊔⊔ ⊓⊔⊔	15
80 – 89	⊓⊔⊔	5
90 – 99	⊓⊔⊔ ||	7
		37

5.

Stems	Leaves
4	1
5	8 2 8 0 7
6	8 2 9 9
7	3 5 9 9 7 5 5 3 3 6 7 1 7 1 5
8	7 3 9 9 1
9	4 6 9 7 5 8 0

Exercise Set 12.1

1. **a.** The *population* is all American men ages 18 and older. The *sample* is the group of 1014 that were randomly selected.

   b. The variable measured was health. The data was qualitative.

2. a. The *population* is all surgical patients. The *sample* is the group of 500 that were randomly selected.

b. The sample is representative of the population because it was randomly selected.

c. The variable measured was herbal medicine use before surgery. The data was qualitative.

3. c

4. c

5. A stress rating of 7 was reported by 31 students.

6. A stress rating of 1 was reported by 1 student.

7. Totaling the frequency column shows that 151 students were involved in the study.

8. 26 + 15 + 14 = 55. Thus, 55 students reported a stress level of 8 or more.

9.

Time Spent on Homework (in hours)	Number of students
15	4
16	5
17	6
18	5
19	4
20	2
21	2
22	0
23	0
24	2
	30

10.

Height (in inches)	Number of students
66	1
67	3
68	2
69	1
70	3
71	7
72	5
73	5
74	1
75	2
	30

11. The lower class limits are 0, 5, 10, 15, 20, 25, 30, 35, 40, and 45.

12. The upper class limits are 4, 9, 14, 19, 24, 29, 34, 39, 44, and 49.

13. The class width is 5, the difference between successive lower limits.

14. Totaling the frequency column shows that 94 students were involved in the study.

15. 4 + 3 + 3 + 3 = 13. Thus, 13 students had at least 30 social interactions.

16. 12 + 16 + 16 = 44. Thus, 44 students had at most 14 social interactions.

17. The 5 – 9 class.

18. The 35 – 39 class.

19.

Age	Frequency
41–45	2
46–50	8
51–55	15
56–60	9
61–65	7
66–70	2
	43

20.

IQ Score	Number of students
85–89	2
90–94	5
95–99	12
100–104	14
105–109	15
110–114	11
115–119	8
120–124	3
	70

21. Histogram for Stress Rating:

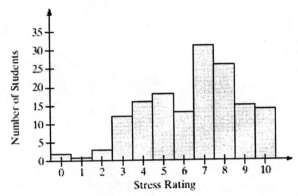

Frequency Polygon for Stress Rating:

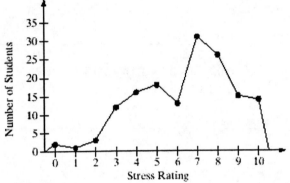

22. Histogram for Time Spent on Homework:

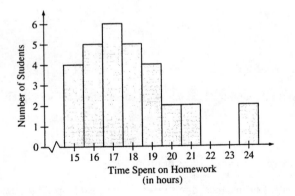

Frequency Polygon for Time Spent on Homework:

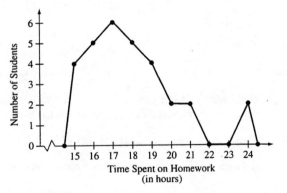

23. Histogram for Height:

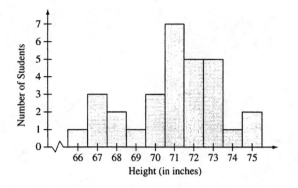

Frequency Polygon for Height:

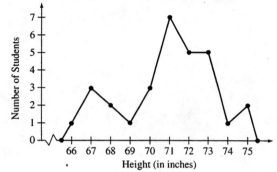

24. c

25. b

26.

Stems	Leaves
4	2 3 6 6 7 8 9 9
5	0 0 1 1 1 1 2 2 4 4 4 4 4 5 5 5 5 6 6 6 7 7 7 7 8
6	0 1 1 1 2 4 4 5 8 9

27.

Stems	Leaves
2	8 8 9 5
3	8 7 0 1 2 7 6 4 0 5
4	8 2 2 1 4 5 4 6 2 0 8 2 7 9
5	9 4 1 9 1 0
6	3 2 3 6 6 3

28. **a.** 31

    b. $80 - 21 = 59$

    c. 56

    d. Actresses tend to win Oscars at younger ages than actors. Explanations will vary.

29. The results are misleading. Explanations will vary but could include the idea that high school girls are less likely to select a choice that contains an absolute such as "always."

30. The title is misleading. Explanations will vary.

31. Unequal intervals on the horizontal axis cause the rapid increase to appear less dramatic.

32. The volumes of the barrels do not fairly compare their costs. For instance, a fair visual comparison would suggest that the $13.34 barrel have a volume that is only about 20% larger than the $10.95 barrel. However, the picture shows a $13.34 barrel that would contain many times the volume of the $10.95 barrel.

33-42. Answers will vary.

43.

River length	Frequency
600–999	12
1000–1399	5
1400–1799	3
1800–2199	3
2200–2599	2
	25

Check Points 12.2

1. a. $\dfrac{10+20+30+40+50}{5} = \dfrac{150}{5} = 30$

b. $\dfrac{3+10+10+10+117}{5} = \dfrac{150}{5} = 30$

2.

x	f	xf
30	3	$30 \cdot 3 = 90$
33	4	$33 \cdot 4 = 132$
40	4	$40 \cdot 4 = 160$
50	1	$50 \cdot 1 = 50$
	12	$\sum xf = 432$

$\text{Mean} = \dfrac{\sum xf}{n} = \dfrac{432}{12} = 36$

3. a. First arrange the data items from smallest to largest: 25, 28, <u>35</u>, 40, 42
The number of data items is odd, so the median is the middle number. The median is 35.

b. First arrange the data items from smallest to largest: 61, 72, <u>79</u>, <u>85</u>, 87, 93
The number of data items is even, so the median is the mean of the two middle data items.
The median is $\dfrac{79+85}{2} = \dfrac{164}{2} = 82$.

4. The data items are arranged from smallest to largest with $n = 19$, which gives $\dfrac{n+1}{2} = \dfrac{19+1}{2} = \dfrac{20}{2} = 10$

The median is in the 10th position, which means the median is 5.

5. The data items are arranged from smallest to largest with $n = 10$, which gives $\dfrac{n+1}{2} = \dfrac{10+1}{2} = \dfrac{11}{2} = 5.5$

The median is in the 5.5 position, which means the median is the mean of the data items in positions 5 and 6.
The median is $\dfrac{23+26}{2} = \dfrac{49}{2} = 24.5$.

6. The total frequency is $1+1+1+3+1+2+2+2+1+2+1+1 = 18$, therefore $n = 18$

   The median's position is $\dfrac{n+1}{2} = \dfrac{18+1}{2} = \dfrac{19}{2} = 9.5$.

   Therefore, the median is the mean of the data items in positions 9 and 10.
   Counting through the frequency row identifies that the 9th data item is 54 and the 10th data item is 55.

   Thus, the median is $\dfrac{54+55}{2} = \dfrac{109}{2} = 54.5$.

7. Mean $= \dfrac{17.1+11.8+5.0+4.5+4.3+4.2+3.1+2.1+2.0+1.0+1.0+0.8+0.7+0.3}{14} = \dfrac{57.9}{14} \approx \$4.1$ million

   The mean salary of \$4.1 million is substantially higher than the median salary of \$2.6 million. This is due to the fact that there are two players that are paid substantially more than the other twelve. These two extreme data items are greatly influencing the mean. These two extreme data items do not greatly influence the median.

8. The number 8 occurs more often than any other. The mode is 8.

9. lowest data value $= \$60,000$, highest data value $= \$151,500$

   Midrange $= \dfrac{\$60,000+\$151,500}{2} = \dfrac{\$211,500}{2} = \$105,750$

10. a. Mean $= \dfrac{173+191+182+190+172+147+146+138+175+136+179+153+107+195+135+140+138}{17}$

    $= \dfrac{2697}{17} = 158.6$ calories

    b. Order the data items: 107, 135, 136, 138, 138, 140, 146, 147, <u>153</u>, 172, 173, 175, 179, 182, 190, 191, 195
    The number of data items is odd, so the median is the middle number. The median is 153 calories.

    c. The number 138 occurs more often than any other. The mode is 138 calories.

    d. Midrange $= \dfrac{107+195}{2} = \dfrac{302}{2} = 151$ calories

Exercise Set 12.2

1. $\dfrac{7+4+3+2+8+5+1+3}{8} = \dfrac{33}{8} = 4.125$

2. $\dfrac{11+6+4+0+2+1+12+0+0}{9} = \dfrac{36}{9} = 4$

3. $\dfrac{91+95+99+97+93+95}{6} = \dfrac{570}{6} = 95$

4. $\dfrac{100+100+90+30+70+100}{6} = \dfrac{490}{6} \approx 81.67$

5. $\dfrac{100+40+70+40+60}{5} = \dfrac{310}{5} = 62$

6. $\dfrac{1+3+5+10+8+5+6+8}{8} = \dfrac{46}{8} = 5.75$

7. $\dfrac{1.6+3.8+5.0+2.7+4.2+4.2+3.2+4.7+3.6+2.5+2.5}{11} = \dfrac{38}{11} \approx 3.45$

8. $\dfrac{1.4+2.1+1.6+3.0+1.4+2.2+1.4+9.0+9.0+1.8}{10} = \dfrac{32.9}{10} = 3.29$

9.

x	f	xf
1	1	$1 \cdot 1 = 1$
2	3	$2 \cdot 3 = 6$
3	4	$3 \cdot 4 = 12$
4	4	$4 \cdot 4 = 16$
5	6	$5 \cdot 6 = 30$
6	5	$6 \cdot 5 = 30$
7	3	$7 \cdot 3 = 21$
8	2	$8 \cdot 2 = 16$
	28	$\sum xf = 132$

$\text{Mean} = \dfrac{\sum xf}{n} = \dfrac{132}{28} \approx 4.71$

10.

x	f	xf
1	2	$1 \cdot 2 = 2$
2	4	$2 \cdot 4 = 8$
3	5	$3 \cdot 5 = 15$
4	7	$4 \cdot 7 = 28$
5	6	$5 \cdot 6 = 30$
6	4	$6 \cdot 4 = 24$
7	3	$7 \cdot 3 = 21$
	31	$\sum xf = 128$

$\text{Mean} = \dfrac{\sum xf}{n} = \dfrac{128}{31} \approx 4.13$

11.

x	f	xf
1	1	$1 \cdot 1 = 1$
2	1	$2 \cdot 1 = 2$
3	2	$3 \cdot 2 = 6$
4	5	$4 \cdot 5 = 20$
5	7	$5 \cdot 7 = 35$
6	9	$6 \cdot 9 = 54$
7	8	$7 \cdot 8 = 56$
8	6	$8 \cdot 6 = 48$
9	4	$9 \cdot 4 = 36$
10	3	$10 \cdot 3 = 30$
	46	$\sum xf = 288$

$\text{Mean} = \dfrac{\sum xf}{n} = \dfrac{288}{46} \approx 6.26$

12.

x	f	xf
1	3	$1 \cdot 3 = 3$
2	4	$2 \cdot 4 = 8$
3	6	$3 \cdot 6 = 18$
4	8	$4 \cdot 8 = 32$
5	9	$5 \cdot 9 = 45$
6	7	$6 \cdot 7 = 42$
7	5	$7 \cdot 5 = 35$
8	2	$8 \cdot 2 = 16$
9	1	$9 \cdot 1 = 9$
10	1	$10 \cdot 1 = 10$
	46	$\sum xf = 218$

$$\text{Mean} = \frac{\sum xf}{n} = \frac{218}{46} \approx 4.74$$

13. First arrange the data items from smallest to largest: 1, 2, 3, 3, 4, 5, 7, 8
The number of data items is even, so the median is the mean of the two middle data items. The median is 3.5.

14. First arrange the data items from smallest to largest: 0, 0, 0, 1, 2, 4, 6, 11, 12
The number of data items is odd, so the median is the middle number.
The median is 2.

15. First arrange the data items from smallest to largest: 91, 93, 95, 95, 97, 99
The number of data items is even, so the median is the mean of the two middle data items.
$$\text{Median} = \frac{95 + 95}{2} = 95$$

16. First arrange the data items from smallest to largest: 30, 70, 90, 100, 100, 100
The number of data items is even, so the median is the mean of the two middle data items.
$$\text{Median} = \frac{90 + 100}{2} = 95$$

17. First arrange the data items from smallest to largest: 40, 40, 60, 70, 100
The number of data items is odd, so the median is the middle number. The median is 60.

18. First arrange the data items from smallest to largest: 1, 3, 5, 5, 6, 8, 8, 10
The number of data items is even, so the median is the mean of the two middle data items.
$$\text{Median} = \frac{5 + 6}{2} = 5.5$$

19. First arrange the data items from smallest to largest: 1.6, 2.5, 2.5, 2.7, 3.2, 3.6, 3.8, 4.2, 4.2, 4.7, 5.0
The number of data items is odd, so the median is the middle number. The median is 3.6.

20. First arrange the data items from smallest to largest:
1.4, 1.4, 1.4, 1.6, 1.8, 2.1, 2.2, 3.0, 9.0, 9.0
The number of data items is even, so the median is the mean of the two middle data items.
$$\text{Median} = \frac{1.8 + 2.1}{2} = 1.95$$

21. $n = 28$
$$\frac{n + 1}{2} = \frac{28 + 1}{2} = \frac{29}{2} = 14.5$$
The median is in the 14.5 position, which means the median is the mean of the data items in positions 14 and 15.

Counting down the frequency column, the 14th and 15th data items are both 5.

$$\text{Median} = \frac{5+5}{2} = 5$$

22. $n = 31$

$$\frac{n+1}{2} = \frac{31+1}{2} = \frac{32}{2} = 16$$

The median is in the 16th position. Counting down the frequency column, the 16th data item is 4. The median is 4.

23. $n = 46$

$$\frac{n+1}{2} = \frac{46+1}{2} = 23.5$$

The median is in the 23.5 position, which means the median is the mean of the data items in positions 23 and 24. Counting down the frequency column, the 23rd and 24th data items are both 6.

$$\text{Median} = \frac{6+6}{2} = 6$$

24. $n = 46$

$$\frac{n+1}{2} = \frac{46+1}{2} = 23.5$$

The median is in the 23.5 position, which means the median is the mean of the data items in positions 23 and 24. Counting down the frequency column, the 23rd and 24th data items are both 5.

$$\text{Median} = \frac{5+5}{2} = 5$$

25. The mode is 3.

26. The mode is 0.

27. The mode is 95.

28. The mode is 100.

29. The mode is 40.

30. The modes are 5 and 8.

31. The modes are 2.5 and 4.2.

32. The mode is 1.4.

33. The mode is 5.

34. The mode is 4.

35. The mode is 6.

36. The mode is 5.

37. lowest data value = 1, highest data value = 8

$$\text{Midrange} = \frac{1+8}{2} = 4.5$$

38. lowest data value = 0, highest data value = 12

$$\text{Midrange} = \frac{0+12}{2} = 6$$

39. lowest data value = 91, highest data value = 99

$$\text{Midrange} = \frac{91+99}{2} = 95$$

40. lowest data value = 30, highest data value = 100

$$\text{Midrange} = \frac{30+100}{2} = 65$$

41. lowest data value = 40, highest data value = 100

$$\text{Midrange} = \frac{40+100}{2} = 70$$

42. lowest data value = 1, highest data value = 10

$$\text{Midrange} = \frac{1+10}{2} = 5.5$$

43. lowest data value = 1.6, highest data value = 5.0

$$\text{Midrange} = \frac{1.6+5.0}{2} = 3.3$$

44. lowest data value = 1.4, highest data value = 9.0

$$\text{Midrange} = \frac{1.4+9.0}{2} = 5.2$$

45. $\text{Midrange} = \dfrac{1+8}{2} = 4.5$

46. $\text{Midrange} = \dfrac{1+7}{2} = 4$

47. $\text{Midrange} = \dfrac{1+10}{2} = 5.5$

48. $\text{Midrange} = \dfrac{1+10}{2} = 5.5$

49. a. $\text{Mean} = \dfrac{79+83+73+67+67+64+55+70+65}{9} = \dfrac{623}{9} \approx 69.2$

    b. Order the data items: 55, 64, 65, 67, <u>67</u>, 70, 73, 79, 83
The number of data items is odd, so the median is the middle number. The median is 67.

    c. The mode is 67.

    d. $\text{Midrange} = \dfrac{55+83}{2} = \dfrac{138}{2} = 69$

50. a. $\text{Mean} = \dfrac{54+59+35+41+46+25+47+60+54+46+49+46+41+34+22}{15} = \dfrac{659}{15} \approx 43.9$

b. Order the data items: 22, 25, 34, 35, 41, 41, 46, <u>46</u>, 46, 47, 49, 54, 54, 59, 60
The number of data items is odd, so the median is the middle number. The median is 46.

c. The mode is 46.

d. Midrange $= \dfrac{22+60}{2} = \dfrac{82}{2} = 41$

51. a. Mean $= \dfrac{25.2+20.0+18.9+18.0+18.0+17.1+17.0+17.0+15.7+15.5}{10} = \dfrac{182.4}{10} = \$18.24$ million

b. The median is $\dfrac{18.0+17.1}{2} = \dfrac{35.1}{2} = \$17.55$ million .

c. The modes are 17.0 and 18.0.

d. Midrange $= \dfrac{25.2+15.5}{2} = \dfrac{40.7}{2} = \$20.35$ million

52.

x	f	xf
2	12	$2 \cdot 12 = 24$
7	16	$7 \cdot 16 = 112$
12	16	$12 \cdot 16 = 192$
17	16	$17 \cdot 16 = 272$
22	10	$22 \cdot 10 = 220$
27	11	$27 \cdot 11 = 297$
32	4	$32 \cdot 4 = 128$
37	3	$37 \cdot 3 = 111$
42	3	$42 \cdot 3 = 126$
47	3	$47 \cdot 3 = 141$
	94	$\sum xf = 1623$

a. Mean $= \dfrac{\sum xf}{n} = \dfrac{1623}{94} \approx 17.3$

b. The median is 17 because the 47th and 48th data items both are 17.

c. The modes are 7, 12, and 17.

d. Midrange $= \dfrac{47+2}{2} = \dfrac{49}{2} = 24.5$

53. Mean $= \dfrac{1\cdot150+2\cdot155+2\cdot160+4\cdot165+6\cdot170+8\cdot175+5\cdot180+4\cdot185+2\cdot190+3\cdot195+1\cdot200+2\cdot205}{40} = 176.875$ lb

54. $n = 40$, $\dfrac{n+1}{2} = \dfrac{40+1}{2} = \dfrac{41}{2} = 20.5$
The median is in the 20.5 position, which means the median is the mean of the data items in positions 20 and 21.
Median $= \dfrac{175+175}{2} = 175$ lb

55. The modal weight is 175 lb.

56. Midrange $= \dfrac{150 + 205}{2} = 177.5$ lb

57. Mean $= \dfrac{17.1 + 11.8 + 5.0 + 4.5 + 4.3 + 4.2 + 3.1 + 2.1 + 2.0 + 1.0 + 1.0 + 0.8 + 0.7 + 0.3}{14 \quad 12} = \dfrac{29.0}{12} \approx \$2.4$ million

Without the highest two data items, the mean of \$2.4 million, is quite close to the median salary of \$2.6 million.

58. a.

Words per Minute	Number of People
600	1
650	2
700	2
750	2
800	3
850	3
900	3
950	2
1000	4
1050	1
1100	1
	24

Mean $= \dfrac{1 \cdot 600 + 2 \cdot 650 + 2 \cdot 700 + 2 \cdot 750 + 3 \cdot 800 + 3 \cdot 850 + 3 \cdot 900 + 2 \cdot 950 + 4 \cdot 1000 + 1 \cdot 1050 + 1 \cdot 1100}{24}$

≈ 854 words per minute

Median $= \dfrac{850 + 850}{2} = 850$ words per minute

Mode $= 1000$ words per minute

Midrange $= \dfrac{600 + 1100}{2} = 850$ words per minute

b. Mode

c. Answers will vary.

59. Find the weighted mean by treating the number of credits as the "frequency."

Course	Grade	Value (x)	Credits (f)	xf
Sociology	A	4	3	$4 \cdot 3 = 12$
Biology	C	2	3.5	$2 \cdot 3.5 = 7$
Music	B	3	1	$3 \cdot 1 = 3$
Math	B	3	4	$3 \cdot 4 = 12$
English	C	2	3	$2 \cdot 3 = 6$
			14.5	$\sum xf = 40$

Mean $= \dfrac{\sum xf}{n} = \dfrac{40}{14.5} \approx 2.76$

60-72. Answers will vary.

73. All 30 students had the same grade.

Check Points 12.3

1. Range $= 11 - 2 = 9$

2. Mean $= \dfrac{2+4+7+11}{4} = \dfrac{24}{4} = 6$

Data item	Deviation: Data item − mean
2	$2 - 6 = -4$
4	$4 - 6 = -2$
7	$7 - 6 = 1$
11	$11 - 6 = 5$

3. Mean $= \dfrac{2+4+7+11}{4} = \dfrac{24}{4} = 6$

Data item	Deviation: Data item − mean	$(\text{Deviation})^2$: $(\text{Data item–mean})^2$
2	$2 - 6 = -4$	$(-4)^2 = 16$
4	$4 - 6 = -2$	$(-2)^2 = 4$
7	$7 - 6 = 1$	$1^2 = 1$
11	$11 - 6 = 5$	$5^2 = 25$
		$\sum(\text{data item–mean})^2 = 46$

Standard deviation $= \sqrt{\dfrac{46}{4-1}} = \sqrt{\dfrac{46}{3}} \approx 3.92$

4. *Sample A*

Mean $= \dfrac{73+75+77+79+81+83}{6} = \dfrac{468}{6} = 78$

Data item	Deviation: Data item − mean	$(\text{Deviation})^2$: $(\text{Data item–mean})^2$
73	$73 - 78 = -5$	$(-5)^2 = 25$
75	$75 - 78 = -3$	$(-3)^2 = 9$
77	$77 - 78 = -1$	$(-1)^2 = 1$
79	$79 - 78 = 1$	$1^2 = 1$
81	$81 - 78 = 3$	$3^2 = 9$
83	$83 - 78 = 5$	$5^2 = 25$
		$\sum(\text{data item–mean})^2 = 70$

Standard deviation $= \sqrt{\dfrac{70}{6-1}} = \sqrt{\dfrac{70}{5}} \approx 3.74$

Sample B

$$\text{Mean} = \frac{40 + 44 + 92 + 94 + 98 + 100}{6} = \frac{468}{6} = 78$$

Data item	Deviation: Data item − mean	(Deviation)^2: (Data item−mean)^2
40	$40 - 78 = -38$	$(-38)^2 = 1444$
44	$44 - 78 = -34$	$(-34)^2 = 1156$
92	$92 - 78 = 14$	$14^2 = 196$
94	$94 - 78 = 16$	$16^2 = 256$
98	$98 - 78 = 20$	$20^2 = 400$
100	$100 - 78 = 22$	$22^2 = 484$

$$\sum (\text{data item−mean})^2 = 3936$$

$$\text{Standard deviation} = \sqrt{\frac{3936}{6-1}} = \sqrt{\frac{3936}{5}} \approx 28.06$$

5. a. Stocks had a greater return on investment.

b. Stocks have the greater risk. The high standard deviation indicates that stocks are more likely to lose money.

Exercise Set 12.3

1. Range $= 5 - 1 = 4$

2. Range $= 20 - 16 = 4$

3. Range $= 15 - 7 = 8$

4. Range $= 17 - 11 = 6$

5. Range $= 5 - 3 = 2$

6. Range $= 5 - 3 = 2$

7. a.

Data item	Deviation: Data item − mean
3	$3 - 12 = -9$
5	$5 - 12 = -7$
7	$7 - 12 = -5$
12	$12 - 12 = 0$
18	$18 - 12 = 6$
27	$27 - 12 = 15$

b. $-9 - 7 - 5 + 0 + 6 + 15 = 0$

8. a.

Data item	Deviation: Data item − mean
84	$84 - 91 = -7$
88	$88 - 91 = -3$
90	$90 - 91 = -1$
95	$95 - 91 = 4$
98	$98 - 91 = 7$

b. $-7 - 3 - 1 + 4 + 7 = 0$

9. a.

Data item	Deviation: Data item – mean
29	$29 - 49 = -20$
38	$38 - 49 = -11$
48	$48 - 49 = -1$
49	$49 - 49 = 0$
53	$53 - 49 = 4$
77	$77 - 49 = 28$

b. $-20 - 11 - 1 + 0 + 4 + 28 = 0$

10. a.

Data item	Deviation: Data item – mean
60	$60 - 65 = -5$
60	$60 - 65 = -5$
62	$62 - 65 = -3$
65	$65 - 65 = 0$
65	$65 - 65 = 0$
65	$65 - 65 = 0$
66	$66 - 65 = 1$
67	$67 - 65 = 2$
70	$70 - 65 = 5$
70	$70 - 65 = 5$

b. $-5 - 5 - 3 + 0 + 0 + 0 + 1 + 2 + 5 + 5 = 0$

11. a. $\text{Mean} = \dfrac{85 + 95 + 90 + 85 + 100}{5} = 91$

b.

Data item	Deviation: Data item – mean
85	$85 - 91 = -6$
95	$95 - 91 = 4$
90	$90 - 91 = -1$
85	$85 - 91 = -6$
100	$100 - 91 = 9$

c. $-6 + 4 - 1 - 6 + 9 = 0$

12. a. $\text{Mean} = \dfrac{94 + 62 + 88 + 85 + 91}{5} = 84$

b.

Data item	Deviation: Data item – mean
94	$94 - 84 = 10$
62	$62 - 84 = -22$
88	$88 - 84 = 4$
85	$85 - 84 = 1$
91	$91 - 84 = 7$

c. $10 - 22 + 4 + 1 + 7 = 0$

13. a. $\text{Mean} = \dfrac{146+153+155+160+161}{5} = 155$

b.

Data item	Deviation: Data item – mean
146	$146 - 155 = -9$
153	$153 - 155 = -2$
155	$155 - 155 = 0$
160	$160 - 155 = 5$
161	$161 - 155 = 6$

c. $-9 - 2 + 0 + 5 + 6 = 0$

14. a. $\text{Mean} = \dfrac{150+132+144+122}{4} = 137$

b.

Data item	Deviation: Data item – mean
150	$150 - 137 = 13$
132	$132 - 137 = -5$
144	$144 - 137 = 7$
122	$122 - 137 = -15$

c. $13 - 5 + 7 - 15 = 0$

15. a. $\text{Mean} = \dfrac{2.25+3.50+2.75+3.10+1.90}{5} = 2.70$

b.

Data item	Deviation: Data item – mean
2.25	$2.25 - 2.70 = -0.45$
3.50	$3.50 - 2.70 = 0.80$
2.75	$2.75 - 2.70 = 0.05$
3.10	$3.10 - 2.70 = 0.40$
1.90	$1.90 - 2.70 = -0.80$

c. $-0.45 + 0.80 + 0.05 + 0.40 - 0.80 = 0$

16. a. $\text{Mean} = \dfrac{0.35+0.37+0.41+0.39+0.43}{5} = 0.39$

b.

Data item	Deviation: Data item – mean
0.35	$0.35 - 0.39 = -0.04$
0.37	$0.37 - 0.39 = -0.02$
0.41	$0.41 - 0.39 = 0.02$
0.39	$0.39 - 0.39 = 0$
0.43	$0.43 - 0.39 = 0.04$

c. $-0.04 - 0.02 + 0.02 + 0 + 0.04 = 0$

17. Mean $= \dfrac{1+2+3+4+5}{5} = 3$

Data item	Deviation: Data item − mean	(Deviation)^2 : (Data item−mean)^2
1	$1-3=-2$	$(-2)^2 = 4$
2	$2-3=-1$	$(-1)^2 = 1$
3	$3-3=0$	$0^2 = 0$
4	$4-3=1$	$1^2 = 1$
5	$5-3=2$	$2^2 = 4$
		$\sum$ (data item−mean)$^2 = 10$

Standard deviation $= \sqrt{\dfrac{10}{5-1}} = \sqrt{\dfrac{10}{4}} \approx 1.58$

18. Mean $= \dfrac{16+17+18+19+20}{5} = 18$

Data item	Deviation: Data item − mean	(Deviation)^2 : (Data item−mean)^2
16	$16-18=-2$	$(-2)^2 = 4$
17	$17-18=-1$	$(-1)^2 = 1$
18	$18-18=0$	$0^2 = 0$
19	$19-18=1$	$1^2 = 1$
20	$20-18=2$	$2^2 = 4$
		$\sum$ (data item−mean)$^2 = 10$

Standard deviation $= \sqrt{\dfrac{10}{5-1}} = \sqrt{\dfrac{10}{4}} \approx 1.58$

19. Mean $= \dfrac{7+9+9+15}{4} = 10$

Data item	Deviation: Data item − mean	(Deviation)^2 : (Data item−mean)^2
7	$7-10=-3$	$(-3)^2 = 9$
9	$9-10=-1$	$(-1)^2 = 1$
9	$9-10=-1$	$(-1)^2 = 1$
15	$15-10=5$	$5^2 = 25$
		$\sum$ (data item−mean)$^2 = 36$

Standard deviation $= \sqrt{\dfrac{36}{4-1}} = \sqrt{\dfrac{36}{3}} \approx 3.46$

20. Mean $= \dfrac{11+13+14+15+17}{5} = 14$

Data item	Deviation: Data item − mean	(Deviation)^2 : (Data item−mean)^2
11	$11 - 14 = -3$	$(-3)^2 = 9$
13	$13 - 14 = -1$	$(-1)^2 = 1$
14	$14 - 14 = 0$	$0^2 = 0$
15	$15 - 14 = 1$	$1^2 = 1$
17	$17 - 14 = 3$	$3^2 = 9$
		$\sum (\text{data item−mean})^2 = 20$

Standard deviation $= \sqrt{\dfrac{20}{5-1}} = \sqrt{\dfrac{20}{4}} \approx 2.24$

21. Mean $= \dfrac{3+3+4+4+5+5}{6} = 4$

Data item	Deviation: Data item − mean	(Deviation)^2 : (Data item−mean)^2
3	$3 - 4 = -1$	$(-1)^2 = 1$
3	$3 - 4 = -1$	$(-1)^2 = 1$
4	$4 - 4 = 0$	$0^2 = 0$
4	$4 - 4 = 0$	$0^2 = 0$
5	$5 - 4 = 1$	$1^2 = 1$
5	$5 - 4 = 1$	$1^2 = 1$
		$\sum (\text{data item−mean})^2 = 4$

Standard deviation $= \sqrt{\dfrac{4}{6-1}} = \sqrt{\dfrac{4}{5}} \approx 0.89$

22. Mean $= \dfrac{3+3+3+4+5+5+5}{7} = 4$

Data item	Deviation: Data item − mean	(Deviation)^2 : (Data item−mean)^2
3	$3 - 4 = -1$	$(-1)^2 = 1$
3	$3 - 4 = -1$	$(-1)^2 = 1$
3	$3 - 4 = -1$	$(-1)^2 = 1$
4	$4 - 4 = 0$	$0^2 = 0$
5	$5 - 4 = 1$	$1^2 = 1$
5	$5 - 4 = 1$	$1^2 = 1$
5	$5 - 4 = 1$	$1^2 = 1$
		$\sum (\text{data item−mean})^2 = 6$

Standard deviation $= \sqrt{\dfrac{6}{7-1}} = \sqrt{\dfrac{6}{6}} = 1$

23. Mean $= \dfrac{1+1+1+4+7+7+7}{7} = 4$

Data item	Deviation: Data item − mean	(Deviation)^2 : (Data item−mean)^2
1	$1 - 4 = -3$	$(-3)^2 = 9$
1	$1 - 4 = -3$	$(-3)^2 = 9$
1	$1 - 4 = -3$	$(-3)^2 = 9$
4	$4 - 4 = 0$	$0^2 = 0$
7	$7 - 4 = 3$	$3^2 = 9$
7	$7 - 4 = 3$	$3^2 = 9$
7	$7 - 4 = 3$	$3^2 = 9$
		$\sum (\text{data item−mean})^2 = 54$

Standard deviation $= \sqrt{\dfrac{54}{7-1}} = \sqrt{\dfrac{54}{6}} = 3$

24. Mean $= \dfrac{6+6+6+6+7+7+7+4+8+3}{10} = 6$

Data item	Deviation: Data item – mean	(Deviation)^2 : (Data item–mean)^2
6	$6-6=0$	$0^2=0$
6	$6-6=0$	$0^2=0$
6	$6-6=0$	$0^2=0$
6	$6-6=0$	$0^2=0$
7	$7-6=1$	$1^2=1$
7	$7-6=1$	$1^2=1$
7	$7-6=1$	$1^2=1$
4	$4-6=-2$	$(-2)^2=4$
8	$8-6=2$	$2^2=4$
3	$3-6=-3$	$(-3)^2=9$
		$\sum$ (data item–mean)$^2=20$

Standard deviation $= \sqrt{\dfrac{20}{10-1}} = \sqrt{\dfrac{20}{9}} \approx 1.49$

25. Mean $= \dfrac{9+5+9+5+9+5+9+5}{8} = 7$

Data item	Deviation: Data item – mean	(Deviation)^2 : (Data item–mean)^2
9	$9-7=2$	$2^2=4$
5	$5-7=-2$	$(-2)^2=4$
9	$9-7=2$	$2^2=4$
5	$5-7=-2$	$(-2)^2=4$
9	$9-7=2$	$2^2=4$
5	$5-7=-2$	$(-2)^2=4$
9	$9-7=2$	$2^2=4$
5	$5-7=-2$	$(-2)^2=4$
		$\sum$ (data item–mean)$^2=32$

Standard deviation $= \sqrt{\dfrac{32}{8-1}} = \sqrt{\dfrac{32}{7}} \approx 2.14$

26. Mean $= \dfrac{6+10+6+10+6+10+6+10}{8} = 8$

Data item	Deviation: Data item – mean	(Deviation)^2: (Data item–mean)^2
6	$6 - 8 = -2$	$(-2)^2 = 4$
10	$10 - 8 = 2$	$2^2 = 4$
6	$6 - 8 = -2$	$(-2)^2 = 4$
10	$10 - 8 = 2$	$2^2 = 4$
6	$6 - 8 = -2$	$(-2)^2 = 4$
10	$10 - 8 = 2$	$2^2 = 4$
6	$6 - 8 = -2$	$(-2)^2 = 4$
10	$10 - 8 = 2$	$2^2 = 4$

$$\sum (\text{data item–mean})^2 = 32$$

Standard deviation $= \sqrt{\dfrac{32}{8-1}} = \sqrt{\dfrac{32}{7}} \approx 2.14$

27. *Sample A*

Mean $= \dfrac{6+8+10+12+14+16+18}{7} = 12$

Range $= 18 - 6 = 12$

Data item	Deviation: Data item – mean	(Deviation)^2: (Data item–mean)^2
6	$6 - 12 = -6$	$(-6)^2 = 36$
8	$8 - 12 = -4$	$(-4)^2 = 16$
10	$10 - 12 = -2$	$(-2)^2 = 4$
12	$12 - 12 = 0$	$0^2 = 0$
14	$14 - 12 = 2$	$2^2 = 4$
16	$16 - 12 = 4$	$4^2 = 16$
18	$18 - 12 = 6$	$6^2 = 36$

$$\sum (\text{data item–mean})^2 = 112$$

Standard deviation $= \sqrt{\dfrac{112}{7-1}} = \sqrt{\dfrac{112}{6}} \approx 4.32$

Sample B

Mean $= \dfrac{6+7+8+12+16+17+18}{7} = 12$

Range $= 18 - 6 = 12$

Data item	Deviation: Data item − mean	$(Deviation)^2$: $(Data\ item–mean)^2$
6	$6 - 12 = -6$	$(-6)^2 = 36$
7	$7 - 12 = -5$	$(-5)^2 = 25$
8	$8 - 12 = -4$	$(-4)^2 = 16$
12	$12 - 12 = 0$	$0^2 = 0$
16	$16 - 12 = 4$	$4^2 = 16$
17	$17 - 12 = 5$	$5^2 = 25$
18	$18 - 12 = 6$	$6^2 = 36$

$$\sum (data\ item–mean)^2 = 154$$

$$\text{Standard deviation} = \sqrt{\frac{154}{7–1}} = \sqrt{\frac{154}{6}} \approx 5.07$$

Sample C

$$\text{Mean} = \frac{6+6+6+12+18+18+18}{7} = 12$$

Range = $18 - 6 = 12$

Data item	Deviation: Data item − mean	$(Deviation)^2$: $(Data\ item–mean)^2$
6	$6 - 12 = -6$	$(-6)^2 = 36$
6	$6 - 12 = -6$	$(-6)^2 = 36$
6	$6 - 12 = -6$	$(-6)^2 = 36$
12	$12 - 12 = 0$	$0^2 = 0$
18	$18 - 12 = 6$	$6^2 = 36$
18	$18 - 12 = 6$	$6^2 = 36$
18	$18 - 12 = 6$	$6^2 = 36$

$$\sum (data\ item–mean)^2 = 216$$

$$\text{Standard deviation} = \sqrt{\frac{216}{7–1}} = \sqrt{\frac{216}{6}} = 6$$

The samples have the same mean and range, but different standard deviations.

28. *Sample A*

$$\text{Mean} = \frac{8+10+12+14+16+18+20}{7} = 14$$

Range = 20 − 8 = 12

Data item	Deviation: Data item − mean	(Deviation)^2: (Data item−mean)^2
8	8 − 14 = −6	$(-6)^2 = 36$
10	10 − 14 = −4	$(-4)^2 = 16$
12	12 − 14 = −2	$(-2)^2 = 4$
14	14 − 14 = 0	$0^2 = 0$
16	16 − 14 = 2	$2^2 = 4$
18	18 − 14 = 4	$4^2 = 16$
20	20 − 14 = 6	$6^2 = 36$

$$\sum (\text{data item−mean})^2 = 112$$

$$\text{Standard deviation} = \sqrt{\frac{112}{7-1}} = \sqrt{\frac{112}{6}} \approx 4.32$$

Sample B

$$\text{Mean} = \frac{8+9+10+14+18+19+20}{7} = 14$$

Range = 20 − 8 = 12

Data item	Deviation: Data item − mean	(Deviation)^2: (Data item−mean)^2
8	8 − 14 = −6	$(-6)^2 = 36$
9	9 − 14 = −5	$(-5)^2 = 25$
10	10 − 14 = −4	$(-4)^2 = 16$
14	14 − 14 = 0	$0^2 = 0$
18	18 − 14 = 4	$4^2 = 16$
19	19 − 14 = 5	$5^2 = 25$
20	20 − 14 = 6	$6^2 = 36$

$$\sum (\text{data item−mean})^2 = 154$$

$$\text{Standard deviation} = \sqrt{\frac{154}{7-1}} = \sqrt{\frac{154}{6}} \approx 5.07$$

Sample C

$$\text{Mean} = \frac{8+8+8+14+20+20+20}{7} = 14$$

Range = 20 − 8 = 12

Data item	Deviation: Data item – mean	$(\text{Deviation})^2$: $(\text{Data item–mean})^2$
8	$8 - 14 = -6$	$(-6)^2 = 36$
8	$8 - 14 = -6$	$(-6)^2 = 36$
8	$8 - 14 = -6$	$(-6)^2 = 36$
14	$14 - 14 = 0$	$0^2 = 0$
20	$20 - 14 = 6$	$6^2 = 36$
20	$20 - 14 = 6$	$6^2 = 36$
20	$20 - 14 = 6$	$6^2 = 36$

$$\sum (\text{data item–mean})^2 = 216$$

$$\text{Standard deviation} = \sqrt{\frac{216}{7-1}} = \sqrt{\frac{216}{6}} = 6$$

The samples have the same mean and range, but different standard deviations.

29. $\text{Mean} = \dfrac{186 + 190 + 195 + 198 + 201 + 206}{6} = 196$

Data item	Deviation: Data item – mean	$(\text{Deviation})^2$: $(\text{Data item–mean})^2$
186	$186 - 196 = -10$	$(-10)^2 = 100$
190	$190 - 196 = -6$	$(-6)^2 = 36$
195	$195 - 196 = -1$	$(-1)^2 = 1$
198	$198 - 196 = 2$	$2^2 = 4$
201	$201 - 196 = 5$	$5^2 = 25$
206	$206 - 196 = 10$	$10^2 = 100$

$$\sum (\text{data item–mean})^2 = 266$$

$$\text{Standard deviation} = \sqrt{\frac{266}{6-1}} = \sqrt{\frac{266}{5}} \approx 7.29$$

30. Mean $= \dfrac{120+134+130+146+142+156}{6} = 138$

Data item	Deviation: Data item − mean	(Deviation)^2: (Data item−mean)^2
120	$120-138 = -18$	$(-18)^2 = 324$
134	$134-138 = -4$	$(-4)^2 = 16$
130	$130-138 = -8$	$(-8)^2 = 64$
146	$146-138 = 8$	$8^2 = 64$
142	$142-138 = 4$	$4^2 = 16$
156	$156-138 = 18$	$18^2 = 324$
		$\sum(\text{data item}-\text{mean})^2 = 808$

Standard deviation $= \sqrt{\dfrac{808}{6-1}} = \sqrt{\dfrac{808}{5}} \approx 12.71$

31. Mean $= \dfrac{9+12+2+0+0+7+12+2+9+1+2}{11} = \dfrac{56}{11} \approx 5.09$

Data item	Deviation: Data item − mean	(Deviation)^2: (Data item−mean)^2
9	$9-5.1 = 3.9$	$3.9^2 = 15.21$
12	$12-5.1 = 6.9$	$6.9^2 = 47.61$
2	$2-5.1 = -3.1$	$(-3.1)^2 = 9.61$
0	$0-5.1 = -5.1$	$(-5.1)^2 = 26.01$
0	$0-5.1 = -5.1$	$(-5.1)^2 = 26.01$
7	$7-5.1 = 1.9$	$1.9^2 = 3.61$
12	$12-5.1 = 6.9$	$6.9^2 = 47.61$
2	$2-5.1 = -3.1$	$(-3.1)^2 = 9.61$
9	$9-5.1 = 3.9$	$3.9^2 = 15.21$
1	$1-5.1 = -4.1$	$(-4.1)^2 = 16.81$
2	$2-5.1 = -3.1$	$(-3.1)^2 = 9.61$
		$\sum(\text{data item}-\text{mean})^2 = 226.91$

Standard deviation $= \sqrt{\dfrac{226.91}{11-1}} = \sqrt{\dfrac{226.91}{10}} \approx 4.76$

32-39. Answers will vary.

Chapter 12: Statistics

40. a

41-42. Answers will vary.

43. a

44 Original data:

$$\text{Mean} = \frac{0+1+3+4+4+6}{6} = \frac{18}{6} = 3$$

$$\text{Standard deviation} = \sqrt{\frac{24}{6-1}} = \sqrt{\frac{24}{5}} \approx 2.19$$

Adjusted data:

$$\text{Mean} = \frac{2+3+5+6+6+8}{6} = \frac{30}{6} = 5$$

$$\text{Standard deviation} = \sqrt{\frac{24}{6-1}} = \sqrt{\frac{24}{5}} \approx 2.19$$

Adding 2 to each data item raises the mean by 2, but does not affect the standard deviation.

Check Points 12.4

1. a. Height $= 70 + 3 \cdot 2.5 = 70 + 7.5 = 77.5$ in.

   b. Height $= 70 - 2 \cdot 2.5 = 70 - 5 = 65$ in.

2. a. 300 is 2 standard deviations below the mean. $500 - 2 \cdot 100 = 300$
   700 is 2 standard deviations above the mean. $500 + 2 \cdot 100 = 700$
   The 68-95-99.7 rule indicates that approximately 95% score between 300 and 700.

   b. 700 is 2 standard deviations above the mean. $500 + 2 \cdot 100 = 700$
   The 68-95-99.7 rule states that approximately 95% score between 2 standard deviations below and 2 standard deviations above the mean. Because the distribution is symmetrical, half of the 95%, or 47.5% score between 500 and 700.

   c. 600 is 1 standard deviation above the mean. $500 + 1 \cdot 100 = 600$
   The 68-95-99.7 rule states that approximately 68% score between 1 standard deviation below and 1 standard deviation above the mean. Therefore, $100\% - 68\% = 32\%$ are farther than 1 standard deviation from the mean. Because the distribution is symmetrical, half of the 32%, or 16% score above 600.

3. a. $z_{342} = \dfrac{\text{data item} - \text{mean}}{\text{standard deviation}} = \dfrac{342 - 336}{3} = \dfrac{6}{3} = 2$

   b. $z_{336} = \dfrac{\text{data item} - \text{mean}}{\text{standard deviation}} = \dfrac{336 - 336}{3} = \dfrac{0}{3} = 0$

   c. $z_{333} = \dfrac{\text{data item} - \text{mean}}{\text{standard deviation}} = \dfrac{333 - 336}{3} = \dfrac{-3}{3} = -1$

4. Find the z-score for each test taken.

   SAT: $z_{550} = \dfrac{\text{data item} - \text{mean}}{\text{standard deviation}} = \dfrac{550 - 500}{100} = \dfrac{50}{100} = 0.5$

   ACT: $z_{24} = \dfrac{\text{data item} - \text{mean}}{\text{standard deviation}} = \dfrac{24 - 18}{6} = \dfrac{6}{6} = 1$

You scored better on the ACT test because the score is 1 standard deviation above the mean. The SAT score is only half a standard deviation above the mean.

5. Score = mean + 2.5 · standard deviation = 100 + 2.5(15) = 100 + 37.5 = 137.5

6. Scoring in the 62nd percentile means that the student did better than about 62% of all those who took the SAT.

7. First, find the z-score. $z_{68} = \dfrac{\text{data item} - \text{mean}}{\text{standard deviation}} = \dfrac{68 - 65}{2.5} = \dfrac{3}{2.5} = 1.2$

   Looking up 1.2 in the z-score column of table 12.14 indicates that the percentile is 88.49.
   Therefore, approximately 88.49% of young women are shorter than 68 inches.

8. First, find the z-score. $z_{145} = \dfrac{\text{data item} - \text{mean}}{\text{standard deviation}} = \dfrac{145 - 110}{25} = \dfrac{35}{25} = 1.4$.

   Looking up 1.4 in the z-score column of table 12.14 indicates that the percentile is 91.92.
   Therefore, approximately 100% – 91.92%, or 8.08% of all IQ scores for this age group are greater than 145.

9. Convert each given data item to a z-score and look up the corresponding percentile in table 12.14.

   $z_{67} = \dfrac{\text{data item} - \text{mean}}{\text{standard deviation}} = \dfrac{67 - 70}{2.5} = \dfrac{-3}{2.5} = -1.2$, which corresponds to a percentile of 11.51.

   $z_{74} = \dfrac{\text{data item} - \text{mean}}{\text{standard deviation}} = \dfrac{74 - 70}{2.5} = \dfrac{4}{2.5} = 1.6$, which corresponds to a percentile of 94.52.

   94.52 – 11.51 = 83.01. Therefore, approximately 83.01% of all young men have heights between 67 in. and 74 in.

10. a. Margin of error $= \pm \dfrac{1}{\sqrt{1082}} \approx \pm 0.03 = \pm 3.0\%$

    b. Note: 64% – 3% = 61% and 64% + 3% = 67%
        We can be 95% confident that between 61% and 67% of all adult Americans think that raising airplane ticket prices $50 to increase security is acceptable.

Exercise Set 12.4

1. Score = 100 + 1 · 20 = 100 + 20 = 120

2. Score = 100 + 2 · 20 = 100 + 40 = 140

3. Score = 100 + 3 · 20 = 100 + 60 = 160

4. Score = 100 + 1.5(20) = 100 + 30 = 130

5. Score = 100 + 2.5(20) = 100 + 50 = 150

6. Score = 100 – 1 · 20 = 100 – 20 = 80

7. Score = 100 – 2 · 20 = 100 – 40 = 60

8. Score = 100 – 3 · 20 = 100 – 60 = 40

9. Score = 100 – 0.5(20) = 100 – 10 = 90

10. Score = 100 – 2.5(20) = 100 – 50 = 50

11. $16,500 is 1 standard deviation below the mean and $17,500 is 1 standard deviation above the mean. The Rule and the figure indicate that 68% of the buyers paid between $16,500 and $17,500.

12. $16,000 is 2 standard deviations below the mean and $18,000 is 2 standard deviations above the mean. The Rule and the figure indicate that 95% of the buyers paid between $16,000 and $18,000.

13. $17,500 is 1 standard deviation above the mean. 68% of the buyers paid between $16,500 and $17,500. Because of symmetry, the percent that paid between $17,000 and $17,500 is $\dfrac{1}{2}(68\%) = 34\%$.

14. $18,000 is 2 standard deviations above the mean. 95% of the buyers paid between $16,000 and $18,000. Because of symmetry, the percent that paid between $17,000 and $18,000 is $\dfrac{1}{2}(95\%) = 47.5\%$.

15. $16,000 is 2 standard deviations below the mean. 95% of the buyers paid between $16,000 and $18,000. Because of symmetry, the percent that paid between $16,000 and $17,000 is $\frac{1}{2}(95\%) = 47.5\%$.

16. $16,500 is 1 standard deviation below the mean. 68% of the buyers paid between $16,500 and $17,500. Because of symmetry, the percent that paid between $16,500 and $17,000 is $\frac{1}{2}(68\%) = 34\%$.

17. $15,500 is 3 standard deviations below the mean. 99.7% of the buyers paid between $15,500 and $18,500. Because of symmetry, the percent that paid between $15,500 and $17,000 is $\frac{1}{2}(99.7\%) = 49.85\%$.

18. $18,500 is 3 standard deviations above the mean. 99.7% of the buyers paid between $15,500 and $18,500. Because of symmetry, the percent that paid between $17,000 and $18,500 is $\frac{1}{2}(99.7\%) = 49.85\%$.

19. $17,500 is 1 standard deviation above the mean. Since 68% of the data items fall within 1 standard deviation of the mean, 100% − 68% = 32% fall farther than 1 standard deviation from the mean. Because of symmetry, the percent that paid more than $17,500 is $\frac{1}{2}(32\%) = 16\%$.

20. $18,000 is 2 standard deviations above the mean. Since 95% of the data items fall within 2 standard deviations of the mean, 100% − 95% = 5% fall farther than 2 standard deviations from the mean. Because of symmetry, the percent that paid more than $18,000 is $\frac{1}{2}(5\%) = 2.5\%$.

21. $16,000 is 2 standard deviations below the mean. Since 95% of the data items fall within 2 standard deviations of the mean, 100% − 95% = 5% fall farther than 2 standard deviations from the mean. Because of symmetry, the percent that paid less than $16,000 is $\frac{1}{2}(5\%) = 2.5\%$.

22. $16,500 is 1 standard deviation below the mean. Since 68% of the data items fall within 1 standard deviation of the mean,
100% − 68% = 32% fall farther than 1 standard deviation from the mean. Because of symmetry, the percent that paid less than $16,500 is $\frac{1}{2}(32\%) = 16\%$.

23. $530 - 2 \cdot 128 = 274$
    $530 + 2 \cdot 128 = 786$
    95% score between 274 and 786.

24. $530 - 1 \cdot 128 = 402$
    $530 + 1 \cdot 128 = 658$
    68% score between 402 and 658.

25. From Exercise 23, we know 95% score between 274 and 786. By symmetry, $\frac{1}{2}(95\%) = 47.5\%$ score between 274 and 530.

26. From Exercise 24, we know 68% score between 402 and 658. By symmetry, $\frac{1}{2}(68\%) = 34\%$ score between 402 and 530.

27. $530 + 1 \cdot 128 = 658$
   68% score within 1 standard deviation of the mean, so $100\% - 68\% = 32\%$ of the scores are farther than 1 standard deviation from the mean. Because of symmetry, the percent that score above 658 is $\frac{1}{2}(32\%) = 16\%$.

28. $530 + 2 \cdot 128 = 786$
   95% score within 2 standard deviations of the mean, so $100\% - 95\% = 5\%$ of the scores are farther than 2 standard deviations from the mean. Because of symmetry, the percent that score above 786 is $\frac{1}{2}(5\%) = 2.5\%$.

29. From Exercise 23, we know 95% score between 274 and 786. That means that $100\% - 95\% = 5\%$ score below 274 or above 786. Because of symmetry, the percent that score below 274 is $\frac{1}{2}(5\%) = 2.5\%$.

30. From Exercise 24, we know 68% score between 402 and 658. That means that $100\% - 68\% = 32\%$ score below 402 or above 658. Because of symmetry, the percent that score below 402 is $\frac{1}{2}(32\%) = 16\%$.

31. $530 + 3 \cdot 128 = 914$
   99.7% score within 3 standard deviations of the mean, so $100\% - 99.7\% = 0.3\%$ of the scores are farther than 3 standard deviations from the mean. Because of symmetry, the percent that score above 914 is $\frac{1}{2}(0.3\%) = 0.15\%$.

32. $530 - 3 \cdot 128 = 146$
   99.7% score within 3 standard deviations of the mean, so $100\% - 99.7\% = 0.3\%$ of the scores are farther than 3 standard deviations from the mean. Because of symmetry, the percent that score below 146 is $\frac{1}{2}(0.3\%) = 0.15\%$.

33. $z_{68} = \dfrac{68 - 60}{8} = \dfrac{8}{8} = 1$

34. $z_{76} = \dfrac{76 - 60}{8} = \dfrac{16}{8} = 2$

35. $z_{84} = \dfrac{84 - 60}{8} = \dfrac{24}{8} = 3$

36. $z_{92} = \dfrac{92 - 60}{8} = \dfrac{32}{8} = 4$

37. $z_{64} = \dfrac{64 - 60}{8} = \dfrac{4}{8} = 0.5$

38. $z_{72} = \dfrac{72 - 60}{8} = \dfrac{12}{8} = 1.5$

39. $z_{74} = \dfrac{74 - 60}{8} = \dfrac{14}{8} = 1.75$

40. $z_{78} = \dfrac{78 - 60}{8} = \dfrac{18}{8} = 2.25$

41. $z_{60} = \dfrac{60 - 60}{8} = \dfrac{0}{8} = 0$

42. $z_{100} = \dfrac{100 - 60}{8} = \dfrac{40}{8} = 5$

43. $z_{52} = \dfrac{52 - 60}{8} = \dfrac{-8}{8} = -1$

44. $z_{44} = \dfrac{44 - 60}{8} = \dfrac{-16}{8} = -2$

45. $z_{48} = \dfrac{48 - 60}{8} = \dfrac{-12}{8} = -1.5$

46. $z_{40} = \dfrac{40 - 60}{8} = \dfrac{-20}{8} = -2.5$

47. $z_{34} = \dfrac{34 - 60}{8} = \dfrac{-26}{8} = -3.25$

48. $z_{30} = \dfrac{30 - 60}{8} = \dfrac{-30}{8} = -3.75$

49. $z_{290} = \dfrac{290 - 266}{16} = \dfrac{24}{16} = 1.5$

50. $z_{294} = \dfrac{294 - 266}{16} = \dfrac{28}{16} = 1.75$

51. $z_{302} = \dfrac{302 - 266}{16} = \dfrac{36}{16} = 2.25$

52. $z_{318} = \dfrac{318 - 266}{16} = \dfrac{52}{16} = 3.25$

53. $z_{258} = \dfrac{258 - 266}{16} = \dfrac{-8}{16} = -0.5$

54. $z_{254} = \dfrac{254 - 266}{16} = \dfrac{-12}{16} = -0.75$

55. $z_{242} = \dfrac{242 - 266}{16} = \dfrac{-24}{16} = -1.5$

56. $z_{226} = \dfrac{226 - 266}{16} = \dfrac{-40}{16} = -2.5$

57. math test:
$$z_{230} = \dfrac{230 - 200}{10} = \dfrac{30}{10} = 3$$
reading test:
$$z_{540} = \dfrac{540 - 500}{15} = \dfrac{40}{15} \approx 2.7$$
The student had the better score on the math test.

58. grammar test:
$$z_{72} = \dfrac{72 - 84}{10} = \dfrac{-12}{10} = -1.2$$
vocabulary test:
$$z_{255} = \dfrac{255 - 300}{30} = \dfrac{-45}{30} = -1.5$$
The student had the better score on the grammar test.

59. $2 \cdot 50 = 100$
The data item is 100 units above the mean.
$400 + 100 = 500$

60. $3 \cdot 50 = 150$
The data item is 150 units above the mean.
$400 + 150 = 550$

61. $1.5(50) = 75$
The data item is 75 units above the mean.
$400 + 75 = 475$

62. $2.5(50) = 125$
The data item is 125 units above the mean.
$400 + 125 = 525$

63. $-3 \cdot 50 = -150$
The data item is 150 units below the mean.
$400 - 150 = 250$

64. $-2 \cdot 50 = -100$
The data item is 100 units below the mean.
$400 - 100 = 300$

65. $-2.5(50) = -125$
The data item is 125 units below the mean.
$400 - 125 = 275$

66. $-1.5(50) = -75$
The data item is 75 units below the mean.
$400 - 75 = 325$

67. a. 72.57%

b. $100\% - 72.57\% = 27.43\%$

68. a. 78.81%

b. $100\% - 78.81\% = 21.19\%$

69. a. 88.49%

b. $100\% - 88.49\% = 11.51\%$

70. a. 91.92%

b. $100\% - 91.92\% = 8.08\%$

71. a. 24.20%

b. $100\% - 24.20\% = 75.8\%$

72. a. 34.46%

b. $100\% - 34.46\% = 65.54\%$

73. a. 11.51%

b. $100\% - 11.51\% = 88.49\%$

74. a. 3.59%

b. $100\% - 3.59\% = 96.41\%$

75. $z = 0.2 \rightarrow 57.93\%$
$z = 1.4 \rightarrow 91.92\%$
$91.92\% - 57.93\% = 33.99\%$

76. $z = 0.3 \rightarrow 61.79\%$
$z = 2.1 \rightarrow 98.21\%$
$98.21\% - 61.79\% = 36.42\%$

77. $z = 1 \rightarrow 84.13\%$
$z = 3 \rightarrow 99.87\%$
$99.87\% - 84.13\% = 15.74\%$

78. $z = 2 \rightarrow 97.72\%$
$z = 3 \rightarrow 99.87\%$
$99.87\% - 97.72\% = 2.15\%$

79. $z = -1.5 \rightarrow 6.68\%$
$z = 1.5 \rightarrow 93.32\%$
$93.32\% - 6.68\% = 86.64\%$

80. $z = -1.2 \rightarrow 11.51\%$
$z = 1.2 \rightarrow 88.49\%$
$88.49\% - 11.51\% = 76.98\%$

81. $z = -2 \rightarrow 2.28\%$
$z = -0.5 \rightarrow 30.85\%$
$30.85\% - 2.28\% = 28.57\%$

82. $z = -2.2 \rightarrow 1.39\%$
$z = -0.3 \rightarrow 38.21\%$
$38.21\% - 1.39\% = 36.82\%$

83. $z_{650} = \dfrac{650 - 500}{100} = \dfrac{150}{100} = 1.5$

$z = 1.5 \rightarrow 93.32\%$
93.32% score below 650.

84. $z_{680} = \dfrac{680 - 500}{100} = \dfrac{180}{100} = 1.8$

$z = 1.8 \rightarrow 96.41\%$
96.41% score below 680.

85. $z_{560} = \dfrac{560 - 500}{100} = \dfrac{60}{100} = 0.6$

$z = 0.6 \rightarrow 72.57\%$
$100\% - 72.57\% = 27.43\%$ score above 560.

86. $z_{590} = \dfrac{590 - 500}{100} = \dfrac{90}{100} = 0.9$

$z = 0.9 \rightarrow 81.59\%$
$100\% - 81.59\% = 18.41\%$ score above 590.

87. $z_{380} = \dfrac{380 - 500}{100} = \dfrac{-120}{100} = -1.2$

$z = -1.2 \rightarrow 11.51\%$
$100\% - 11.51\% = 88.49\%$ score above 380.

88. $z_{360} = \dfrac{360 - 500}{100} = \dfrac{-140}{100} = -1.4$

$z = -1.4 \rightarrow 8.08\%$
$100\% - 8.08\% = 91.92\%$ score above 360

89. $z_{640} = \dfrac{640 - 500}{100} = \dfrac{140}{100} = 1.4$

$z = 1.4 \rightarrow 91.92\%$

$z_{710} = \dfrac{710 - 500}{100} = \dfrac{210}{100} = 2.1$

$z = 2.1 \rightarrow 98.21\%$
$98.21\% - 91.92\% = 6.29\%$ score between 640 and 710.

90. $z_{660} = \dfrac{660 - 500}{100} = \dfrac{160}{100} = 1.6$

$z = 1.6 \rightarrow 94.52\%$

$z_{740} = \dfrac{740 - 500}{100} = \dfrac{240}{100} = 2.4$

$z = 2.4 \rightarrow 99.18\%$
$99.18\% - 94.52\% = 4.66\%$ score between 660 and 740.

91. $z_{440} = \dfrac{440 - 500}{100} = \dfrac{-60}{100} = -0.6$

$z = -0.6 \rightarrow 27.43\%$

$z_{560} = \dfrac{560 - 500}{100} = \dfrac{60}{100} = 0.6$

$z = 0.6 \rightarrow 72.57\%$
$72.57\% - 27.43\% = 45.14\%$ score between 440 and 560.

92. $z_{420} = \dfrac{420 - 500}{100} = \dfrac{-80}{100} = -0.8$

$z = -0.8 \rightarrow 21.19\%$

$z_{580} = \dfrac{580 - 500}{100} = \dfrac{80}{100} = 0.8$

$z = 0.8 \rightarrow 78.81\%$
$78.81\% - 21.19\% = 57.62\%$ score between 420 and 580.

93. $z_{25.8} = \dfrac{25.8 - 22.5}{2.2} = 1.5$

$z = 1.5 \rightarrow 93.32\%$
$100\% - 93.32\% = 6.68\%$ weigh more than 25.8 pounds.

94. $z_{23.6} = \dfrac{23.6 - 22.5}{2.2} = 0.5$

$z = 0.5 \rightarrow 69.15\%$
$100\% - 69.15\% = 30.85\%$ weigh more than
23.6 pounds.

95. $z_{19.2} = \dfrac{19.2 - 22.5}{2.2} = -1.5$

$z = -1.5 \rightarrow 6.68\%$
$z_{21.4} = \dfrac{21.4 - 22.5}{2.2} = -0.5$

$z = -0.5 \rightarrow 30.85\%$
$30.85\% - 6.68\% = 24.17\%$ weigh between 19.2 and
21.4 pounds.

96. $z_{18.1} = \dfrac{18.1 - 22.5}{2.2} = -2$

$z = -2 \rightarrow 2.28\%$
$z_{19.2} = \dfrac{19.2 - 22.5}{2.2} = -1.5$

$z = -1.5 \rightarrow 6.68\%$
$6.68\% - 2.28\% = 4.4\%$ weigh between 18.1 and
19.2 pounds.

97. a. margin of error $= \pm \dfrac{1}{\sqrt{397}}$

$\approx \pm 0.050$

$\approx \pm 5.0\%$

b. $26\% - 5\% = 21\%$
$26\% + 5\% = 31\%$
We can be 95% confident that between 21%
and 31% of all parents feel that crime is a bad
thing about being a kid.

98. a. margin of error $= \pm \dfrac{1}{\sqrt{397}}$

$\approx \pm 0.050$

$\approx \pm 5.0\%$

b. $5\% - 5\% = 0\%$
$5\% + 5\% = 10\%$
We can be 95% confident that between 0% and
10% of all parents feel that drugs are a bad
thing about being a kid.

99. a. margin of error $= \pm \dfrac{1}{\sqrt{4000}}$

$\approx \pm 0.016$

$\approx \pm 1.6\%$

b. $60.2\% - 1.6\% = 58.6\%$
$60.2\% + 1.6\% = 61.8\%$
We can be 95% confident that between 58.6%
and 61.8% of all TV households watched the
final episode of $M*A*S*H$.

100. a. margin of error $= \pm \dfrac{1}{\sqrt{4000}}$

$\approx \pm 0.016$

$\approx \pm 1.6\%$

b. $51.1\% - 1.6\% = 49.5\%$
$51.1\% + 1.6\% = 52.7\%$
We can be 95% confident that between 49.5%
and 52.7% of all TV households watched
Roots, Part 8.

101. new margin of error $= \pm \dfrac{1}{\sqrt{5000}}$

$\approx \pm 0.014$

$\approx \pm 1.4\%$
improvement $= 1.6\% - 1.4\% = 0.2\%$

102. new margin of error $= \pm \dfrac{1}{\sqrt{10,000}}$

$= \pm 0.010$

$= \pm 1.0\%$
improvement $= 1.4\% - 1.0\% = 0.4\%$

103. No, explanations will vary.

104. No, explanations will vary.

105-118. Answers will vary.

119. $\dfrac{1}{400} = 0.0025 = 0.25\%$

A z-score of -2.8 has 0.26% of the data items below
it. So find the height corresponding to $z = -2.8$.
$69 - 2.8(2.5) = 62$ inches
The woman is 62 inches tall.

120. A z-score of 1.3 has 90.32% of the data items below
it, and 9.68% above it. So find the score
corresponding to $z = 1.3$.
$500 + 1.3(100) = 630$
The cutoff score is 630.

Check Points 12.5

1. 0.51 would indicate a moderate correlation between the two.

2.

x	y	xy	x^2	y^2
2.5	211	527.5	6.25	44,521
3.9	167	651.3	15.21	27,889
2.9	131	379.9	8.41	17,161
2.4	191	458.4	5.76	36,481
2.9	220	638	8.41	48,400
0.8	297	237.6	0.64	88,209
9.1	71	646.1	82.81	5041
0.8	211	168.8	0.64	44,521
0.7	300	210	0.49	90,000
7.9	107	845.3	62.41	11,449
1.8	167	300.6	3.24	27,889
1.9	266	505.4	3.61	70,756
0.8	227	181.6	0.64	51,529
6.5	86	559	42.25	7396
1.6	207	331.2	2.56	42,849
5.8	115	667	33.64	13,225
1.3	285	370.5	1.69	81,225
1:2	199	238.8	1.44	39,601
2.7	172	464.4	7.29	29,584

$\sum x = 57.5 \quad \sum y = 3630 \quad \sum xy = 8381.4 \quad \sum x^2 = 287.39 \quad \sum y^2 = 777,726$

$\left(\sum x\right)^2 = (57.5)^2 = 3306.25$ and $\left(\sum y\right)^2 = (3630)^2 = 13,176,900$

$$r = \frac{19(8381.4)-(57.5)(3630)}{\sqrt{19(287.39)-3306.25}\sqrt{19(777,726)-13,176,900}} = \frac{-49,478.4}{\sqrt{2154.16}\sqrt{1599894}} \approx -0.84$$

This value for r is fairly close to -1 and indicates a strong negative correlation. This means the more a person drinks, the less likely the person is to die from heart disease.

3. $m = \dfrac{19(8381.4)-(57.5)(3630)}{19(287.39)-3306.25} = \dfrac{-49,478.4}{2154.16} \approx -22.97$

$b = \dfrac{3630-(-22.97)(57.5)}{19} = \dfrac{4950.775}{19} \approx 260.56$

The equation of the regression line is $y = -22.97x + 260.56$.

The predicted heart disease death rate in a country where adults average 10 liters of alcohol per person per year can be found by substituting 10 for x.

$y = -22.97x + 260.56$

$= -22.97(10) + 260.56$

$= 30.86$

4. Yes, $|r| = 0.84$. Since $0.84 > 0.456$ and 0.575 (using table 12.16), we may conclude that a correlation does exist.

Exercise Set 12.5

1. There appears to be a positive correlation.

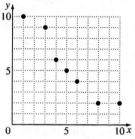

2. There appears to be a positive correlation.

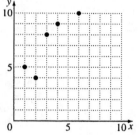

3. There appears to be a negative correlation.

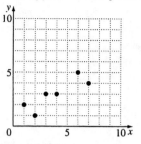

4. There does not appear to be a correlation.

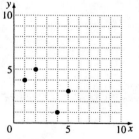

5. There appears to be a positive correlation.

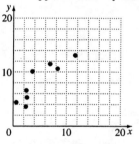

6. There appears to be a strong positive correlation.

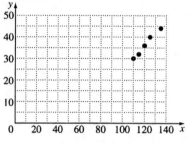

7. There appears to be a positive correlation.

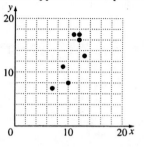

8. There appears to be a negative correlation.

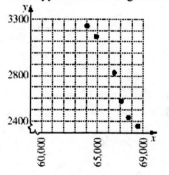

9. False; the correlation is negative.

10. False; there is a negative correlation.

11. True

12. False; correlation does not indicate causality.

13. True

14. False; there are 5 births per woman in Vietnam.

15. False; see for example, Syria and Vietnam.

16. False; Kenya has the greatest number of births per woman, but it does not have the smallest percentage of women using contraceptives.

17. False; there is some positive correlation.

18. False; the correlation is weak.

19. True

20. True

21. False; very few of the points lie on the regression line.

22. False; there are only about 40 students in the sample.

23. False

24. False

25. False; both correlations are negative.

26. False; the regression line indicates that sometime around 2015 women will start to swim faster than men in this Olympic event.

27. True

28. False; the correlation coefficients should be closer to -1.

29. a

30. b

31. d

32. e

33.

x	y	xy	x^2	y^2
1	2	2	1	4
6	5	30	36	25
4	3	12	16	9
3	3	9	9	9
7	4	28	49	16
2	1	2	4	1

$$\sum x = 23 \quad \sum y = 18 \quad \sum xy = 83 \quad \sum x^2 = 115 \quad \sum y^2 = 64$$

$$\left(\sum x\right)^2 = (23)^2 = 529 \text{ and } \left(\sum y\right)^2 = (18)^2 = 324$$

$$r = \frac{6(83) - (23)(18)}{\sqrt{6(115) - 529}\sqrt{6(64) - (324)}}$$

$$= \frac{84}{\sqrt{161}\sqrt{60}}$$

$$\approx 0.855$$

34.

x	y	xy	x^2	y^2
2	4	8	4	16
1	5	5	1	25
6	10	60	36	100
3	8	24	9	64
4	9	36	16	81

$$\sum x = 16 \quad \sum y = 36 \quad \sum xy = 133 \quad \sum x^2 = 66 \quad \sum y^2 = 286$$

$$\left(\sum x\right)^2 = (16)^2 = 256 \text{ and } \left(\sum y\right)^2 = (36)^2 = 1296$$

$$r = \frac{5(133) - (16)(36)}{\sqrt{5(66) - 256}\sqrt{5(286) - 1296}}$$

$$= \frac{89}{\sqrt{74}\sqrt{134}}$$

$$\approx 0.894$$

35.

x	y	xy	x^2	y^2
8	2	16	64	4
6	4	24	36	16
1	10	10	1	100
5	5	25	25	25
4	6	24	16	36
10	2	20	100	4
3	9	27	9	81

$\sum x = 37 \qquad \sum y = 38 \qquad \sum xy = 146 \qquad \sum x^2 = 251 \qquad \sum y^2 = 266$

$$\left(\sum x\right)^2 = (37)^2 = 1369 \text{ and } \left(\sum y\right)^2 = (38)^2 = 1444$$

$$r = \frac{7(146) - (37)(38)}{\sqrt{7(251) - 1369}\sqrt{7(266) - 1444}}$$

$$= \frac{-384}{\sqrt{388}\sqrt{418}}$$

$$\approx -0.954$$

36.

x	y	xy	x^2	y^2
4	1	4	16	1
5	3	15	25	9
2	5	10	4	25
1	4	4	1	16

$\sum x = 12 \qquad \sum y = 13 \qquad \sum xy = 33 \qquad \sum x^2 = 46 \qquad \sum y^2 = 51$

$$\left(\sum x\right)^2 = (12)^2 = 144 \text{ and } \left(\sum y\right)^2 = (13)^2 = 169$$

$$r = \frac{4(33) - (12)(13)}{\sqrt{4(46) - 144}\sqrt{4(51) - 169}}$$

$$= \frac{-24}{\sqrt{40}\sqrt{35}}$$

$$\approx -0.641$$

37. a.

x	y	xy	x^2	y^2
13	13	169	169	169
9	11	99	81	121
7	7	49	49	49
12	16	192	144	256
12	17	204	144	289
10	8	80	100	64
11	17	187	121	289

$\sum x = 74 \qquad \sum y = 89 \qquad \sum xy = 980 \qquad \sum x^2 = 808 \qquad \sum y^2 = 1237$

$\left(\sum x\right) = (74)^2 = 5476$ and $\left(\sum y\right)^2 = (89)^2 = 7921$

$r = \dfrac{7(980) - (74)(89)}{\sqrt{7(808) - 5476}\sqrt{7(1237) - 7921}}$

$= \dfrac{274}{\sqrt{180}\sqrt{738}}$

≈ 0.75

b. $m = \dfrac{7(980) - (74)(89)}{7(808) - 5476} = \dfrac{274}{180} \approx 1.52$

$b = \dfrac{89 - 1.52(74)}{7} = \dfrac{-23.48}{7} \approx -3.38$

$y = 1.52x - 3.38$

c. $x = 16$
$y = 1.52(16) - 3.38 = 20.98$
21 years

38. a.

x	y	xy	x^2	y^2
110	30	3300	12,100	900
115	32	3680	13,225	1024
120	36	4320	14,400	1296
125	40	5000	15,625	1600
135	44	5940	18,225	1936

$\sum x = 605 \qquad \sum y = 182 \qquad \sum xy = 22,240 \qquad \sum x^2 = 73,575 \qquad \sum y^2 = 6756$

$\left(\sum x\right)^2 = (605)^2 = 366,025$ and $\left(\sum y\right)^2 = (182)^2 = 33,124$

$r = \dfrac{5(22,240) - (605)(182)}{\sqrt{5(73,575) - 366,025}\sqrt{5(6756) - 33,124}}$

$= \dfrac{1090}{\sqrt{1850}\sqrt{656}}$

≈ 0.989

b. $m = \dfrac{5(22,240) - (605)(182)}{5(73,575) - 366,025} = \dfrac{1090}{1850} \approx 0.59$

$b = \dfrac{182 - 0.59(605)}{5} = \dfrac{-174.95}{5} \approx -34.89$

$y = 0.59x - 34.89$

c. $x = 123$

$y = 0.59(123) - 34.89 = 37.68$

$\$37,680$

39. a.

x	y	xy	x^2	y^2
11.6	13.1	151.96	134.56	171.61
8.3	10.6	87.98	68.89	112.36
6.9	11.5	79.35	47.61	132.25
3.6	10.1	36.36	12.96	102.01
2.6	5.3	13.78	6.76	28.09
2.5	6.6	16.50	6.25	43.56
2.4	3.6	8.64	5.76	12.96
0.6	4.4	2.64	0.36	19.36

$\sum x = 38.5 \quad \sum y = 65.2 \quad \sum xy = 397.21 \quad \sum x^2 = 283.15 \quad \sum y^2 = 622.2$

$\left(\sum x\right)^2 = (38.5)^2 = 1482.25$ and $\left(\sum y\right)^2 = (65.2)^2 = 4251.04$

$r = \dfrac{8(397.21) - (38.5)(65.2)}{\sqrt{8(283.15) - 1482.25}\sqrt{8(622.2) - 4251.04}}$

$= \dfrac{667.48}{\sqrt{782.95}\sqrt{726.56}}$

≈ 0.885

b. $m = \dfrac{8(397.21) - (38.5)(65.2)}{8(283.15) - 1482.25} = \dfrac{667.48}{782.95} \approx 0.8525 \approx 0.85$

$b = \dfrac{65.2 - 0.8525(38.5)}{8} = \dfrac{32.378}{8} \approx 4.05$

$y = 0.85x + 4.05$

c. $x = 14$

$y = 0.85(14) + 4.05 = 15.95$

16 murders per 100,000 people

40. a.

x	y	xy	x^2	y^2
64,085	3239	207,571,315	4,106,887,225	10,491,121
64,897	3147	204,230,859	4,211,620,609	9,903,609
66,524	2826	187,996,824	4,425,442,576	7,986,276
67,134	2580	173,205,720	4,506,973,956	6,656,400
67,761	2433	164,862,513	4,591,553,121	5,919,489
68,580	2350	161,163,000	4,703,216,400	5,522,500

$\sum x = 398,981 \quad \sum y = 16,575 \quad \sum xy = 1,099,030,231 \quad \sum x^2 = 26,545,693,887 \quad \sum y^2 = 46,479,395$

$$\left(\sum x\right)^2 = (398,981)^2 \approx 1.5919 \times 10^{11} \text{ and } \left(\sum y\right)^2 = (16,575)^2 = 274,730,625$$

$$r = \frac{6(1,099,030,231) - (398,981)(16,575)}{\sqrt{6(26,545,693,887) - (398,981)^2}\sqrt{6(46,479,395) - 274,730,625}}$$

$$\approx -0.989$$

b. $m = \dfrac{6(1,099,030,231) - (398,981)(16,575)}{6(26,545,693,887) - (398,981)^2} \approx -0.21$

$b = \dfrac{16,575 - (-0.21)(398,981)}{6} \approx 17,013.26$

$y = -0.21x + 17,013.26$

c. $x = 70,000$

$y = -0.21x + 17,013.26$

$\quad = -0.21(70,000) + 17,013.26$

$\quad \approx 2313.26$ thousand unemployed males

$\quad \approx 2,313,260$ unemployed males

41. $|r| = 0.5$

Since 0.5 > 0.444, conclude that a correlation does exist.

42. $|r| = 0.4$

Since 0.4 > 0.381, conclude that a correlation does exist.

43. $|r| = 0.5$

Since 0.5 < 0.576, conclude that a correlation does not exist.

44. $|r| = 0.04$

Since 0.04 < 0.423, conclude that a correlation does not exist.

45. $|r| = 0.351$

Since 0.351 > 0.232, conclude that a correlation does exist.

46. $|r| = 0.37$

Since 0.37 > 0.325, conclude that a correlation does exist.

47. $|r| = 0.37$

Since 0.37 < 0.444, conclude that a correlation does not exist.

48. $|r| = 0.73$

Since 0.73 > 0.602, conclude that a correlation does exist.

49-59. Answers will vary.

60. a

61. Answers will vary.

62.

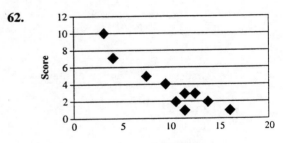

63.

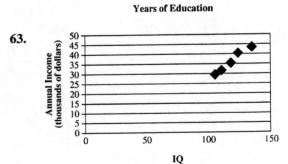

Chapter 12: Statistics

Chapter 12 Review Exercises

1. The *population* is all American mothers with children under 18. The *sample* is the group of 181 that were randomly selected.

2. The variable measured is the mothers' perceived change in the likelihood of terrorist attacks due to the war with Iraq.

3. a

4.

Time Spent on Homework (in hours)	Number of students
6	1
7	3
8	3
9	2
10	1
	10

5.

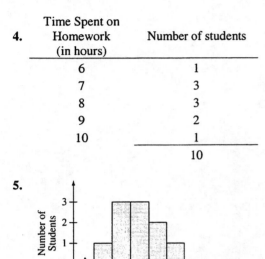

6.

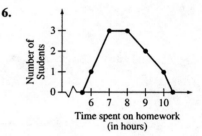

7.

Grades	Number of students
0–39	19
40–49	8
50–59	6
60–69	6
70–79	5
80–89	3
90–100	3
	50

8.

Stems	Leaves
1	3 4 1 3 7 8
2	4 9 6 9 2 7
3	4 9 6 5 1 1 1
4	4 0 2 7 9 1 2 5
5	7 9 6 4 0 1
6	3 3 7 0 8 9
7	2 3 4 0 5
8	7 1 6
9	5 1 0

9. Though the left edge of each bar lines up with the appropriate value in the vertical axis, the right edge of each bar extends well above the correct value.

10. Mean $= \dfrac{84+90+95+89+98}{5}$

    $= \dfrac{456}{5}$

    $= 91.2$

11. Mean $= \dfrac{33+27+9+10+6+7+11+23+27}{9}$

    $= \dfrac{153}{9}$

    $= 17$

12. Mean $= \dfrac{1\cdot2+2\cdot4+3\cdot3+4\cdot1}{10}$

    $= \dfrac{2+8+9+4}{10}$

    $= \dfrac{23}{10}$

    $= 2.3$

13. First arrange the data items from smallest to largest.
    6, 7, 9, 10, <u>11</u>, 23, 27, 27, 33
    There is an odd number of data items, so the median is the middle number. The median is 11.

14. First arrange the data items from smallest to largest.
    16, 22, <u>28</u>, 28, 34
    There is an odd number of data items, so the median is the middle number. The median is 28.

15. The median is the value in the $\dfrac{n+1}{2} = \dfrac{10+1}{2} = \dfrac{11}{2} = 5.5$ position, which means the median is the mean of the 5th and 6th values. The 5th and 6th values are both 2, therefore the median is 2.

16. The number 27 occurs most frequently, so the mode is 27.

17. Bimodal; 585 and 587 each occur twice.

18. The number 2 occurs most frequently, so the mode is 2.

19. lowest data value = 84, highest data value = 98
    Midrange $= \dfrac{84+98}{2} = \dfrac{182}{2} = 91$

20. lowest data value = 6, highest data value = 33
    Midrange $= \dfrac{6+33}{2} = \dfrac{39}{2} = 19.5$

21. lowest data value = 1, highest data value = 4
    Midrange $= \dfrac{1+4}{2} = \dfrac{5}{2} = 2.5$

22-23. Answers will vary.

24. a.

Age at first inauguration	Number of Presidents
42	1
43	1
44	0
45	0
46	2
47	1
48	1
49	2
50	1
51	5
52	2
53	0
54	5
55	4
56	3
57	4
58	1
59	0
60	1
61	3
62	1
63	0
64	2
65	1
66	0
67	0
68	1
69	1
	43

b. Mean $= \dfrac{\left(\begin{array}{c}42\cdot1+43\cdot1+46\cdot2+47\cdot1+48\cdot1+49\cdot2+50\cdot1+51\cdot5+52\cdot2+54\cdot5+55\cdot4\\+56\cdot3+57\cdot4+58\cdot1+60\cdot1+61\cdot3+62\cdot1+64\cdot2+65\cdot1+68\cdot1+69\cdot1\end{array}\right)}{43} = \dfrac{2357}{43} \approx 54.81$ years

The median is the value in the $\dfrac{n+1}{2} = \dfrac{43+1}{2} = \dfrac{44}{2} = 22$ position, which means the median is 22nd value.

Median = 55 years

The model ages are 51 and 54 years (bimodal).

Midrange $= \dfrac{42+69}{2} = 55.5$ years

25. Range = 34 − 16 = 18

26. Range = 783 − 219 = 564

27. a.

Data item	Deviation: Data item – mean
29	$29 - 35 = -6$
9	$9 - 35 = -26$
8	$8 - 35 = -27$
22	$22 - 35 = -13$
46	$46 - 35 = 11$
51	$51 - 35 = 16$
48	$48 - 35 = 13$
42	$42 - 35 = 7$
53	$53 - 35 = 18$
42	$42 - 35 = 7$

b. $-6 - 26 - 27 - 13 + 11 + 16 + 13 + 7 + 18 + 7 = 0$

28. a. $\text{Mean} = \dfrac{36 + 26 + 24 + 90 + 74}{5} = \dfrac{250}{5} = 50$

b.

Data item	Deviation: Data item – mean
36	$36 - 50 = -14$
26	$26 - 50 = -24$
24	$24 - 50 = -26$
90	$90 - 50 = 40$
74	$74 - 50 = 24$

c. $-14 - 24 - 26 + 40 + 24 = 0$

29. $\text{Mean} = \dfrac{3 + 3 + 5 + 8 + 10 + 13}{6} = \dfrac{42}{6} = 7$

Data item	Deviation: Data item – mean	$(\text{Deviation})^2$: $(\text{Data item–mean})^2$
3	$3 - 7 = -4$	$(-4)^2 = 16$
3	$3 - 7 = -4$	$(-4)^2 = 16$
5	$5 - 7 = -2$	$(-2)^2 = 4$
8	$8 - 7 = 1$	$1^2 = 1$
10	$10 - 7 = 3$	$3^2 = 9$
13	$13 - 7 = 6$	$6^2 = 36$
		$\sum (\text{data item–mean})^2 = 82$

$\text{Standard deviation} = \sqrt{\dfrac{82}{6-1}} = \sqrt{\dfrac{82}{5}} \approx 4.05$

30. Mean $= \dfrac{20 + 27 + 23 + 26 + 28 + 32 + 33 + 35}{8} = \dfrac{224}{8} = 28$

Data item	Deviation: Data item – mean	(Deviation)^2 : (Data item–mean)^2
20	$20 - 28 = -8$	$(-8)^2 = 64$
27	$27 - 28 = -1$	$(-1)^2 = 1$
23	$23 - 28 = -5$	$(-5)^2 = 25$
26	$26 - 28 = -2$	$(-2)^2 = 4$
28	$28 - 28 = 0$	$0^2 = 0$
32	$32 - 28 = 4$	$4^2 = 16$
33	$33 - 28 = 5$	$5^2 = 25$
35	$35 - 28 = 7$	$7^2 = 49$
		$\sum$(data item–mean)$^2 = 184$

Standard deviation $= \sqrt{\dfrac{184}{8-1}} = \sqrt{\dfrac{184}{7}} \approx 5.13$

31. Mean $= \dfrac{10 + 30 + 37 + 40 + 43 + 44 + 45 + 69 + 86 + 86}{10} = \dfrac{490}{10} = 49$

Range $= 86 - 10 = 76$

Data item	Deviation: Data item – mean	(Deviation)^2 : (Data item–mean)^2
10	$10 - 49 = -39$	$(-39)^2 = 1521$
30	$30 - 49 = -19$	$(-19)^2 = 361$
37	$37 - 49 = -12$	$(-12)^2 = 144$
40	$40 - 49 = -9$	$(-9)^2 = 81$
43	$43 - 49 = -6$	$(-6)^2 = 36$
44	$44 - 49 = -5$	$(-5)^2 = 25$
45	$45 - 49 = -4$	$(-4)^2 = 16$
69	$69 - 49 = 20$	$20^2 = 400$
86	$86 - 49 = 37$	$37^2 = 1369$
86	$86 - 49 = 37$	$37^2 = 1369$
		$\sum$(data item–mean)$^2 = 5322$

Standard deviation $= \sqrt{\dfrac{5322}{10-1}} = \sqrt{\dfrac{5322}{9}} \approx 24.32$

32. Set A:

$$\text{Mean} = \frac{80+80+80+80}{4} = \frac{320}{4} = 80$$

Data item	Deviation: Data item − mean	$(\text{Deviation})^2$: $(\text{Data item−mean})^2$
80	$80-80=0$	$0^2 = 0$
80	$80-80=0$	$0^2 = 0$
80	$80-80=0$	$0^2 = 0$
80	$80-80=0$	$0^2 = 0$
		$\sum(\text{data item−mean})^2 = 0$

$$\text{Standard deviation} = \sqrt{\frac{0}{4-1}} = \sqrt{\frac{0}{3}} = 0$$

Set B:

$$\text{Mean} = \frac{70+70+90+90}{4} = \frac{320}{4} = 80$$

Data item	Deviation: Data item − mean	$(\text{Deviation})^2$: $(\text{Data item−mean})^2$
70	$70-80=-10$	$(-10)^2 = 100$
70	$70-80=-10$	$(-10)^2 = 100$
90	$90-80=10$	$10^2 = 100$
90	$90-80=10$	$10^2 = 100$
		$\sum(\text{data item−mean})^2 = 400$

$$\text{Standard deviation} = \sqrt{\frac{400}{4-1}} = \sqrt{\frac{400}{3}} \approx 11.55$$

Written descriptions of the similarities and differences between the two sets of data will vary.

33. Answers will vary.

34. $70 + 2 \cdot 8 = 70 + 16 = 86$

35. $70 + 3.5(8) = 70 + 28 = 98$

36. $70 - 1.25(8) = 70 - 10 = 60$

37. 64 is one standard deviation below the mean and 72 is one standard deviation above the mean, so 68% of the people in the retirement community are between 64 and 72 years old.

38. 60 is two standard deviations below the mean and 76 is two standard deviations above the mean, so 95% of the people in the retirement community are between 60 and 76 years old.

39. 68 is the mean and 72 is one standard deviation above the mean, so half of 68%, or 34% of the people in the retirement community are between 68 and 72 years old.

40. 56 is three standard deviations below the mean and 80 is three standard deviations above the mean, so 99.7% of the people in the retirement community are between 56 and 80 years old.

41. 72 is one standard deviation above the mean, so 16% of the people in the retirement community are over 72 years old. (Note: 100% − 68% = 32%, half of 32% is 16%).

42. 72 is one standard deviation above the mean, so 84% of the people in the retirement community are under 72 years old. (Note: Question #41 showed that 16% is above 72, 100% − 16% = 84%)

43. 76 is two standard deviations above the mean, so 2.5% of the people in the retirement community are over 76 years old. (Note: 100% − 95% = 5%, half of 5% is 2.5%).

44. $z_{50} = \dfrac{50-50}{5} = \dfrac{0}{5} = 0$

45. $z_{60} = \dfrac{60-50}{5} = \dfrac{10}{5} = 2$

46. $z_{58} = \dfrac{58-50}{5} = \dfrac{8}{5} = 1.6$

47. $z_{35} = \dfrac{35-50}{5} = \dfrac{-15}{5} = -3$

48. $z_{44} = \dfrac{44-50}{5} = \dfrac{-6}{5} = -1.2$

49. vocabulary test: $z_{60} = \dfrac{60-50}{5} = \dfrac{10}{5} = 2$

grammar test: $z_{80} = \dfrac{80-72}{6} = \dfrac{8}{6} \approx 1.3$

The student scored better on the vocabulary test because it has a higher z-score.

50. 1.5(4000) = 6000
32,000 + 6000 = 38,000 miles

51. 2.25(4000) = 9000
32,000 + 9000 = 41,000 miles

52. −2.5(4000) = −10,000
32,000 − 10,000 = 22,000 miles

53. $z_{221} = \dfrac{221-200}{15} = \dfrac{21}{15} = 1.4$
$z = 1.4 \rightarrow 91.92\%$
91.92% have cholesterol less than 221.

54. $z_{173} = \dfrac{173-200}{15} = \dfrac{-27}{15} = -1.8$
$z = -1.8 \rightarrow 3.59\%$
100% − 3.59% = 96.41% have cholesterol greater than 173.

55. $z_{173} = \dfrac{173-200}{15} = \dfrac{-27}{15} = -1.8$
and $z = -1.8 \rightarrow 3.59\%$
$z_{221} = \dfrac{221-200}{15} = \dfrac{21}{15} = 1.4$
and $z = 1.4 \rightarrow 91.92\%$
91.92% − 3.59% = 88.33% have cholesterol between 173 and 221.

56. $z_{164} = \dfrac{164-200}{15} = \dfrac{-36}{15} = -2.4$
and $z = -2.4 \rightarrow 0.82\%$
$z_{182} = \dfrac{182-200}{15} = \dfrac{-18}{15} = -1.2$
and $z = -1.2 \rightarrow 11.51\%$
11.51% − 0.82% = 10.69% have cholesterol between 164 and 182.

57. 75%

58. 100% − 86% = 14%

59. 86% − 75% = 11%

60. a. margin of error $= \pm \dfrac{1}{\sqrt{1014}} \approx \pm 0.031 \approx \pm 3.1\%$

b. We can be 95% confident that between 29.9% and 36.1% of all American men ages 18 and older have suffered from depression or anxiety disorder.

61. There appears to be a positive correlation.

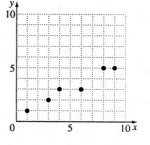

62. There appears to be a negative correlation.

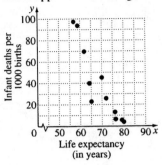

Life expectancy
(in years)

63. False; the correlation is only moderate.

64. True

65. False

66. False; data points that are vertically aligned dispute this statement.

67. True

68. False; there is a moderate negative correlation.

69. True

70. c

71. a.

x	y	xy	x^2	y^2
1	1	1	1	1
3	2	6	9	4
4	3	12	16	9
6	3	18	36	9
8	5	40	64	25
9	5	45	81	25
$\sum x = 31$	$\sum y = 19$	$\sum xy = 122$	$\sum x^2 = 207$	$\sum y^2 = 73$

$$\left(\sum x\right)^2 = (31)^2 = 961 \text{ and } \left(\sum y\right)^2 = (19)^2 = 361$$

$$r = \frac{6(122)-(31)(19)}{\sqrt{6(207)-961}\sqrt{6(73)-361}} = \frac{143}{\sqrt{281}\sqrt{77}} \approx 0.972$$

b. $m = \dfrac{6(122)-(31)(19)}{6(207)-961} = \dfrac{143}{281} \approx 0.509$

$b = \dfrac{19-(0.509)(31)}{6} = \dfrac{3.221}{6} \approx 0.537$

$y = 0.509x + 0.537$

72. a.

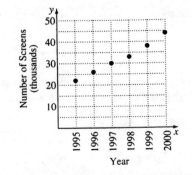

Year

447

b.

x	y	xy	x^2	y^2
0	22	0	0	484
1	26	26	1	676
2	30	60	4	900
3	33	99	9	1089
4	38	152	16	1444
5	44	220	25	1936

$$\sum x = 15 \qquad \sum y = 193 \qquad \sum xy = 557 \qquad \sum x^2 = 55 \qquad \sum y^2 = 6529$$

$$\left(\sum x\right)^2 = (15)^2 = 225 \text{ and } \left(\sum y\right)^2 = (193)^2 = 37,249$$

$$r = \frac{6(557) - (15)(193)}{\sqrt{6(55) - 225}\sqrt{6(6529) - 37,249}} = \frac{447}{\sqrt{105}\sqrt{1925}} \approx 0.994$$

c. Since $0.994 > 0.811$, we can, indeed, conclude that there is a correlation.

Chapter 12 Test

1. d

2.

Score	Frequency
3	1
4	2
5	3
6	2
7	2
8	3
9	2
10	1
	16

3.

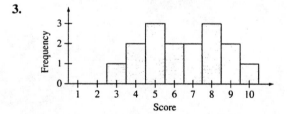

4.

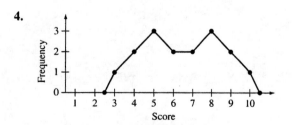

5.

Class	Frequency
40–49	3
50–59	6
60–69	6
70–79	7
80–89	6
90–99	2
	30

6.

Stems	Leaves
4	1 8 6
5	9 1 0 5 0 0
6	2 3 7 0 1 1
7	9 3 1 5 8 9 1
8	8 9 9 1 3 0
9	0 3

7. Mean $= \dfrac{3+6+2+1+7+3}{6} = \dfrac{22}{6} \approx 3.67$

8. First arrange the numbers from smallest to largest.
1, 2, 3, 3, 6, 7
There is an even number of data items, so the median is the mean of the middle two data values.
Median $= \dfrac{3+3}{2} = \dfrac{6}{2} = 3$

9. lowest data value $= 1$
highest data value $= 7$
Midrange $= \dfrac{1+7}{2} = \dfrac{8}{2} = 4$

10.

Data item	Deviation: Data item – mean	(Deviation)^2: (Data item–mean)^2
3	$3 - 3.7 = -0.7$	$(-0.7)^2 = 0.49$
6	$6 - 3.7 = 2.3$	$(2.3)^2 = 5.29$
2	$2 - 3.7 = -1.7$	$(-1.7)^2 = 2.89$
1	$1 - 3.7 = -2.7$	$(-2.7)^2 = 7.29$
7	$7 - 3.7 = 3.3$	$(3.3)^2 = 10.89$
3	$3 - 3.7 = -0.7$	$(-0.7)^2 = 0.49$

$$\sum (\text{data item–mean})^2 = 27.34$$

$$\text{Standard deviation} = \sqrt{\frac{27.34}{6-1}} = \sqrt{\frac{27.34}{5}} \approx 2.34$$

11. $\text{Mean} = \dfrac{1 \cdot 3 + 2 \cdot 5 + 3 \cdot 2 + 4 \cdot 2}{12}$

$\quad\quad = \dfrac{3 + 10 + 6 + 8}{12}$

$\quad\quad = \dfrac{27}{12}$

$\quad\quad = 2.25$

12. The median is in the $\dfrac{n+1}{2} = \dfrac{12+1}{2} = \dfrac{13}{2} = 6.5$ position, which means the median is the mean of the values in the 6th and 7th positions.

$\text{Median} = \dfrac{2+2}{2} = \dfrac{4}{2} = 2$

13. Mode = 2

14. Answers will vary.

15. $7 + 1(5.3) = 12.3$

68% of the data values are within 1 standard deviation of the mean. Because of symmetry, $\dfrac{1}{2}(68\%) = 34\%$ of college freshmen study between 7 and 12.3 hours per week.

16. $7 + 2(5.3) = 17.6$

95% of the data values are within 2 standard deviations of the mean. $100\% - 95\% = 5\%$ of the values are farther than 2 standard deviations from the mean. Because of symmetry, $\dfrac{1}{2}(5\%) = 2.5\%$ of college freshmen study more than 17.6 hours per week.

17. student: $z_{120} = \dfrac{120-100}{10} = \dfrac{20}{10} = 2$

professor: $z_{128} = \dfrac{128-100}{15} = \dfrac{28}{15} \approx 1.9$

The student scored better, because the student's z-score is higher.

18. $z_{88} = \dfrac{88 - 74}{10} = \dfrac{14}{10} = 1.4$

$z = 1.4 \rightarrow 91.92\%$

$100\% - 91.92\% = 8.08\%$ of the scores are above 88.

19. $49\% - 8\% = 41\%$

20. a.   margin of error $= \pm \dfrac{1}{\sqrt{n}}$

$= \pm \dfrac{1}{\sqrt{100}}$

$= \pm 0.1$

$= \pm 10\%$

b.   We can be 95% confident that between 50% and 70% of all students are very satisfied with their professors.

21.   There appears to be a strong negative correlation.

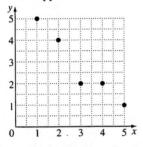

22.   False; Though the data shows that there is a <u>correlation</u>, it does not prove <u>causation</u>.

23.   False

24.   True

25.   Answers will vary.

Chapter 13
Mathematical Systems

Check Points 13.1

1. $O + O = E$. This means that the sum of two odd numbers is an even number.

2. No, the set is not closed under addition. Example: 2 + 2 = 4; 4 is not an element of the set.

3. Yes, the natural numbers are closed under multiplication.

4. No, the natural numbers are not closed under division. Example: 2 divided by 3 is not a natural number.

5. We must show that $(1 \oplus 3) \oplus 2 = 1 \oplus (3 \oplus 2)$.
$$(1 \oplus 3) \oplus 2 = 1 \oplus (3 \oplus 2)$$
$$0 \oplus 2 = 1 \oplus 1$$
$$2 = 2$$

6. The identity element is g, because it does not change anything.

7. The inverse is -12. (because $12 + (-12) = 0$)

8. The inverse is $\dfrac{1}{12}$. (because $12 \cdot \dfrac{1}{12} = 1$)

9. **a.** The identity element is k, because it does not change anything.

   b. The inverse of j is l because $j \circ l = k$
   The inverse of k is k because $k \circ k = k$
   The inverse of l is j because $l \circ j = k$
   The inverse of m is m because $m \circ m = k$

Exercise Set 13.1

1. $\{e, a, b, c\}$

2. The binary operation is $\circ$.

3. $a \circ b = c$

4. $c \circ a = b$

5. $b \circ c = a$

6. $c \circ b = a$

7. $e \circ e = e$

8. $e \circ a = a$

9. $b \circ e = b$

10. $c \circ e = c$

11. $a \circ a = e$

12. $(b \circ b) \circ c = e \circ c = c$

13. $(c \circ c) \circ a = e \circ a = a$

14. Yes. The answer to any possible combination of two elements of the set is an element that is in the set.

15. No. For example, $4 + 1 = 5$, and 5 is not in the set.

16. No. For example, $5 + 1 = 6$, and 6 is not in the set.

17. Yes. The answer to any possible combination of two elements of the set is an element that is in the set.

18. Yes. The answer to any possible combination of two elements of the set is an element that is in the set.

19. No. For example, $1 - 2 = -1$, and -1 is not in the set.

20. No. For example, $1 \div 2 = \dfrac{1}{2}$, and $\dfrac{1}{2}$ is not in the set.

21. No, the system is not closed under $*$. $b * a = c$, and c is not in the set.

22. No, the system is not closed under $*$. $d * f = g$, and g is not in the set.

23. $2 \oplus 4 = 1$
$4 \oplus 2 = 1$
So $2 \oplus 4 = 4 \oplus 2$

24. $3 \oplus 4 = 2$
$4 \oplus 3 = 2$
So $3 \oplus 4 = 4 \oplus 3$

25. $4 \oplus 1 = 0$
$1 \oplus 4 = 0$
So $4 \oplus 1 = 1 \oplus 4$

451

26. $2 \oplus 3 = 0$
$3 \oplus 2 = 0$
So $2 \oplus 3 = 3 \oplus 2$

27. The Commutative Property; since table entries are mirror images of each other across the main diagonal, $\oplus$ is commutative.

28. $(3 \oplus 2) \oplus 4 = 0 \oplus 4 = 4$
$3 \oplus (2 \oplus 4) = 3 \oplus 1 = 4$
$(3 \oplus 2) \oplus 4 = 3 \oplus (2 \oplus 4)$

29. $(4 \oplus 3) \oplus 2 = 2 \oplus 2 = 4$
$4 \oplus (3 \oplus 2) = 4 \oplus 0 = 4$
$(4 \oplus 3) \oplus 2 = 4 \oplus (3 \oplus 2)$

30. $(2 \oplus 2) \oplus 3 = 4 \oplus 3 = 2$
$2 \oplus (2 \oplus 3) = 2 \oplus 0 = 2$
$(2 \oplus 2) \oplus 3 = 2 \oplus (2 \oplus 3)$

31. $(4 \oplus 4) \oplus 2 = 3 \oplus 2 = 0$
$4 \oplus (4 \oplus 2) = 4 \oplus 1 = 0$
$(4 \oplus 4) \oplus 2 = 4 \oplus (4 \oplus 2)$

32. The Associative Property

33. a. $(b \circ c) \circ b = c \circ b = b$

   b. $b \circ (c \circ b) = b \circ b = a$

   c. No. $(b \circ c) \circ b \neq b \circ (c \circ b)$
   When the grouping changed, the answer changed.

34. a. $(b \circ b) \circ c = b \circ c = a$

   b. $b \circ (b \circ c) = b \circ a = b$

   c. No. $(b \circ b) \circ c \neq b \circ (b \circ c)$
   When the grouping changed, the answer changed.

35-36. Answers will vary.

37. $29 + (-29) = 0$
-29 is the inverse of 29 under the operation of addition.

38. $43 + (-43) = 0$
-43 is the inverse of 43 under the operation of addition.

39. $29 \cdot \dfrac{1}{29} = 1$

$\dfrac{1}{29}$ is the inverse of 29 under the operation of multiplication.

40. $43 \cdot \dfrac{1}{43} = 1$

$\dfrac{1}{43}$ is the inverse of 43 under the operation of multiplication.

41. $a \circ a = a$

42. $a \circ b = b$

43. $a \circ c = c$

44. $a \circ d = d$

45. $a \circ e = e$

46. $b \circ a = b$

47. $c \circ a = c$

48. $d \circ a = d$

49. $e \circ a = e$

50. a is the identity element under the operation $\circ$.

51. a

52. e

53. d

54. c

55. b

56. The elements are inverses under the operation $\circ$.

57. 0 is the identity element.

58. $0 \circ 0 = 0$
0 is the inverse for 0.

59. $1 \oplus 4 = 0$
4 is the inverse for 1.

60. $2 \circ 3 = 0$
3 is the inverse for 2.

61. $3 \oplus 2 = 0$
2 is the inverse for 3.

62. $4 \circ 1 = 0$
1 is the inverse for 4.

63. a. d is the identity element.

b.

element	inverse
a	none
b	none
c	none
d	d

64. a. c is the identity element.

b.

element	inverse
a	none
b	none
c	c
d	e
e	d

65. The mathematical system shows all possible starting and ending positions for the four-way switch. The 25 entries in the table represent the final position of the switch for each starting position (shown in the left column) and number of clockwise turns (shown across the top).

66. The mathematical system shows the ending position relative to the starting position after the person completes a command shown in the left column followed by a command in the top row.

67–72.

×	E	O
E	E	E
O	E	O

67. Yes. The answer to any possible combination of two elements of the set is an element that is in the set.

68. $E \times O = E$ and $O \times E = E$

69. $(O \times E) \times O = E$ and $O \times (E \times O) = E$

70. O is the identity element.

71. E does not have an inverse.

72. $O \circ O = O$; O is the inverse of O.

73-80. Answers will vary.

81. a. $\begin{bmatrix} 2 & 3 \\ 4 & 7 \end{bmatrix} \times \begin{bmatrix} 0 & 1 \\ 5 & 6 \end{bmatrix}$

$= \begin{bmatrix} 2 \cdot 0 + 3 \cdot 5 & 2 \cdot 1 + 3 \cdot 6 \\ 4 \cdot 0 + 7 \cdot 5 & 4 \cdot 1 + 7 \cdot 6 \end{bmatrix}$

$= \begin{bmatrix} 0 + 15 & 2 + 18 \\ 0 + 35 & 4 + 42 \end{bmatrix}$

$= \begin{bmatrix} 15 & 20 \\ 35 & 46 \end{bmatrix}$

b. $\begin{bmatrix} 0 & 1 \\ 5 & 6 \end{bmatrix} \times \begin{bmatrix} 2 & 3 \\ 4 & 7 \end{bmatrix}$

$= \begin{bmatrix} 0 \cdot 2 + 1 \cdot 4 & 0 \cdot 3 + 1 \cdot 7 \\ 5 \cdot 2 + 6 \cdot 4 & 5 \cdot 3 + 6 \cdot 7 \end{bmatrix}$

$= \begin{bmatrix} 0 + 4 & 0 + 7 \\ 10 + 24 & 15 + 42 \end{bmatrix}$

$= \begin{bmatrix} 4 & 7 \\ 34 & 57 \end{bmatrix}$

c. Matrix multiplication is not commutative.

Check Points 13.2

1. a. 1. The set is closed under the binary operation because the entries in the body of the table are all elements of the set.

2. Associative Property: For example,
$(O \circ E) \circ O = O \circ (E \circ O)$
$O \circ O = O \circ O$
$E = E$
and
$(E \circ O) \circ O = E \circ (O \circ O)$
$O \circ O = E \circ E$
$E = E$

3. E is the identity element.

4.

element	inverse
E	E
O	O

Each element has an inverse.
Since the system meets the four requirements, the system is a group.

b. The Commutative Property holds for this group (as can be seen by the symmetry along the diagonal from the upper left to lower right). Therefore, this system is a commutative group.

2. a. $(8+5)+11 = 8+(5+11)$

$1+11 = 8+4$

$0 = 0$

b. Locating 9 on the left and 4 across the top indicates that $9+4 = 1$.
Locating 4 on the left and 9 across the top indicates that $4+9 = 1$.

3. a. true; $61 \equiv 5 \pmod 7$ because
$61 \div 7 = 8$, remainder 5.

b. true; $36 \equiv 0 \pmod 6$ because
$36 \div 6 = 6$, remainder 0.

c. false; $57 \equiv 2 \pmod{11}$ because
$57 \div 11 = 5$, remainder 2 (not 3).

4. a. $(1+3)(\bmod 5) \equiv 4(\bmod 5)$

b. $(5+4)(\bmod 7) \equiv 9(\bmod 7) \equiv 2(\bmod 7)$

c. $(8+10)(\bmod 13) \equiv 18(\bmod 13) \equiv 5(\bmod 13)$

5. $97 \equiv 6(\bmod 7)$ thus, the desired day of the week is 6 days past Wednesday, or Tuesday.

Exercise Set 13.2

1. 8-fold rotational symmetry.

2. 5-fold rotational symmetry.

3. 18-fold rotational symmetry.

4. 4-fold rotational symmetry.

5. For any 2 elements in the set, the result is also in the set.

6. $(p \circ s) \circ t = t \circ t = e$ and
$p \circ (s \circ t) = p \circ q = e$
So $(p \circ s) \circ t = p \circ (s \circ t)$

7. $(r \circ t) \circ q = p \circ q = e$ and
$r \circ (t \circ q) = r \circ r = e$
So $(r \circ t) \circ q = r \circ (t \circ q)$

8. The Associative Property.

9. e is the identity element.

10. $e \circ e = e$
e is the inverse of e.

11. $p \circ q = e$
q is the inverse of p.

12. $q \circ p = e$
p is the inverse of q.

13. $r \circ r = e$
r is the inverse of r.

14. $s \circ s = e$
s is the inverse of s.

15. $t \circ t = e$
t is the inverse of t.

16. This mathematical system is a group.

17. $r \circ p = t$

18. $p \circ r = s$

19. This mathematical system is not commutative.

20. The natural numbers do not have an identity element under addition.

21. Most elements do not have an inverse. For example, no natural number will satisfy the expression $2 \times ? = 1$.

22. The system lacks the associative property. For example, $10-(5-2) \neq (10-5)-2$

23. a.

+	0	1	2	3	4	5
0	0	1	2	3	4	5
1	1	2	3	4	5	0
2	2	3	4	5	0	1
3	3	4	5	0	1	2
4	4	5	0	1	2	3
5	5	0	1	2	3	4

b. 1. The set is closed under the operation of clock addition because the entries in the body of the table are all elements of the set.

2. Associative Property: For example,
$$(2+3)+4 = 2+(3+4)$$
$$5+4 = 2+1$$
$$3 = 3$$
and
$$(3+4)+0 = 3+(4+0)$$
$$1+0 = 3+4$$
$$1 = 1$$

3. 0 is the identity element.

4.

element	inverse
0	0
1	5
2	4
3	3
4	2
5	1

Each element has an inverse.

5. The table is symmetric, so the Commutative Property holds. Therefore, this system is a commutative group.

24. a.

+	0	1	2	3	4	5	6
0	0	1	2	3	4	5	6
1	1	2	3	4	5	6	0
2	2	3	4	5	6	0	1
3	3	4	5	6	0	1	2
4	4	5	6	0	1	2	3
5	5	6	0	1	2	3	4
6	6	0	1	2	3	4	5

b. 1. The set is closed under the operation of clock addition because the entries in the body of the table are all elements of the set.

2. Associative Property: For example,
$$(2+4)+6 = 2+(4+6)$$
$$6+6 = 2+3$$
$$5 = 5$$
and
$$(1+3)+5 = 1+(3+5)$$
$$4+5 = 1+1$$
$$2 = 2$$

3. 0 is the identity element.

4.

element	inverse
0	0
1	6
2	5
3	4
4	3
5	2
6	1

Each element has an inverse.

5. The table is symmetric, so the Commutative Property holds. Therefore, this system is a commutative group.

25. $7 \equiv 2 \pmod 5$
$7 \div 5 = 1$, remainder 2
True

26. $8 \equiv 3 \pmod 5$
$8 \div 5 = 1$, remainder 3
True

27. $41 \equiv 6 \pmod 7$
$41 \div 7 = 5$, remainder 6
True

28. $77 \equiv 5 \pmod{12}$
$77 \div 12 = 6$, remainder 5
True

29. $84 \equiv 1 \pmod 7$
$84 \div 7 = 12$, remainder 0
False
A true statement is $84 \equiv 0 \pmod 7$

30. $21 \equiv 5 \pmod 7$
$21 \div 7 = 3$, remainder 0
False
A true statement is $21 \equiv 0 \pmod 7$

31. $23 \equiv 2 \pmod 4$
$23 \div 4 = 5$, remainder 3
False
A true statement is $23 \equiv 3 \pmod 4$

32. $29 \equiv 3 \pmod 4$
$29 \div 4 = 7$, remainder 1
False
A true statement is $29 \equiv 1 \pmod 4$

33. $55 \equiv 0 \pmod{11}$
$55 \div 11 = 5$, remainder 0
True

34. $75 \equiv 0 \pmod{25}$
$75 \div 25 = 3$, remainder 0
True

35. $(3 + 2) \pmod 6$
$3 + 2 = 5,\ 5 < 6$
$3 + 2 \equiv 5 \pmod 6$

36. $(3 + 4) \pmod 8$
$3 + 4 = 7,\ 7 < 8$
$3 + 4 \equiv 7 \pmod 8$

37. $(4 + 5) \pmod 6$
$4 + 5 = 9,\ 9 > 6$
$9 \div 6 = 1$, remainder 3
$4 + 5 \equiv 3 \pmod 6$

38. $(5 + 6) \pmod 8$
$5 + 6 = 11,\ 11 > 8$
$11 \div 8 = 1$, remainder 3
$5 + 6 \equiv 3 \pmod 8$

39. $(6 + 5) \pmod 7$
$6 + 5 = 11,\ 11 > 7$
$11 \div 7 = 1$, remainder 4
$6 + 5 \equiv 4 \pmod 7$

40. $(8 + 7) \pmod 9$
$8 + 7 = 15,\ 15 > 9$
$15 \div 9 = 1$, remainder 6
$8 + 7 \equiv 6 \pmod 9$

41. $(49 + 49) \pmod 5$
$49 + 49 = 98,\ 98 > 50$
$98 \div 50 = 1$, remainder 48
$49 + 49 \equiv 48 \pmod{50}$

42. $(75 + 75) \pmod{100}$
$75 + 75 = 150,\ 150 > 100$
$150 \div 100 = 1$, remainder 50
$75 + 75 \equiv 50 \pmod{100}$

43. $(1200 + 0600) \pmod{2400}$
$1200 + 0600 = 1800,\ 1800 < 2400$
$1200 + 0600 \equiv 1800 \pmod{2400}$

44. $(1300 + 1900) \pmod{2400}$
$1300 + 1900 = 3200,\ 3200 > 2400$
$3200 \div 2400 = 1$, remainder 800
$1300 + 1900 \equiv 0800 \pmod{2400}$

45. $(0830 + 1550) \pmod{2400}$
$0830 + 1550 = 2380,$
23 hr 80 min $\equiv$ 24 hr 20 min
$2420 \equiv 0020 \pmod{2400}$

46. $(1315 + 0945) \pmod{2400}$
$1315 + 0945 = 2260,$
22 hr 60 min $\equiv$ 23 hr 0 min
$2300 \equiv 2300 \pmod{2400}$

47. $67 \div 7 = 9$, remainder 4
$67 \equiv 4 \pmod 7$
Thus, the desired day of the week is 4 days past Wednesday, or Sunday.

48. $147 \div 7 = 21$, remainder 0

$147 \equiv 0 \pmod 7$

Thus, the desired day of the week is 0 days past Tuesday, or Tuesday.

49. *Beam me up*

Code:	9	12	8	20	7	20	12	7	1	23
Add 20:	29	32	28	40	27	40	32	27	21	43
Mod 27:	2	5	1	13	0	13	5	0	21	16
Letter:	B	E	A	M	_	M	E	_	U	P

50-57. Answers will vary.

58. E(conditional): $p \rightarrow q$

C(converse): $q \rightarrow p$

I(inverse): $\sim p \rightarrow \sim q$

CP(contrapositive): $\sim q \rightarrow \sim p$

a. C followed by CP changes $q \rightarrow p$ to $\sim p \rightarrow \sim q$, which is inverse, I. C followed by I changes $q \rightarrow p$ to $\sim q \rightarrow \sim p$ which is the contrapositive, CP.

b.

$\circ$	E	C	I	CP
E	E	C	I	CP
C	C	E	CP	I
I	I	CP	E	C
CP	CP	I	C	E

c. 1. Closure. The mathematical system is closed since every entry of the table in part **b** is an element of the set $\{E, C, I, CP\}$.

2. Associative. Examples may vary.

$(C \circ I) \circ CP = CP \circ CP = E$

$C \circ (I \circ CP) = C \circ C = E$

Thus, $(C \circ I) \circ CP = C \circ (I \circ CP)$.

$(CP \circ I) \circ C = C \circ C = E$

$CP \circ (I \circ C) = CP \circ CP = E$

Thus, $(CP \circ I) \circ C = CP \circ (I \circ C)$

3. Identity. E is the identity element, since E does not change the conditional statement.

4. Inverse.

$E \circ E = E, C \circ C = E,$

$I \circ I = E$, and $CP \circ CP = E,$

so each element has an inverse. Actually, each element is its own inverse.

Thus this is a group. To show that the group is commutative, note that the parts of the table above and below the main diagonal (upper left to lower right) are mirror images.

59-60. Answers will vary.

61. $99,999,999 \div 24 = 4,166,666$, remainder 15

$99,999,999 = 15 \pmod{24}$

It will be 15 hours past 5:00 P.M., or 8:00 A.M.

62. a. $(3-6)(\bmod 7) \equiv 4$

b. $(2-4)(\bmod 5) \equiv 3$

63. $x+3 \equiv 5 \pmod 7$ for $x = 2, 9, 16, 23, 30,$ and 37

64. We must find multiples of 3 cannot have a remainder of 3 when divided by 9. Values of x that make the statement true are 1, 4, 7, 10, 13, and 16

Chapter 13 Review Exercises

1. $\{e, c, f, r\}$

2. Yes. Any possible combination of two elements of the set is an element of the set.

3. $c \circ f = r$

4. $r \circ r = f$

5. $e \circ c = c$

6. $c \circ r = e$

$r \circ c = e$

7. $f \circ r = c$

$r \circ f = c$

8. $f \circ e = f$

$e \circ f = f$

9. The Commutative Property

10. Since the table entries are symmetric about the main diagonal, the operation is commutative.

11. $(c \circ r) \circ f = e \circ f = f$

$c \circ (r \circ f) = c \circ c = f$

12. $(r \circ e) \circ c = r \circ c = e$

$r \circ (e \circ c) = r \circ c = e$

13. The Associative Property

14. e is the identity element.

15. $e \circ e = e$

e is the inverse for e.

16. $c \circ r = e$

r is the inverse for c.

17. $f \circ f = e$

f is the inverse for f.

18. $r \circ c = e$

c is the inverse for r.

19. No. $1 + 1 = 2$, and 2 is not in the set.

20. Yes. Any possible combination of two elements of the set is an element of the set.

21. No. For example, $1 \div 2 = \dfrac{1}{2}$, and $\dfrac{1}{2}$ is not in the set.

22. $123 + (-123) = 0$

-123 is the additive inverse of 123.

23. $123 \cdot \dfrac{1}{123} = 1$

$\dfrac{1}{123}$ is the multiplicative inverse of 123.

24. a.

+	0	1	2	3	4
0	0	1	2	3	4
1	1	1	2	3	4
2	2	2	2	3	4
3	3	3	3	3	4
4	4	4	4	4	4

b. Zero is the identity element.

c. No. There is no element in the set such that $2 \circ ? = 0$.

25. 3-fold rotational symmetry

26. 18-fold rotational symmetry

27. a.

+	0	1	2	3	4
0	0	1	2	3	4
1	1	2	3	4	0
2	2	3	4	0	1
3	3	4	0	1	2
4	4	0	1	2	3

b. 1. The set is closed under the operation of clock addition because the entries in the body of the table are all elements of the set.

2. Associative Property: For example,
$$(1+2)+3 = 1+(2+3)$$
$$3+3 = 1+0$$
$$1 = 1$$

3. 0 is the identity element.

4.

element	inverse
0	0
1	4
2	3
3	2
4	1

Each element has an inverse.

5. The table is symmetric, so the Commutative Property holds. Therefore, this system is a commutative group.

28. $17 \equiv 2 \pmod 8$
$17 \div 8 = 2$, remainder 1
False
A true statement is $17 \equiv 1 \pmod 8$.

29. $37 \equiv 3 \pmod 5$
$37 \div 5 = 7$, remainder 2
False
A true statement is $37 \equiv 2 \pmod 5$.

30. $60 \equiv 0 \pmod{10}$
$60 \div 10 = 6$, remainder 0
True

31. $(4+3) \pmod 6$
$4+3 = 7, 7 > 6$
$7 \div 6 = 1$, remainder 1
$4+3 \equiv 1 \pmod 6$

32. $(7+7) \pmod 8$
$7+7 = 14, 14 > 8$
$14 \div 8 = 1$, remainder 6
$7+7 \equiv 6 \pmod 8$

33. $(4+3) \pmod 9$
$4+3 = 7, 7 < 9$
$4+3 = 7 \pmod 9$

34. $(3+18) \pmod{20}$
$3+18 = 21, 21 > 20$
$21 \div 20 = 1$, remainder 1
$3+18 \equiv 1 \pmod{20}$

Chapter 13 Test

1. Yes. Any possible combination of two elements of the set is an element of the set.

2. $z \circ y = x$
$y \circ z = x$
This illustrates the Commutative Property.

3. $(x \circ z) \circ z = z \circ z = y$
$x \circ (z \circ z) = x \circ y = y$
This illustrates the Associative Property.

4. x is the identity element.

5.

element	inverse
x	x
y	z
z	y

6. No. For example, $1 + 1 = 2$, and 2 is not in the set.

7. $5 \cdot \dfrac{1}{5} = 1$

$\dfrac{1}{5}$ is the multiplicative inverse of 5.

8. 6-fold symmetry; Answers will vary.

9.

+	0	1	2	3
0	0	1	2	3
1	1	2	3	0
2	2	3	0	1
3	3	0	1	2

10. 1. The set is closed under the operation of clock addition because the entries in the body of the table are all elements of the set.

    2. Associative Property:
For example,
$$(1+2)+3 = 1+(2+3)$$
$$3+3 = 1+1$$
$$2 = 2$$

    3. 0 is the identity element.

    4.

element	inverse
0	0
1	3
2	2
3	1

Each element has an inverse.

    5. The table is symmetric, so the Commutative Property holds. Therefore, this system is a commutative group.

11. $39 \equiv 3 \pmod 6$
$39 \div 6 = 6$, remainder 3
True

12. $14 \equiv 2 \pmod 7$
$14 \div 7 = 2$, remainder 0
False
A true statement is $14 \equiv 0 \pmod 7$

13. $(9+1) \pmod{11}$
$9+1 = 10, \ 10 < 11$
$9+1 \equiv 10 \pmod{11}$

14. $(9+6) \pmod{10}$
$9+6 = 15, \ 15 > 10$
$15 \div 10 = 1$, remainder 5
$9+6 \equiv 5 \pmod{10}$

Chapter 14
Voting and Apportionment

14.1   Voting Methods

Check Point 1.

a.   We find the number of people who voted in the election by adding the numbers in the row labeled Number of Votes: 2100 + 1305 + 765 + 40 = 4210. Thus, 4210 people voted in the election.

b.   We find how many people selected the candidates in the order B, S, A, C by referring to the fourth column of letters in the preference table. Above this column is the number 40. Thus, 40 people voted in the order B, S, A, C.

c.   We find the number of people who selected S as their first choice by reading across the row that says First Choice: 2100 + 765 = 2865. Thus, 2865 students selected S (Samir) as their first choice for student body president.

Check Point 2.

The candidate with the most first-place votes is the winner. When using Table 14.2, it is only necessary to look at the row which indicates the number of first-place votes. This indicates that A (Antonio) gets 130 first-place votes, C (Carmen) gets 150 first-place votes, and D (Donna) gets 120 + 100 = 220 first-place votes. Thus Donna is declared the winner using the plurality method.

Check Point 3.

Because there are four candidates, a first-place vote is worth 4 points, a second-place vote is worth 3 points, a third-place vote is worth 2 points, and a fourth-place vote is worth 1 point. We show the points produced by the votes in the preference table.

Number of Votes	130	120	100	150
First Choice: 4 points	A: $130 \times 4 = 520$ pts	D: $120 \times 4 = 480$ pts	D: $100 \times 4 = 400$ pts	C: $150 \times 4 = 600$ pts
Second Choice: 3 points	B: $130 \times 3 = 390$ pts	B: $120 \times 3 = 360$ pts	B: $100 \times 3 = 300$ pts	B: $150 \times 3 = 450$ pts
Third Choice: 2 points	C: $130 \times 2 = 260$ pts	C: $120 \times 2 = 240$ pts	A: $100 \times 2 = 200$ pts	A: $150 \times 2 = 300$ pts
Fourth Choice: 1 point	D: $130 \times 1 = 130$ pts	A: $120 \times 1 = 120$ pts	C: $100 \times 1 = 100$ pts	D: $150 \times 1 = 150$ pts

Now we read down each column and total the points for each candidate separately.

A gets 520 + 120 + 200 + 300 = 1140 points
B gets 390 + 360 + 300 + 450 = 1500 points
C gets 260 + 240 + 100 + 600 = 1200 points
D gets 130 + 480 + 400 + 150 = 1160 points

Because B (Bob) has received the most points, he is the winner and the new mayor of Smallville.

Check Point 4.

There are 130 + 120 + 100 + 150, or 500, people voting. In order to receive a majority, a candidate must receive more than 50% of the votes, meaning more than 250 votes. The number of first-place votes for each candidate is
A (Antonio) = 130   B (Bob) = 0   C (Carmen) = 150   D (Donna) = 220

We see that no candidate receives a majority of first-place votes. Because Bob received the fewest first-place votes, he is eliminated in the next round. We construct a new preference table in which B is removed. Each candidate below B moves up one place, while the positions of candidates above B remain unchanged.

Number of Votes	130	120	100	150
First Choice	A	D	D	C
Second Choice	C	C	A	A
Third Choice	D	A	C	D

The number of first-place votes for each candidate is now A (Antonio) = 130; C (Carmen) = 150; D (Donna) = 220

No candidate receives a majority of first-place votes. Because Antonio received the fewest first-place votes, he is eliminated in the next round.

Number of Votes	130	120	100	150
First Choice	C	D	D	C
Second Choice	D	C	C	D

The number of first-place votes for each candidate is now C (Carmen) = 280; D (Donna) = 220

Because Carmen has received the majority of first-place votes, she is the winner and the new mayor of Smallville.

Check Point 5.

A vs. B

130	120	100	150
A	D	D	C
B	**B**	**B**	**B**
C	C	A	A
D	*A*	C	D

130 voters prefer A to B.
120 + 100 + 150 = 370 voters prefer B to A.

Conclusion: B wins this comparison and gets one point.

A vs. C

130	120	100	150
A	D	D	**C**
B	B	B	B
C	**C**	*A*	*A*
D	*A*	C	D

130 + 100 = 230 voters prefer A to C.
120 + 150 = 270 voters prefer C to A.

Conclusion: C wins this comparison and gets one point.

A vs. D

130	120	100	150
A	D	D	**C**
B	B	B	B
C	C	A	A
D	*A*	*D*	*D*

130 + 150 = 280 voters prefer A to D.
120 + 100 = 220 voters prefer D to A.

Conclusion: A wins this comparison and gets one point.

B vs. C

130	120	100	150
A	D	D	**C**
B	**B**	**B**	*B*
C	*C*	A	A
D	A	C	D

130 + 120 + 100 = 350 voters prefer B to C.
150 voters prefer C to B.

Conclusion: B wins this comparison and gets one point.

	B vs. D		
130	120	100	150
A	D	D	C
B	B	B	B
C	C	A	A
D	A	C	D

130 + 150 = 280 voters prefer B to D.
120 + 100 = 220 voters prefer D to B.

Conclusion: B wins this comparison and gets one point.

	C vs. D		
130	120	100	150
A	D	D	C
B	B	B	B
C	C	A	A
D	A	C	D

130 + 150 = 280 voters prefer C to D.
120 + 100 = 220 voters prefer D to C.

Conclusion: C wins this comparison and gets one point.

We now use each of the six conclusions and add points for the six comparisons.

    A gets 1 point.
    B gets 1 + 1 + 1 = 3 points.
    C gets 1 + 1 = 2 points.

After all comparisons have been made, the candidate receiving the most points is B (Bob). He is the winner and the new mayor of Smallville.

Exercise Set 14.1

1.

Number of Votes	7	5	4
First Choice	A	B	C
Second Choice	B	C	B
Third Choice	C	A	A

2.

Number of Votes	8	6	2
First Choice	A	B	C
Second Choice	B	C	B
Third Choice	C	A	A

3.

Number of Votes	5	1	4	2
First Choice	A	B	C	C
Second Choice	B	D	B	B
Third Choice	C	C	D	A
Fourth Choice	D	A	A	D

4.

Number of Votes	4	1	5	2
First Choice	A	B	C	C
Second Choice	B	D	B	B
Third Choice	C	C	A	D
Fourth Choice	D	A	D	A

5. **a.** $14 + 8 + 3 + 1 = 126$

   b. 8

   c. $14 + 8 = 22$

   d. 3

6. **a.** $70 + 30 + 10 + 5 = 115$

   b. 10

   c. $30 + 10 = 40$

   d. $70 + 10 = 80$

7. "Musical" received 12 first-place votes, "comedy" received 10 first-place votes, and "drama" received 8 first-place votes, so the type of play selected is a musical.

8. New York received 14 first-place votes, San Francisco received 16 first-place votes, and Chicago received 4 first-place votes, so the city selected is San Francisco.

9. Darwin received 30 first-place votes, Einstein received 22 first-place votes, Freud received 20 first-place votes, and Hawking received 14 first-place votes, so the professor declared chair is Darwin.

10. Disney received 10 first-place votes, Ford received 30 first-place votes, Gates received 24 first-place votes, and Sarnoff received 18 first-place votes, so the professor declared president is Ford.

11.

Number of Votes	10	6	6	4	2	2
First Choice: 3 points	M: $10 \times 3 = 30$	C: $6 \times 3 = 18$	D: $6 \times 3 = 18$	C: $4 \times 3 = 12$	D: $2 \times 3 = 6$	M: $2 \times 3 = 6$
Second Choice: 2 points	C: $10 \times 2 = 20$	M: $6 \times 2 = 12$	C: $6 \times 2 = 12$	D: $4 \times 2 = 8$	M: $2 \times 2 = 4$	D: $2 \times 2 = 4$
Third Choice: 1 point	D: $10 \times 1 = 10$	D: $6 \times 1 = 6$	M: $6 \times 1 = 6$	M: $4 \times 1 = 4$	C: $2 \times 1 = 2$	C: $2 \times 1 = 2$

C gets $20 + 18 + 12 + 12 + 2 + 2 = 66$ points.
D gets $10 + 6 + 18 + 8 + 6 + 4 = 52$ points.
M gets $30 + 12 + 6 + 4 + 4 + 6 = 62$ points.

C (Comedy) receives the most points, and is selected.

12.

Number of Votes	16	8	6	4
First Choice: 3 points	S: $16 \times 3 = 48$	N: $8 \times 3 = 24$	N: $6 \times 3 = 18$	C: $4 \times 3 = 12$
Second Choice: 2 points	N: $16 \times 2 = 32$	S: $8 \times 2 = 16$	C: $6 \times 2 = 12$	N: $4 \times 2 = 8$
Third Choice: 1 point	C: $16 \times 1 = 16$	C: $8 \times 1 = 8$	S: $6 \times 1 = 6$	S: $4 \times 1 = 4$

N gets $32 + 24 + 18 + 8 = 82$ points
S gets $48 + 16 + 6 + 4 = 74$ points
C gets $16 + 8 + 12 + 12 = 48$ points

N (New York) receives the most points and is selected.

13.

Number of Votes	30	22	20	12	2
First Choice: 4 points	D: $30 \times 4 = 120$	E: $22 \times 4 = 88$	F: $20 \times 4 = 80$	H: $12 \times 4 = 48$	H: $2 \times 4 = 8$
Second Choice: 3 points	H: $30 \times 3 = 90$	F: $22 \times 3 = 66$	E: $20 \times 3 = 60$	E: $12 \times 3 = 36$	F: $2 \times 3 = 6$
Third Choice: 2 points	F: $30 \times 2 = 60$	H: $22 \times 2 = 44$	H: $20 \times 2 = 40$	F: $12 \times 2 = 24$	D: $2 \times 2 = 4$
Fourth Choice: 1 point	E: $30 \times 1 = 30$	D: $22 \times 1 = 22$	D: $20 \times 1 = 20$	D: $12 \times 1 = 12$	E: $2 \times 1 = 2$

D gets $120 + 22 + 20 + 12 + 4 = 178$ points.
E gets $30 + 88 + 60 + 36 + 2 = 216$ points.
F gets $60 + 66 + 80 + 24 + 6 = 236$ points.
H gets $90 + 44 + 40 + 48 + 8 = 230$ points.

F (Freud) receives the most points and is declared the new division chair.

14.

Number of Votes	30	22	18	10	2
First Choice: 4 points	F: $30 \times 4 = 120$	G: $22 \times 4 = 88$	S: $18 \times 4 = 72$	D: $10 \times 4 = 40$	G: $2 \times 4 = 8$
Second Choice: 3 points	D: $30 \times 3 = 90$	D: $22 \times 3 = 66$	G: $18 \times 3 = 54$	S: $10 \times 3 = 30$	S: $2 \times 3 = 6$
Third Choice: 2 points	G: $30 \times 2 = 60$	S: $22 \times 2 = 44$	D: $18 \times 2 = 36$	G: $10 \times 2 = 20$	D: $2 \times 2 = 4$
Fourth Choice: 1 point	S: $30 \times 1 = 30$	F: $22 \times 1 = 22$	F: $18 \times 1 = 18$	F: $10 \times 1 = 10$	F: $2 \times 1 = 2$

D gets $90 + 66 + 36 + 40 + 4 = 236$ points.
F gets $120 + 22 + 18 + 10 + 2 = 172$ points.
G gets $60 + 88 + 54 + 20 + 8 = 230$ points.
S gets $30 + 44 + 72 + 30 + 6 = 182$ points.

D (Disney) receives the most points, and is declared the new president.

15. There are 30 people voting, so the winner needs more than 15 votes for a majority.
The number of first-place votes for each candidate is

C (Comedy) = 10   D (Drama) = 8   M (Musical) = 12

No candidate has a majority. Drama received the fewest first-place votes, so we eliminate it in the next round.

Number of Votes	10	6	6	4	2	2
First Choice	M	C	C	C	M	M
Second Choice	C	M	M	M	C	C

The number of first-place votes for each candidate is now

   C (Comedy) = 16   M (Musical) = 14

C (Comedy) has 16 votes, which is a majority, so "Comedy" is selected.

16. There are 34 people voting, so the winner needs more than 17 votes for a majority. The number of first-place votes for each candidate is

   N (New York) = 14   S (San Francisco) = 16   C (Chicago) = 4

No candidate has a majority. Chicago received the fewest first-place votes, so we eliminate it in the next round.

Number of Votes	16	8	6	4
First Choice	S	N	N	N
Second Choice	N	S	S	S

The number of first-place votes for each candidate is now

N (New York) = 18   S (San Francisco) = 16

N (New York) has 18 votes, which is a majority, so New York is selected.

17. There are 86 people voting, so the winner needs more than 43 votes for a majority. The number of first-place votes for each candidate is

   D (Darwin) = 30   E (Einstein) = 22
   F (Freud) = 20   H (Hawking) = 14

No candidate has a majority. Hawking received the fewest first-place votes, so we eliminate him in the next round.

Number of Votes	30	22	20	12	2
First Choice	D	E	F	E	F
Second Choice	F	F	E	F	D
Third Choice	E	D	D	D	E

The number of first-place votes for each candidate is now

D (Darwin) = 30 E (Einstein) = 34 F (Freud) = 22

No candidate has a majority. Freud received the fewest first-place votes, so we eliminate him in the next round:

Number of Votes	30	22	20	12	2
First Choice	D	E	E	E	D
Second Choice	E	D	D	D	E

The number of first-place votes for each candidate is now

D (Darwin) = 32 E (Einstein) = 54

E (Einstein) has 54 votes, which is a majority, so Einstein is declared the new division chair.

18. There are 82 people voting, so the winner needs more than 41 votes for a majority. The number of first-place votes for each candidate is

    D (Disney) = 10   F (Ford) = 30
    G (Gates) = 24   S (Sarnoff) = 18

    No candidate has a majority. Disney received the fewest first-place votes, so we eliminate him in the next round.

Number of Votes	30	22	18	10	2
First Choice	F	G	S	S	G
Second Choice	G	S	G	G	S
Third Choice	S	F	F	F	F

The number of first-place votes for each candidate is now F (Ford) = 30; G (Gates) = 24; S (Sarnoff) = 28

No candidate has a majority. Gates received the fewest first-place votes, so we eliminate him in the next round.

Number of Votes	30	22	18	10	2
First Place	F	S	S	S	S
Second Place	S	F	F	F	F

The number of first-place votes for each candidate is now F (Ford) = 30; S (Sarnoff) = 52

S (Sarnoff) has 52 votes, which is a majority, so Sarnoff is declared the new president.

19. With $n = 5$, there are $\dfrac{5(5-1)}{2} = 10$ comparisons.

20. With $n = 6$, there are $\dfrac{6(6-1)}{2} = 15$ comparisons.

21. With $n = 8$, there are $\dfrac{8(8-1)}{2} = 28$ comparisons.

22. With $n = 9$, there are $\dfrac{9(9-1)}{2} = 36$ comparisons.

23.

10	6	6	4	2	2
M	C	D	C	D	M
C	M	C	D	M	D
D	D	M	M	C	C

C vs. D
$10 + 6 + 4 = 20$ voters prefer C to D.
$6 + 2 + 2 = 10$ voters prefer D to C.
C wins this comparison and gets one point.

D vs. M
$6 + 4 + 2 = 12$ voters prefer D to M.
$10 + 6 + 2 = 18$ voters prefer M to D.
M wins this comparison and gets one point.

C vs. M
$6 + 6 + 4 = 16$ voters prefer C to M.
$10 + 2 + 2 = 14$ voters prefer M to C.
C wins this comparison and gets one point

Adding points for the three comparisons:
C gets $1 + 1 = 2$ points.
D gets 0 points.
M gets 1 point.

C (Comedy) receives the most points, so a comedy is selected.

24.

16	8	6	4
S	N	N	C
N	S	C	N
C	C	S	S

N vs. S
8 + 6 + 4 = 18 voters prefer N to S.
16 voters prefer S to N.
N wins this comparison and gets one point.

N vs. C
16 + 8 + 6 = 30 voters prefer N to C.
4 voters prefer C to N.
N wins this comparison and gets one point.

S vs. C
16 + 8 = 24 voters prefer S to C.
6 + 4 = 10 voters prefer C to S.
S wins this comparison and gets one point.

Adding points for the three comparisons:
N gets 1 + 1 = 2 points.
S gets 1 point.
C gets 0 points.

N (New York) receives the most points, so New York is selected.

25.

30	22	20	12	2
D	E	F	H	H
H	F	E	E	F
F	H	H	F	D
E	D	D	D	E

D vs. E
30 + 2 = 32 voters prefer D to E.
22 + 20 + 12 = 54 voters prefer E to D.
E wins the comparison and gets one point

D vs. F
30 voters prefer D to F.
22 + 20 + 12 + 2 = 56 voters prefer F to D.
F wins this comparison and gets one point.

D vs. H
30 voters prefer D to H.
22 + 20 + 12 + 2 = 56 voters prefer H to D.
H wins this comparison and gets one point.

E vs. F
22 + 12 = 34 voters prefer E to F.
30 + 20 + 2 = 52 voters prefer F to E.
F wins this comparison and gets one point

E vs. H
22 + 20 = 42 voters prefer E to H.
30 + 12 + 2 = 44 voters prefer H to E.
H wins this comparison and gets one point.

F vs. H
22 + 20 = 42 voters prefer F to H.
30 + 12 + 2 = 44 voters prefer H to F.
H wins this comparison and gets one point.

Adding points for the six comparisons:
D gets 0 points.
E gets 1 point.
F gets 1 + 1 = 2 points.
H gets 1 + 1 + 1 = 3 points.

H (Hawking) receives the most points, so Hawking is declared the new division chair.

26.

30	22	18	10	2
F	G	S	D	G
D	D	G	S	S
G	S	D	G	D
S	F	F	F	F

D vs. F
22 + 18 + 10 + 2 = 52 voters prefer D to F.
30 voters prefer F to D.
D wins this comparison and gets one point.

D vs. S
30 + 22 + 10 = 62 voters prefer D to S.
18 + 2 = 20 voters prefer S to D.
D wins this comparison and gets one point

F vs. S
30 voters prefer F to S.
22 + 18 + 10 + 2 = 52 voters prefer S to F.
S wins this comparison and gets one point.

D vs. G
30 + 10 = 40 voters prefer D to G.
22 + 18 + 2 = 42 voters prefer G to D.
G wins this comparison and gets one point.

F vs. G
30 voters prefer F to G.
22 + 18 + 10 + 2 = 52 voters prefer G to F.
G wins this comparison and gets one point

G vs. S
30 + 22 + 2 = 54 voters prefer G to S.
18 + 10 = 28 voters prefer S to G.
G wins this comparison and gets one point.

Adding points for the three comparisons:
D gets 1 + 1 = 2 points.
F gets 0 points.
G gets 1 + 1 + 1 = 3 points.
S gets 1 point.

G (Gates) receives the most points, so Gates is declared the new president.

27. A received 34 first-place votes, B received 30 first-place votes, C received 6 first-place votes, and D received 2 first-place votes, so A is the winner.

28.

Number of Votes	34	30	6	2
First Choice: 4 points	A: $34 \times 4 = 136$	B: $30 \times 4 = 120$	C: $6 \times 4 = 24$	D: $2 \times 4 = 8$
Second Choice: 3 points	B: $34 \times 3 = 102$	C: $30 \times 3 = 90$	D: $6 \times 3 = 18$	B: $2 \times 3 = 6$
Third Choice: 2 points	C: $34 \times 2 = 68$	D: $30 \times 2 = 60$	B: $6 \times 2 = 12$	C: $2 \times 2 = 4$
Fourth Choice: 1 point	D: $34 \times 1 = 34$	A: $30 \times 1 = 30$	A: $6 \times 1 = 6$	A: $2 \times 1 = 2$

A gets $136 + 30 + 6 + 2 = 174$ points.
B gets $102 + 120 + 12 + 6 = 240$ points.
C gets $68 + 90 + 24 + 4 = 186$ points.
D gets $34 + 60 + 18 + 8 = 120$ points.

B receives the most points and is the winner.

29. There are 72 people voting, so the winner needs more than 36 votes for a majority. The number of first-place votes for each candidate is: A = 34;   B = 30;   C = 6;   D = 2

No candidate has a majority. D received the fewest first-place votes, so we eliminate it in the next round.

Number of Voters	34	30	6	2
First Choice	A	B	C	B
Second Choice	B	C	B	C
Third Choice	C	A	A	A

The number of first-place votes for each candidate is now A = 34;   B = 32;   C = 6

No candidate has a majority. C received the fewest first-place votes, so we eliminate it in the next round.

Number of Voters	34	30	6	2
First Choice	A	B	B	B
Second Choice	B	A	A	A

The number of first-place votes for each candidate is now A = 34;   B = 38

B has 38 votes, which is a majority, so B is selected.

30.

34	30	6	2
A	B	C	D
B	C	D	B
C	D	B	C
D	A	A	A

A vs. B
34 voters prefer A to B.
30 + 6 + 2 = 38 voters prefer B to A.
B wins this comparison and gets one point.

A vs. C
34 voters prefer A to C.
30 + 6 + 2 = 38 voters prefer C to A.
C wins this comparison and gets one point.

A vs. D
34 voters prefer A to D.
30 + 6 + 2 = 38 voters prefer D to A.
D wins this comparison and gets one point.

B vs. C
34 + 30 + 2 = 66 voters prefer B to C.
6 voters prefer C to B.
B wins this comparison and gets one point.

B vs. D
34 + 30 = 64 voters prefer B to D.
6 + 2 = 8 voters prefer D to B.
B wins this comparison and gets one point

C vs. D
34 + 30 + 6 = 70 voters prefer C to D.
2 voters prefer D to C.
C wins this comparison and gets one point.

Adding points for the six comparisons:
A gets 0 points.
B gets 1 + 1 + 1 = 3 points.
C gets 1 + 1 = 2 points.
D gets 1 point.

B receives the most points, so B is the winner.

31.

Number of Votes	5	5	4	3	3	2
First choice: 5 points	C: $5 \times 5 = 25$	S: $5 \times 5 = 25$	C: $4 \times 5 = 20$	W: $3 \times 5 = 15$	W: $3 \times 5 = 15$	P: $2 \times 5 = 10$
Second choice: 4 points	R: $5 \times 4 = 20$	R: $5 \times 4 = 20$	P: $4 \times 4 = 16$	P: $3 \times 4 = 12$	R: $3 \times 4 = 12$	S: $2 \times 4 = 8$
Third choice: 3 points	P: $5 \times 3 = 15$	W: $5 \times 3 = 15$	R: $4 \times 3 = 12$	R: $3 \times 3 = 9$	S: $3 \times 3 = 9$	C: $2 \times 3 = 6$
Fourth choice: 2 points	W: $5 \times 2 = 10$	P: $5 \times 2 = 10$	S: $4 \times 2 = 8$	S: $3 \times 2 = 6$	C: $3 \times 2 = 6$	R: $2 \times 2 = 4$
Fifth choice: 1 point	S: $5 \times 1 = 5$	C: $5 \times 1 = 5$	W: $4 \times 1 = 4$	C: $3 \times 1 = 3$	P: $3 \times 1 = 3$	W: $2 \times 1 = 2$

C gets $25 + 5 + 20 + 3 + 6 + 6 = 65$ points.
P gets $15 + 10 + 16 + 12 + 3 + 10 = 66$ points.
R gets $20 + 20 + 12 + 9 + 12 + 4 = 77$ points.
S gets $5 + 25 + 8 + 6 + 9 + 8 = 61$ points.
W gets $10 + 15 + 4 + 15 + 15 + 2 = 61$ points.

R (Rent) receives the most points and is selected.

32. C received 9 first-place votes, P received 2 first-place votes, R received 0 first-place votes, S received 5 first-place votes, and W received 6 first-place votes, so C (Cabaret) is the winner.

33.

5	5	4	3	3	2
C	S	C	W	W	P
R	R	P	P	R	S
P	W	R	R	S	C
W	P	S	S	C	R
S	C	W	C	P	W

C vs. P
$5 + 4 + 3 = 12$ voters prefer C to P.
$5 + 3 + 2 = 10$ voters prefer P to C.
C wins this comparison and gets one point.

C vs. R
$5 + 4 + 2 = 11$ voters prefer C to R.
$5 + 3 + 3 = 11$ voters prefer R to C.
C and R are tied. Each gets $\frac{1}{2}$ point.

C vs. S
$5 + 4 = 9$ voters prefer C to S.
$5 + 3 + 3 + 2 = 13$ voters prefer S to C.
S wins this comparison and gets one point.

C vs. W
$5 + 4 + 2 = 11$ voters prefer C to W.
$5 + 3 + 3 = 11$ voters prefer W to C.
C and W are tied. Each gets $\frac{1}{2}$ point.

P vs. R
$4 + 3 + 2 = 9$ voters prefer P to R.
$5 + 5 + 3 = 13$ voters prefer R to P.
R wins this comparison and gets one point.

P vs. S
$5 + 4 + 3 + 2 = 14$ voters prefer P to S.
$5 + 3 = 8$ voters prefer S to P.
P wins this comparison and gets one point.

P vs. W

$5 + 4 + 2 = 11$ voters prefer P to W.

$5 + 3 + 3 = 11$ voters prefer W to P.

P and W are tied. Each gets $\frac{1}{2}$ point.

R vs. W

$5 + 5 + 4 + 2 = 16$ voters prefer R to W.

$3 + 3 = 6$ voters prefer W to R.

R wins this comparison and gets one point.

R vs. S

$5 + 4 + 3 + 3 = 15$ voters prefer R to S.

$5 + 2 = 7$ voters prefer S to R.

R wins this comparison and gets one point.

S vs. W

$5 + 4 + 2 = 11$ voters prefer S to W.

$5 + 3 + 3 = 11$ voters prefer W to S.

S and W are tied. Each gets $\frac{1}{2}$ point.

Adding points for 10 comparisons:

C gets $1 + \frac{1}{2} + \frac{1}{2} = 2$ points.

P gets $1 + \frac{1}{2} = 1\frac{1}{2}$ points.

R gets $\frac{1}{2} + 1 + 1 + 1 = 3\frac{1}{2}$ points.

S gets $1 + \frac{1}{2} = 1\frac{1}{2}$ points.

W gets $\frac{1}{2} + \frac{1}{2} + \frac{1}{2} = 1\frac{1}{2}$ points.

R (Rent) receives the most points, so Rent is the winner.

34. There are 22 people voting, so the winner needs more than 11 votes for a majority. The number of first-place votes for each candidate is

$C = 9 \quad P = 2 \quad R = 0 \quad S = 5 \quad W = 6$

No candidate has a majority. R received the fewest first-place votes, so we eliminate it in the next round.

Number of Votes	5	5	4	3	3	2
First Choice	C	S	C	W	W	P
Second Choice	P	W	P	P	S	S
Third Choice	W	P	S	S	C	C
Fourth Choice	S	C	W	C	P	W

The number of first-place votes for each candidate is now

$C = 9 \quad P = 2 \quad S = 5 \quad W = 6$

No candidate has a majority. P received the fewest first-place votes, so we eliminate it in the next round.

Number of Votes	5	5	4	3	3	2
First Choice	C	S	C	W	W	S
Second Choice	W	W	S	S	S	C
Third Choice	S	C	W	C	C	W

The number of first-place votes for each candidate is now

$C = 9 \quad S = 7 \quad W = 6$

No candidate has a majority. W received the fewest first-place votes, so we eliminate it in the next round.

472

Number of Votes	5	5	4	3	3	2
First Choice	C	S	C	S	S	S
Second Choice	S	C	S	C	C	C

The number of first-place votes for each candidate is now

$C = 9$ $S = 13$

S (Sweeney Todd) has 13 votes, which is a majority, so Sweeney Todd is selected.

35. a.

Number of Votes	5	5	3	3	3	2
First Choice: 5 points	A: $5 \times 5 = 25$	C: $5 \times 5 = 25$	D: $3 \times 5 = 15$	A: $3 \times 5 = 15$	B: $3 \times 5 = 15$	D: $2 \times 5 = 10$
Second Choice: 4 points	B: $5 \times 4 = 20$	E: $5 \times 4 = 20$	C: $3 \times 4 = 12$	D: $3 \times 4 = 12$	E: $3 \times 4 = 12$	C: $2 \times 4 = 8$
Third Choice: 3 points	C: $5 \times 3 = 15$	D: $5 \times 3 = 15$	B: $3 \times 3 = 9$	B: $3 \times 3 = 9$	A: $3 \times 3 = 9$	B: $2 \times 3 = 6$
Fourth Choice: 2 points	D: $5 \times 2 = 10$	A: $5 \times 2 = 10$	E: $3 \times 2 = 6$	C: $3 \times 2 = 6$	C: $3 \times 2 = 6$	A: $2 \times 2 = 4$
Fifth Choice: 1 point	E: $5 \times 1 = 5$	B: $5 \times 1 = 5$	A: $3 \times 1 = 3$	E: $3 \times 1 = 3$	D: $3 \times 1 = 3$	E: $2 \times 1 = 2$

A gets $25 + 10 + 3 + 15 + 9 + 4 = 66$ points.
B gets $20 + 5 + 9 + 9 + 15 + 6 = 64$ points.
C gets $15 + 25 + 12 + 6 + 6 + 8 = 72$ points.
D gets $10 + 15 + 15 + 12 + 3 + 10 = 65$ points.
E gets $5 + 20 + 6 + 3 + 12 + 2 = 48$ points.

C receives the most points and is the winner.

b.

Number of Votes	5	5	3	3	3	2
First Choice: 4 points	A: $5 \times 4 = 20$	C: $5 \times 4 = 20$	D: $3 \times 4 = 12$	A: $3 \times 4 = 12$	B: $3 \times 4 = 12$	D: $2 \times 4 = 8$
Second Choice: 3 points	B: $5 \times 3 = 15$	D: $5 \times 3 = 15$	C: $3 \times 3 = 9$	D: $3 \times 3 = 9$	A: $3 \times 3 = 9$	C: $2 \times 3 = 6$
Third Choice: 2 points	C: $5 \times 2 = 10$	A: $5 \times 2 = 10$	B: $3 \times 2 = 6$	B: $3 \times 2 = 6$	C: $3 \times 2 = 6$	B: $2 \times 2 = 4$
Fourth Choice: 1 points	D: $5 \times 1 = 5$	B: $5 \times 1 = 5$	A: $3 \times 1 = 3$	C: $3 \times 1 = 3$	D: $3 \times 1 = 3$	A: $2 \times 1 = 2$

A gets $20 + 10 + 3 + 12 + 9 + 2 = 56$ points.
B gets $15 + 5 + 6 + 6 + 12 + 4 = 48$ points.
C gets $10 + 20 + 9 + 3 + 6 + 6 = 54$ points.
D gets $5 + 15 + 12 + 9 + 3 + 8 = 52$ points.

A receives the most points and is the winner.

36. a.

5	5	3	3	3	2
A	C	D	A	B	D
B	E	C	D	E	C
C	D	B	B	A	B
D	A	E	C	C	A
E	B	A	E	D	E

A vs. B
5 + 5 + 3 = 13 voters prefer A to B.
3 + 3 + 2 = 8 voters prefer B to A.
A wins this comparison and gets one point.

A vs. C
5 + 3 + 3 = 11 voters prefer A to C.
5 + 3 + 2 = 10 voters prefer C to A.
A wins this comparison and gets one point.

A vs. D
5 + 3 + 3 = 11 voters prefer A to D.
5 + 3 + 2 = 10 voters prefer D to A.
A wins this comparison and gets one point.

A vs. E
5 + 3 + 2 = 10 voters prefer A to E.
5 + 3 + 3 = 11 voters prefer E to A.
E wins this comparison and gets one point.

B vs. C
5 + 3 + 3 = 11 voters prefer B to C.
5 + 3 + 2 = 10 voters prefer C to B.
B wins this comparison and gets one point.

B vs. D
5 + 3 = 8 voters prefer B to D.
5 + 3 + 3 + 2 = 13 voters prefer D to B.
D wins this comparison and gets one point.

B vs. E
5 + 3 + 3 + 3 + 2 = 16 voters prefer B to E.
5 voters prefer E to B.
B wins this comparison and gets one point.

C vs. D
5 + 5 + 3 = 13 voters prefer C to D.
3 + 3 + 2 = 8 voters prefer D to C.
C wins this comparison and gets one point.

C vs. E
5 + 5 + 3 + 3 + 2 = 18 voters prefer C to E.
3 voters prefer E to C.
C wins this comparison and gets one point.

D vs. E
5 + 3 + 3 + 2 = 13 voters prefer D to E.
5 + 3 = 8 voters prefer E to D.
D wins this comparison and gets one point.

Adding points for the ten comparisons:
A gets 1 + 1 + 1 = 3 points.
B gets 1 + 1 = 2 points.
C gets 1 + 1 = 2 points.
D gets 1 + 1 = 2 points.
E gets 1 point.

A receives the most points, so A is declared the new division chair.

b.

Number of Votes	5	5	3	3	3	2
First Choice	A	C	D	A	B	D
Second Choice	B	D	C	D	A	C
Third Choice	C	A	B	B	C	B
Fourth Choice	D	B	A	C	D	A

A vs. B
5 + 5 + 3 = 13 voters prefer A to B.
3 + 3 + 2 = 8 voters prefer B to A.
A wins this comparison and gets one point.

A vs. C
5 + 3 + 3 = 11 voters prefer A to C.
5 + 3 + 2 = 10 voters prefer C to A.
A wins this comparison and gets one point.

A vs. D
5 + 3 + 3 = 11 voters prefer A to D.
5 + 3 + 2 = 10 voters prefer D to A.
A wins this comparison and gets one point.

B vs. C
5 + 3 + 3 = 11 voters prefer B to C.
5 + 3 + 2 = 10 voters prefer C to B.
B wins this comparison and gets one point.

B vs. D
5 + 3 = 8 voters prefer B to D.
5 + 3 + 3 + 2 = 13 voters prefer D to B.
D wins this comparison and gets one point.

C vs. D
5 + 5 + 3 = 13 voters prefer C to D.
3 + 3 + 2 = 8 voters prefer D to C.
C wins this comparison and gets one point.

Adding points for the six comparisons:
A gets 1 + 1 + 1 = 3 points.
B gets 1 point.
C gets 1 point.
D gets 1 point.

A receives the most points, so A is declared the new division chair.

37. First use the plurality method: C receives 12,000 first-place votes, and A receives 12,000 first-place votes. This results in a tie, so we use the Borda count method.

Number of Votes	12,000	7500	4500
First Choice: 3 points	C: 12,000 × 3 = 36,000	A: 7500 × 3 = 22,500	A: 4500 × 3 = 13,500
Second Choice: 2 points	B: 12,000 × 2 = 24,000	B: 7500 × 2 = 15,000	C: 4500 × 3 = 9000
Third Choice: 1 points	A: 12,000 × 1 = 12,000	C: 7500 × 1 = 7500	B: 4500 × 1 = 4500

A gets 12,000 + 22,500 + 13,500 = 48,000 points.
B gets 24,000 + 15,000 + 4500 = 43,500 points.
C gets 36,000 + 7500 + 9000 = 52,500 points.
C receives the most points and is the winner.

38. First use the pairwise comparison method.

60,000	40,000	40,000	20,000	20,000
A	C	B	A	C
B	A	C	C	B
C	B	A	B	A

A vs. B
60,000 + 40,000 + 20,000 = 120,000 voters prefer A to B.
40,000 + 20,000 = 60,000 voters prefer B to A.
A wins this comparison and gets one point.

A vs. C
60,000 + 20,000 = 80,000 voters prefer A to C.
40,000 + 40,000 + 20,000 = 100,000 voters prefer C to A.
C wins this comparison and gets one point.

B vs. C
60,000 + 40,000 = 100,000 voters prefer B to C.
40,000 + 20,000 + 20,000 = 80,000 voters prefer C to B.
B wins this comparison and gets one point.

Adding points for the three comparisons:
A gets 1 point.
B gets 1 point.
C gets 1 point.

We have a tie. We next try the Borda count method.

Number of Votes	60,000	40,000	40,000	20,000	20,000
First Choice: 3 points	A: 60,000 × 3 = 180,000	C: 40,000 × 3 = 120,000	B: 40,000 × 3 = 120,000	A: 20,000 × 3 = 60,000	C: 20,000 × 3 = 60,000
Second Choice: 2 points	B: 60,000 × 2 = 120,000	A: 40,000 × 2 = 80,000	C: 40,000 × 2 = 80,000	C: 20,000 × 2 = 40,000	B: 20,000 × 2 = 40,000
Third Choice: 1 point	C: 60,000 × 1 = 60,000	B: 40,000 × 1 = 40,000	A: 40,000 × 1 = 40,000	B: 20,000 × 1 = 20,000	A: 20,000 × 1 = 20,000

A gets 180,000 + 80,000 + 40,000 + 60,000 + 20,000 = 380,000 points.
B gets 120,000 + 40,000 + 120,000 + 20,000 + 40,000 = 340,000 points.
C gets 60,000 + 120,000 + 80,000 + 40,000 + 60,000 = 360,000 points.

A receives the most points, so A becomes the new mayor.

39-48. Answers will vary.

49. b

50. Using the pairwise comparison method in an election with 20 candidates, there are $\frac{20(19)}{2} = 190$ comparisons. If each pairwise comparison takes 2 minutes, it will take $2 \times 190 = 380$ minutes, or 6 hours and 20 minutes, to calculate the election results.

51-54. Answers will vary.

14.2 Flaws of Voting Methods

Check Point 1.

a. There are 14 first-place votes. A candidate with more than half of these receives a majority. The first-choice row shows that candidate A received 8 first-place votes. Thus, candidate A has a majority of first-place votes.

b. Using the Borda count method with four candidates, a first-place vote is worth 4 points, a second-place vote is worth 3 points, a third-place vote is worth 2 points, and a fourth-place vote is worth 1 point.

Number of Votes	6	4	2	2
First Choice: 4 points	A: 6 × 4 = 24 pts	B: 4 × 4 = 16 pts	B: 2 × 4 = 8 pts	A: 2 × 4 = 8 pts
Second Choice: 3 points	B: 6 × 3 = 18 pts	C: 4 × 3 = 12 pts	D: 2 × 3 = 6 pts	B: 2 × 3 = 6 pts
Third Choice: 2 points	C: 6 × 2 = 12 pts	D: 4 × 2 = 8 pts	C: 2 × 2 = 4 pts	D: 2 × 2 = 4 pts
Fourth Choice: 1 point	D: 6 × 1 = 6 pts	A: 4 × 1 = 4 pts	A: 2 × 1 = 2 pts	C: 2 × 1 = 2 pts

Now we read down the columns and total the points for each candidate.
A gets 24 + 4 + 2 + 8 = 38 points.
B gets 18 + 16 + 8 + 6 = 48 points.
C gets 12 + 12 + 4 + 2 = 30 points.
D gets 6 + 8 + 6 + 4 = 24 points.

Because candidate B has received the most points, candidate B is declared the new principal using the Borda count method.

Check Point 2.

a. We begin by comparing A and B. A is favored over B in column 1, giving A 3 votes. B is favored over A in columns 2 and 3, giving B 2 + 2, or 4, votes. Thus, B is favored when compared to A.

Now we compare B to C. B is favored over C in columns 1 and 2, giving B 3 + 2, or 5, votes. C is favored over B in column 3, giving C 2 votes. Thus, B is favored when compared to C.

We see that B is favored over both A and C using a head-to-head comparison.

b. Using the plurality method, the brand with the most first-place votes is the winner. In the row indicating first choice, A received 3 votes, B received 2 votes, and C received 2 votes. A wins using the plurality method.

Check Point 3.

a. There are 120 people voting. No candidate initially receives more than 60 votes. Because C receives the fewest first-place votes, C is eliminated in the next round. The new preference table is

Number of Votes	42	34	28	16
First Choice	A	A	B	B
Second Choice	B	B	A	A

Because A has received a majority of first-place votes, A is the winner of the straw poll.

b. No candidate initially receives more than 60 votes. Because B receives the fewest first-place votes, B is eliminated in the next round. The new preference table is

Number of Votes	54	34	28	4
First Choice	A	C	C	A
Second Choice	C	A	A	C

Because C has received a majority of first-place votes, C is the winner of the second election.

c. A won the first election. A then gained additional support with the 12 voters who changed their ballots to make A their first choice. A lost the second election. This violates the monotonicity criterion.

Check Point 4.

a. Because there are 4 candidates, $n = 4$ and the number of comparisons we must make is $\frac{n(n-1)}{2} = \frac{4(4-1)}{2} = \frac{4 \cdot 3}{2} = \frac{12}{2} = 6$.

The following table shows the results of these 6 comparisons.

Comparison	Vote Results	Conclusion
A vs. B	270 voters prefer A to B. 90 voters prefer B to A.	A wins and gets 1 point.
A vs. C	270 voters prefer A to C. 90 voters prefer C to A.	A wins and gets 1 point.
A vs. D	150 voters prefer A to D. 210 voters prefer D to A.	D wins and gets 1 point.
B vs. C	180 voters prefer B to C. 180 voters prefer C to B.	B and C tie. Each gets $\frac{1}{2}$ point.
B vs. D	240 voters prefer B to D. 120 voters prefer D to B.	B wins and gets 1 point.
C vs. D	240 voters prefer C to D. 120 voters prefer D to C.	C wins and gets 1 point.

Thus A gets 2 points, B gets $1\frac{1}{2}$ points, C gets $1\frac{1}{2}$ points, and D gets 1 point. Therefore A is the winner.

b. After B and C withdraw, there is a new preference table:

Number of Votes	150	90	90	30
First Choice	A	D	D	D
Second Choice	D	A	A	A

Using the pairwise comparison test with 2 candidates, there is only one comparison to make namely A vs. D.

150 voters prefer A to D, and 210 voters prefer D to A. D gets 1 point, A gets 0 points, and D wins the election.

c. The first election count produced A as the winner. The removal of B and C from the ballots produced D as the winner. This violates the irrelevant alternatives criterion.

Exercise Set 14.2

1. a. D has 300 first-place votes, which is more than half of the 570 total votes, so D has a majority of first-place votes.

b.

Number of Votes	300	120	90	60
First Choice: 4 points	D: $300 \times 4 = 1200$	C: $120 \times 4 = 480$	C: $90 \times 4 = 360$	A: $60 \times 4 = 240$
Second Choice: 3 points	A: $300 \times 3 = 900$	A: $120 \times 3 = 360$	A: $90 \times 3 = 270$	D: $60 \times 3 = 180$
Third Choice: 2 points	B: $300 \times 2 = 600$	B: $120 \times 2 = 240$	D: $90 \times 2 = 180$	B: $60 \times 2 = 120$
Fourth Choice: 1 point	C: $300 \times 1 = 300$	D: $120 \times 1 = 120$	B: $90 \times 1 = 90$	C: $60 \times 1 = 60$

A gets $900 + 360 + 270 + 240 = 1770$ points.
B gets $600 + 240 + 90 + 120 = 1050$ points.
C gets $300 + 480 + 360 + 60 = 1200$ points.
D gets $1200 + 120 + 180 + 180 = 1680$ points.

A receives the most points, so A is the chosen design.

c. No. D receives a majority of first-place votes, but A is chosen by the Borda count method.

2. a. A has 27 first-place votes, which is more than half of the 53 total votes, so A has a majority of first-place votes.

b.

Number of Votes	27	24	2
First Choice: 3 points	A: $27 \times 3 = 81$	B: $24 \times 3 = 72$	C: $2 \times 3 = 6$
Second Choice: 2 points	C: $27 \times 2 = 54$	C: $24 \times 2 = 48$	B: $2 \times 2 = 4$
Third Choice: 1 point	B: $27 \times 1 = 27$	A: $24 \times 1 = 24$	A: $2 \times 1 = 2$

A gets $81 + 24 + 2 = 107$ points.
B gets $27 + 72 + 4 = 103$ points.
C gets $54 + 48 + 6 = 108$ points.

C receives the most points, so C is the winner.

c. No. A receives the majority of first-place votes, but C is chosen by the Borda count method.

3. a. A is favored over R in columns 1 and 3, giving A 12 + 4, or 16, votes. R is favored over A in columns 2 and 4, giving R 9 + 4, or 13, votes. Thus, A is favored when compared to R.

A is favored over V in columns 1 and 4, giving A 12 + 4, or 16, votes. V is favored over A in columns 2 and 3, giving V 9 + 4, or 13, votes. Thus, A is favored when compared to V.

We see that A is favored over the other two cities using a head-to-head comparison.

b. A gets 12 first-place votes, V gets 13 first-place votes, and R gets 4 first-place votes, so V wins using the plurality method.

c. No. A wins the head-to-head comparison, but V wins the election.

4. a. B is favored over A in columns 2 and 3, giving B 19 + 5, or 24, votes. A is favored over B in column 1, giving A 20 votes. Thus, B is favored when compared to A.

B is favored over C in columns 1 and 2, giving B 20 + 19, or 39, votes. C is favored over B in column 3, giving C 5 votes. Thus, B is favored when compared to C. We see that B is favored over the other two cities using a head-to-head comparison.

b. A gets 20 first-place votes, B gets 19 first-place votes, and C gets 5 first-place votes, so A wins using the plurality method.

c. No. B wins the head-to-head comparison, but A wins the election.

5. a. A is favored over B in columns 1 and 4, giving A 120 + 30, or 150, votes. B is favored over A in columns 2, 3, and 5, giving B 60 + 30 + 30, or 120 votes. Thus, A is favored when compared to B.

A is favored over C in columns 1 and 3, giving A 120 + 30, or 150 votes. C is favored over A in columns 2, 4, and 5, giving C 60 + 30 + 30, or 120, votes. Thus, A is favored when compared to C.

We see that A is favored over the other two options using a head-to-head comparison.

b.

Number of Votes	120	60	30	30	30
First Choice: 3 points	A: $120 \times 3 = 360$	C: $60 \times 3 = 180$	B: $30 \times 3 = 90$	C: $30 \times 3 = 90$	B: $30 \times 3 = 90$
Second Choice: 2 points	C: $120 \times 2 = 240$	B: $60 \times 2 = 120$	A: $30 \times 2 = 60$	A: $30 \times 2 = 60$	C: $30 \times 2 = 60$
Third Choice: 1 point	B: $120 \times 1 = 120$	A: $60 \times 1 = 60$	C: $30 \times 1 = 30$	B: $30 \times 1 = 30$	A: $30 \times 1 = 30$

A gets 360 + 60 + 60 + 60 + 30 = 570 points.
B gets 120 + 120 + 90 + 30 + 90 = 450 points.
C gets 240 + 180 + 30 + 90 + 60 = 600 points.

C receives the most points, so C is the winner.

c. No. A wins the head-to-head comparison, but C wins the election.

6. a. C is favored over A in column 1, giving C 200 votes. A is favored over C in columns 2 and 3, giving A 80 + 80, or 160, votes. Thus, C is favored when compared to A. C is favored over B in column 1, giving C 200 votes. B is favored over C in columns 2 and 3, giving B 80 + 80, or 160, votes. Thus, C is favored when compared with B.

We see that C is favored over the other two options using a head-to-head comparison.

b.

Number of Votes	200	80	80
First Choice: 3 points	C: $200 \times 3 = 600$	B: $80 \times 3 = 240$	A: $80 \times 3 = 240$
Second Choice: 2 points	A: $200 \times 2 = 400$	A: $80 \times 2 = 160$	B: $80 \times 2 = 160$
Third Choice: 1 point	B: $200 \times 1 = 200$	C: $80 \times 1 = 80$	C: $80 \times 1 = 80$

A gets 400 + 160 + 240 = 800 points.
B gets 200 + 240 + 160 = 600 points.
C gets 600 + 80 + 80 = 760 points.

A receives the most points, so A is the favored option.

c. No. C wins the head-to-head comparison, but A wins the election.

7. a. There are 29 people voting. No one receives the 15 first-place votes needed for a majority. B receives the fewest first-place votes and is eliminated in the next round.

Number of Votes	18	11
First Choice	C	A
Second Choice	A	C

C receives the majority of first-place votes, so C is the winner.

b. With the voting change, a new preference table results.

Number of Votes	14	8	7
First Choice	C	B	A
Second Choice	A	C	B
Third Choice	B	A	C

No one receives a majority of first-place votes. A receives the fewest first-place votes, and is eliminated in the next round.

Number of Votes	14	15
First Choice	C	B
Second Choice	B	C

B receives the majority of first-place votes, so B is the winner.

c. No. C wins the straw vote, and the only change increases the number of first-place votes for C, but B wins the election.

8. a. There are 42 people voting. No one receives the 22 first-place votes needed for a majority. B receives the fewest first-place votes and is eliminated in the next round.

Number of Votes	26	16
First Choice	C	A
Second Choice	A	C

C receives the majority of first-place votes, so C is the winner.

b. With the voting change, a new preference table results.

Number of Votes	20	12	10
First Choice	C	B	A
Second Choice	A	C	B
Third Choice	B	A	C

No one receives a majority of first-place votes. A receives the fewest first-place votes, and is eliminated in the next round.

Number of Votes	20	22
First Choice	C	B
Second Choice	B	C

B receives the majority of first-place votes, so B is the winner.

c. No. C wins the straw vote, and the only change increases the number of first-place votes for C, but B wins the election.

9. a. There are 3 candidates, so $n = 3$ and the number of comparisons we must make is $\frac{n(n-1)}{2} = \frac{3(2)}{2} = 3$.

Comparison	Vote Results	Conclusion
H vs. L	10 voters prefer H to L. 13 voters prefer L to H.	L wins and gets one point.
H vs. S	10 voters prefer H to S. 13 voters prefer S to H.	S wins and gets one point.
L vs. S	8 voters prefer L to S. 15 voters prefer S to L.	S wins and gets one point.

Thus, L gets 1 point and S gets 2 points. Therefore, S is the winner when candidates H and L are included.

b. New preference table:

Number of Votes	15	8
First Choice	S	L
Second Choice	L	S

With only two candidates, we can only make one comparison. We see that S wins, defeating L by 15 votes to 8 votes. Thus S gets 1 point, L gets 0 points, and S is the winner.

c. Yes. S wins whether or not H withdraws.

10. a. There are 3 candidates, so $n = 3$ and the number of comparisons we must make is $\frac{n(n-1)}{2} = \frac{3(2)}{2} = 3$.

Comparison	Vote Results	Conclusion
G vs. M	14 voters prefer G to M. 12 voters prefer M to G.	G wins and gets one point.
G vs. R	18 voters prefer G to R. 8 voters prefer R to G.	G wins and gets one point.
M vs. R	12 voters prefer M to R. 14 voters prefer R to M.	R wins and gets one point.

Thus G gets 2 points and R gets 1 point. Therefore, G is the winner when candidates M and R are included.

b. New preference table:

Number of Votes	18	8
First Choice	G	R
Second Choice	R	G

With only two candidates, we can only make one comparison. We see that G wins, defeating R by 18 votes to 8 votes. Thus, G gets 1 point, R gets 0 points, and G is the winner.

c. Yes. G is the winner whether or not M withdraws.

11. a.

Number of Votes	20	16	10	4
First Choice: 4 points	D: $20 \times 4 = 80$	C: $16 \times 4 = 64$	C: $10 \times 4 = 40$	A: $4 \times 4 = 16$
Second Choice: 3 points	A: $20 \times 3 = 60$	A: $16 \times 3 = 48$	B: $10 \times 3 = 30$	B: $4 \times 3 = 12$
Third Choice: 2 points	B: $20 \times 2 = 40$	B: $16 \times 2 = 32$	D: $10 \times 2 = 20$	D: $4 \times 2 = 8$
Fourth Choice: 1 point	C: $20 \times 1 = 20$	D: $16 \times 1 = 16$	A: $10 \times 1 = 10$	C: $4 \times 1 = 4$

A gets $60 + 48 + 10 + 16 = 134$ points.
B gets $40 + 32 + 30 + 12 = 114$ points.
C gets $20 + 64 + 40 + 4 = 128$ points.
D gets $80 + 16 + 20 + 8 = 124$ points.

A receives the most points, so A is the winner.

b. No. A has only 4 first-place votes, out of 50 total votes. C has 26 first-place votes, which is a majority, but A wins the election.

12. a.

Number of Votes	20	15	3	1
First Choice: 4 points	A: $20 \times 4 = 80$	B: $15 \times 4 = 60$	C: $3 \times 4 = 12$	D: $1 \times 4 = 4$
Second Choice: 3 points	B: $20 \times 3 = 60$	C: $15 \times 3 = 45$	D: $3 \times 3 = 9$	B: $1 \times 3 = 3$
Third Choice: 2 points	C: $20 \times 2 = 40$	D: $15 \times 2 = 30$	B: $3 \times 2 = 6$	C: $1 \times 2 = 2$
Fourth Choice: 1 point	D: $20 \times 1 = 20$	A: $15 \times 1 = 15$	A: $3 \times 1 = 3$	A: $1 \times 1 = 1$

A gets $80 + 15 + 3 + 1 = 99$ points.
B gets $60 + 60 + 6 + 3 = 129$ points.
C gets $40 + 45 + 12 + 2 = 99$ points.
D gets $20 + 30 + 9 + 4 = 63$ points.

B receives the most points, so B is the winner.

b. No. A receives 20 first-place votes out of 39 total votes, which is a majority, but B wins the election.

13. a. There are 70 people voting. No one receives the 36 first-place votes needed for a majority. B receives the fewest first-place votes and is eliminated in the next round.

Number of Votes	24	20	10	8	8
First Choice	D	C	A	A	C
Second Choice	A	A	D	C	D
Third Choice	C	D	C	D	A

No one receives a majority of first-place votes. A receives the fewest first-place votes and is eliminated in the next round.

Number of Votes	34	36
First Choice	D	C
Second Choice	C	D

C receives 36 first-place votes, which is a majority, so C is the winner.

b. No. When compared individually to B, A wins with 60 votes to 10. Compared with C, A wins with 42 votes to 28. Compared with D, A wins with 38 votes to 32. So A is favored in all head-to-head contests but C wins the election.

14. a. There are 51 people voting. No one receives the 26 first-place votes needed for a majority. B and D tie for the fewest first-place votes, so both are eliminated in the next round.

Number of Votes	22	29
First Choice	A	C
Second Choice	C	A

C has a majority of first-place votes, so C is the winner.

b. No. D wins the head-to-head comparison against A, B, and C, but C wins using the plurality-with-elimination method.

15. a.

Number of Votes	14	8	4
First Choice: 4 points	A: $14 \times 4 = 56$	B: $8 \times 4 = 32$	D: $4 \times 4 = 16$
Second Choice: 3 points	B: $14 \times 3 = 42$	D: $8 \times 3 = 24$	A: $4 \times 3 = 12$
Third Choice: 2 points	C: $14 \times 2 = 28$	C: $8 \times 2 = 16$	C: $4 \times 2 = 8$
Fourth Choice: 1 point	D: $14 \times 1 = 14$	A: $8 \times 1 = 8$	B: $4 \times 1 = 4$

A gets $56 + 8 + 12 = 76$ points.
B gets $42 + 32 + 4 = 78$ points.
C gets $28 + 16 + 8 = 52$ points.
D gets $14 + 24 + 16 = 54$ points.

B receives the most points, so B is the winner.

b. No. A receives the majority of first-place votes, but B wins the election.

c. No. A wins all head-to-head comparisons, but B wins the election.

d. Using the Borda count method with C removed:

Number of Votes	14	8	4
First Choice: 3 points	A: $14 \times 3 = 42$	B: $8 \times 3 = 24$	D: $4 \times 3 = 12$
Second Choice: 2 points	B: $14 \times 2 = 28$	D: $8 \times 2 = 16$	A: $4 \times 2 = 8$
Third Choice: 1 point	D: $14 \times 1 = 14$	A: $8 \times 1 = 8$	B: $4 \times 1 = 4$

A gets $42 + 8 + 8 = 58$ points.
B gets $28 + 24 + 4 = 56$ points.
D gets $14 + 16 + 12 = 42$ points.

A receives the most points, and wins the election.

The irrelevant alternatives criterion is not satisfied. Candidate C's dropping out changed the outcome of the election.

16. a. There are 42 people voting. No one receives the 22 first-place votes needed for a majority. D receives the fewest first-place votes and is eliminated in the next round.

Number of Votes	14	12	16
First Choice	A	B	C
Second Choice	B	A	B
Third Choice	C	C	A

No one receives a majority of first-place votes. B receives the fewest first-place votes and is eliminated in the next round.

Number of Votes	26	16
First Choice	A	C
Second Choice	C	A

A receives 26 first-place votes, which is a majority, so A is the winner.

b. New preference table:

Number of Votes	14	12	10	6
First Choice	A	B	C	A
Second Choice	B	A	B	D
Third Choice	C	C	A	C
Fourth Choice	D	D	D	B

No one receives a majority of first-place votes. C receives the fewest first-place votes and is eliminated in the next round.

Number of Votes	14	22	6
First Choice	A	B	A
Second Choice	B	A	D
Third Choice	D	D	B

B receives 22 first-place votes, which is a majority, so B is the winner. The monotonicity criterion is not satisfied because the only change gave A more first-place votes, but resulted in A's losing the election.

17. a.

Number of Votes	16	14	12	4	2
First Choice: 5 points	A: $16 \times 5 = 80$	D: $14 \times 5 = 70$	D: $12 \times 5 = 60$	C: $4 \times 5 = 20$	E: $2 \times 5 = 10$
Second Choice: 4 points	B: $16 \times 4 = 64$	B: $14 \times 4 = 56$	B: $12 \times 4 = 48$	A: $4 \times 4 = 16$	A: $2 \times 4 = 8$
Third Choice: 3 points	C: $16 \times 3 = 48$	A: $14 \times 3 = 42$	E: $12 \times 3 = 36$	B: $4 \times 3 = 12$	D: $2 \times 3 = 6$
Fourth Choice: 2 points	D: $16 \times 2 = 32$	C: $14 \times 2 = 28$	C: $12 \times 2 = 24$	D: $4 \times 2 = 8$	B: $2 \times 2 = 4$
Fifth Choice: 1 point	E: $16 \times 1 = 16$	E: $14 \times 1 = 14$	A: $12 \times 1 = 12$	E: $4 \times 1 = 4$	C: $2 \times 1 = 2$

A gets $80 + 42 + 12 + 16 + 8 = 158$ points.
B gets $64 + 56 + 48 + 12 + 4 = 184$ points.
C gets $48 + 28 + 24 + 20 + 2 = 122$ points.
D gets $32 + 70 + 60 + 8 + 6 = 176$ points.
E gets $16 + 14 + 36 + 4 + 10 = 80$ points.

B receives the most points, so B is the winner.

b. No. D gets a majority of first-place votes, but B wins the election.

c. No. D wins all head-to-head comparisons, but B wins the election.

18. a. There are 5 candidates, so the number of pairwise comparisons is $\frac{n(n-1)}{2} = \frac{5(5-1)}{2} = \frac{5(4)}{2} = 10$.

Comparison	Vote Results	Conclusion
A vs. B	14 voters prefer A to B. 18 voters prefer B to A.	B wins and gets 1 point.
A vs. C	28 voters prefer A to C. 4 voters prefer C to A.	A wins and gets 1 point.
A vs. D	28 voters prefer A to D. 4 voters prefer D to A.	A wins and gets 1 point.
A vs. E	28 voters prefer A to E. 4 voters prefer E to A.	A wins and gets 1 point.
B vs. C	14 voters prefer B to C. 18 voters prefer C to B.	C wins and gets 1 point.
B vs. D	18 voters prefer B to D. 14 voters prefer D to B.	B wins and gets 1 point.
B vs. E	16 voters prefer B to E. 16 voters prefer E to B.	B and E tie. Each gets $\frac{1}{2}$ point.
C vs. D	18 voters prefer C to D. 14 voters prefer D to C.	C wins and gets 1 point.
C vs. E	16 voters prefer C to E. 16 voters prefer E to C.	C and E tie. Each gets $\frac{1}{2}$ point.
D vs. E	26 voters prefer D to E. 6 voters prefer E to D.	D wins and gets 1 point.

Thus A gets 3 points, B gets $2\frac{1}{2}$ points, C gets $2\frac{1}{2}$ points, D gets 1 point, and E gets 1 point. Therefore, A is the winner.

b. After eliminating C, we have 4 candidates, and need 6 comparisons.

Comparison	Vote Results	Conclusion
A vs. B	14 voters prefer A to B. 18 voters prefer B to A.	B wins and gets 1 point.
A vs. D	28 voters prefer A to D. 4 voters prefer D to A.	A wins and gets 1 point.
A vs. E	28 voters prefer A to E. 4 voters prefer E to A.	A wins and gets 1 point.
B vs. D	18 voters prefer B to D. 14 voters prefer D to B.	B wins and gets 1 point.
B vs. E	16 voters prefer B to E. 16 voters prefer E to B.	B and E tie. Each gets $\frac{1}{2}$ point.
D vs. E	26 voters prefer D to E. 6 voters prefer E to D.	D wins and gets 1 point.

Thus A gets 2 points, B gets $2\frac{1}{2}$ points, D gets 1 point, and E gets $\frac{1}{2}$ point. Therefore, B is the winner.

The irrelevant alternatives criterion is not satisfied, since removing one candidate changed the outcome of the election.

19. a. A receives the most first-place votes, and is the winner.

 b. Yes. A has a majority of the first-place votes, and wins.

 c. Yes. A wins in comparisons to B and C.

 d. New preference table:

Number of Votes	7	3	2
First Choice	A	B	A
Second Choice	B	C	C
Third Choice	C	A	B

A has the majority of first-place votes, and wins using the plurality method.

 e. Yes. A still receives the most first-place votes, and wins.

 f. No. The fact that all four criteria are satisfied in a particular case does not mean that the method used always satisfies all four criteria.

20-32. Answers will vary.

14.3 Apportionment Methods

Check Point 1.

a. Standard divisor $= \dfrac{\text{total population}}{\text{number of allocated items}} = \dfrac{10,000}{200} = 50$

b. Standard quota for state A $= \dfrac{\text{population of state A}}{\text{standard divisor}} = \dfrac{1112}{50} = 22.24$

 Standard quota for state B $= \dfrac{\text{population of state B}}{\text{standard divisor}} = \dfrac{1118}{50} = 22.36$

 Standard quota for state C $= \dfrac{\text{population of state C}}{\text{standard divisor}} = \dfrac{1320}{50} = 26.4$

 Standard quota for state D $= \dfrac{\text{population of state D}}{\text{standard divisor}} = \dfrac{1515}{50} = 30.3$

 Standard quota for state E $= \dfrac{\text{population of state E}}{\text{standard divisor}} = \dfrac{4935}{50} = 98.7$

Table 14.27   Population of Amador by State

State	A	B	C	D	E	Total
Population (in thousands)	1112	1118	1320	1515	4935	10,000
Standard quota	22.24	22.36	26.4	30.3	98.7	200

Check Point 2.

State	Population (in thousands)	Standard Quota	Lower Quota	Fractional Part	Surplus	Final Apportionment
A	1112	22.24	22	0.24		22
B	1118	22.36	22	0.36		22
C	1320	26.4	26	0.4 (next largest)	1	27
D	1515	30.3	30	0.3		30
E	4935	98.7	98	0.7 (largest)	1	99
Total	10,000	200	198			200

Check Point 3.

State	Population (in thousands)	Modified Quota (using $d = 49.3$)	Modified Lower Quota	Final Apportionment
A	1112	22.56	22	22
B	1118	22.68	22	22
C	1320	26.77	26	26
D	1515	30.73	30	30
E	4935	100.10	100	100
Total	10,000		200	200

Check Point 4.

State	Population (in thousands)	Modified Quota (using $d = 50.5$)	Modified Upper Quota
A	1112	22.02	23
B	1118	22.14	23
C	1320	26.14	27
D	1515	30	30
E	4935	97.72	98
Total	10,000		201

This sum should be 200, not 201.

State	Population (in thousands)	Modified Quota (using $d = 50.6$)	Modified Upper Quota	Final Apportionment
A	1112	21.98	22	22
B	1118	22.09	23	23
C	1320	26.09	27	27
D	1515	29.94	30	30
E	4935	97.53	98	98
Total	10,000		200	200

Check Point 5.

State	Population (in thousands)	Modified Quota (using $d = 49.8$)	Modified Rounded Quota
A	1112	22.33	22
B	1118	22.45	22
C	1320	26.51	27
D	1515	30.42	30
E	4935	99.10	99
Total	10,000		200

Exercise Set 14.3

1. a. Standard divisor $= \frac{1600}{80} = 20$. There are 20,000 people for each seat in congress.

b–c.

State	A	B	C	D
Standard quota	$\frac{138}{20} = 6.9$	$\frac{266}{20} = 13.3$	$\frac{534}{20} = 26.7$	$\frac{662}{20} = 33.1$
Lower quota	6	13	26	33
Upper Quota	7	14	27	34

2. a. Standard divisor $= \frac{1600}{200} = 8$. There are 8000 people for each seat in congress.

b–c.

State	A	B	C	D
Standard quota	$\frac{138}{8} = 17.25$	$\frac{266}{8} = 33.25$	$\frac{534}{8} = 66.75$	$\frac{662}{8} = 82.75$
Lower quota	17	33	66	82
Upper Quota	18	34	67	83

3.

State	Population (in thousands)	Standard Quota	Lower Quota	Fractional Part	Surplus	Final Apportionment
A	138	6.9	6	0.9	1	7
B	266	13.3	13	0.3		13
C	534	26.7	26	0.7	1	27
D	662	33.1	33	0.1		33
Total	1600	80	78			80

4.

State	Population (in thousands)	Standard Quota	Lower Quota	Fractional Part	Surplus	Final Apportionment
A	138	17.25	17	0.25		17
B	266	33.25	33	0.25		33
C	534	66.75	66	0.75	1	67
D	662	82.75	82	0.75	1	83
Total	1600	200	198			200

5.

School	Enrollment	Standard Quota	Lower Quota	Fractional Part	Surplus	Final Apportionment
Humanities	1050	30.26	30	0.26		30
Social Science	1410	40.63	40	0.63	1	41
Engineering	1830	52.74	52	0.74	1	53
Business	2540	73.20	73	0.20		73
Education	3580	103.17	103	0.17		103
Total	10,410	300	298			300

We use $\frac{10,410}{300} = 34.7$ as the standard divisor.

6.

School	Enrollment	Standard Quota	Lower Quota	Fractional Part	Surplus	Final Apportionment
Liberal Arts	1180	32.60	32	0.60		32
Education	1290	35.64	35	0.64	1	36
Business	2140	59.12	59	0.12		59
Engineering	2930	80.94	80	0.94	1	81
Sciences	3320	91.71	91	0.71	1	92
Total	10,860	300.01	297			300

We use $\frac{10,860}{300} = 36.2$ as the standard divisor.

7.

State	Population	Modified Quota ($d = 32,920$)	Modified Lower Quota	Final Apportionment
A	126,316	3.84	3	3
B	196,492	5.97	5	5
C	425,264	12.92	12	12
D	526,664	15.998	15	15
E	725,264	22.03	22	22
Total	2,000,000		57	57

8.

State	Population	Modified Quota ($d = 7.82$)	Modified Lower Quota	Final Apportionment
A	424	54.22	54	54
B	664	84.91	84	84
C	892	114.07	114	114
D	1162	148.59	148	148
Total	3142		400	400

9. There are 15,000 patients. The standard divisor is $\frac{15,000}{150}$, or 100. Try a modified divisor of 98.

Clinic	Average Weekly Patient Load	Modified Quota	Modified Lower Quota	Final Apportionment
A	1714	17.49	17	17
B	5460	55.71	55	55
C	2440	24.90	24	24
D	5386	54.96	54	54
Total	15,000		150	150

10. There are 2914 patients. The standard divisor is $\frac{2914}{70}$, or 41.63. Try a modified divisor of 39.8.

Clinic	Average Weekly Patient Load	Modified Quota	Modified Lower Quota	Final Apportionment
A	316	7.94	7	7
B	598	15.03	15	15
C	396	9.95	9	9
D	692	17.39	17	17
E	426	10.70	10	10
F	486	12.21	12	12
Total	2914		70	70

11.

Precinct	Crimes	Modified Quota ($d = 16$)	Modified Upper Quota	Final Apportionment
A	446	27.88	28	28
B	526	32.88	33	33
C	835	52.19	53	53
D	227	14.19	15	15
E	338	21.13	22	22
F	456	28.5	29	29
Total	2828		180	180

12.

Person	Contribution	Modified Quota ($d = 108$)	Modified Upper Quota	Final Apportionment
A	2013	18.64	19	19
B	187	1.73	2	2
C	290	2.69	3	3
D	3862	35.76	36	36
Total	6352		60	60

13. There is a total of $2025 to be invested. The standard divisor is $\frac{2025}{30}$, or 67.5. Try a modified divisor of 72.

Person	Amount	Modified Quota	Modified Upper Quota	Final Apportionment
A	795	11.04	12	12
B	705	9.79	10	10
C	525	7.29	8	8
Total	2025		30	30

14. There are 15,000 patients. The standard divisor is $\frac{15,000}{150}$, or 100. Try a modified divisor of 101.2.

Clinic	Average Weekly Patient Load	Modified Quota	Modified Upper Quota	Final Apportionment
A	1714	16.94	17	17
B	5460	53.95	54	54
C	2440	24.11	25	25
D	5386	53.22	54	54
Total	15,000		150	150

15.

Course	Enrollment	Modified Quota ($d = 29.6$)	Modified Rounded Quota	Final Apportionment
Introductory Algebra	130	4.39	4	4
Intermediate Algebra	282	9.53	10	10
Liberal Arts Math	188	6.35	6	6
Total	600		20	20

16.

State	Population (in thousands)	Modified Quota ($d = 9.98$)	Modified Rounded Quota	Final Apportionment
A	424	42.48	42	42
B	664	66.53	67	67
C	892	89.38	89	89
D	1162	116.43	116	116
Total	3142		314	314

17. The total number of passengers is 11,060. The standard divisor is $\frac{11,060}{200}$ or 55.3. Try a modified divisor of 55.5.

Route	Average Number of Passengers	Modified Quota	Modified Rounded Quota	Final Apportionment
A	1087	19.59	20	20
B	1323	23.84	24	24
C	1592	28.68	29	29
D	1596	28.76	29	29
E	5462	98.41	98	98
Total	11,060		200	200

18. The total number of crimes is 2828. The standard divisor is $\frac{2828}{180}$, or 15.71. Try a modified divisor of 15.7.

Precinct	Crimes	Modified Quota	Modified Rounded Quota	Final Apportionment
A	446	28.41	28	28
B	526	33.50	34	34
C	835	53.18	53	53
D	227	14.46	14	14
E	338	21.53	22	22
E	456	29.04	29	29
Total	2828		180	180

19. The total number of patients is 2000. The standard divisor is $\frac{2000}{250}$, or 8. Use Hamilton's method.

Shift	Average Number of Patients	Standard Quota	Lower Quota	Fractional Part	Surplus	Final Apportionment
A	453	56.625	56	0 .625	1	57
B	650	81.25	81	0.25		81
C	547	68.375	68	0.375		68
D	350	43.75	43	0.75	1	44
Total	2000	250	248			250

20. Try a modified divisor of 7.93. Use Jefferson's method.

Shift	Average Number of Patients	Modified Quota	Modified Lower Quota	Final Apportionment
A	453	57.12	57	57
B	650	81.97	81	81
C	547	68.98	68	68
D	350	44.14	44	44
Total	2000		250	250

21. Try a modified divisor of 8.06. Use Adams' method.

Shift	Average Number of Patients	Modified Quota	Modified Upper Quota	Final Apportionment
A	453	56.20	57	57
B	650	80.65	81	81
C	547	67.87	68	68
D	350	43.42	44	44
Total	2000		250	250

22. Try a modified divisor of 8. Use Webster's method.

Shift	Average Number of Patients	Modified Quota	Modified Rounded Quota	Final Apportionment
A	453	56.625	57	57
B	650	81.25	81	81
C	547	68.375	68	68
D	350	43.75	44	44
Total	2000		250	250

23. The total population is 3,615,920. The standard divisor is $\frac{3,615,920}{105}$, or 34,437.333. Use Hamilton's method.

State	Population	Standard Quota	Lower Quota	Fractional Part	Surplus	Final Apportionment
Connecticut	236,841	6.88	6	0.88	1	7
Delaware	55,540	1.61	1	0.61	1	2
Georgia	70,835	2.06	2	0.06		2
Kentucky	68,705	1.995	1	0.995	1	2
Maryland	278,514	8.09	8	0.09		8
Massachusetts	475,327	13.80	13	0.80	1	14
New Hampshire	141,822	4.12	4	0.12		4
New Jersey	179,570	5.21	5	0.21		5
New York	331,589	9.63	9	0.63	1	10
North Carolina	353,523	10.27	10	0.27		10
Pennsylvania	432,879	12.57	12	0.57	1	13
Rhode Island	68,446	1.99	1	0.99	1	2
South Carolina	206,236	5.99	5	0.99	1	6
Vermont	85,533	2.48	2	0.48		2
Virginia	630,560	18.31	18	0.31		18
Total	3,615,920	105.005	97			105

24. Use Jefferson's method with $d = 33,000$.

State	Population	Modified Quota	Modified Lower Quota	Final Apportionment
Connecticut	236,841	7.18	7	7
Delaware	55,540	1.68	1	1
Georgia	70,835	2.15	2	2
Kentucky	68,705	2.08	2	2
Maryland	278,514	8.44	8	8
Massachusetts	475,327	14.40	14	14
New Hampshire	141,822	4.30	4	4
New Jersey	179,570	5.44	5	5
New York	331,589	10.05	10	10
North Carolina	353,523	10.71	10	10
Pennsylvania	432,879	13.12	13	13
Rhode Island	68,446	2.07	2	2
South Carolina	206,236	6.25	6	6
Vermont	85,533	2.59	2	2
Virginia	630,560	19.11	19	19
Total	3,615,920		105	105

25. Use Adams' method with $d = 36,100$.

State	Population	Modified Quota	Modified Upper Quota	Final Apportionment
Connecticut	236,841	6.56	7	7
Delaware	55,540	1.54	2	2
Georgia	70,835	1.96	2	2
Kentucky	68,705	1.90	2	2
Maryland	278,514	7.72	8	8
Massachusetts	475,327	13.17	14	14
New Hampshire	141,822	3.93	4	4
New Jersey	179,570	4.97	5	5
New York	331,589	9.19	10	10
North Carolina	353,523	9.79	10	10
Pennsylvania	432,879	11.99	12	12
Rhode Island	68,446	1.90	2	2
South Carolina	206,236	5.71	6	6
Vermont	85,533	2.37	3	3
Virginia	630,560	17.47	18	18
Total	3,615,920		105	105

26. Use Webster's method with $d = 34,500$.

State	Population	Modified Quota	Modified Rounded Quota	Final Apportionment
Connecticut	236,841	6.86	7	7
Delaware	55,540	1.61	2	2
Georgia	70,835	2.05	2	2
Kentucky	68,705	1.99	2	2
Maryland	278,514	8.07	8	8
Massachusetts	475,327	13.78	14	14
New Hampshire	141,822	4.11	4	4
New Jersey	179,570	5.20	5	5
New York	331,589	9.61	10	10
North Carolina	353,523	10.25	10	10
Pennsylvania	432,879	12.55	13	13
Rhode Island	68,446	1.98	2	2
South Carolina	206,236	5.98	6	6
Vermont	85,533	2.48	2	2
Virginia	630,560	18.28	18	18
Total	3,615,920		105	105

27-41. Answers will vary.

42. Rearranging the formula

standard quota = $\frac{\text{population of a group}}{\text{standard divisor}}$, we find that standard divisor = $\frac{\text{population of a group}}{\text{standard quota}}$, so for Alabama, the standard

divisor is $\frac{1,262,505}{7.671}$, or 164,581.5409. By rearranging the formula

standard divisor = $\frac{\text{total population}}{\text{number of allocated items}}$, we find that total population = (standard divisor)(number of allocated items).

So for the U.S., the total population is (164,581.5409)(300), or 49,374,462.26. The nearest whole number is 49,374,462.

43-45. Answers will vary.

14.4 Flaws of Apportionment Methods

Check Point 1.

We begin with 99 seats in the Congress.

First we compute the standard divisor: Standard divisor = $\frac{\text{total population}}{\text{number of allocated items}} = \frac{20,000}{99} = 202.02$

Using this value, make a table showing apportionment using Hamilton's method.

State	Population	Standard Quota	Lower Quota	Fractional Part	Surplus Seats	Final Apportionment
A	2060	10.20	10	0.20		10
B	2080	10.30	10	0.30	1	11
C	7730	38.26	38	0.26		38
D	8130	40.24	40	0.24		40
Total	20,000	99	98			99

Now let's see what happens with 100 seats in Congress.

First we compute the standard divisor: Standard divisor $\frac{\text{total population}}{\text{number of allocated items}} = \frac{20,000}{100} = 200$.

Using this value, make a table showing apportionment using Hamilton's method.

State	Population	Standard Quota	Lower Quota	Fractional Part	Surplus Seats	Final Apportionment
A	2060	10.3	10	0.3		10
B	2080	10.4	10	0.4		10
C	7730	38.65	38	0.65	1	39
D	8130	40.65	40	0.65	1	41
Total	20,000	100	98			100

The final apportionments are summarized in the following table.

State	Apportionment with 99 seats	Apportionment with 100 seats
A	10	10
B	11	10
C	38	39
D	40	41

When the number of seats increased from 99 to 100, B's apportionment decreased from 11 to 10.

Check Point 2.

a. We use Hamilton's method to find the apportionment for each state with its original population. First we compute the standard divisor.

$$\text{Standard divisor} = \frac{\text{total population}}{\text{number of allocated items}} = \frac{200,000}{100} = 2000$$

Using this value, we show the apportionment in the following table.

State	Original Population	Standard Quota	Lower Quota	Fractional Part	Surplus Seats	Final Apportionment
A	19,110	9.56	9	0.56	1	10
B	39,090	19.55	19	0.55		19
C	141,800	70.9	70	0.9	1	71
Total	200,000	100.01	98			100

b. The fraction for percent increase is the amount of increase divided by the original amount. The percent increase in the population of each state is determined as follows.

State A: $\dfrac{19,302-19,110}{19,110} = \dfrac{192}{19,110} \approx 0.01005 = 1.005\%$

State B: $\dfrac{39,480-39,090}{39,090} = \dfrac{390}{39,090} \approx 0.00998 = 0.998\%$

State A is increasing at a rate of 1.005%. This is faster than State B, which is increasing at a rate of 0.998%.

c. We use Hamilton's method to find the apportionment for each state with its new population. First we compute the standard divisor.

$$\text{Standard divisor} = \frac{\text{total population}}{\text{number of allocated items}} = \frac{200,582}{100} = 2005.82$$

Using this value, we show the apportionment in the following table.

State	New Population	Standard Quota	Lower Quota	Fractional Part	Surplus Seats	Final Apportionment
A	19,302	9.62	9	0.62		9
B	39,480	19.68	19	0.68	1	20
C	141,800	70.69	70	0.69	1	71
Total	200,582	99.99	98			100

The final apportionments are summarized in the following table.

State	Growth Rate	Original Apportionment	New Apportionment
A	1.005%	10	9
B	0.998%	19	20
C	0%	71	71

State A loses a seat to State B, even though the population of State A is increasing at a faster rate. This is an example of the population paradox.

Check Point 3.

a. We use Hamilton's method to find the apportionment for each school. First we compute the standard divisor.

$$\text{Standard divisor} = \frac{\text{total population}}{\text{number of allocated items}} = \frac{12,000}{100} = 120$$

Using this value, we show the apportionment in the following table.

School	Enrollment	Standard Quota	Lower Quota	Fractional Part	Surplus	Final Apportionment
East High	2574	21.45	21	0.45		21
West High	9426	78.55	78	0.55	1	79
Total	12,000	100	99			100

b. Again we use Hamilton's method.

$$\text{Standard divisor} = \frac{\text{total population}}{\text{number of allocated items}} = \frac{12,750}{106} = 120.28$$

Using this value, we show the apportionment in the following table

School	Enrollment	Standard Quota	Lower Quota	Fractional Part	Surplus	Final Apportionment
East High	2574	21.40	21	0.40	1	22
West High	9426	78.37	78	0.37		78
North High	750	6.24	6	0.24		6
Total	12,750	106.01	105			106

West High has lost a counselor to East High.

Exercise Set 14.4

1. a. The standard divisor is $\frac{1800}{30}$, or 60.

Course	Enrollment	Standard Quota	Lower Quota	Fractional Part	Surplus	Final Apportionment
College Algebra	978	16.30	16	0.30		16
Statistics	500	8.33	8	0.33		8
Liberal Arts Math	322	5.37	5	0.37	1	6
Total	1800	30	29			30

b. The standard divisor is $\frac{1800}{31}$, or 58.06.

Course	Enrollment	Standard Quota	Lower Quota	Fractional Part	Surplus	Final Apportionment
College Algebra	978	16.84	16	0.84	1	17
Statistics	500	8.61	8	0.61	1	9
Liberal Arts Math	322	5.55	5	0.55		5
Total	1800	31	29			31

Liberal Arts Math loses a teaching assistant when the total number of teaching assistants is raised from 30 to 31. This is an example of the Alabama paradox.

2. a. The standard divisor is $\frac{14,250}{57} = 250$.

School	Enrollment	Standard Quota	Lower Quota	Fractional Part	Surplus	Final Apportionment
A	5040	20.16	20	0.16		20
B	4560	18.24	18	0.24		18
C	4040	16.16	16	0.16		16
D	610	2.44	2	0.44	1	3
Total	14,250	57	56			57

b. The standard divisor is $\frac{14,250}{58} = 245.69$.

School	Enrollment	Standard Quota	Lower Quota	Fractional Part	Surplus	Final Apportionment
A	5040	20.51	20	0.51	1	21
B	4560	18.56	18	0.56	1	19
C	4040	16.44	16	0.44		16
D	610	2.48	2	0.48		2
Total	14,250	57.99	56			58

D loses one laptop when the total number of laptops is increased from 57 to 58. This is an example of the Alabama paradox.

3. Standard divisor with 40 seats: $\frac{20,000}{40} = 500$. Use Hamilton's method.

State	Population	Standard Quota	Lower Quota	Fractional Part	Surplus	Final Apportionment
A	680	1.36	1	0.36	1	2
B	9150	18.30	18	0.30		18
C	10,170	20.34	20	0.34		20
Total	20,000	40	39			40

Standard divisor with 41 seats: $\frac{20,000}{41} = 487.8$. Use Hamilton's method.

State	Population	Standard Quota	Lower Quota	Fractional Part	Surplus	Final Apportionment
A	680	1.39	1	0.39		1
B	9150	18.76	18	0.76	1	19
C	10,170	20.85	20	0.85	1	21
Total	20,000	41	39			41

State A loses a seat when the total number of seats increases from 40 to 41.

4. Standard divisor with 24 seats: $\frac{3760}{24} = 156.7$. Use Hamilton's method.

State	Population (in thousands)	Standard Quota	Lower Quota	Fractional Part	Surplus	Final Apportionment
A	530	3.38	3	0.38	1	4
B	990	6.32	6	0.32		6
C	2240	14.30	14	0.30		14
Total	3760	24	23			24

Standard divisor with 25 seats: $\frac{3760}{25} = 150.4$. Use Hamilton's method.

State	Population (in thousands)	Standard Quota	Lower Quota	Fractional Part	Surplus	Final Apportionment
A	530	3.52	3	0.52		3
B	990	6.58	6	0.58	1	7
C	2240	14.89	14	0.89	1	15
Total	3760	25	23			25

A loses a seat when the total number of seats increases from 24 to 25.

5. a. Standard divisor: $\frac{3760}{24} = 156.7$. Use Hamilton's method.

State	Original Population	Standard Quota	Lower Quota	Fractional Part	Surplus	Final Apportionment
A	530	3.38	3	0.38	1	4
B	990	6.32	6	0.32		6
C	2240	14.30	14	0.30		14
Total	3760	24	23			24

b. Percent increase for state A: $\frac{680 - 530}{530} \approx 0.283 = 28.3\%$

Percent increase for state B: $\frac{1250 - 990}{990} \approx 0.263 = 26.3\%$

Percent increase for state C: $\frac{2570 - 2240}{2240} \approx 0.147 = 14.7\%$

c. Standard divisor: $\frac{4500}{24} = 187.5$. Use Hamilton's method.

State	New Population	Standard Quota	Lower Quota	Fractional Part	Surplus	Final Apportionment
A	680	3.63	3	0.63		3
B	1250	6.67	6	0.67	1	7
C	2570	13.71	13	0.71	1	14
Total	4500	24.01	22			24

A loses a seat while B gains, even though A has a faster increasing population. The population paradox does occur.

6. a. Standard divisor: $\frac{20,000}{200} = 100$.

State	Original Population	Standard Quota	Lower Quota	Fractional Part	Surplus	Final Apportionment
A	2224	22.24	22	0.24		22
B	2236	22.36	22	0.36		22
C	2640	26.40	26	0.40	1	27
D	3030	30.30	30	0.30		30
E	9870	98.70	98	0.70	1	99
Total	20,000	200	198			200

b. State A: $\dfrac{2424 - 2224}{2224} \approx 0.090 = 9.0\%$

State B: $\dfrac{2436 - 2236}{2236} \approx 0.089 = 8.9\%$

State C: $\dfrac{2740 - 2640}{2640} \approx 0.038 = 3.8\%$

State D: $\dfrac{3130 - 3030}{3030} \approx 0.033 = 3.3\%$

State E: $\dfrac{10,070 - 9870}{9870} \approx 0.020 = 2.0\%$

c. Standard divisor: $\dfrac{20,800}{200} = 104$

State	New Population	Standard Quota	Lower Quota	Fractional Part	Surplus	Final Apportionment
A	2424	23.31	23	0.31		23
B	2436	23.42	23	0.42	1	24
C	2740	26.35	26	0.35		26
D	3130	30.10	30	0.10		30
E	10,070	96.83	96	0.83	1	97
Total	20,800	200.01	198			200

State A has a larger percent population change than state B, but B gains more seats. This is a paradoxical result, but it is not technically an instance of the population paradox, since no state actually loses seats to another state with a lower percent population change. Notice also that state C has a larger percent population change than state D, but C loses a seat while D remains unchanged. If C lost a seat and D gained one, that would be an example of the population paradox.

7. Original standard divisor: $\dfrac{8880}{40} = 222$

District	Original Population	Standard Quota	Lower Quota	Fractional Part	Surplus	Final Apportionment
A	1188	5.35	5	0.35		5
B	1424	6.41	6	0.41		6
C	2538	11.43	11	0.43	1	12
D	3730	16.80	16	0.80	1	17
Total	8880	39.99	38			40

New standard divisor: $\dfrac{9000}{40} = 225$

District	New Population	Standard Quota	Lower Quota	Fractional Part	Surplus	Final Apportionment
A	1188	5.28	5	0.28		5
B	1420	6.311	6	0.311	1	7
C	2544	11.307	11	0.307		11
D	3848	17.10	17	0.10		17
Total	9000	39.998	39			40

Percent increase by state:

A: 0% (no change)

B: $\dfrac{1420 - 1424}{1424} \approx -0.0028 = -0.28\%$

C: $\dfrac{2544 - 2538}{2538} \approx 0.0024 = 0.24\%$

D: $\dfrac{3848 - 3730}{3730} \approx 0.032 = 3.2\%$

C loses a truck to B even though C increased in population faster than B. This shows the population paradox occurs.

8. Original standard divisor: $\dfrac{9000}{50} = 180$

District	Original Population	Standard Quota	Lower Quota	Fractional Part	Surplus	Final Apportionment
A	780	4.33	4	0.33		4
B	1500	8.33	8	0.33		8
C	1730	9.61	9	0.61	1	10
D	2040	11.33	11	0.33		11
E	2950	16.39	16	0.39	1	17
Total	9000	49.99	48			50

New standard divisor: $\dfrac{9090}{50} = 181.8$

District	New Population	Standard Quota	Lower Quota	Fractional Part	Surplus	Final Apportionment
A	780	4.29	4	0.29	1	5
B	1500	8.25	8	0.25		8
C	1810	9.96	9	0.96	1	10
D	2040	11.22	11	0.22		11
E	2960	16.28	16	0.28		16
Total	9090	50	48			50

Percent increase by state: A, B, D: 0% (no change)

C: $\dfrac{1810 - 1730}{1730} \approx 0.046 = 4.6\%$

E: $\dfrac{2960 - 2950}{2950} \approx 0.0034 = 0.34\%$

E loses a truck to A even though E has a faster population increase. This shows that the population paradox occurs.

9. a. Standard divisor: $\dfrac{10,000}{100} = 100$

Branch	Employees	Standard Quota	Lower Quota	Fractional Part	Surplus	Final Apportionment
A	1045	10.45	10	0.45		10
B	8955	89.55	89	0.55	1	90
Total	10,000	100	99			100

b. New standard divisor: $\dfrac{10,525}{105} = 100.238$

Branch	Employees	Standard Quota	Lower Quota	Fractional Part	Surplus	Final Apportionment
A	1045	10.43	10	0.43	1	11
B	8955	89.34	89	0.34		89
C	525	5.24	5	0.24		5
Total	10,525	105.01	104			105

Branch B loses a promotion when branch C is added. This means the new-states paradox has occurred.

10. a. Standard divisor: $\dfrac{3000}{60} = 50$

Branch	Employees	Standard Quota	Lower Quota	Fractional Part	Surplus	Final Apportionment
A	209	4.18	4	0.18		4
B	769	15.38	15	0.38		15
C	2022	40.44	40	0.44	1	41
Total	3000	60	59			60

b. New standard divisor: $\dfrac{3260}{65} = 50.15$

Branch	Employees	Standard Quota	Lower Quota	Fractional Part	Surplus	Final Apportionment
A	209	4.17	4	0.17		4
B	769	15.33	15	0.33	1	16
C	2022	40.32	40	0.32		40
D	260	5.18	5	0.18		5
Total	3260	65	64			65

Branch C loses a promotion when branch D is added. This means the new-states paradox has occurred.

11. a. Standard divisor: $\dfrac{9450 + 90,550}{100} = 1000$

State	Population	Standard Quota	Lower Quota	Fractional Part	Surplus	Final Apportionment
A	9450	9.45	9	0.45		9
B	90,550	90.55	90	0.55	1	91
Total	100,000	100	99			100

b. New standard divisor: $\dfrac{100,000 + 10,400}{110} = 1003.64$

State	Population	Standard Quota	Lower Quota	Fractional Part	Surplus	Final Apportionment
A	9450	9.42	9	0.42	1	10
B	90,550	90.22	90	0.22		90
C	10,400	10.36	10	0.36		10
Total	110,400	110	109			110

State B loses a seat when state C is added.

12. a. Standard divisor: $\dfrac{99,000 + 214,000 + 487,000}{50} = 16,000$

State	Population	Standard Quota	Lower Quota	Fractional Part	Surplus	Final Apportionment
A	99,000	6.19	6	0.19		6
B	214,000	13.38	13	0.38		13
C	487,000	30.44	30	0.44	1	31
Total	800,000	50.01	49			50

b. New standard divisor: $\dfrac{800,000 + 116,000}{57} = 16,070.175$

State	Population	Standard Quota	Lower Quota	Fractional Part	Surplus	Final Apportionment
A	99,000	6.16	6	0.16		6
B	214,000	13.32	13	0.32	1	14
C	487,000	30.30	30	0.30		30
D	116,000	7.22	7	0.22		7
Total	916,000	57	56			57

State C loses a seat when State D is added.

13. a.

State	Population	Modified Quota	Modified Lower Quota	Final Apportionment
A	99,000	6.39	6	6
B	214,000	13.81	13	13
C	487,000	31.42	31	31
Total	800,000		50	50

b.

State	Population	Modified Quota	Modified Lower Quota	Final Apportionment
A	99,000	6.39	6	6
B	214,000	13.81	13	13
C	487,000	31.42	31	37
D	116,000	7.48	7	7
Total	916,000		57	57

The new-states paradox does not occur. As long as the modified divisor, d, remains the same, adding a new state cannot change the number of seats held by existing states.

14-18. Answers will vary.

19. The only true statement is d.

20. Answers will vary.

Review Exercises

1.

Number of Votes	4	3	3	2
First Choice	A	B	C	C
Second Choice	B	D	B	B
Third Choice	C	C	D	A
Fourth Choice	D	A	A	D

2. $9 + 5 + 4 + 2 + 2 + 1 = 23$

3. 4

4. $9 + 5 + 2 = 16$

5. $9 + 5 = 14$

6. M receives 12 first-choice votes, compared to 10 for C and 2 for D, so M (Musical) is selected.

7.

Number of Votes	10	8	4	2
First Choice: 3 points	C: $10 \times 3 = 30$	M: $8 \times 3 = 24$	M: $4 \times 3 = 12$	D: $2 \times 3 = 6$
Second Choice: 2 points	D: $10 \times 2 = 20$	C: $8 \times 2 = 16$	D: $4 \times 2 = 8$	M: $2 \times 2 = 4$
Third Choice: 1 point	M: $10 \times 1 = 10$	D: $8 \times 1 = 8$	C: $4 \times 1 = 4$	C: $2 \times 1 = 2$

C gets $30 + 16 + 4 + 2 = 52$ points.
D gets $20 + 8 + 8 + 6 = 42$ points.
M gets $10 + 24 + 12 + 4 = 50$ points.

C (Comedy) gets the most points and is chosen.

8. There are 24 voters, so 13 votes are needed for a majority. None of the candidates has 13 first-place votes. D has the fewest first-place votes and is eliminated in the next round.

Number of Votes	10	14
First Choice	C	M
Second Choice	M	C

M (Musical) has 14 first-place votes, a majority, so a musical is selected.

9. There are 3 choices so we make $\frac{3(3-1)}{2} = 3$ comparisons.

Comparison	Vote Results	Conclusion
C vs. D	18 voters prefer C to D. 6 voters prefer D to C.	C wins and gets 1 point.
C vs. M	10 voters prefer C to M. 14 voters prefer M to C.	M wins and gets 1 point.
D vs. M	12 voters prefer D to M. 12 voters prefer M to D.	D and M tie. Each gets $\frac{1}{2}$ point.

C gets 1 point, D gets $\frac{1}{2}$ point, and M gets $1\frac{1}{2}$ points. So M (Musical) wins, and is selected.

10. A receives 40 first-place votes, compared to 30 for B, 6 for C, and 2 for D. So A wins.

11.

Number of Votes	40	30	6	2
First Choice: 4 points	A: $40 \times 4 = 160$	B: $30 \times 4 = 120$	C: $6 \times 4 = 24$	D: $2 \times 4 = 8$
Second Choice: 3 points	B: $40 \times 3 = 120$	C: $30 \times 3 = 90$	D: $6 \times 3 = 18$	B: $2 \times 3 = 6$
Third Choice: 2 points	C: $40 \times 2 = 80$	D: $30 \times 2 = 60$	B: $6 \times 2 = 12$	C: $2 \times 2 = 4$
Fourth Choice: 1 point	D: $40 \times 1 = 40$	A: $30 \times 1 = 30$	A: $6 \times 1 = 6$	A: $2 \times 1 = 2$

A gets $160 + 30 + 6 + 2 = 198$ points.
B gets $120 + 120 + 12 + 6 = 258$ points.
C gets $80 + 90 + 24 + 4 = 198$ points.
D gets $40 + 60 + 18 + 8 = 126$ points.

B receives the most points, and wins.

12. There are 78 voters, so 40 first-place votes are needed for a majority. A has 40 first-place votes, and wins.

13. There are 4 candidates, so $\frac{4(4-1)}{2} = 6$ comparisons are needed.

Comparison	Vote Results	Conclusion
A vs. B	40 voters prefer A to B. 38 voters prefer B to A.	A wins and gets 1 point.
A vs. C	40 voters prefer A to C. 38 voters prefer C to A.	A wins and gets 1 point.
A vs. D	40 voters prefer A to D. 38 voters prefer D to A.	A wins and gets 1 point.
B vs. C	72 voters prefer B to C. 6 voters prefer C to B.	B wins and gets 1 point.
B vs. D	70 voters prefer B to D. 8 voters prefer D to B.	B wins and gets 1 point.
C vs. D	76 voters prefer C to D. 2 voters prefer D to C.	C wins and gets 1 point.

A gets 3 points, B gets 2 points, C gets 1 point, and D gets 0 points. So A wins.

14.

Number of Votes	1500	600	300
First Choice: 4 points	A: $1500 \times 4 = 6000$	B: $600 \times 4 = 2400$	C: $300 \times 4 = 1200$
Second Choice: 3 points	B: $1500 \times 3 = 4500$	D: $600 \times 3 = 1800$	B: $300 \times 3 = 900$
Third Choice: 2 points	C: $1500 \times 2 = 3000$	C: $600 \times 2 = 1200$	D: $300 \times 2 = 600$
Fourth Choice: 1 point	D: $1500 \times 1 = 1500$	A: $600 \times 1 = 600$	A: $300 \times 1 = 300$

A gets $6000 + 600 + 300 = 6900$ points.
B gets $4500 + 2400 + 900 = 7800$ points.
C gets $3000 + 1200 + 1200 = 5400$ points.
D gets $1500 + 1800 + 600 = 3900$ points.

B receives the most points, and wins.

15. A has a majority of first-place votes. In Exercise 14, B wins and so the majority criterion is not satisfied.

16. A is favored above all others using a head-to-head comparison. This is automatically true, since A has a majority of first-place votes. In Exercise 14, B wins and so the head-to-head criterion is not satisfied.

17. There are 2500 voters. 1251 first-place votes are needed for a majority. B has 1500 first-place votes, and is the winner.

18. B is favored above all others using a head-to-head comparison. This is automatically true, since B has a majority of first-place votes. In Exercise 17, B wins and so the head-to-head criterion is satisfied.

19. A receives 180 first-place votes, compared with 100 for B, 30 for C, and 40 for D. Therefore A wins.

20.

Number of Votes	180	100	40	30
First Choice: 4 points	A: $180 \times 4 = 720$	B: $100 \times 4 = 400$	D: $40 \times 4 = 160$	C: $30 \times 4 = 120$
Second Choice: 3 points	B: $180 \times 3 = 540$	D: $100 \times 3 = 300$	B: $40 \times 3 = 120$	B: $30 \times 3 = 90$
Third Choice: 2 points	C: $180 \times 2 = 360$	A: $100 \times 2 = 200$	C: $40 \times 2 = 80$	A: $30 \times 2 = 60$
Fourth Choice: 1 point	D: $180 \times 1 = 180$	C: $100 \times 1 = 100$	A: $40 \times 1 = 40$	D: $30 \times 1 = 30$

A gets $720 + 200 + 40 + 60 = 1020$ points.
B gets $540 + 400 + 120 + 90 = 1150$ points.
C gets $360 + 100 + 80 + 120 = 660$ points.
D gets $180 + 300 + 160 + 30 = 670$ points.

B gets the most points, and wins.

21. There are 350 voters. 176 first-place votes are needed for a majority. A has 180 votes, a majority, and wins.

22. There are 4 candidates, and therefore $\frac{4(4-1)}{2} = 6$ comparisons.

Comparison	Vote Results	Conclusion
A vs. B	180 voters prefer A to B. 170 voters prefer B to A.	A wins and gets 1 point.
A vs. C	280 voters prefer A to C. 70 voters prefer C to A.	A wins and gets 1 point.
A vs. D	210 voters prefer A to D. 140 voters prefer D to A.	A wins and gets 1 point.
B vs. C	320 voters prefer B to C. 30 voters prefer C to B.	B wins and gets 1 point.
B vs. D	310 voters prefer B to D. 40 voters prefer D to B.	B wins and gets 1 point.
C vs. D	210 voters prefer C to D. 140 voters prefer D to C.	C wins and gets 1 point.

A gets 3 points, B gets 2 points, C gets 1 point, and D gets 0 points. Therefore A wins.

23. A has a majority of first-place votes. Based on Exercises 19–22, only the Borda count method violates the majority criterion. B wins by the Borda count method.

24. There are 1450 voters. 726 first-place votes are needed for a majority. No candidate has a majority. A has the fewest first-place votes and is eliminated in the next round.

Number of Votes	900	550
First Choice	B	C
Second Choice	C	B

B has the majority of first-place votes, and wins.

25. There is a new preference table:

Number of Votes	700	400	350
First Choice	B	A	C
Second Choice	C	B	A
Third Choice	A	C	B

No candidate has a majority of first-place votes. C has the fewest first-place votes, and is eliminated in the next round.

Number of Votes	700	750
First Choice	B	A
Second Choice	A	B

A has a majority of first-place votes, and wins. This does not satisfy the monotonicity criterion, since the only change gave B more first-place votes, but after the change B lost the election.

26. A has 400 first-place votes, compared to 200 for B and 250 for C. Therefore A wins.

27.

Number of Votes	400	450
First Choice	A	C
Second Choice	C	A

C has the majority of first-place votes, and wins this election. The irrelevant alternatives criterion is not satisfied, because removing B changes the winner from A to C.

28.

Number of Votes	400	250	200
First Choice: 3 points	A: $400 \times 3 = 1200$	C: $250 \times 3 = 750$	B: $200 \times 3 = 600$
Second Choice: 2 points	B: $400 \times 2 = 800$	B: $250 \times 2 = 500$	C: $200 \times 2 = 400$
Third Choice: 1 point	C: $400 \times 1 = 400$	A: $250 \times 1 = 250$	A: $200 \times 1 = 200$

A gets $1200 + 250 + 200 = 1650$ points.
B gets $800 + 500 + 600 = 1900$ points.
C gets $400 + 750 + 400 = 1550$ points.

B gets the most points, and wins.

29.

Number of Votes	400	450
First Choice: 2 points	A: $400 \times 2 = 800$	B: $450 \times 2 = 900$
Second Choice: 1 point	B: $400 \times 1 = 400$	A: $450 \times 1 = 450$

A gets $800 + 450 = 1250$ points.
B gets $400 + 900 = 1300$ points.

B still gets the most points, and wins. The same thing happens if A drops out instead of C, and so the irrelevant alternatives criterion is satisfied.

30. $\dfrac{275 + 392 + 611 + 724}{40} = \dfrac{2002}{40} = 50.05$

31. With a standard divisor of 50.05:

Clinic	A	B	C	D
Average weekly patient load	275	392	611	724
Standard Quota	5.49	7.83	12.21	14.47

32. Using the results of Exercise 31:

Clinic	Standard Quota	Lower Quota	Upper Quota
A	5.49	5	6
B	7.83	7	8
C	12.21	12	13
D	14.47	14	15

33.

Clinic	Standard Quota	Lower Quota	Fractional Part	Surplus	Final Apportionment
A	5.49	5	0.49	1	6
B	7.83	7	0.83	1	8
C	12.21	12	0.21		12
D	14.47	14	0.47		14
Total	40	38			40

34.

Clinic	Average Weekly Patient Load	Modified Quota $(d = 48)$	Modified Lower Quota	Final Apportionment
A	275	5.73	5	5
B	392	8.17	8	8
C	611	12.73	12	12
D	724	15.08	15	15
Total	2002		40	40

35.

Clinic	Average Weekly Patient Load	Modified Quota $(d = 52)$	Modified Upper Quota	Final Apportionment
A	275	5.29	6	6
B	392	7.54	8	8
C	611	11.75	12	12
D	724	13.92	14	14
Total	2002		40	40

36.

Clinic	Average Weekly Patient Load	Modified Quota $(d = 49.95)$	Modified Rounded Quota	Final Apportionment
A	275	5.51	6	6
B	392	7.85	8	8
C	611	12.23	12	12
D	724	14.49	14	14
Total	2002		40	40

37. Standard divisor: $\dfrac{3320 + 10,060 + 15,020 + 19,600}{200} = \dfrac{48,000}{200} = 240$

State	Population	Standard Quota	Lower Quota	Fractional Part	Surplus	Final Apportionment
A	3320	13.83	13	0.83	1	14
B	10,060	41.92	41	0.92	1	42
C	15,020	62.58	62	0.58		62
D	19,600	81.67	81	0.67	1	82
Total	48,000	200	197			200

38. Try modified divisor $d = 238$.

State	Population	Modified Quota	Modified Lower Quota	Final Apportionment
A	3320	13.95	13	13
B	10,060	42.27	42	42
C	15,020	63.11	63	63
D	19,600	82.35	82	82
Total	48,000		200	200

39. Try modified divisor $d = 242$.

State	Population	Modified Quota	Modified Upper Quota	Final Apportionment
A	3320	13.72	14	14
B	10,060	41.57	42	42
C	15,020	62.07	63	63
D	19,600	80.99	81	81
Total	48,000		200	200

40. Try modified divisor $d = 240.4$.

State	Population	Modified Quota	Modified Rounded Quota	Final Apportionment
A	3320	13.81	14	14
B	10,060	41.85	42	42
C	15,020	62.48	62	62
D	19,600	81.53	82	82
Total	48,000		200	200

41. a. Standard divisor: $\dfrac{7500}{150} = 50$

School	Enrollment	Standard Quota	Lower Quota	Fractional Part	Surplus	Final Apportionment
A	370	7.4	7	0.4	1	8
B	3365	67.3	67	0.3		67
C	3765	75.3	75	0.3		75
Total	7500	150	149			150

b. Standard divisor: $\dfrac{7500}{151} = 49.67$

School	Enrollment	Standard Quota	Lower Quota	Fractional Part	Surplus	Final Apportionment
A	370	7.45	7	0.45		7
B	3365	67.75	67	0.75	1	68
C	3765	75.80	75	0.80	1	76
Total	7500	151	149			151

The Alabama paradox occurs. A loses a laptop when the overall number of laptops changes from 150 to 151.

42. a. Standard divisor: $\dfrac{200,000}{100} = 2000$

School	Original Population	Standard Quota	Lower Quota	Fractional Part	Surplus	Final Apportionment
A	143,796	71.90	71	0.90	1	72
B	41,090	20.55	20	0.55		20
C	15,114	7.56	7	0.56	1	8
Total	200,000	100.01	98			100

b. Percent increase of B: $\dfrac{41,420 - 41,090}{41,090} \approx 0.0080 = 0.8\%$

Percent increase of C: $\dfrac{15,304 - 15,114}{15,114} \approx 0.0126 \approx 1.3\%$

c. Standard divisor: $\dfrac{200,520}{100} = 2005.2$

School	New Population	Standard Quota	Lower Quota	Fractional Part	Surplus	Final Apportionment
A	143,796	71.71	71	0.71	1	72
B	41,420	20.66	20	0.66	1	21
C	15,304	7.63	7	0.63		7
Total	200,520	100	98			100

The population paradox occurs. C loses a seat to B, even though C is growing faster.

43. a. Standard divisor: $\dfrac{1650}{33} = 50$

Branch	Employees	Standard Quota	Lower Quota	Fractional Part	Surplus	Final Apportionment
A	372	7.44	7	0.44		7
B	1278	25.56	25	0.56	1	26
Total	1650	33	32			33

b. Standard divisor: $\dfrac{2005}{40} = 50.125$

Branch	Employees	Standard Quota	Lower Quota	Fractional Part	Surplus	Final Apportionment
A	372	7.42	7	0.42		7
B	1278	25.50	25	0.50	1	26
C	355	7.08	7	0.08		7
Total	2005	40	39			40

The new-states paradox does not occur. Neither branch A nor branch B loses any promotions.

44. False. Answers will vary.

Chapter 14 Test

1. $1200 + 900 + 900 + 600 = 3600$

2. 600

3. $900 + 600 = 1500$

4. $900 + 600 = 1500$

5. A received 1200 first-place votes, B received 1500, and C received 900. Therefore B wins.

6.

Number of Votes	1200	900	900	600
First Choice: 3 points	A: $1200 \times 3 = 3600$	C: $900 \times 3 = 2700$	B: $900 \times 3 = 2700$	B: $600 \times 3 = 1800$
Second Choice: 2 points	B: $1200 \times 2 = 2400$	A: $900 \times 2 = 1800$	C: $900 \times 2 = 1800$	A: $600 \times 2 = 1200$
Third Choice: 1 point	C: $1200 \times 1 = 1200$	B: $900 \times 1 = 900$	A: $900 \times 1 = 900$	C: $600 \times 1 = 600$

A gets $3600 + 1800 + 900 + 1200 = 7500$ points.
B gets $2400 + 900 + 2700 + 1800 = 7800$ points.
C gets $1200 + 2700 + 1800 + 600 = 6300$ points.

B receives the most points and is the winner.

7. There are 3600 voters. 1801 first-place votes are needed for a majority. No candidate has a majority. C receives the fewest first-place votes and is eliminated in the next round.

Number of Votes	2100	1500
First Choice	A	B
Second Choice	B	A

A receives the majority of first-place votes, and wins.

8. There are 3 candidates. The number of comparisons is $\frac{3(3-1)}{2}$, or 3.

Comparison	Vote Results	Conclusion
A vs. B	2100 voters prefer A to B. 1500 voters prefer B to A.	A wins and gets 1 point.
A vs. C	1800 voters prefer A to C. 1800 voters prefer C to A.	A and C tie. Each gets $\frac{1}{2}$ point.
B vs. C	2700 voters prefer B to C. 900 voters prefer C to B.	B wins and gets 1 point.

A gets $1\frac{1}{2}$ points, B gets 1 point, and C gets $\frac{1}{2}$ point. Therefore A wins.

9.

Number of Votes	240	160	60
First Choice: 4 points	A: $240 \times 4 = 960$	C: $160 \times 4 = 640$	D: $60 \times 4 = 240$
Second Choice: 3 points	B: $240 \times 3 = 720$	B: $160 \times 3 = 480$	A: $60 \times 3 = 180$
Third Choice: 2 points	C: $240 \times 2 = 480$	D: $160 \times 2 = 320$	C: $60 \times 2 = 120$
Fourth Choice: 1 point	D: $240 \times 1 = 240$	A: $160 \times 1 = 160$	B: $60 \times 1 = 60$

A gets $960 + 160 + 180 = 1300$ points.
B gets $720 + 480 + 60 = 1260$ points.
C gets $480 + 640 + 120 = 1240$ points.
D gets $240 + 320 + 240 = 800$ points.

A gets the most points, and wins.

10. A has the majority of first-place votes. Based on Exercise 9, the majority criterion is satisfied.

11. A has 1500 first-place votes, whereas B and C have 1000 each. Therefore A wins.

12. B is favored when compared to A, by 2000 votes to 1500. B is favored when compared to C, by 2500 votes to 1000. So B is favored in each head-to-head comparison. Based on Exercise 11, the head-to-head criterion is not satisfied, because A wins the election.

13. There are 210 voters. 106 votes are needed for a majority. No candidate has a majority. B receives the fewest first-place votes and is eliminated in the next round.

Number of Votes	130	80
First Choice	C	A
Second Choice	A	C

C receives a majority of votes, and wins.

14. New preference table:

Number of Votes	100	60	50
First Choice	C	B	A
Second Choice	A	C	B
Third Choice	B	A	C

No candidate has a majority. A has the fewest first-place votes and is eliminated in the next round.

Number of Votes	100	110
First Choice	C	B
Second Choice	B	C

B has the majority of first-place votes, and wins. The monotonicity criterion is not satisfied, because the only change gave more first-place votes to C, but C lost the second election.

15. B has 90 first-place votes, C has 75, and A has 45. Therefore B wins. If C drops out, there is a new preference table:

Number of Votes	90	120
First Choice	B	A
Second Choice	A	B

A has a majority of first-place votes, and wins. This changed outcome shows that the irrelevant alternatives criterion is not satisfied.

16. $\dfrac{119 + 165 + 216}{10} = \dfrac{500}{10} = 50$

17. A: $\dfrac{119}{50} = 2.38$ B: $\dfrac{165}{50} = 3.3$ C: $\dfrac{216}{50} = 4.32$

18. A: 2, 3; B: 3, 4; C: 4, 5

19.

Clinic	Average Weekly Patient Load	Standard Quota	Lower Quota	Fractional Part	Surplus	Final Apportionment
A	119	2.38	2	0.38	1	3
B	165	3.3	3	0.3		3
C	216	4.32	4	0.32		4
Total	500	10	9			10

20.

Clinic	Average Weekly Patient Load	Modified Quota ($d = 42$)	Modified Lower Quota	Final Apportionment
A	119	2.83	2	2
B	165	3.93	3	3
C	216	5.14	5	5
Total	500		10	10

21.

Clinic	Average Weekly Patient Load	Modified Quota ($d = 56$)	Modified Upper Quota	Final Apportionment
A	119	2.13	3	3
B	165	2.95	3	3
C	216	3.86	4	4
Total	500		10	10

22.

Clinic	Average Weekly Patient Load	Modified Quota ($d = 47.7$)	Modified Rounded Quota	Final Apportionment
A	119	2.49	2	2
B	165	3.46	3	3
C	216	4.52	5	5
Total	500		10	10

23. New standard divisor: $\frac{500}{11} = 45.45$

Clinic	Average Weekly Patient Load	Standard Quota	Lower Quota	Fractional Part	Surplus	Final Apportionment
A	119	2.62	2	0.62		2
B	165	3.63	3	0.63	1	4
C	216	4.75	4	0.75	1	5
Total	500	11	9			11

The Alabama paradox occurs. Clinic A loses one doctor when the total number of doctors is raised from 10 to 11.

24. New standard divisor: $\frac{500 + 110}{12} = \frac{610}{12} = 50.83$

Clinic	Average Weekly Patient Load	Standard Quota	Lower Quota	Fractional Part	Surplus	Final Apportionment
A	119	2.34	2	0.34	1	3
B	165	3.25	3	0.25		3
C	216	4.25	4	0.25		4
D	110	2.16	2	0.16		2
Total	610	12	11			12

The new-states paradox does not occur. No clinic loses doctors when a new clinic is added.

25. Answers will vary.

Chapter 15
Graph Theory

15.1 Graphs, Paths, and Circuits

Check Point 1.

Graphs (a) and (b) both have vertices *A, B, C, D,* and *E*. Also, both graphs have edges *AB, AC, BD, BE, CD, CE,* and *DE*.

Because the two graphs have the same number of vertices connected to each other in the same way, they are the same. And in fact graph (b) is just graph (a) rotated clockwise and bent out of shape.

Check Point 2.

Draw points for the five land masses and label them *N, S, A, B,* and *C*.

There is one bridge that connects North Metroville to Island A, so one edge is drawn connecting vertex *N* to vertex *A*. Similarly, one edge connects vertex *A* with vertex *B*, and one edge connects vertex *B* with vertex *C*. Since there are two bridges connecting Island C to South Metroville, two edges connect vertex *C* with vertex *S*.

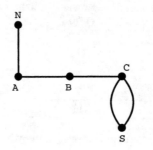

Check Point 3.

We use the abbreviations for the states to label the vertices: ID for Idaho, MT for Montana, WY for Wyoming, UT for Utah, and CO for Colorado. The precise placement of these vertices is not important.

Whenever two states share a common border, we connect the respective vertices with an edge. For example, Idaho shares a common border with Montana, with Wyoming, and with Utah. Continuing in this manner, we obtain the following graph.

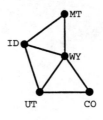

Check Point 4.

We use the letters in Figure 15.13 to label each vertex. Only one door connects the outside, *E*, with room *B*, so we draw one edge from vertex *E* to vertex *B*. Two doors connect the outside, *E*, to room *D*, so we draw two edges from *E* to *D*. Counting doors between the rooms, we complete the following graph.

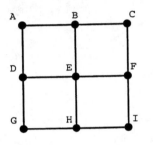

Check Point 5.

We label each of the corners and intersections with an upper-case letter and use points to represent the corners and street intersections. Now we are ready to draw the edges that represent the streets the security guard has to walk. Each street only needs to be walked once, so we draw one edge to represent each street. This results in the following graph.

Check Point 6.

We systematically list which pairs of vertices are adjacent, working alphabetically. Thus, the adjacent vertices are *A* and *B*, *A* and *C*, *A* and *D*, *A* and *E*, *B* and *C*, and *E* and *E*.

Exercise Set 15.1

1. There are six edges attached to the Pittsburgh vertex, so Pittsburgh plays six games during the week. One edge connects the Pittsburgh vertex to the St. Louis vertex, so one game is against St. Louis. One edge connects the Pittsburgh vertex to Chicago, so one game is against Chicago. Two edges connect the Pittsburgh vertex to the Philadelphia vertex, so two games are against Philadelphia. Two edges connect the Pittsburgh vertex to the Montreal vertex, so two games are against Montreal.

2. There are five edges attached to the Montreal vertex, so Montreal plays five games during the week. One edge connects the Montreal vertex to the Philadelphia vertex, so one game is against Philadelphia. One edge connects the Montreal vertex to the St. Louis vertex, so one game is against St. Louis. Two edges connect the Montreal vertex to the Pittsburgh vertex, so two games are against Pittsburgh. One edge connects the Montreal vertex to the New York vertex, so one game is against New York.

3. No. Montreal is farther north than New York but is drawn lower on the graph. However, the graph is not drawn incorrectly. Only the games between teams are important, and these are represented by the edges. Geographic position is not relevant.

4. No. Chicago is west of New York, but not farther south. On the graph, Chicago's position appears to be southwest of New York's. However, the graph is not drawn incorrectly. Only the games between teams are important, and these are represented by the edges. Geographic position is not relevant.

5. Possible answers:

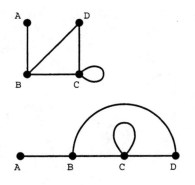

6. Possible answers:

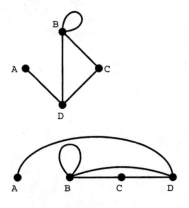

7. Both graphs have vertices *A*, *B*, *C*, and *D* and edges *AB*, *AC*, *AD*, and *BD*. The two graphs have the same number of vertices connected in the same way, so they are the same.

Possible answer:

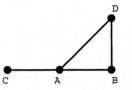

8. Both graphs have vertices *A*, *B*, *C*, and *D* and edges *AB*, *AC*, *BC*, and *BD*. The two graphs have the same number of vertices connected in the same way, so they are the same.
Possible answer:

9. We label each student's vertex with the first letter of his or her name. An edge connecting two vertices represents a friendship prior to forming the homework group. The following graph results.

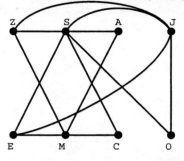

10. Use vertices to represent the three committees. The Preserving Open Space and Fund Raising Committees have two members in common (B and D), the Fund Raising and Wetlands Protection Committees have two members in common (C and D), and the Preserving Open Space and Wetlands Protection Committees have one member in Common (D).

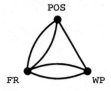

11. Label one vertex *N*, for North Gothamville. Label another *S*, for South Gothamville. Label the islands, from left to right, *A*, *B*, and *C*. Label three vertices accordingly. Use edges to represent bridges. The following graph results.

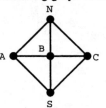

12. Label one vertex *N*, for North Wisdomville. Label another *S*, for South Wisdomville. Label the islands, from left to right, *A*, *B*, and *C*. Label three vertices accordingly. Use edges to represent bridges. The following graph results.

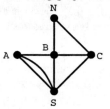

13. We use the abbreviations WA, OR, ID, MT, and WY to label the vertices representing Washington, Oregon, Idaho, Montana, and Wyoming. The following graph results.

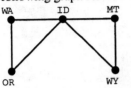

14. We use the abbreviations WA, OR, CA, AZ, NV, and ID to label the vertices representing Washington, Oregon, California, Arizona, Nevada, and Idaho. The following graph results.

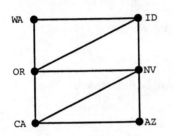

15.

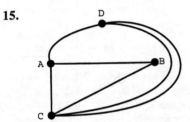

16.

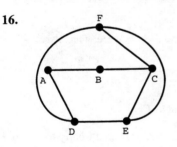

17.

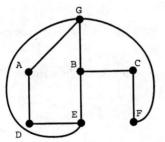

18.

19.

20.

21.

22.

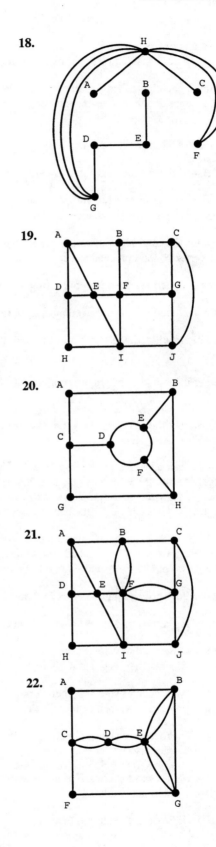

23. The degree of a vertex is the number of edges at that vertex. Thus, vertex *A* has degree 2, vertex *B* has degree 2, vertex *C* has degree 3, vertex *D* has degree 3, vertex *E* has degree 3, and vertex *F* has degree 1. (The loop at *E* counts for 2.)

24. Vertices *A* and *B* each have 2 edges, an even number, attached to them, so *A* and *B* are even vertices. Vertices *C*, *D*, and *E* each have 3 edges attached to them, and vertex *F* has 1 edge attached to it. Since these are all odd numbers, *C*, *D*, *E*, and *F* are odd vertices.

25. Vertices *B* and *C* each have an edge connecting to *A*, so *B* and *C* are adjacent to *A*.

26. Vertices *C*, *E*, and *F* are each connected to vertex *D* by an edge, so *C*, *E*, and *F* are adjacent to *D*.

27. Starting at vertex *A*, we proceed to vertex *C*, then vertex *D*. This is one path from *A* to *D*. For a second path, start at vertex *A*, then proceed to vertex *B*, then *C*, then *D*.

28. Starting at vertex *B*, we proceed to vertex *A*, then vertex *C*, then vertex *D*. This is one path from *B* to *D*. For a second path, start at vertex *B*, then proceed to vertex *C*, then *D*.

29. The edges not included are the edge connecting *A* to *C*, and the edge connecting *D* to *F*.

30. The edges not included are the edges connecting *B* to *C*, and the edge connecting *D* to *F*.

31. While edge *CD* is included, the graph is connected. If we remove *CD*, the graph will be disconnected. Thus, *CD* is a bridge.

32. While edge *DE* is included, the graph is connected. If we remove *DE*, the graph will be disconnected. Thus, *DE* is a bridge.

33. Edge *DF* is also a bridge. With it, the graph is connected. If *DF* is removed, vertex *F* stands alone, so the graph is disconnected.

34. Vertex *A* has 2 attached edges, so *A* has degree 2. Vertex *B* has 2 attached edges, so *B* has degree 2. Vertex *C* has 5 attached edges (counting the loop twice), so *C* has degree 5. Vertex *D* has 3 attached edges, so *D* has degree 3. Vertex *E* has 1 attached edge, so *E* has degree 1. Vertex *F* has 3 attached edges, so *F* has degree 3. Vertex *G* has 2 attached edges, so *G* has degree 2. Vertex *H* has 2 attached edges, so *H* has degree 2. Vertex *I* has 2 attached edges, so *I* has degree 2.

35. Vertices *A*, *B*, *G*, *H*, and *I* each have two attached edges, which is an even number of edges. Thus *A*, *B*, *G*, *H*, and *I* are even vertices. Vertex *C* has five attached edges, vertex *E* has one, and vertices *D* and *F* have three. These are odd numbers of edges. Thus *C*, *E*, *D*, and *F* are odd vertices.

36. Vertex *E* has an edge connecting to vertex *D*. Thus *D* is adjacent to *E*.

37. Vertex *F* has edges connecting to vertices *D*, *G*, and *I*. Thus *D*, *G*, and *I* are adjacent to *F*.

38. Begin at vertex *A*. Proceed to vertex *C*, next along the loop back to vertex *C*, next to vertex *D*, and finally to vertex *F*. This is one path. For another, begin at *A*, then proceed to *B*, then *C*, then *D*, then *F*.

39. Begin at vertex *B*. Proceed to vertex *C*, then vertex *D*, then vertex *F*. This is one path from *B* to *F*. For a second path, begin at *B*, then proceed to *A*, then *C*, then *D*, then *F*.

40. Begin at vertex *F*. Proceed to vertex *I*, then vertex *H*, then vertex *G*, and finally to vertex *F*. This is a circuit. (The counterclockwise order also works.)

41. Begin at vertex *G*. proceed to vertex *F*, then vertex *I*, then vertex *H*, then vertex *G*. This is a circuit. (The counterclockwise order also works.)

42. Begin at vertex *H*. Proceed to vertex *I*, then vertex *F*, then vertex *D*, then vertex *E*.

43. Begin at vertex A. Proceed to vertex B, then vertex C, then around the loop to C again, then vertex D, then vertex F, then vertex G, then vertex H, then vertex I.

44. A, C, D, E, D requires that the edge DE be traversed twice. This is not allowed within a path.

45. G, F, D, E, D requires that edge DE be traversed twice. This is not allowed within a path.

46. A, C, D, G is not a path because no edge connects vertices D and G.

47. H, I, F, E is not a path because no edge connects vertices F and E.

48. Edge CD is a bridge. When it is removed, the following graph results.

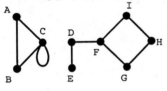

Edge DE is a bridge. When it is removed, the following graph results.

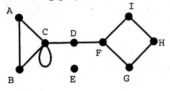

Edge DF is a bridge. When it is removed, the following graph results.

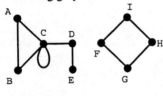

49. Possible answer:

Each vertex has degree 2.

50. Possible answer:

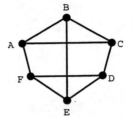

Each vertex has degree 3.

51. Possible answer:

Vertex A has degree 1, and the rest have degree 3.

52. Possible answer:

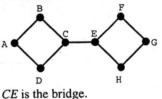

CE is the bridge.

53–66. Answers will vary.

67. Use vertices to represent the six members.

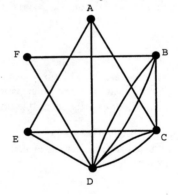

68. The sum of the degree of the vertices is twice the number of edges.

15.2 Euler Paths and Euler Circuits

Check Point 1.

We use trial and error to find one such path. The following figure shows a result.

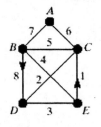

Using vertex letters to name the path, we write *E, C, D, E, B, C, A, B, D.*

Check Point 2.

We use trial and error to find an Euler circuit that starts at *G*. The following figure shows a result.

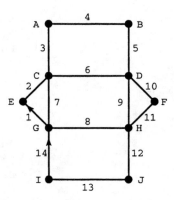

Using vertex letters to name the circuit, we write *G, E, C, A, B, D, C, G, H, D, F, H, J, I, G.*

Check Point 3.

a. A walk through every room and the outside, using each door exactly once, means that we are looking for an Euler path or Euler circuit on the graph in Figure 15.34(b). This graph has exactly two odd vertices, namely *B* and *E*. By Euler's theorem, the graph has at least one Euler path, but no Euler circuit. It is possible to walk through every room and the outside, using each door exactly once. It is not possible to begin and end the walk in the same place.

b. Euler's theorem tells us that a possible Euler path must start at one of the odd vertices and end at the other. We use trial and error to find such a path, starting at vertex *B* (room *B* in the floor plan), and ending at vertex *E* (outside in the floor plan). Possible paths follow.

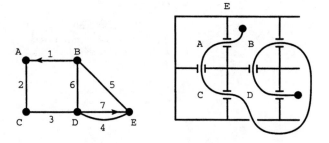

Check Point 4.

The graph has no odd vertices, so we can begin at any vertex. We choose vertex C as the starting point. From C we can travel to A, B, or D. We choose to travel to D.

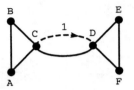

Now the remaining edge CD is a bridge, so we must travel to either E or F. We choose F.

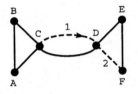

We have no choices for our next three steps, which are bridges. We must travel to E, then D, then C.

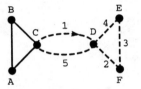

From C, we may travel to either A or B. We choose B. Then we must travel to A, then back to C.

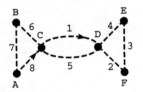

The above figure shows the completed Euler circuit. Written using the letters of the vertices, the path is C, D, F, E, D, C, B, A, C.

Exercise Set 15.2

1.

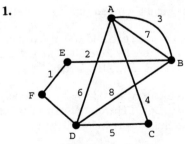

This path does not include edge FD, so it is neither an Euler path nor an Euler circuit.

2.

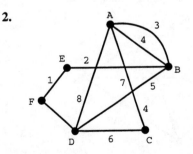

This path does not include edge FD, so it is neither an Euler path nor an Euler circuit.

3.

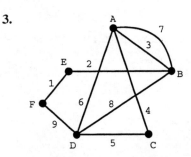

This path travels through each edge of the graph once, and only once. It begins and ends at *F*. Therefore, it is an Euler circuit.

4.

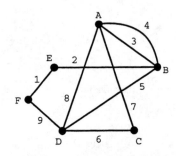

This path travels through each edge of the graph once, and only once. It begins and ends with *F*. Therefore, it is an Euler circuit.

5.

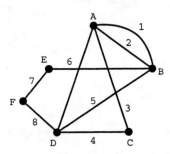

This path does not include edge *AD*, so it is neither an Euler path nor an Euler circuit.

6.

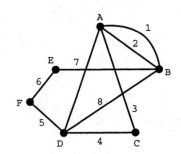

This path does not include edge *AD*, so it is neither an Euler path nor an Euler circuit.

7. a. There are exactly two odd vertices, namely *A* and *B*, so by Euler's theorem there is at least one Euler path.

b.

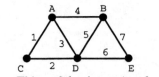

This path begins at *A* and ends at *B*.

8. a. There are exactly two odd vertices, namely *A* and *C*, so by Euler's theorem there is at least one Euler path.

b.

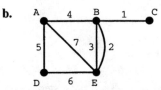

This path begins at *C* and ends at *A*.

9. a. There are no odd vertices, so by Euler's theorem, there is at least one Euler circuit.

b.

This circuit begins and ends at *C*.

10. a. There are no odd vertices, so by Euler's theorem, there is at least one Euler circuit.

b.

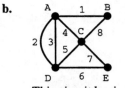

This circuit begins and ends at *B*.

11. There are more than two odd vertices, namely *B, D, G,* and *K*. Therefore by Euler's theorem, there are no Euler paths and no Euler circuits.

12. There are more than two odd vertices, namely *B, C, E, I, H, L, N,* and *O*. Therefore by Euler's theorem, there are no Euler paths and no Euler circuits.

13. Since the graph has no odd vertices, it must have an Euler circuit, by Euler's theorem.

14. Since the graph has no odd vertices, it must have an Euler circuit, by Euler's theorem.

15. Since the graph has exactly two odd vertices, it has an Euler path, but no Euler circuit, by Euler's theorem.

16. Since the graph has exactly two odd vertices, it has an Euler path, but no Euler circuit, by Euler's theorem.

17. Since the graph has more than two odd vertices, it has neither an Euler path nor an Euler circuit, by Euler's theorem.

18. Since the graph has more than two odd vertices, it has neither an Euler path nor an Euler circuit, by Euler's theorem.

19. a. All vertices are even, so there must be an Euler circuit.

b.

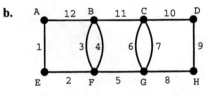

20. a. All vertices are even, so there must be an Euler circuit.

b.

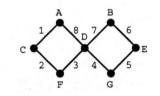

21. a. There are exactly two odd vertices, so there must be an Euler path.

b.

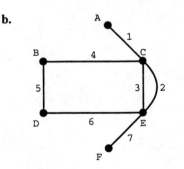

22. a. There are exactly two odd vertices, so there must be an Euler path.

b.

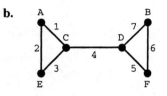

23. a. There are more than two odd vertices, so there is neither an Euler path nor an Euler circuit.

24. a. There are more than two odd vertices, so there is neither an Euler path nor an Euler circuit.

25. a. There are exactly two odd vertices, so there is an Euler path.

b.

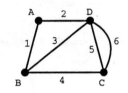

26. a. There are exactly two odd vertices, so there is an Euler path.

b.

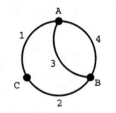

27. a. There are no odd vertices, so there is an Euler circuit.

b.

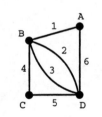

28. a. There are no odd vertices, so there is an Euler circuit.

b.

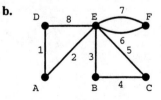

29. a. There are more than two odd vertices, so there is neither an Euler path nor an Euler circuit.

30. a. There are more than two odd vertices, so there is neither an Euler path nor an Euler circuit.

31. a. There are exactly two odd vertices, so there is an Euler path.

b.

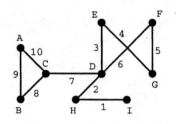

32. a. There are exactly two odd vertices, so there is an Euler path.

b.

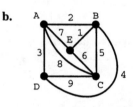

33. The two odd vertices in the graph are A and C. We start with A, so we must progress next to B. From B, we may travel to C, D, or E. We choose C.

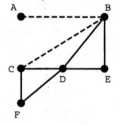

Next we travel to F, then D, then E.

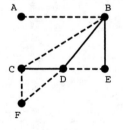

Finally we travel to B, then D, and last, to C. We label each step taken.

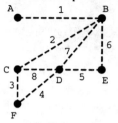

34. The two odd vertices in the graph are A and B. We start with B and progress to A, then D, then E.

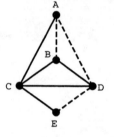

From E, we travel to C, then D, then B, then C, and last, to A. We label each step taken.

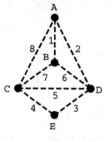

35. The two odd vertices in the graph are A and C. We start with A, then travel to B, C, and E.

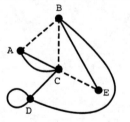

We continue on to B, D, D, C, A, and C. We label each step taken.

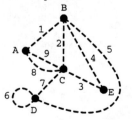

36. The two odd vertices in the graph are *A* and *B*. We start with *B*, then travel to *D*, *F*, *E*, *C*, and *A*.

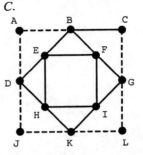

We continue on to *B*, then *C*, *D*, *E*, *B*, *F*, and *A*. We label each step taken.

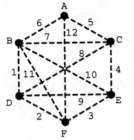

37. We begin with *A*, and travel to *D*, *H*, *G*, *F*, *E*, *B*, and *C*.

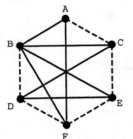

We continue on to *F*, *D*, *C*, and back to *A*. We label each step.

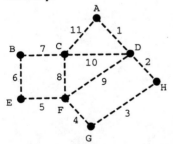

38. We begin with *B*, and travel to *A*, *D*, *J*, *K*, *L*, *G*, and *C*.

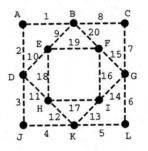

We continue on to *B*, *E*, *D*, *H*, *K*, *I*, *G*, *F*, *I*, *H*, *E*, *F*, and back to *B*. We label each step.

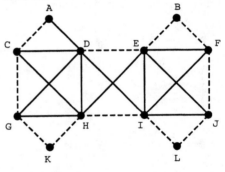

39. We begin with *A*, and travel to *C*, *G*, *K*, *H*, *I*, *L*, *J*, *F*, *B*, *E*, and *D*.

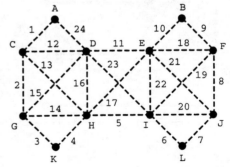

We continue on to *C*, *H*, *G*, *D*, *H*, *E*, *F*, *I*, *J*, *E*, *I*, *D*, and back to *A*. We label each step.

527

40. We begin with *A*, and travel to *F, J, K, L, M, N, I, E, D, C,* and *B*.

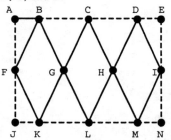

We continue on to *F, K, G, L, H, M, I, D, H, C, G, B,* and back to *A*. We label each step.

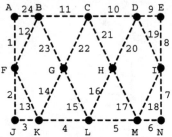

41. The graph that models the neighborhood has no odd vertices, so an Euler circuit exists with any vertex, including *B*, as the starting point.

42.

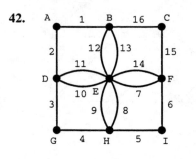

43.

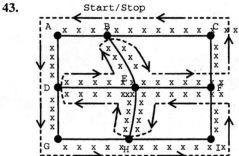

44. First we draw a graph that models the streets walked by the security guard.

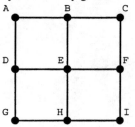

The graph has more than two odd vertices, namely *B, D, F,* and *H*. Therefore there is no route the security guard can take in order to walk each street exactly once.

45. a.

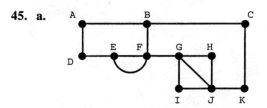

b. There are exactly two odd vertices, namely *E* and *B*. Therefore the guard should begin at one of these vertices and end at the other.

46. a.

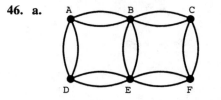

b. The graph depicts an Euler circuit, since each vertex is even. Therefore the carrier can park at any intersection and deliver all the mail without retracing the side of any street.

c.

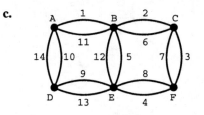

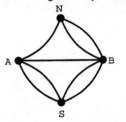

47. a. Label the vertices *N* for North Bank, *S* for South Bank, and *A* and *B* for the two islands. Draw edges to represent bridges.

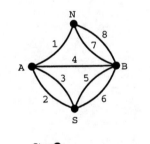

b. The graph has exactly two odd vertices, *N* and *B*, so residents can walk across all the bridges without crossing the same bridge twice.

c.

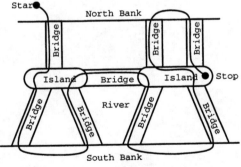

48. a. Label the vertices *N* for North Bank, *S* for South Bank, and *A* and *B* for the two islands.

Draw edges to represent bridges.

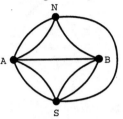

b. The graph has exactly two odd vertices, *A* and *S*, so residents can walk across all the bridges without crossing the same bridge twice.

c.

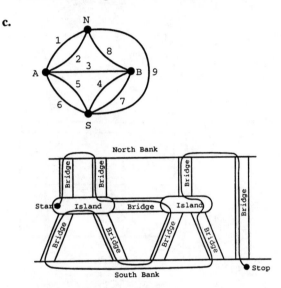

49. Use NJ to label the New Jersey vertex, M for Manhattan, SI for Staten Island, and LI for Long Island. Each edge represents a bridge.

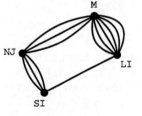

There are exactly two odd vertices, M and LI, so the graph has an Euler path. Therefore it is possible to visit each location, using each bridge or tunnel exactly once.

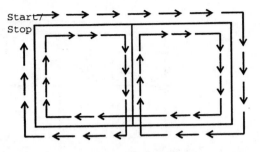

50. a.

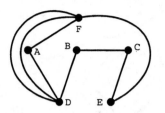

b. There are no odd vertices, so the graph has an Euler circuit. Therefore, it is possible to walk through each room and the outside, using each door exactly once.

c.

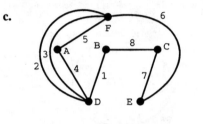

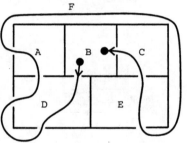

51. a.

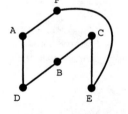

b. There are no odd vertices, so the graph has an Euler circuit. Therefore, it is possible to walk through each room and the outside, using each door exactly once.

c.

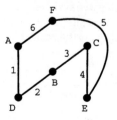

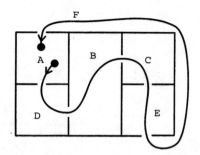

52. There are exactly two odd vertices on the graph, so an Euler path exists, by Euler's theorem. Thus, we can travel each border exactly once while visiting these states.

53.

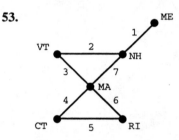

54.

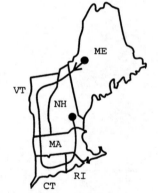

55. a.

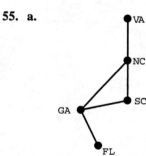

b. There are more than two odd vertices, so no Euler path exists. Therefore it is not possible to travel through these states, crossing each border exactly once.

d. For the same reason as in (b), this is not possible.

56. a.

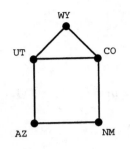

b. There are exactly two odd vertices, so there is an Euler path. Therefore it is possible to travel through these states, crossing each border exactly once.

c.

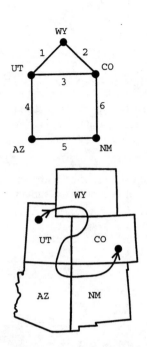

d. Because there are two odd vertices, there is no Euler circuit. Hence the trip cannot start and end in the same state.

57-67. Answers will vary.

15.3   Hamilton Paths and Hamilton Circuits

Check Point 1.

a. A Hamilton path must pass through each vertex exactly once. The graph has many Hamilton paths. An example of such a path is *E, C, D, G, B, A, F.*

b. A Hamilton circuit must pass through every vertex exactly once and begin and end at the same vertex. The graph has many Hamilton circuits. An example of such a circuit is *E, C, D, G, B, F, A, E.*

Check Point 2.

In each case, we use the expression $(n - 1)!$. For three vertices, substitute 3 for n in the expression. For six and ten vertices, substitute 6 and 10, respectively, for n.

a. A complete graph with three vertices has $(3 - 1)! = 2! = 2 \cdot 1 = 2$ Hamilton circuits.

b. A complete graph with six vertices has $(6 - 1)! = 5! = 5 \cdot 4 \cdot 3 \cdot 2 \cdot 1 = 120$ Hamilton circuits.

c. A complete graph with ten vertices has $(10 - 1)! = 9! = 9 \cdot 8 \cdot 7 \cdot 6 \cdot 5 \cdot 4 \cdot 3 \cdot 2 \cdot 1 = 362,880$ Hamilton circuits.

Check Point 3.

The trip described by the Hamilton circuit A, C, B, D, A involves the sum of four costs:

$124 + $126 + $155 + $157 = $562.

Here, $124 is the cost of the trip from A to C; $126 is the cost from C to B; $155 is the cost from B to D; and $157 is the cost from D to A. The total cost of the trip is $562.

Check Point 4.

The graph has four vertices. Thus, using $(n-1)!$, there are $(4-1)! = 3! = 6$ possible Hamilton circuits. The 6 possible Hamilton circuits and their costs are shown.

Hamilton Circuit	Sum of the Weights of the Edges	=	Total Cost
A, B, C, D, A	$20 + 15 + 50 + 30$	=	$115
A, B, D, C, A	$20 + 10 + 50 + 70$	=	$150
A, C, B, D, A	$70 + 15 + 10 + 30$	=	$125
A, C, D, B, A	$70 + 50 + 10 + 20$	=	$150
A, D, B, C, A	$30 + 10 + 15 + 70$	=	$125
A, D, C, B, A	$30 + 50 + 15 + 20$	=	$115

The two Hamilton circuits having the lowest cost of $115 are A, B, C, D, A and A, D, C, B, A.

Check Point 5.

The Nearest Neighbor method is carried out as follows:

- Start at A.

- Choose the edge with the smallest weight: 13. Move along this edge to B.

- From B, choose the edge with the smallest weight that does not lead to A: 5. Move along this edge to C.

- From C, choose the edge with the smallest weight that does not lead to a city already visited: 12. Move along this edge to D.

- From D, the only choice is to fly to E, the only city not yet visited: 154.

- From E, close the circuit and return home to A: 14.

An approximate solution is the Hamilton circuit A, B, C, D, E, A. The total weight is $13 + 5 + 12 + 154 + 14 = 198$.

Exercise Set 15.3

1. One such path is A, G, C, F, E, D, B.

2. One such path is G, A, D, B, F, C, E.

3. One such circuit is A, B, G, C, F, E, D, A.

4. One such circuit is A, G, C, B, F, E, D, A.

5. One such path is A, F, G, E, C, B, D.

6. One such path is A, F, D, B, C, E, G.

7. One such circuit is A, B, C, E, G, F, D, A.

8. One such circuit is F, G, E, C, B, A, D, F.

9. a. This graph is not complete. For example, no edge connects A and B. Therefore it may not have Hamilton circuits.

10. **a.** This graph is not complete. For example, no edge connects B and G. Therefore it may not have Hamilton circuits.

11. **a.** This graph is complete: there is an edge between each pair of vertices. Therefore it must have Hamilton circuits.

    b. There are 6 vertices, so the number of Hamilton circuits is $(6-1)! = 5! = 120$.

12. **a.** This graph is complete: there is an edge between each pair of vertices. Therefore it must have Hamilton circuits.

    b. There are 7 vertices, so the number of Hamilton circuits is $(7-1)! = 6! = 720$.

13. **a.** This graph is not complete. For example, no edge connects G and F. Therefore it may not have Hamilton circuits.

14. **a.** This graph is not complete. For example, no edge connects A and K. Therefore it may not have Hamilton circuits.

15. $(3-1)! = 2! = 2$

16. $(4-1)! = 3! = 6$

17. $(12-1)! = 11! = 39,916,800$

18. $(13-1)! = 12! = 479,001,600$

19. 11

20. 7

21. $9 + 8 + 11 + 6 + 2 = 36$

22. $9 + 7 + 4 + 11 + 10 = 41$

23. $9 + 7 + 6 + 11 + 3 = 36$

24. $9 + 5 + 11 + 4 + 2 = 31$

25. $40 + 24 + 10 + 14 = 88$

26. $40 + 12 + 10 + 20 = 82$

27. $20 + 24 + 12 + 14 = 70$

28. $20 + 10 + 12 + 40 = 82$

29. $14 + 12 + 24 + 20 = 70$

30. $14 + 10 + 24 + 40 = 88$

31. On a complete graph with four vertices, there are 6 distinct Hamilton circuits. These are listed in Exercises 25–30. We have already computed the weight of each possible Hamilton circuit, as required by the Brute Force Method. The optimal solutions have the smallest weight, 70. They are A, C, B, D, A, and A, D, B, C, A.

32. Starting from A, the edge with smallest weight is AD, with weight 14. Therefore proceed to D. From D, the edge having smallest weight and not returning to A is DC, with weight 10. The only edge from C which does not lead to a previously visited vertex is CB, with weight 24. Last, return to A. Edge BA has weight 40. The total weight of this Hamilton circuit is
$14 + 10 + 24 + 40 = 88$.

33. Starting from B, the edge with smallest weight is BD, with weight 12. Therefore, proceed to D. From D, the edge having smallest weight and not leading back to B is DC, with weight 10. From C, our only choice is CA, with weight 20. From A, return to B. Edge AB has weight 40. The total weight of the Hamilton circuit is
$12 + 10 + 20 + 40 = 82$.

34. Starting from C, the edge with smallest weight is CD, with weight 10. Therefore proceed to D. From D, the edge having smallest weight and not leading back to C is DB, with weight 12. From B, our only choice is edge BA, with weight 40. From A, we return to C. Edge AC has weight 20. The total weight of this Hamilton circuit is
$10 + 12 + 40 + 20 = 82$.

35.

Hamilton Circuit	Sum of the Weights of the Edges	=	Total Weight
A, B, C, D, E, A	500 + 305 + 320 + 302 + 205	=	1632
A, B, C, E, D, A	500 + 305 + 165 + 302 + 185	=	1457
A, B, D, C, E, A	500 + 360 + 320 + 165 + 205	=	1550
A, B, D, E, C, A	500 + 360 + 302 + 165 + 200	=	1527
A, B, E, C, D, A	500 + 340 + 165 + 320 + 185	=	1510
A, B, E, D, C, A	500 + 340 + 302 + 320 + 200	=	1662
A, C, B, D, E, A	200 + 305 + 360 + 302 + 205	=	1372
A, C, B, E, D, A	200 + 305 + 340 + 302 + 185	=	1332
A, C, D, B, E, A	200 + 320 + 360 + 340 + 205	=	1425
A, C, E, B, D, A	200 + 165 + 340 + 360 + 185	=	1250
A, D, B, C, E, A	185 + 360 + 305 + 165 + 205	=	1220
A, D, C, B, E, A	185 + 320 + 305 + 340 + 205	=	1355

Using the Brute Force method, we compute the sum of the weights of the edges for each possible Hamilton circuit, as in the table above. The smallest weight sum is 1220, representing a total cost of $1220 for airfare. This results from the Hamilton circuit *A, D, B, C, E, A.* Thus, the sales director should fly to the cities in this order.

36. Starting from *A*, the edge with smallest weight is *AD*, with weight 185. Proceed to edge *D*. From *D*, the edge having smallest weight and not leading back to *A* is *DE*, with weight 302. From *E*, the edge with smallest weight and not leading back to *A* or *D* is *EC*, with weight 165. From *C*, the only option is *CB*, with weight 305. From *B*, return to *A*. Edge *BA* has weight 500. The total weight for this Hamilton circuit is 185 + 302 + 165 + 305 + 500 = 1457, meaning the cost is $1457.

37.

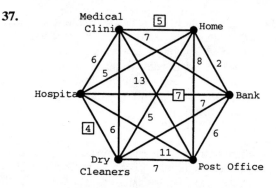

38. There are six vertices; so there are $(6 - 1)! = 5! = 120$ possible routes.

39. $2 + 6 + 7 + 4 + 6 + 5 = 30$

40. Start at Home. The shortest distance is 2, to the Bank. From the Bank, the shortest distance to another errand is 6, to the Post Office. From there, the shortest distance to an undone errand is 7, to the Dry Cleaners. From there, the shortest distance to an undone errand is 4, to the Hospital. The only errand remaining is the Medical Center, at a distance of 6 from the Hospital. The return Home from the Medical Center is a distance of 5. This is the same route found in Exercise 39.

41. Label the vertices H for Home, B for Bank, P for Post Office, and M for Market.

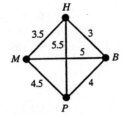

42. The distances are the same in both directions, so we only need to check half the possible Hamilton circuits. There are $(4-1)! = 3! = 6$ Hamilton circuits.

Hamilton Circuit	Sum of the Weights of the Edges	=	Total Distance
H, B, P, M, H	3 + 4 + 4.5 + 3.5	=	15
H, B, M, P, H	3 + 5 + 4.5 + 5.5	=	18
H, P, B, M, H	5.5 + 4 + 5 + 3.5	=	18

The minimum distance is 15 miles, along the route H, B, P, M, H.

43. From Home, the closest errand is the Bank, 3 miles away. From the Bank, the closest remaining errand is the Post Office, 4 miles away. From the Post Office, the last remaining errand is the Market, 4.5 miles away. From the Market, Home is 3.5 miles away. The total distance for this Hamilton circuit is $3 + 4 + 4.5 + 3.5 = 15$ miles. This is the same route found in Exercise 42.

44. Answers will vary.

45-55. Answers will vary.

56. $120 = 5! = (6-1)!$. Therefore, the graph has 6 vertices.

57-58. Answers will vary.

15.4 Trees

Check Point 1.

The graph in Figure 15.51(c) is a tree. It is connected and has no circuits. There is only one path joining any two vertices. Every edge is a bridge; if removed, each edge would create a disconnected graph. Finally, the graph has 7 vertices and $7 - 1$, or 6, edges.

The graph in Figure 15.51(a) is not a tree because it is disconnected. There are 7 vertices and only 5 edges, not the 6 edges required for a tree.

The graph in Figure 15.51(b) is not a tree because it has a circuit, namely A, B, C, D, A. There are 7 vertices and 7 edges, not the 6 edges required for a tree.

Check Point 2.

A spanning tree must contain all six vertices shown in the connected graph in Figure 15.55. The spanning tree must have one edge less than it has vertices, so it must have five edges. The graph in Figure 15.55 has eight edges, so we must remove three edges. We elect to remove the edges of the circuit *C, D, E, C*. This leaves us the following spanning tree.

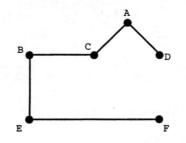

Check Point 3.

Step 1. Find the edge with the smallest weight. This is edge *DE*; mark it.

Step 2. Find the next-smallest edge in the graph. This is edge *DC*; mark it.

Step 3. Find the next-smallest edge in the graph that does not create a circuit. This is edge *DA*; mark it.

Step 4. Find the next-smallest edge in the graph that does not create a circuit. This is *AB*; mark it.

The resulting minimum spanning tree is complete. It contains all 5 vertices of the graph, and has 5 − 1, or 4, edges. Its total weight is 12 + 14 + 21 + 22 = 69. It is shown below.

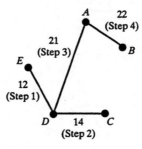

Exercise Set 15.4

1. Yes, this graph is a tree. It has 3 edges on 4 vertices, is connected, and has no circuits. Every edge is a bridge.

2. Yes, this graph is a tree. It has 5 edges on 6 vertices, is connected, and has no circuits. Every edge is a bridge.

3. No, this graph is not a tree. It is disconnected.

4. No, this graph is not a tree. It is disconnected.

5. Yes, this graph is a tree. It has 3 edges on 4 vertices, is connected, and has no circuits. Every edge is a bridge.

6. Yes, this graph is a tree. It has 3 edges on 4 vertices, is connected, and has no circuits. Every edge is a bridge.

7. No, this graph is not a tree. It has a circuit.

8. No, this graph is not a tree. It has a circuit.

9. Yes, this graph is a tree. It has 6 edges on 7 vertices, is connected, and has no circuits. Every edge is a bridge.

10. Yes, this graph is a tree. It has 8 edges on 9 vertices, is connected, and has no circuits. Every edge is a bridge.

11. i.; If the graph contained any circuits, some points would have more than one path joining them.

12. i.; Since every edge is a bridge, there are no circuits.

13. ii.; a tree with n vertices must have $n - 1$ edges.

14. ii.; a tree with n vertices must have $n - 1$ edges.

15. ii.; a tree has no circuits.

16. ii.; a tree has no circuits.

17. iii.

18. iii.

19.
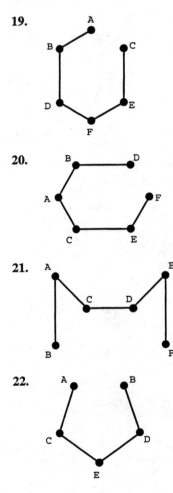

20.

21.

22.

23.
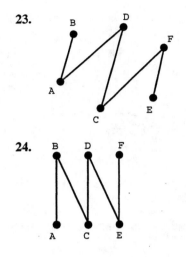

24.
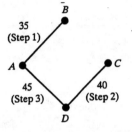

25. Kruskal's algorithm results in the following figure.

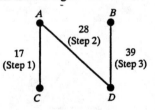

This minimum spanning tree has weight
$35 + 40 + 45 = 120.$

26. Kruskal's algorithm results in the following figure.

This minimum spanning tree has weight
$17 + 28 + 39 = 84.$

27. Kruskal's algorithm results in the following figure.

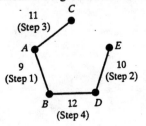

This minimum spanning tree has weight
$9 + 10 + 11 + 12 = 42.$

28. Kruskal's algorithm results in the following figure.

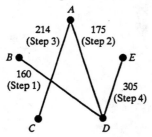

This minimum spanning tree has weight
160 + 175 + 214 + 305 = 854.

29. Kruskal's algorithm results in the following figure.

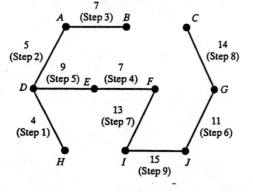

This minimum spanning tree has weight
4 + 5 + 7 + 7 + 9 + 11 + 13 + 14 + 15 = 85.

30. Kruskal's algorithm results in the following figure.

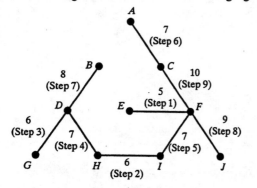

This minimum spanning tree has weight
5 + 6 + 6 + 7 + 7 + 7 + 8 + 9 + 10 = 65.

31. Kruskal's algorithm results in the following figure.

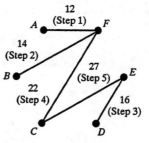

This minimum spanning tree has weight
12 + 14 + 16 + 22 + 27 = 91.

32. Kruskal's algorithm results in the following figure.

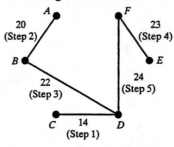

This minimum spanning tree has weight
14 + 20 + 22 + 23 + 24 = 103.

33.

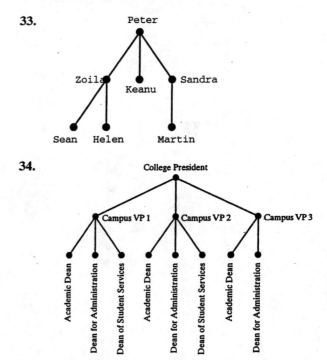

34.

538

35. a.

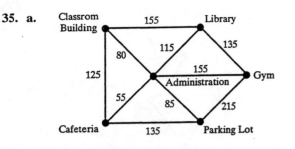

b. Kruskal's algorithm is shown in the following figure.

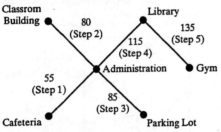

The total length of the sidewalks that need to be sheltered by awnings is
$55 + 80 + 85 + 115 + 135 = 470$ feet.

36. a.

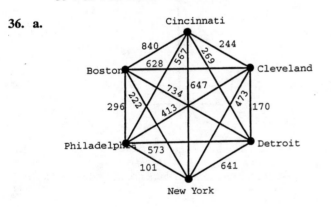

b. Kruskal's algorithm is shown in the following figure.

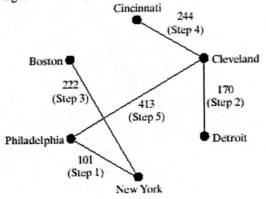

The total length of cable needed is
$101 + 170 + 222 + 244 + 413 = 1150$ miles.

37. Kruskal's method is shown in the figure.

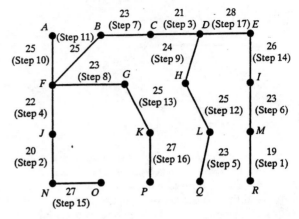

The smallest number of feet of underground pipes is
$19 + 20 + 21 + 22 + 23 + 23 + 23 + 23 + 24 + 25 + 25 + 25 + 25 + 26 + 27 + 27 + 28 = 406$ feet.

38. Kruskal's algorithm is shown in the figure.

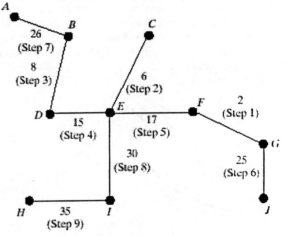

The minimum mileage for the bike trail is
$2 + 6 + 8 + 15 + 17 + 25 + 26 + 30 + 35 = 164$ miles.

39-47. Answers will vary.

48. Choose the largest-weight edge first, then the next-largest, then the next-largest that does not produce a circuit, etc.

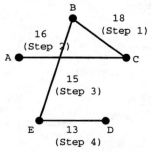

49. The graph has 6 vertices and 6 edges. A spanning tree on 6 vertices has 5 edges. Only three edges are able to be removed without a disconnected graph resulting. These are *BC, BF,* and *CF.* The result of removing any one of these edges is a spanning tree.

50. Answers will vary.

Review Exercises

1. Each graph has 5 vertices, *A, B, C, D,* and *E.* Each has one edge connecting *A* and *B,* one connecting *A* and *C,* one connecting *A* and *D,* one connecting *A* and *E,* and one connecting *B* and *C.* Both graphs have the same number of vertices, and these vertices are connected in the same ways. A third way to draw the same graph is

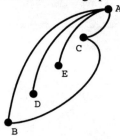

2. *A*: 5 (A loop add degree 2.); *B*: 4; *C*: 5; *D*: 4; *E*: 2

3. Even: *B, D, E*; odd: *A, C*

4. *B, C,* and *E*

5. Possible answer: *E, D, B, A* and *E, C, A*

6. Possible answer: *E, D, C, E*

7. Yes. A path can be found from any vertex to any other vertex.

8. No. There is no edge which can be removed to leave a disconnected graph.

9. *AD, DE,* and *DF*

10.

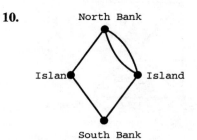

11. Use the states' abbreviations to label the vertices representing them.

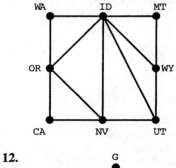

12.

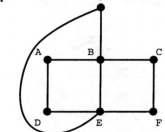

13. a. Neither. There are more than two odd vertices.

14. a. Euler circuit: there are no odd vertices.

b.

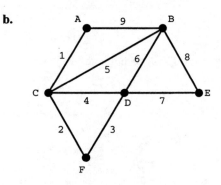

15. a. Euler path: there are exactly two odd vertices.

b.

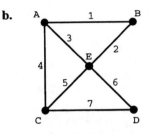

16. There are exactly two odd vertices, G and I. We start at G and continue to D, A, B, C, F, I, H, and E.

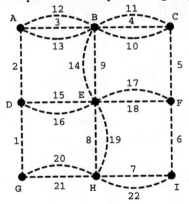

We continue erasing edges as we go, till we have completed an Euler path ending at I.

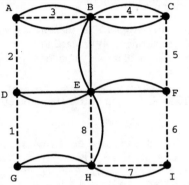

17. We may begin anywhere, since there are no odd vertices. We erase edges as we go, till we have the Euler circuit. We begin at A.

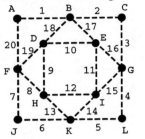

18. a. Yes, they would. The graph has exactly two odd vertices, so there is an Euler path.

b.

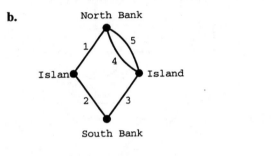

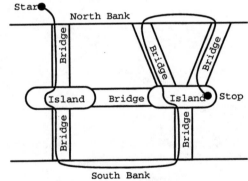

c. No; there is no such path. Since the graph has odd vertices, it does not have an Euler circuit.

19. Yes, it is possible. There are exactly two odd vertices, and therefore there is an Euler path (but no Euler circuit).

20. a. Yes it is possible. There are no odd vertices, so there is an Euler circuit.

b.

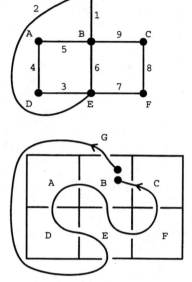

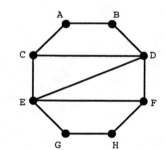

21. a.

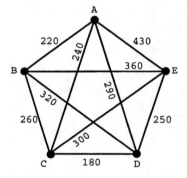

b. Yes. There are exactly two odd vertices C and F, so there is an Euler path.

c. The guard should begin at C and end at F, or vice versa.

22. A, E, C, B, D, A

23. D, B, A, E, C, D

24. a. No, because this is not a complete graph. It may not have Hamilton circuits.

25. a. Yes, because this is a complete graph.

b. $(4 - 1)! = 3! = 6$

26. a. No, because this is not a complete graph. It may not have Hamilton circuits.

27. a. Yes, because this is a complete graph.

b. $(5 - 1)! = 4! = 24$

28.

A, B, C, D, A:	$4 + 6 + 5 + 4$	$=$	19
A, B, D, C, A:	$4 + 7 + 5 + 2$	$=$	18
A, C, B, D, A:	$2 + 6 + 7 + 4$	$=$	19
A, C, D, B, A:	$2 + 5 + 7 + 4$	$=$	18
A, D, B, C, A:	$4 + 7 + 6 + 2$	$=$	19
A, D, C, B, A:	$4 + 5 + 6 + 4$	$=$	19

29. These are the only possible Hamilton circuits on a graph with 4 vertices. The lowest weight, 18, occurs on the circuits A, B, D, C, A and A, C, D, B, A. These are the optimal solutions.

30. Start with A. Then edge AC has the smallest weight, 2, of all edges starting at A. Proceed to C. From C, edge CD has the smallest weight, 5, of edges not returning to A. From D, we must travel DB, with weight 7, to B. We return to A along BA, with weight 4. The total weight of this Hamilton circuit is $2 + 5 + 7 + 4 = 18$.

31. Start with A. Of all paths leading from A, the path with smallest weight is AB, with weight 4. Proceed to B. The path with smallest weight leading from B, but not to A, is BE, with weight 6. The path with smallest weight leading from E, but not to A or B, is ED, with weight 4. From D, we proceed along DC, with weight 3, to C, the only remaining vertex. We then return to A along CA, with weight 7. The total weight is $4 + 6 + 4 + 3 + 7 = 24$.

32.

33. Start at A. The lowest cost from A, \$220, is on edge AB. From B, the lowest cost other than returning to A is \$260, on edge BC. From C, the lowest cost to a new city is \$180, on edge CD. From D, the salesman must fly to E for \$250, then return to A for \$430. The total cost of this circuit is $220 + 260 + 180 + 250 + 430 = \$1340$.

34. Yes. It is connected, has no circuits, has 6 edges on 7 vertices, and each edge is a bridge.

35. No. It has a circuit.

36. No. It is disconnected.

37.

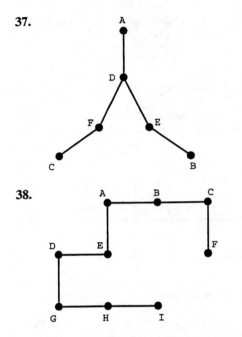

38.

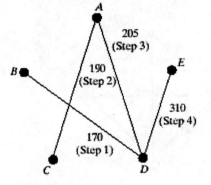

39. Kruskal's algorithm is demonstrated in the figure.

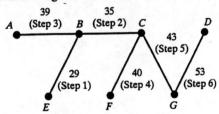

The total weight is
170 + 190 + 205 + 310 = 875.

40. Kruskal's algorithm is demonstrated in the figure.

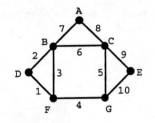

The total weight is
29 + 35 + 39 + 40 + 43 + 53 = 239.

41. The figure demonstrates Kruskal's algorithm and the layout of the cable system.

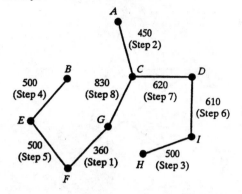

The smallest length of cable needed is
360 + 450 + 500 + 500 + 500 + 610 + 620 + 830 = 4370 miles.

Chapter Test

1. A: 2; B: 2; C: 4; D: 3; E: 2; F: 1

2. A, D, E and A, B, C, E

3. B, A, D, E, C, B

4. CF

5.

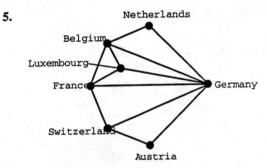

6. a. Euler path: there are exactly two odd vertices.

b.

7. a. Neither: there are more than two odd vertices.

b. N/A

543

8. a. Euler circuit: there are no odd vertices.

b.

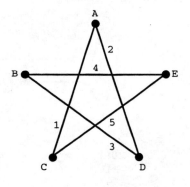

9. We begin at *A*, then proceed to *E, I, H*, and so on, erasing edges once they have been crossed. The result is shown in the figure.

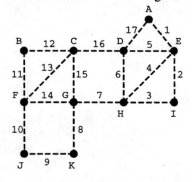

10. a.

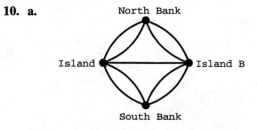

b. Yes: there are exactly two odd vertices.

c. It should begin at one of the islands, and end at the other island.

11. a.

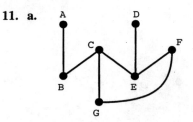

b. No: there are more than two odd vertices.

12. a. Let vertices represent intersections, and let edges represent streets.

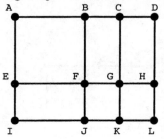

b. No: there are more than two odd vertices.

13. A, B, C, D, G, F, E, A and A, F, G, D, C, B, E, A.

14. $(5 - 1)! = 4! = 24$

15.

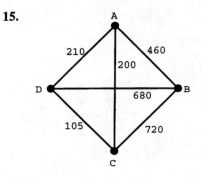

16.

Hamilton Circuit	Sum of the Weights of the Edges	=	Total Cost
A, B, C, D, A	460 + 720 + 105 + 210	=	$1495
A, B, D, C, A	460 + 680 + 105 + 200	=	$1445
A, C, B, D, A	200 + 720 + 680 + 210	=	$1810
A, C, D, B, A	200 + 105 + 680 + 460	=	$1445
A, D, B, C, A	210 + 680 + 720 + 200	=	$1810
A, D, C, B, A	210 + 105 + 720 + 460	=	$1495

The optimal route is *A, B, D, C, A* or *A, C, D, B, A*. The total cost for this route is $1445.

17. Starting from *A*, the edge with smallest weight is *AE*, with weight 5. Proceed to *E*. From *E*, the edge with smallest weight, and not leading back to *A*, is *ED*, with weight 8. From *D*, the edge with smallest weight, and to a new vertex, is *DC*, with weight 4. From *C*, only *B* remains. Edge *CB* has weight 5. Return to *A* by edge *BA*, with weight 11. The total weight of this Hamilton circuit is
$5 + 8 + 4 + 5 + 11 = 33$.

18. No; it has a circuit, namely *C, D, E, C*.

19.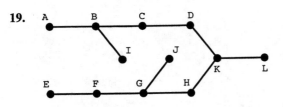

20. Kruskal's algorithm is shown in the figure.

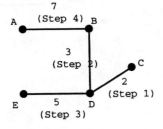

The total weight of the minimum spanning tree is $2 + 3 + 5 + 7 = 17$.